THE HOLT PHYSICAL SCIENCE PROGRAM

Basic Text: MODERN PHYSICAL SCIENCE

by Brooks, Tracy, Tropp, and Friedl

SUPPLEMENTARY MATERIALS TO THE BASIC TEXT:

Teacher's Edition, Modern Physical Science   Annotated copy of the student book with a separate section of professional material on the teaching of the basic text.

Exercises and Investigations for Modern Physical Science   by the authors of the basic text. A combination workbook-laboratory manual to accompany the basic text.

Tests for Modern Physical Science

Answer Book for Exercises and Investigations and Key to Tests for Modern Physical Science

Designs of the Cosmos   by the Physical Science Curriculum Committee, Portland, Oregon. A teacher's guide and sourcebook for a course of study in physical sciences.

Geology and Earth Sciences Sourcebook   by the American Geological Institute, Robert L. Heller, Editor.

Radioactivity: Fundamentals and Experiments   by Hermias and Joecile

FROM THE HOLT LIBRARY OF SCIENCE:

Interplanetary Navigation, by Robert A. Park and Thomas Magness
Ours Is the Earth, by Allan A. Sollers
Satellite Tracking Facilities, by Shirley Thomas
Optics, by Irvin Gluck
Orbital Space Flight, by Howard S. and Mary H. Seifert
Chemistry in the Space Age, by Marjorie H. Gardner
Thrust into Space, by Maxwell W. Hunter, II
Unmanned Space Flight, by John E. Naugle
The Physics of Space, by Richard M. Sutton
Meteorological Satellites, by William K. Widger, Jr.

RELATED BASIC TEXTS:

MODERN LIFE SCIENCE, by Fitzpatrick and Hole
MODERN EARTH SCIENCE, by William L. Ramsey and Raymond A. Burckley

WILLIAM O. BROOKS

GEORGE R. TRACY

HARRY E. TROPP

ALFRED E. FRIEDL

MODERN PHYSICAL SCIENCE

Holt, Rinehart and Winston, Inc.
New York   Toronto   London

William O. Brooks was a member of the Science Department, Technical High School, Springfield, Massachusetts.

George R. Tracy, Science Department, Polytechnic High School, Long Beach, California.

Harry E. Tropp is Science Consultant, Hillsborough County Public Schools, Tampa, Florida.

Alfred E. Friedl is Curriculum Coordinator, San Diego County Department of Education, San Diego, California.

Cover photograph: light reflected from a thin film of soap, *Fundamental Photographs.* Title page photograph: a beam of light strikes a rectangular bar of glass, showing reflection, refraction, total internal reflection, and diffusion, *Fundamental Photographs.* Block opening photographs: Block One, crystals of calcium tartaricum, *Monkmeyer Press Photo Service;* Block Two, mercury switch and bimetalic coil in a thermostat, *Fundamental Photographs;* Block Three, circular waves on water, *Fundamental Photographs;* Block Four, a magnet deflects the electron beam of a television set showing the words "American League," *Fundamental Photographs;* Block Five, a radio-telescope antenna, *Monkmeyer Press Photo Service.*

66VH7

1–1098–2016

PREFACE

Modern Physical Science is an outgrowth of many years of science teaching. It was designed to be especially useful to teachers who feel the need for relating the study of science to the experiences of the students.

At an age when we are surrounded by many scientific breakthroughs, all students should possess a minimum literacy in the basic sciences. To this end, this textbook was written as a part of the general education program in the high school. It provides for a development and an understanding of basic concepts in chemistry and physics. It also relates these concepts to many applications in meteorology, space science, astronomy, geology, and oceanography.

Too often, teachers place an excessive amount of stress on the highly technical and mathematical end-products of scientific knowledge. This approach frequently creates an environment which inhibits student interest and learning. This text, on the other hand, presents a well-balanced science course stressing the processes and activities of science as well as the basic fundamentals. All of these are developed fully using a nonmathematical approach. However, there are numerous problems used which require the recall of simple computational skills. These problems are selected to provide students with an opportunity to experience the quantitative aspects of science. Included in the text are many simple demonstrations and experiments, many of which can be performed individually by students either at school or at home. Adventures in the exploration of nature, and the development of models to fit observed behavior of matter are also emphasized.

The text is arranged into five blocks, each of which explores a major subdivision in physical science. Each teacher must, of course, select those blocks which fall within the scope and needs of his class. Those teachers who like the pupil-motivation, functional, and individualized methods of instruction will find this text a valuable resource tool, readily accessible to the so-called "average student."

The blocks are further subdivided into chapters which are structured in such a manner as to develop and apply basic principles and applications of science. The chapter-end material is enriched with a short summary, a matching review exercise, *Group A* questions for essential recall information, and *Group B* questions for interpretation and application of the material presented in the chapter. Numerical problems are also included in chapters where appropriate.

For added convenience, each chapter is delineated into several sections. A short *Quick Quiz* is included as section-end material to be used as classroom discussion questions or for student evaluations.

The *Teacher's Edition* of *Modern Physical Science* contains a listing of student activities of an investigative nature and selected reference and collateral reading material as additional chapter-end materials. The Teacher's Edition also contains significant annotations as part of the text as well as answers to questions and numerical problems. Suggested skeletal lesson plans are also included for teacher use.

The combined workbook-laboratory manual, *Exercises and Investigations for Modern Physical Science* contains a series of exercises and investigations, following the organization of the text, and is available to the student as supplementary material. In addition, a series of eighteen objective-essay type tests that follows the sequence of the material in the textbook is available for teacher use.

The authors wish to thank Victor Kirsch, Commack Public Schools, Commack, New York; Gerald M. Rees, Ann Arbor High School, Ann Arbor, Michigan; and John G. Weihaupt, USAFI, Madison, Wisconsin, who read the manuscript.

The authors also extend their thanks to George Mass and his staff for the preparation of the drawings, and to Frances L. Orkin who obtained the photographs.

CONTENTS

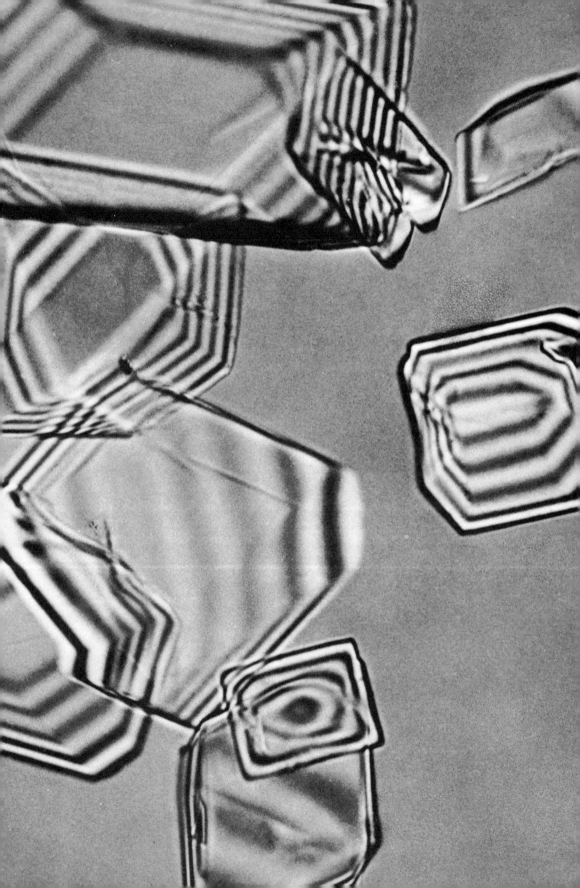

UNDERSTANDING CHEMISTRY

1 THE WORLD OF MATTER

A SCIENCE: A PRODUCT OF MAN'S INTELLIGENCE

Science and curiosity are related. Science begins with man's desire to understand the environment in which he lives. People by nature are basically curious and want to know the *why* and *how* of things. They want to know what makes things "tick," what they are made of, and why they act the way they do. They want to understand the material universe and seek explanations about its behavior. Science seeks to answer many of these questions. (See Fig. 1-1.)

Is the flame of a lighted candle caused by a burning gas? How can we find out?

Observe that the candle wax melts into a pool of liquid. This liquid is soaked up by the wick. Perhaps the melted wax turns into a gas as it gets near the hot flame. You can see through the lower part of the flame, just as you can see through most gases, such as the air. We can assume then that the lower part of the flame is made of an invisible gas.

Draw off some of this gas with a short piece of glass tubing as shown in

1-1. A scientist engages in a controlled series of observations in an experiment. (E. I. du Pont de Nemours & Co., Inc.)

Burning gas

1-2. The flame of a candle is produced by the burning of an invisible gas.

Fig. 1-2. Try to burn it. A flame is obtained at the end of the tube. Evidently, in the lighted candle, flame is caused by the burning gas.

Scientists learn through reading, thinking, *experimenting*, and by sharing ideas with each other. A more complete understanding of nature is the goal of a scientist. Information is gathered from many sources, processed, and then evaluated in order that various problems may be solved. This is the spirit of science. It begins with curiosity!

What is science? In man's continuous search for knowledge about *how* things behave under different conditions, and *why*, he seeks to develop *generalizations* about his environment which will allow him to *predict* the behavior of things. *Science is a process by which new knowledge is acquired, and by which we increase our understanding of the material universe.* Science is *not* a "book of answers," but essentially a method of learning! With the development of new knowledge, the scientist seeks to improve man's living conditions. Thus, science has made possible such things as polio vaccine, weather satellites, television, faster-than-sound jets, and atomic power. (See Fig. 1-3.)

In physical science we are concerned with those sciences *not directly connected with living things*. This includes such branches as chemistry, physics, geology, meteorology, astronomy and astronautics, astrophysics, and oceanography.

1-3. Scientists often use complicated equipment in seeking solutions to their problems. In this photograph, scientists are using a Van de Graaff generator to produce a beam of protons. (Brookhaven National Laboratory)

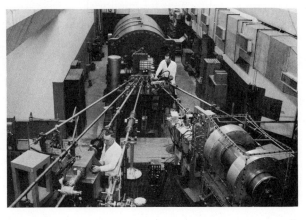

Why study science? We get up in the morning and wash with water that has been scientifically treated and purified. Pressure makes heated water flow from the tap. We use electric lights and enjoy the comforts of a heated home.

During the day, we use machines that simplify tasks of daily living. We can buy better clothing because our knowledge of science has provided improved textiles. Science helps us develop better soaps and soapless cleaners to clean our clothes, more nourishing foods for our bodies, better materials for building homes and more effective drugs to cure or prevent diseases.

Other products of science include motor vehicles for transportation and telephones for communication. Radios and television sets bring us news broadcasts, classroom instruction, and entertainment. We live in a dynamic age of electronic computers, mechanical "brains," miracle drugs, spaceships, and guided missiles.

All of these advances affect our daily lives. Science plays an important role in nearly everything we do!

Fears and superstitions. When you drop a fork, will you have visitors? Do you carry a rabbit's foot for good luck? Are you afraid that if you break a mirror you will have seven years of bad luck? These may seem like silly questions, but some people still believe such superstitions.

Our study of science can help us to distinguish *fact* from superstition, and truth from falsehood. Before the scientific age, people were frightened by mysterious comets, eclipses, thunder, and lightning. Understanding the nature of such events helps eliminate fear.

Science and citizenship. Good citizenship requires an understanding of science. Your community may have to decide on problems of roads, bridges, civil defense measures, parks, airports, sewage disposal, or the water supply. Questions about fluoridation of your drinking water, pollution of air and water, conservation of our national resources, new sources of food supply for peoples of the world, and flood and pest control require an understanding of science for their solutions. (See Fig. 1-4.)

Only if you have learned and understood some principles of science can you help decide these problems wisely. The welfare of our country depends upon effective decisions by well-informed citizens.

Science and measurement. Many of the problems of science require definite answers to such questions as "How much force?"—"How much time?"—

1-4. A Federal Food and Drug Administration inspector checks a crop that will be shipped out-of-state in order to enforce the law that protects consumers from unsafe pesticide residues on the crop. (FDA Photo)

"How fast?"—"How high?" When you say, "The building is high," your remark has various meanings to different people. Such a statement is very *indefinite*. The listener does not know whether the height of the building is 300 ft or 500 ft or 700 ft. When you say, "The building is 770 ft high," then you are being *definite*. You can now compare this measure with heights of other buildings.

You may say that an automobile is traveling fast. One person may think of 50 miles per hour as being fast. Another may think of 70 miles per hour as being fast. Or, in a 15 mile-per-hour school zone, the automobile would be traveling fast even though the speed were only 30 miles per hour.

Unless information is specific and definite, it is of little scientific value and significance.

The metric unit of length. The *metric system* is used by scientists all over the world. In most countries it is the only system of weights and measures used by the people in general. In the United States the *English system* (pounds, feet, etc.) is more commonly used by the people. However, the use of the metric system is rapidly increasing and we should become familiar with it. It is much simpler than our English system because, like our monetary system, it is based on decimals.

The basic unit of length in the metric system is the **meter.** For many years, the *standard meter* was defined as the distance between two parallel lines scratched on a platinum-iridium bar kept near Paris, France. From this standard many copies have been made. A more meaningful standard is now in effect. Arbitrarily, scientists of the world have defined the meter as being

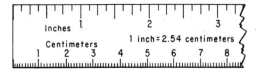

1-5. Can you approximate from the above figure the number of centimeters equivalent to 3 inches?

equivalent to 1,650,763.73 wavelengths of the orange-red spectral line of krypton-86. The scientist needs only to set a krypton gas lamp aglow under proper conditions in his own laboratory and check any given measurement against the standard light when it becomes necessary to do so.

The meter is equivalent to 39.37 inches, or a little over a yard. The meter is conveniently divided into 100 equal parts called *centimeters*. The prefix *centi-* means 1/100. A **centimeter** is 1/100 part of a meter just as a cent is 1/100 part of a dollar. A **millimeter** is 1/1000 part of a meter. The prefix *milli-* means 1/1000. The prefix *kilo-* means 1000. Hence there are 1000 meters in a **kilometer.** Study carefully the table below.

10 millimeters (mm)	= 1 centimeter (cm)
100 centimeters	= 1 meter (m)
1000 meters	= 1 kilometer (km)

The following table and a study of Fig. 1-5 enable us to convert units of length from one system to the other.

1 meter	= 39.37 inches (in.)
1 inch	= 2.54 centimeters

What is weight? Suppose your pencil falls to the floor, or a bomb drops from an airplane. In these cases, the object is attracted or pulled to the earth. A push or a pull on an object is called *force*. *The measure of the pull of the earth on an object is called weight.* When you say that a boy weighs 120 pounds, you mean that the earth and the boy are attracted to each other by a force of 120 pounds.

The weight of a small object can be easily determined by hanging it from a *spring balance.* (See Fig. 1-6.) We can also find the weight of objects with a *platform balance* by placing the object to be weighed on one end and known "weights" on the other end. When the two platforms balance, the weight of the object is equal to the total of the "weights" used on the other end. (See Fig. 1-7.)

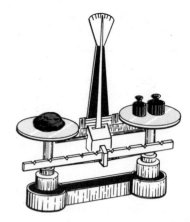

1-7. A platform balance is used in the laboratory to compare masses of small objects.

Even air can be weighed. The familiar saying "as light as air" suggests that air does not weigh very much. A cubic foot of water, rock, or metal weighs much more than the same volume of air. You can determine the weight of a given volume of air in the laboratory. Carefully weigh a globe like the one in Fig. 1-8, with its stopcock open. Then attach the stopcock opening to a vacuum pump and take out as much air as you can. You should be able to remove about 90 percent of the air. Finally, close the stopcock and weigh the globe again. The difference between the two weights gives the weight of the air removed. What happens to the weight when you let the air back in?

Matter and mass. Examine a rubber sponge, a glass of water, or a book. Observe that each occupies a certain space and that each has a definite weight. As you found in the above experiment with the evacuated globe, even gases such as air have weight. *Anything that occupies space and has weight is matter.*

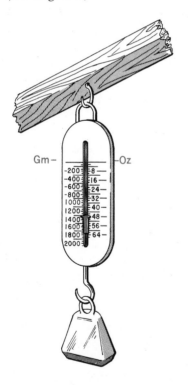

Gm— ——Oz

1-6. What are the approximate readings on the above scale of the spring balance?

Suppose you place a bowling ball and a baseball on a table. Observe that it requires a *greater* force to start the bowling ball moving than it does to start the baseball. This means that the bowling ball contains more *matter* than the baseball. Under these conditions, scientists say that the *mass* of the bowling ball is greater than the mass of the baseball. *Mass is a measure of the amount of matter.*

Experiments show that the mass of an object increases with an increase in its velocity. For example, when electrons are moving with speeds approaching that of light, the increase of mass becomes appreciable. In this text we shall concern ourselves with *rest mass* (the mass of an object when it is not moving), since the velocities we normally deal with are small compared with that of light.

Weight and mass are different. The easiest way to determine the mass of an object is by comparing its mass with

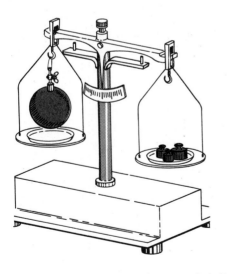

1-8. After the metal globe is evacuated, it weighs less than it did when it contained air.

that of some known standard previously agreed upon by everybody concerned. This can be done in the laboratory by means of the platform balance. Even though weight and mass are directly related to each other, *they are not the same thing.*

Unfortunately, sometimes weight and mass are expressed in the same unit, for example, the pound. But a *pound mass* is a definite amount of matter and remains the same anywhere in the universe. A *pound weight* is the force with which the earth attracts a pound mass at sea level and 45° latitude. *The weight of an object is different in various locations of the universe while the rest mass of the same object does not change.* If we were to attach an object to a spring balance, we would find that it weighs less when taken farther away from the center of the earth.

What is the kilogram? *The kilogram is the unit of mass in the metric system.* The unit of mass is not a matter to be settled by discovery but merely by general agreement of the nations of the world. Under such agreement, the unit of mass is established as the mass of a certain block of platinum preserved with elaborate precautions at the International Bureau of Weights and Measures in France. The mass of this block is called the **kilogram.** Two good copies of this world standard of mass are in possession of the U.S. Bureau of Standards in Washington, D.C. Every kilogram mass that you are likely to see is a direct descendant of one of the American standards. (See Fig. 1-9.)

The *gram* is also a metric unit of mass. It is 1/1000 of the kilogram. Our 5-cent coin (a nickel) has a *mass* of about 5 grams. The same prefixes for fractions of a gram are used as for fractions of a meter. Thus, a *centigram* is 1/100 part of a gram, and a **milligram** is 1/1000 part of a gram. You may wish to change from one system to the other by using the following table.

---

1 pound (lb)   = 454 grams (g)
1 kilogram (kg) = 2.2 pounds

The metric unit of volume. All matter occupies a certain amount of space. An automobile takes up more space than a book, and a battleship takes up more space than an automobile. *The measure of space occupied by an object is called its volume.* The volume of an object of regular shape can be obtained by multiplying its length, width, and depth.

The **liter** (*lee*-ter) is the metric unit for measuring volume. The same prefixes are used for fractions of a liter as are used for fractions of a meter.

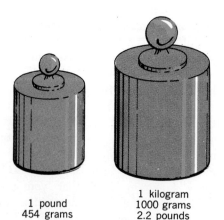

1 pound
454 grams

1 kilogram
1000 grams
2.2 pounds

1-9. The kilogram is the standard unit of rest mass in the metric system and is equivalent to 2.2 pounds in the English system.

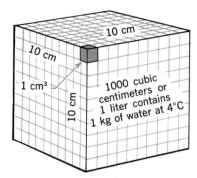

10 cm

10 cm

10 cm

1 cm³

10 cm

1000 cubic centimeters or 1 liter contains 1 kg of water at 4°C

1-10. The large cube represents a volume of one liter or 1000 cm³. The small corner cube is 1/1000 of a liter or 1 milliliter.

A cube 10 cm on each side has a volume of 1000 cubic centimeters (10 cm × 10 cm × 10 cm = 1000 cm³), which in turn is one liter. (See Fig. 1-10.) Observe then, that one **milliliter** (ml) is the same as one cubic centimeter (cm³). The volume of liquid contained in a teaspoon is approximately 5 milliliters. The liter is about 6 percent larger than one liquid quart.

---

1 liter (l) = 1.06 quart (qt)
1 liter   = 1000 cm³ (or 1000 ml)

Determination of volume. To find the volume of a regular object like a cube or other rectangular solid, measure its length, width, and height, and multiply these measurements together.

SAMPLE PROBLEM

A rectangular wooden crate is 6.0 ft long, 2.5 ft wide, and 36 in. high. Find the volume of the crate.

SOLUTION:

Step 1. First write the formula for the volume:

Volume = length × width × height

Step 2. Substitute, using the proper units, and multiply the *numbers* together and then the *units* together.

Volume = 6.0 ft × 2.5 ft × 3.0 ft
       = 45 ft³ (cubic feet)

To find the volume of a small irregular object like a piece of stone, another method is used. Fill a *graduated cylinder* approximately half full with water and note the reading of the water level. (See Fig. 1-11.) Then put the object into the water. Since two objects cannot take up the same space at the same time, the water level will rise in the cylinder. Now take a second reading of the water level. The difference in readings between the second and first water levels is the volume of the stone. What are some of the limitations of this method? What would happen if you tried this with a lump of sugar instead of the stone?

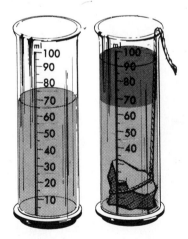

1-11. A graduated cylinder may be used to determine the volume of small irregular objects by liquid displacement. How many milliliters is the volume of the stone in the cylinder on the right?

Quick Quiz

1. What happens to a person's rest mass as his distance from the earth increases? What happens to his weight?
2. Explain how you would determine the weight of small objects in the laboratory.
3. How would you find the volume of a small irregular piece of metal? A piece of candy?
4. What are the basic units of length, mass, and volume in the metric system? How were they determined?
5. Make a list of reasons for favoring the introduction of the metric system in the United States for everyday use. Also prepare a list of several reasonable objections.
6. Discuss the importance of measurement in science.
7. Explain a method by which you could determine whether air has weight. Does air have mass? Explain.
8. From the information contained in Fig. 1-10, determine the weight of 1 ml of water.

B MATTER AND ITS CHANGES

Phases of matter. We recognize many kinds of matter such as wood, water, air, concrete, and gasoline by certain observable characteristics that are familiar to us. For convenience in studying the characteristics of substances, scientists have arranged them in three groups: *solids, liquids,* and *gases.* These are called the *phases or states of matter.* Wood and steel are examples of matter in the solid phase, water and gasoline are in the liquid phase, and the air about you is in the gaseous phase.

In the *solid phase,* matter takes up a definite volume and has a definite shape. Matter in a *liquid phase* takes up a definite volume but has no definite shape. Liquids take the shape of the container they are in, such as milk in a glass or water in a pitcher. Matter in the *gaseous phase* has no definite shape and no definite volume. A gas takes the shape and size of the container. Air filling a toy balloon is a good example of how a gas completely fills its container.

Scientists sometimes speak of a fourth state of matter called *plasma.* This is a special gaseous-like form of matter that exists under extreme conditions of temperature and pressure. Plasma is quite common throughout the universe, being largely the material of the stars. The aurora borealis in our upper atmosphere and solar prominences on the sun provide impressive examples of matter in a plasma state. Scientists have estimated that over 99 percent of all the matter in the universe is in this phase.

Phase changes of matter. Some kinds of matter can be changed from one phase to another by *changing the temperature.* Water is a familiar example. When a piece of ice (solid) is sufficiently heated, water (liquid) results. When water is heated sufficiently, it turns into steam (gas). Other changes in phase are brought about by *changing the pressure.* Pressure applied to ice causes it to melt.

Sometimes matter passes from a solid into a gas without passing through the liquid phase. This process is called *sublimation* (sub-lih-*may*-shun). Dry ice (carbon dioxide in the solid phase) is an example of matter having no liquid phase at ordinary temperatures and pressures. At room temperature, it *sublimes* directly into a gas.

Physical and chemical changes. Countless changes in matter are continually taking place. Ice changes into water. Paraffin melts when heated. Gasoline evaporates rapidly unless kept in a tight container. A piece of blackboard chalk can be ground into a fine

1-12. In the research laboratory, the quest for knowledge never ends. A research chemist ponders a problem that may lead to a new or improved plastic. (E. I. du Pont de Nemours & Co., Inc.)

powder. All of these are *physical changes*. **Physical changes** are those that *do not produce a new substance*. Water is the same chemically whether it is ice or steam. The chalk particles remain chalk no matter what the size or shape of the pieces. Gasoline is chemically unchanged after it evaporates.

Changes that *produce new substances* are called **chemical changes.** The decay of plants, the souring of milk, the rusting of iron, and the digestion of food are examples of chemical changes produced in matter. In each of these processes, new substances are produced whose chemical composition and characteristics are different from those of the original substances. The burning of magnesium produces a white powder called magnesium oxide. Magnesium oxide has none of the color or metallic luster of magnesium; iron rust is different from iron; sweet milk is not the same chemically as sour milk.

How substances are recognized. When you walk down a street, you can easily tell a house built of bricks from one made of wood. In the same way, a scientist recognizes the substances he studies. You might guess that a yellow metal was gold, but you would have to know more about it to be sure.

Each substance has certain qualities or characteristics that identify it. These are called the *properties* of the substance. **Physical properties** of a substance include color, density, hardness, solubility, brittleness, and freezing and boiling temperatures. They are characteristics that can be observed and measured.

There are other kinds of properties, too. Gold does not tarnish. Water and

1-13. A dynamite explosion (chemical change) causes rock to break into small pieces (physical change). (E. I. du Pont de Nemours & Co., Inc.)

common acids do not affect it either. Magnesium burns with a dazzling white flame as it unites with oxygen of the air to form magnesium oxide. *Properties that tell about the reaction of a substance with other substances are called chemical properties.*

What is density? An important physical property of matter which scientists use in distinguishing one substance from another is *density*. Gold, for example, is a very heavy metal; that is, it has a high density. A cubic foot of gold weighs over 1000 lb. *The density of a substance is the weight (or mass) of a certain volume of it.* A cubic inch of gold weighs 0.7 lb. Hence, we say that the density of gold is 0.7 lb per cubic inch, or 0.7 lb/in.^{3}

Generally, density is expressed in pounds per cubic foot (lb/ft^3) in the English system, or in grams per cubic

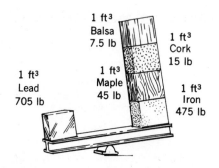

1-14. These blocks show that equal volumes of different materials have different weights, and hence, different densities.

centimeter (gm/cm³) in the metric system. The density of fresh water in the English system is 62.4 lb/ft³. In metric units it is defined as 1.0 g/cm³. (See Fig. 1-14.)

SAMPLE PROBLEM

A piece of wood 8 ft long, 1 ft wide, and 6 in. thick weighs 96 lb. What is the density of the wood?

SOLUTION:

Step 1. The density can be determined if two quantities are known: the *volume* and the *weight* or *mass*. Since the weight is given (96 lb), we need first to compute the volume from the data given in the problem.

$$\text{Volume} = \text{length} \times \text{width} \times \text{thickness}$$
$$= (8\,\text{ft}) \times (1\,\text{ft}) \times (\tfrac{1}{2}\,\text{ft})$$
$$= 4\,\text{ft}^3$$

Step 2. From the definition of density,

$$\text{Density} = \frac{\text{weight}}{\text{volume}}$$
$$= \frac{96\,\text{lb}}{4\,\text{ft}^3}$$
$$= 24\,\text{lb/ft}^3$$

How does the density of this wood compare with that of water?

Electrolysis of water. Figure 1-15 is a diagram of apparatus used to show that water is made of two different gases. This process shows that water is not a basic substance but can be broken up, or *decomposed*, into simpler substances. The apparatus is filled with water that has a small quantity of sulfuric acid in it to make it an electrical conductor. An electric current flowing through the water breaks it up into two gases, **hydrogen** and **oxygen**, which collect in separate tubes. The reason the two gases form as they do will be discussed later in this chapter.

When a *chemical change* results from the passing of an electric current through a liquid, the process is called *electrolysis* (eh-lek-*trol*-uh-sis). This is an important industrial process, and will be referred to often in our study of physical science.

Observe from the diagram, that there is *twice* as much of one gas (hydrogen) as there is of the other (oxygen). Both are colorless gases. Pure hydrogen burns with an almost color-

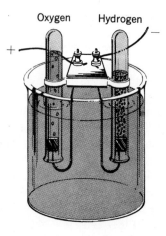

1-15. An electric current separates the compound water into its elements, oxygen and hydrogen.

less flame, and as the hydrogen burns, it combines chemically with oxygen of the air to form water.

The oxygen collected does not burn. However, when you thrust a glowing splint of wood into the oxygen, the wood bursts into flame. This illustrates two chemical properties of oxygen: it does not burn; and it actively supports the burning of other substances.

Elements are basic substances. We have seen that water is made up of two gases, hydrogen and oxygen, which have different chemical properties. These gases have been found to be *basic* substances. No further chemical change will reduce these two gases into simpler substances. *A substance that cannot be broken up into simpler substances by ordinary chemical means is called an* **element.** Elements are nature's building blocks because all different substances in the universe are made from them.

There are over one hundred different elements, many of which exist on the earth in varying amounts. Some are very common while others are extremely rare. Scientists have been able to make a few of these elements artificially. You will have the opportunity to learn about some man-made elements later in our study.

The table below shows the relative average abundance of the most common elements found in the earth's crust. It must be remembered that these elements are not distributed uniformly in the earth's crust. Thus these percentages may not hold for each specific part of the crust.

Notice from the above list that many of the familiar elements such as copper, lead, zinc, silver, and gold are

ELEMENTS IN THE EARTH'S CRUST

Oxygen	49.5%	Sodium	2.6%
Silicon	25.8%	Potassium	2.4%
Aluminum	7.5%	Magnesium	1.9%
Iron	4.7%	Hydrogen	0.9%
Calcium	3.4%	Others	1.3%

not even included. The fact that an element is not relatively abundant does not necessarily mean that it is not important.

Each element has a symbol. Chemists label the elements by using *symbols* of one or two letters. For example, **O** is the chemical symbol for oxygen, **C** for carbon, **H** for hydrogen, **Al** for aluminum, **Mg** for magnesium, **S** for sulfur, **Cl** for chlorine, and **Ca** for calcium. The symbols for the early-known elements were taken from the abbreviation of their Latin names, such as **Au** for gold, **Ag** for silver, **Pb** for lead, **Cu** for copper, and **Fe** for iron. A more complete chart of the common elements and symbols appears in Section C, page 26.

Elements form mixtures and compounds. From the twenty-six letters in our alphabet, we can make an almost endless number of words. Similarly, from about a hundred elements, an unlimited number of mixtures and compounds can be produced. Hence, there are many more mixtures and compounds than there are elements.

When you mix some powdered iron and sulfur, a grayish material results. These two elements have been brought very close together but they have *not combined with each other* to form a new substance. A strong magnet may be used to separate the powdered iron from the sulfur. In other words, the ingredients in this *mixture* retain their original properties. *A **mixture** is a material containing substances that have not been chemically united.* Air is a mixture of many gases, mainly nitrogen and oxygen. Can you suggest a way to separate a mixture of powdered iron and sugar without the use of a magnet?

In a mixture, the component substances may be present in any proportions. It is possible to use a large amount of iron and a small amount of sulfur, or a large amount of sulfur and a small portion of powdered iron.

When you put a sample of iron-sulfur mixture in a test tube and vigorously heat it, the iron unites *chemically* with the sulfur to form a new substance, a *compound,* called *iron sulfide.* (See Fig. 1-16.) The physical and chemical properties of iron sulfide are different from either of the two original elements. The iron can no longer be separated from the iron sulfide by a magnet.

*A **compound** is a substance that is composed of two or more different elements that are united chemically.* The iron sulfide produced in this reaction is an example of a compound. While mixtures can be separated by physical means, a compound can be broken up only by chemical means. The substances listed in the table below are some common examples of elements, mixtures, and compounds.

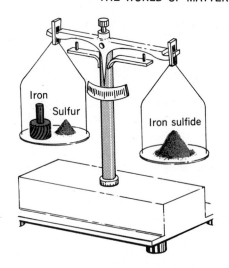

1-16. The element iron (Fe) unites chemically with the element sulfur (S), when heated, to form the compound iron sulfide (FeS). The substances on each side of the balance weigh the same.

What are molecules? Think of a lump of sugar. Imagine dividing it in two—then the two into four—and the four into eight—and so on. Finally, you arrive at a point when you attain the smallest particle that is still identified as sugar. This would be one *molecule* of sugar. Any further dividing would separate the compound sugar into its elements. *The smallest particle that exhibits all the properties of an element or compound is called a **molecule.*** Molecules are so small that even with an electron microscope only a few of

Elements	Mixtures	Compounds
tin (Sn)	milk	water (H_2O)
iron (Fe)	butter	sugar ($C_{12}H_{22}O_{11}$)
aluminum (Al)	toothpaste	table salt (NaCl)
silver (Ag)	baking powder	baking soda ($NaHCO_3$)
oxygen (O)	paint	ethyl alcohol (C_2H_5OH)

the very large ones have ever been observed.

You will have some idea of the size of a molecule when you realize there are more molecules in one tiny grain of sugar than there are grains of sugar contained in a 5-lb bag. Actually, each tiny grain is made up of many billions of sugar molecules.

Perhaps another example will help you to realize how small molecules are. Water is a compound that is made up of molecules. Comparing the size of a molecule of water to a drop of water is like comparing the size of a baseball to the size of the earth.

Molecules are composed of atoms. You learned previously that iron sulfide is made from the elements of iron and sulfur. Each molecule of iron sulfide must contain both iron and sulfur. Hence, each molecule must be made of still smaller particles. These particles are called *atoms. An atom is the smallest particle of an element that can combine chemically with other elements.* A molecule is made up of atoms that are chemically united.

One atom of iron combines with one atom of sulfur to form one molecule of iron sulfide. Each molecule of a compound is composed of two or more different atoms. Molecules of some gaseous elements, for example oxygen and hydrogen, are made up of two *identical* atoms. Atoms of different elements unite in many combinations. A conservative estimate of the number of compounds that have been identified is about 1,000,000. And new compounds are being produced every day in research laboratories all over the world. (See Fig. 1-17.)

Chemical formulas are convenient. With so many known compounds and

new ones continually being prepared, it would be extremely difficult to keep track of them if each were referred to only by name. *Chemical formulas identify compounds by indicating the kind and number of atoms present in them.*

You probably know that H_2O is the formula for water. It can also be written as **HOH.** The simple chemical formula of water tells you that it is a compound of hydrogen and oxygen. It also tells you that one molecule of water consists of two atoms of hydrogen and one atom of oxygen.

Notice that *chemical symbols* are used in writing *formulas.* When a number follows a symbol, written slightly below the line, it tells how many atoms of that element are contained in the molcule. Thus, one molecule of table sugar, $C_{12}H_{22}O_{11}$, contains 12 atoms of carbon, 22 of hydrogen, and 11 of oxygen. In reading this formula, we

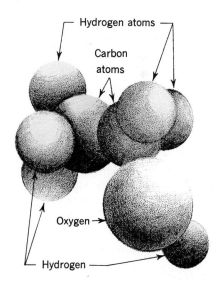

1-17. Chemists use molecular models such as this one for ethyl alcohol to show the possible arrangement of atoms in molecules.

say, C-twelve, H-twenty-two, O-eleven. This makes a total of 45 atoms in one molecule of this sugar. With further study, you will learn the formulas for many other compounds. The table below gives examples of several compounds.

Name of Compound	Formula
Magnesium oxide	MgO
Sodium chloride (table salt)	NaCl
Sodium bicarbonate (baking soda)	$NaHCO_3$
Iron sulfide	FeS
Table sugar	$C_{12}H_{22}O_{11}$
Sulfuric acid	H_2SO_4
Ammonium hydroxide (household ammonia)	NH_4OH

Law of conservation of matter. In ordinary physical and chemical changes, no additional matter is created and none is lost. We can demonstrate this by using the apparatus shown in Fig. 1-18. A chemical change occurs when a solution of sodium chloride (NaCl) is mixed with a solution of silver nitrate ($AgNO_3$). Put common table salt solution in a flask and some silver nitrate solution in the test tube which is placed upright in the flask. Then a stopper is placed in the flask and the whole apparatus is weighed. When the flask is turned upside down, a chemical change takes place forming a white substance that is neither sodium chloride nor silver nitrate. This substance, which *separates* from the liquid, or forms a *precipitate*, is a new substance silver chloride (AgCl). Weighing the flask again, we find that the apparatus has the same weight as before. *No matter has been gained or lost in the reaction.*

This experiment illustrates the *law of conservation of matter: matter cannot be created or destroyed by ordinary chemical means.* In science a *law* is a generalization about the way matter behaves under certain conditions. Laws have been evolved only after many careful experiments. Later we shall learn that matter can be converted into heat energy in nuclear reactions but these are not *ordinary* chemical changes.

Chemical equations. An *equation* is an expression that shows what happens during a chemical reaction. We have seen that heating a mixture of iron and sulfur produces iron sulfide. This may be expressed as a *word equation* as

$$iron + sulfur \rightarrow iron\ sulfide$$

The arrow ($\rightarrow$) means "produces." The equation does not tell us what had to be done to the iron-sulfur mixture to obtain iron sulfide. If we want to express the fact that heat was applied, the equation may be written as

$$iron + sulfur \xrightarrow{heat} iron\ sulfide$$

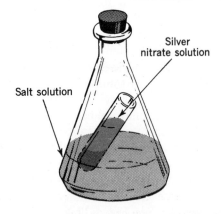

Silver nitrate solution

Salt solution

1-18. A chemical change is produced by turning the flask upside down. No matter is gained or lost.

Chemists prefer to write equations using symbols and formulas because they tell more about the arrangement of the atoms taking part in a chemical reaction. These are called **chemical equations.** The above reaction would then be written as

$$Fe + S \xrightarrow{\text{heat}} FeS$$

The equation reads, "one atom of iron and one atom of sulfur when sufficiently heated produce one molecule of iron sulfide." We have seen that electrolysis of water produces hydrogen and oxygen, and we can express this fact in the following word equation

$$\text{water} \xrightarrow{\text{electricity}} \text{hydrogen} + \text{oxygen}$$

Careful experiments show that a molecule of oxygen gas is composed of two oxygen atoms and is written as O_2. Similarly, a molecule of hydrogen gas is composed of two hydrogen atoms and is written as H_2. Since water was broken up into two volumes of hydrogen and one volume of oxygen, chemists express this fact by the chemical equation

$$2H_2O \rightarrow 2H_2 + O_2$$

This equation reads, "two molecules of water produce two molecules of hydrogen and one molecule of oxygen." While we shall have more to say about equations later in this chapter, notice that there are the *same* number of hydrogen and oxygen atoms on the left side of the arrow as there are on the right. There are four hydrogen atoms and two oxygen atoms on each side. Would you suspect this from the law of conservation of matter?

The law of definite proportions. Iron sulfide is *always* made up of seven parts by *weight* of iron and four parts by *weight* of sulfur. While the composition of mixtures can vary, *the elements that unite to form compounds always unite in the same proportions.* If there is too much iron in proportion to sulfur, some of it does not combine with the sulfur but remains as iron. If there is too much sulfur in proportion to the iron, then some of the sulfur remains uncombined. This fact is expressed as the *law of definite proportions: every compound always has the same proportion by weight of the elements composing it.* The scientific reasons why compounds "obey" this law will be studied in the next section.

Water is our most common solvent. When a cube of sugar is placed in a cup of water and stirred, the sugar disappears. We then say that the sugar has *dissolved.* In this example, the liquid water in which the sugar was dissolved is called the *solvent.* And the solid (sugar) that is dissolved is called the **solute** (*sol*-yoot). We say then that sugar is *soluble* in water. Water is an excellent solvent because it dissolves very many substances.

Some substances, such as oils, gums, and resins, will not dissolve in water. These substances are said to be *insoluble* in water, but usually dissolve in other liquids such as alcohol, gasoline, turpentine, or carbon tetrachloride (tet-rah-*cloh*-ride). Different solvents are used to meet different needs. For example, cleaning fluids like benzene and carbon tetrachloride will remove grease spots. Turpentine is used to dissolve certain paints. The resulting liquid formed by *dissolving a solute in a solvent* is called a **solution.**

Types of solutions. Different words are used to describe solutions with varying amounts of solute in them. If we dissolve a spoonful of sugar in a quart of water, we have an example of a *dilute* solution. But if we dissolve a cupful of sugar in the same amount of water, we say that the solution is *concentrated.*

From the above remarks, it is seen that *dilute* and *concentrated* are not very definite terms. These terms imply "little or much" quantity of solute in the solvent. Frequently in laboratories, you see bottles labeled "Concentrated Sulfuric Acid" or "Concentrated H_2SO_4." This often indicates that there is relatively little water (solvent) present in the acid.

What are saturated solutions? If we keep adding sugar to the quart of water and stirring the solution constantly, we finally reach a point where no more sugar will dissolve at that temperature. This solution is now called a **saturated solution.** Such a solution contains a definite percentage of solute which is always the same for a particular substance at a given temperature. In this example, only a fixed maximum amount of sugar will dissolve in the quart of water at a definite temperature.

Now if we heat a saturated solution of sugar and water, we find that more sugar can be dissolved. In fact, a hot saturated solution contains a much greater percentage of solute than the saturated solution does at room temperature. *Many experiments indicate that most solids are more soluble in hot solvents than they are in cold solvents.*

Gases are more soluble in cold liquids than in hot ones. Just the op-posite of solids, gases dissolve better in cold liquids. Very cold water has a lot of air dissolved in it. If you let a glass of cold water stand in a warm room, you soon observe gas bubbles collecting on the sides of the vessel. As the water warms up, it no longer retains as much air in solution. (See Fig. 1-19.)

We can dissolve larger amounts of gas in a liquid if we apply *pressure* to it. "Soda pop" is water in which carbon dioxide gas has been dissolved under pressure. When the cap is taken off the bottle the pressure is released and the gas comes out of solution.

What is an emulsion? Liquids that are not very soluble in each other form an *emulsion* (ee-*mul*-shun) when they are shaken together. An **emulsion** consists of tiny droplets of one liquid scattered throughout another. The milky-looking sap of some plants is a natural emulsion. Milk is another common example. On standing, the tiny fat particles in the milk go together and rise to the top as cream. When

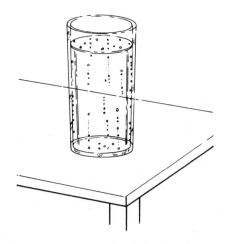

1-19. As cold water warms up, bubbles of air (nitrogen and oxygen gases) collect on the sides of the container.

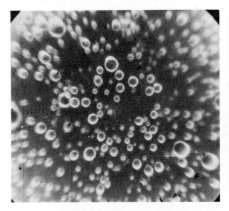 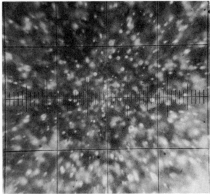

1-20. Notice the difference in size between the fat globules of raw milk (left) and homogenized milk (right) as viewed through the microscope. (Creamery Package Mfg. Co.)

the milk is *homogenized,* the fat is broken up into smaller particles. This forms a smoother mixture that stays *emulsified* longer. (See Fig. 1-20.)

We know that kerosene and water do not mix. However, if some soap solution is added to the mixture, and shaken, we observe that the kerosene and water form an emulsion that does not separate for a long time. In this case, the soap is called an *emulsifier.*

Another form of mixture is used today. Numerous commodities are sold in "spray" cans as *aerosols*. Aerosols are suspensions of tiny liquid or solid particles dispersed in a gaseous medium.

Quick Quiz

1. Describe three phases of matter. Give several examples of each.
2. What is the difference between a physical and a chemical change?
3. Explain how you would determine the density of a rectangular piece of steel.
4. What compound is formed when hydrogen burns in air?
5. State two differences between a mixture and a compound.
6. What does a chemical formula tell us? What information does a chemical equation give us?
7. Write two chemical equations and tell the meanings of each.
8. What is the difference between a solute, solvent, and solution?
9. What is the difference between a dilute, concentrated, and saturated solution?
10. Name five common solvents.
11. What two conditions help to dissolve more gas in a liquid?
12. Why is milk homogenized? How is it done?

C ATOMS AND MOLECULES

The atomic theory. Some of the early Greek scientists believed that matter was made of very small particles called *atoms,* a word meaning indivisible. It was not until the early nineteenth century that the English chemist, John Dalton, proposed the first useful theory concerning the nature and properties of matter. His theory made use of some of the old ideas concerning atoms, and he explained why every compound has a definite composition.

Our modern atomic model is a modified version of the one proposed by Dalton. Today, scientists have a great deal of evidence for believing that:

1. Matter is made up of very small particles called atoms.
2. Atoms of the same element are chemically alike; atoms of different elements are chemically different.
3. While individual atoms of a given element may not have the same weight, they have a definite *average* weight.
4. Atoms of different elements have a different average weight.
5. Atoms do not break up in ordinary chemical changes.

Single atoms of any element are much too small to see, even with the most powerful microscopes. However, the way matter behaves makes us fairly sure that the atomic theory is correct. We learned previously that one atom of iron unites chemically with one atom of sulfur to form one molecule of iron sulfide. A piece of iron sulfide, for example, is simply many of these molecules grouped together. Each molecule in the sample is made the same way. In other words, every iron atom acts like every other iron atom. Each atom of sulfur acts like every other sulfur atom. It is no surprise to find that a molecule of iron sulfide acts like every other molecule of iron sulfide and that these molecules always have the same properties and the same composition by weight of iron and sulfur.

The structure of an atom. For the past sixty years, scientists have been accumulating considerable evidence about the structure of atoms. We know now that atoms contain three different kinds of *basic* particles, called *elec-*

1-21. Particles that comprise the atomic nuclei are studied in this accelerator at Brookhaven National Laboratory. (Brookhaven National Laboratory)

1-22. Diagram of an ordinary hydrogen atom showing one proton in the nucleus (center) and one revolving electron.

trons, protons, and *neutrons.* The first two of these particles (the electron and the proton) carry opposite electrical charges; the third particle is uncharged (neutral).

An *electron is a negatively charged atomic particle;* a *proton* is a much heavier particle than an electron, and has an *equal but positive charge.* A *neutron is a nuclear particle with no electric charge;* it is neutral. The mass of a proton and that of a neutron are very nearly the same.

Although scientists have now discovered some thirty other particles by using cyclotrons and other "atom-smashing" devices, we shall consider only the three basic atomic particles that make up the atom at this time. (See Fig. 1-21.)

The simplest atom is the common form of hydrogen, which has one proton and one electron. The single electron travels in a path around the proton somewhat as shown in Fig. 1-22. The atoms of other elements have 2, 3, 4, or more electrons in motion. The most complex of the naturally-occurring elements, uranium, has a total of 92

electrons in rapid, constant motion. Several additional elements have been produced by scientists. Lawrencium, a recent edition to the man-made elements, contains 103 planetary electrons. *In each case, the neutral atoms of a particular element have the same number of protons as they have electrons.*

The nucleus of the atom. All atoms, except the most common form of hydrogen, contain neutrons. The protons and neutrons are grouped closely together to form the *nucleus,* as shown in Fig. 1-23, and the electrons move rapidly around it.

An atom of gold has the same kinds of basic particles in it as an atom of oxygen, iron, sulfur, or uranium. The differences between these elements are due to the different *numbers* of electrons, protons and neutrons they contain.

In spite of the small size of atoms, scientists have been able to find out a great deal about them. Almost all

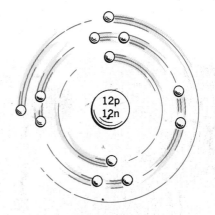

1-23. A simplified diagram of a magnesium atom showing 12 protons (P) and 12 neutrons (N) in the nucleus. Twelve electrons revolve in shells around the nucleus.

the weight of an atom is in the nucleus. This is understandable because each proton and each neutron has a mass about 1840 times as great as that of an electron.

The electrons move rapidly around the nucleus in oval paths or *orbits* at relatively great distances from the nucleus. All 92 electrons of the uranium atom, for example, do not move in the same orbit. In fact, there are 7 different sets of orbits, one inside the other, which scientists often refer to as electron shells, or energy levels.

The electron cloud. Electrons move about the nucleus so fast that they appear to form a cloud. To give you an idea why this is so, think of the appearance of a spinning airplane propeller. The propeller blades sweep out a hazy circular area and can no longer be seen. In a similar manner, the electron also sweeps out a hazy oval area.

You can imagine how complicated this motion becomes when you add more electrons in many different orbits, and also when you extend your imagination to include a spherical volume instead of a flat circular propeller-sweep area. Figure 1-24 shows how

Shell or energy level	Maximum total in completed shell	Maximum totals in completed sub-shell
— P —		
— O —		
— N —	32	
— M —	18	2,6,10
— L —	8	2,6
— K —	2	2
Nucleus (+)		

1-25. The distribution of electrons in shells about the nucleus of an atom.

a hydrogen atom may be represented on a flat surface. Since electrons constantly move in spherical regions instead of simple flat orbits, scientists often like to think of these regions as *electron clouds*. Of course, the electron cloud model of more complex atoms represents a region occupied by all the electrons of an atom, not just the region of one electron as represented by the hydrogen atom.

Electrons are distributed in definite shells about the atomic nucleus. We learned that electrons occupy certain shells about the nucleus of an atom. According to our latest atomic model, each of these shells can hold only a certain *maximum* number of electrons and no more. The innermost region, called the **K** shell, can hold no more than 2 electrons. The second shell, **L**, consisting of *two sub-shells*, can hold no more than a total of 8 electrons.

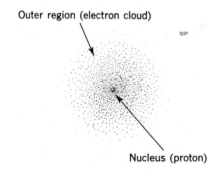

Outer region (electron cloud)

Nucleus (proton)

1-24. A convenient model of an atom of ordinary hydrogen. Imagine the electron cloud decreasing in density away from the nucleus.

The third shell, **M**, consisting of *three sub-shells,* can hold no more than a total of 18 electrons. The **N** shell can hold as many as 32 electrons. Study Fig. 1-25 and the table below to see how the electrons are distributed for the first 18 elements.

Remember that in a neutral atom, the total number of electrons in all of the various shells is equal to the number of protons contained in the nucleus. No two elements have atoms with the same number of electrons (or protons). From the table below, observe that oxygen has *8 protons* in the nucleus and hence a total of 8 *electrons* in the various shells distributed as follows: two in the **K** shell (the maximum number) and six in the **L** shell. Of

these six, two are in the first sub-shell and four in the second.

Chemists believe that the way atoms combine to form molecules is determined by the number of electrons in the outer shell of the atoms.

What is the atomic number of an element? The number of protons in the nucleus of an atom definitely identifies the element. Ordinary hydrogen, for example, consists of one proton as a nucleus. The *atomic number* is 1. The nucleus of the helium atom has 2 protons, hence the atomic number is 2. Lithium has an atomic number of 3, and so on until we reach the last naturally-occurring atom, uranium, with an atomic number of 92. *The atomic number of an element is the*

Name of element	Symbol	Atomic number (protons)	K Shell	L Shell		M Shell		
				1st sub-shell	2nd sub-shell	1st sub-shell	2nd sub-shell	3rd sub-shell
Hydrogen	H	1	1					
Helium	He	2	2					
Lithium	Li	3	2	1				
Beryllium	Be	4	2	2				
Boron	B	5	2	2	1			
Carbon	C	6	2	2	2			
Nitrogen	N	7	2	2	3			
Oxygen	O	8	2	2	4			
Fluorine	F	9	2	2	5			
Neon	Ne	10	2	2	6			
Sodium	Na	11	2	2	6	1		
Magnesium	Mg	12	2	2	6	2		
Aluminum	Al	13	2	2	6	2	1	
Silicon	Si	14	2	2	6	2	2	
Phosphorus	P	15	2	2	6	2	3	
Sulfur	S	16	2	2	6	2	4	
Chlorine	Cl	17	2	2	6	2	5	
Argon	Ar	18	2	2	6	2	6	

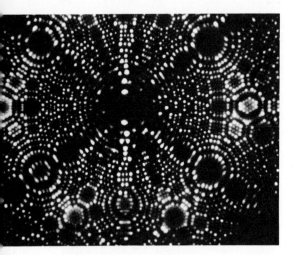

1-26. Scientists can study the patterns formed by atoms in different substances. In this photograph, a tungsten crystal was magnified 4,000,000 times. (Dr. Erwin Muller, Penn. State University)

number of protons contained in the nucleus of an atom. Notice that the elements in the table are arranged according to their atomic numbers.

The Periodic Table. To study the properties of the elements and to predict the behavior of compounds formed from various elements, chemists have found it convenient to classify the elements in a certain arrangement in order of their atomic numbers. Such a classification is called a *Periodic Table,* as shown at the end of this text.

All the elements in the standard-type Periodic Table are placed in seven horizontal rows called *periods.* These are numbered from 1 to 7. The vertical columns numbered from IA to VIIIA are called *groups.* Elements arranged in groups have similar chemical properties and predictable physical properties. For example, the six elements in group IA are very active chemically; that is, they combine read-

ily with certain other elements. Group VIIIA is the family of *inert* gases. These elements are very stable, and chemists have been able to prepare only a very few compounds containing these elements.

On the left of the Periodic Table, the most active elements are at the bottom; on the right, the most active elements are at the top.

How much does an atom weigh? Since atoms are extremely small, we find it inconvenient to express their weights in ordinary units. For example, the weight of a hydrogen atom is approximately 0.000,000,000,000,000,-000,000,000,06 of an ounce!

By international agreement, chemists decided to establish the mass of a carbon atom (an isotope of carbon, C-12) to be 12 mass units. This number represents the atomic mass of carbon. The comparative masses of all other atoms are based on the standard mass of 12 for carbon-12. The mass of a hydrogen atom is about $\frac{1}{12}$ that of the carbon atom. Therefore, ordinary hydrogen is assigned the atomic weight of 1. The *atomic mass* of any element is the *average mass of its atoms based on those of carbon-12 taken as a standard of 12 mass units.* The atomic mass of an atom is rarely a whole number. For our purpose, we shall use whole numbers to express atomic masses.

We mentioned that the hydrogen atom consists of one proton and one electron. Since the mass of either a proton or a neutron is about 1840 times as much as an electron, we disregard the mass of the electron in stating atomic masses and say that the mass of the proton or the neutron is one atomic mass unit. Study the following table.

Particle	Charge	Atomic Mass Units
electron	negative (−)	1/1840
proton	positive (+)	.1
neutron	neutral (0)	1
hydrogen atom	neutral (0)	1
carbon atom	neutral (0)	12
oxygen atom	neutral (0)	16

How many neutrons are in the nucleus of an atom? We have pointed out that the mass of an atom of hydrogen is approximately equal to the mass of its nucleus since the mass of an electron is so small by comparison, and may be neglected. We have also pointed out that the mass of a proton or a neutron is equivalent to one atomic mass unit. Since the nucleus of any atom, except the common form of hydrogen, is made of protons and neutrons, the *atomic mass of an atom is considered to be numerically equal to the sum of the protons and neutrons. Its atomic number, however, is equal to the number of protons.* To find the number of neutrons in an atom, we have only to subtract the atomic number (protons) from the atomic mass. For example, observe in the table on page 26 that the atomic mass of chlorine atom is 35 and its atomic number is 17. Subtracting 17 from 35 gives us 18, which is the number of neutrons in an atom of chlorine.

SAMPLE PROBLEM

How many protons are contained in the nucleus of a sodium atom? How many neutrons? What is the total number of electrons?

SOLUTION:

Step 1. From the table of elements, observe that sodium has an atomic number of 11, which means that there are 11 protons in the nucleus.

Step 2. The atomic mass of sodium is 23. Therefore, the number of neutrons is 23 − 11, or 12 neutrons.

Step 3. In a neutral atom, the total number of electrons about the nucleus is numerically equal to the atomic number. Therefore, the number of electrons is 11.

Note the distribution of these electrons in the various shells. (See table, page 23.)

Valence numbers. We are now ready to see how two different atoms may unite chemically to form a compound. Let us consider a particle of sodium chloride, ordinary table salt. We have seen that sodium has an atomic number of 11 and an atomic mass of 23. Let us first imagine how a sodium atom might appear if we could see it and stop its motion for a moment. There would be 11 protons and 12 neutrons in a closely packed nucleus. Of the 11 electrons about the nucleus, we would have 2 electrons in the *K* shell, 8 electrons in the *L* shell, leaving 1 electron in the outermost *M* shell. (See Fig. 1-27.)

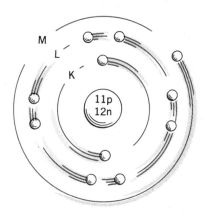

1-27. Diagram of the sodium atom. Notice the single electron in the M shell.

Now picture the chlorine atom. From the table of elements, we see that chlorine has an atomic number of 17 and an atomic mass of 35. This means that there are 17 protons and 18 neutrons tightly packed in the nucleus. Further, there are a total of 17 electrons outside the nucleus. Of this total,

COMMON ELEMENTS

Element	Symbol	Atomic Number	Atomic Mass
Aluminum	Al	13	27
Antimony	Sb	51	122
Argon	Ar	18	40
Arsenic	As	33	75
Barium	Ba	56	137
Boron	B	5	11
Bromine	Br	35	80
Calcium	Ca	20	40
Carbon	C	6	12
Chlorine	Cl	17	35
Chromium	Cr	24	52
Copper	Cu	29	64
Fluorine	F	9	19
Gold	Au	79	197
Helium	He	2	4
Hydrogen	H	1	1
Iodine	I	53	127
Iron	Fe	26	56
Lead	Pb	82	207
Magnesium	Mg	12	24
Manganese	Mn	25	55
Mercury	Hg	80	201
Neon	Ne	10	20
Nickel	Ni	28	59
Nitrogen	N	7	14
Oxygen	O	8	16
Phosphorus	P	15	31
Potassium	K	19	39
Silicon	Si	14	28
Silver	Ag	47	108
Sodium	Na	11	23
Sulfur	S	16	32
Tin	Sn	50	119
Uranium	U	92	238
Zinc	Zn	30	65

2 electrons are in the *K* shell, 8 in the *L* shell, and the remaining 7 electrons in the outer *M* shell. Of the outer *M*-shell electrons, 2 fill the first sub-shell completely, and *one* electron is *lacking* in filling the second sub-shell (see table, page 23). Study Fig. 1-28.

We see that the sodium atom has only one electron in its *outer shell,* while the chlorine *lacks* one electron in filling its outer sub-shell. There appears to be a great tendency for atoms under proper conditions to form complete outer sub-shells. Chemists have learned that a sodium atom will *give up* (lend) its outer electron (with its negative charge) readily in chemical reactions, leaving it with an electrical charge of +1. Similarly, a chlorine atom will readily *accept* (borrow) an electron for its outer sub-shell, giving that atom an electrical charge of −1.

The tendency of atoms to lend or borrow electrons determines, in many cases, how one element will combine with another in a chemical reaction. An element's ability to combine with other elements is usually expressed as *valence numbers, which means the*

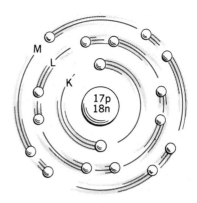

1-28. Diagram of the chlorine atom. Notice that one electron is needed to complete the M sub-shell.

number of electrons that an atom of an element will give up or accept during a chemical reaction. Thus, the sodium atom is said to have a valence number of +1, because it becomes positively charged by one unit when it gives up its outer electron. The valence number of chlorine is said to be −1 because it becomes negatively charged by one unit in accepting the electron. Valence numbers of some common elements are shown in the table below.

USUAL VALENCE NUMBERS OF SOME COMMON ELEMENTS

Name	Symbol	Valence Number	Name	Symbol	Valence Number
Aluminum	Al	+3	Potassium	K	+1
Barium	Ba	+2	Silver	Ag	+1
Calcium	Ca	+2	Sodium	Na	+1
Copper (II), cupric	Cu	+2	Zinc	Zn	+2
Copper (I), cuprous	Cu	+1	Bromine	Br	−1
Iron (III), ferric	Fe	+3	Chlorine	Cl	−1
Iron (II), ferrous	Fe	+2	Fluorine	F	−1
Hydrogen	H	+1	Iodine	I	−1
Lead	Pb	+2	Oxygen	O	−2
Magnesium	Mg	+2	Sulfur	S	−2

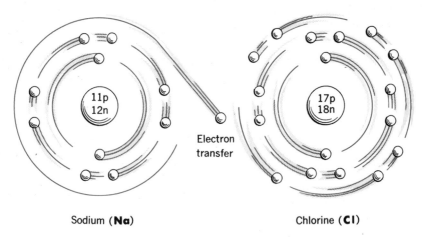

Sodium (**Na**)   Chlorine (**Cl**)

1-29. Sodium chloride is formed when the single electron of the outer shell of the sodium atom fills a vacancy that exists in the outer shell of the chlorine atom. Notice that only the electrons farthest away from the nucleus take part in the reaction.

Notice that some elements have *more than one valence number.* Iron has a valence number of +2 in some compounds and +3 in others. When iron has a valence number of +3, its compounds are called *ferric,* or iron (III); and when +2, they are called *ferrous,* or iron (II). Hence, we have two chlorides of iron, ferric chloride ($FeCl_3$) and ferrous chloride ($FeCl_2$). Copper is another element with two valence numbers, +2 and +1. Can you name the two chlorides of copper?

Many compounds are formed by electron transfer. We have seen that the sodium atom readily *gives up* its outer electron, and that the chlorine atom readily *accepts* an electron, to complete the outer sub-shells of both elements. The electrons farthest from the nucleus of an atom are the ones that are involved in ordinary chemical reactions. Hence, when the electron from the sodium atom is *transferred* to the chlorine atom, we have a chem-

ical reaction in which a white solid *compound* called sodium chloride (table salt) is formed. We may write this compound as $Na^{+1}Cl^{-1}$. However, formulas are commonly written without the valence numbers, as **NaCl.** Study Fig. 1-29 and Fig. 1-30.

Valence numbers are convenient for writing formulas directly. Sodium has a valence number of +1 and chlorine −1. Because all compounds are electrically neutral, these two elements must combine in a 1 to 1 ratio to form the neutral compound, NaCl.

We explain the formation of calcium chloride, $CaCl_2$, similarly. From the valence table, observe that calcium has a valence number of +2. The total valence number of the *positive* part of a compound must equal the total valence number of the *negative* part. Since chlorine has a valence number of −1, *two* atoms of chlorine are required to react with *one* calcium atom. Therefore, we write $CaCl_2$ as the formula for this compound. In the same way, we must write aluminum chloride as $AlCl_3$, since aluminum has a valence number of +3. Explain how you would write the formula for lead oxide.

No nuclei are changed by a chemical process, and no chemical process creates or destroys electrons. Under certain conditions, outer electrons are removed from some elements to fill sub-shell vacancies in other elements, thus bringing about a chemical reaction.

The use of valence numbers makes it easy for us to write formulas of those compounds formed by the *transfer* of electrons.

What are radicals? Some *atom groups* act like a single atom. Certain groups of atoms stay united during a chemical reaction. These groups, called *radicals,* act just as though they were single atoms; they also have definite valence numbers. One of the common radicals is the *hydroxide group, OH.* Another important radical is the *sul-*

VALENCE NUMBERS OF SOME COMMON RADICALS

Name	Formula	Valence Number
Ammonium	NH_4	+1
Acetate	$C_2H_3O_2$	−1
Bicarbonate	HCO_3	−1
Carbonate	CO_3	−2
Chlorate	ClO_3	−1
Hydroxide	OH	−1
Nitrate	NO_3	−1
Phosphate	PO_4	−3
Sulfate	SO_4	−2
Sulfite	SO_3	−2

fate group, SO₄. The table above shows the valence numbers of some common radicals.

Sometimes you see a radical in parenthesis ( ). This is true when you use *more* than one radical. For example, sodium hydroxide is NaOH, but calcium hydroxide is $Ca(OH)_2$, and aluminum hydroxide is $Al(OH)_3$.

1-30. The loss of an electron from the sodium atom leaves it positively charged; the gain of an electron in the chlorine atom makes it negatively charged.

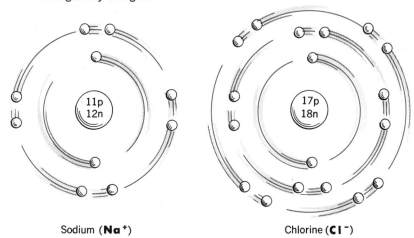

Sodium (**Na⁺**)   Chlorine (**Cl⁻**)

The compounds discussed in the above paragraphs are examples of a large class of compounds that are formed by transfer, or loss and gain, of electrons. An important general property of these compounds is that when dissolved or melted they *conduct an electric current*. We will study more about this class of compounds in section E.

Naming of compounds from their formulas. Observe that in writing formulas for the above class of compounds, the element (or radical) with the *positive* valence number is written first, followed by the element (or radical) with the *negative* valence number. Further, in the naming of almost all compounds of *two* elements, the last element ends in "*ide*." For example, **KI** is potassium iod*ide*, **NaF** is sodium fluor*ide*, and **CaO** is calcium ox*ide*.

The ending "*ate*" indicates that the compound contains *oxygen* along with other elements mentioned in the name. For example, sodium nitr*ate* is **NaNO₃**, calcium carbon*ate* is **CaCO₃**, copper (II) sulf*ate* is **CuSO₄**, and potassium chlor*ate* is **KClO₃**. How would you

1-31. The top diagram (A) shows two atoms of hydrogen and one atom of oxygen. The diagram (B) shows a molecule of water formed by the sharing of common electrons to complete the shells of both elements.

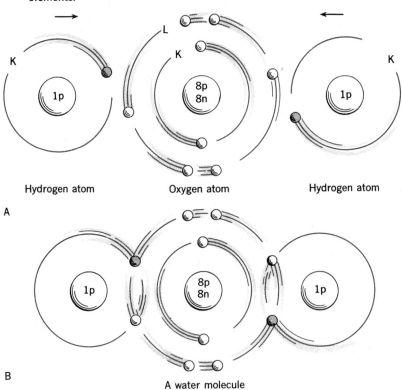

Hydrogen atom   Oxygen atom   Hydrogen atom

A

B   A water molecule

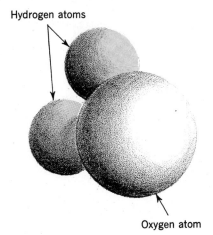

Hydrogen atoms

Oxygen atom

1-32. A three-dimensional drawing of a laboratory model of a water molecule.

write the formula for sodium bicarbon*ate*? Ammonium chlor*ide*?

Molecules formed by sharing electrons. Not all compounds are formed by the transfer of electrons from one atom to another. Some atoms *share* a

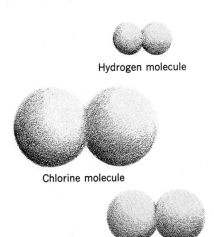

Hydrogen molecule

Chlorine molecule

Oxygen molecule

1-33. Models of molecules formed by sharing electrons. Remember that atoms and molecules are not solid spheres.

common electron with each other to form a compound. Water is a notable example of a molecule formed by the sharing of electrons. From the table on page 23 observe that the oxygen atom needs *two* electrons to complete the *L* shell and the hydrogen atom needs *one* electron to complete the *K* shell. The electron from each of two hydrogen atoms and two electrons from the oxygen atom are *shared* by each atom, thus forming a molecule of water, H_2O, as shown in Fig. 1-31. A laboratory model of a molecule of water is shown in Fig. 1-32.

Molecules of common gases such as oxygen, hydrogen, chlorine, and nitrogen are formed by the sharing of electrons. The hydrogen atom, for example, has only one electron. Since the first shell can hold two electrons, two hydrogen atoms share their electrons with each other to form a hydrogen molecule. Chemists write this as H_2 (say "H-two"). Molecules of other common gases are written as O_2 for oxygen, Cl_2 for chlorine, and N_2 for nitrogen. Compounds formed by the sharing of electrons *do not usually conduct an electric current.* (See Fig. 1-33.)

Molecules are in constant motion. If a gas jet is opened in the front of the room, you will smell the gas odor in the rear of the room within a very short time, even if there are no air currents.

Put a few drops of *hydrochloric acid* on a wad of paper in the bottom of one cylinder and some strong *ammonia water* in the bottom of another cylinder. When you bring the two cylinders together, as shown in Fig. 1-34, a white smoke forms. This smoke is the compound *ammonium chloride,*

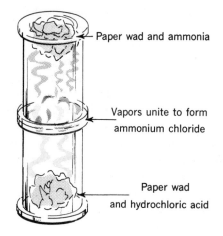

Paper wad and ammonia

Vapors unite to form
ammonium chloride

Paper wad
and hydrochloric acid

1-34. Diagram showing evidence of molecular motion. Hydrochloric acid (HCl) and
ammonia (NH_3) vapors react to form ammonium chloride (NH_4Cl).

formed by the reaction of ammonia
and hydrochloric acid vapors. Because
of their random rapid motion, molecules of the two vapors mix with each
other, as evidenced by the white smoke.

*The mixing of substances because of
molecular motion is called diffusion.*
Gases also diffuse through *porous*
solids. This process is extremely important because it occurs constantly
through membranes of plants and animals, including man. It allows oxygen
to reach the cells and waste to escape.

Liquids evaporate because their
molecules are constantly moving. At
room temperature, molecules are moving at high speeds, up to a mile-a-sec-
ond. From numerous experiments and
observations of the behavior of large
groups of molecules, scientists have arrived at this important generalization:
Molecules are in constant motion and
hence have kinetic energy or energy
of motion. The average *kinetic energy*
of the molecules depends on the *temperature* of the substance. *The higher
the temperature, the faster the molecules of a substance move and, hence,
the greater is their energy of motion.*

1-35. Molecular motion compared in solids, liquids, and gases. As
the temperature increases, the molecular motion also increases.

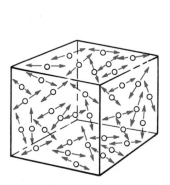

Molecules of a solid vibrate about
fixed positions

Molecules of a liquid
slide over one another
freely

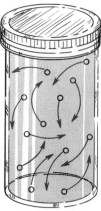

Molecules of a gas are
widely separated and
move most rapidly

Molecules of gases move most rapidly; molecules of liquids less rapidly; and molecules of solids least rapidly. Can you give a good reason why this should be so? (See Fig. 1-35.)

The statement that matter is made of molecules in constant motion is part of the *kinetic theory* of matter, a far-reaching scientific development. This theory has proven to be useful in explaining experimental observations and in predicting the discovery of new facts.

Quick Quiz

1. How does an atom of potassium differ in make-up from an atom of gold?
2. What generalization can you make about the elements in a particular group in the Periodic Table?
3. Where on the Periodic Table are the most active elements located?
4. What is the maximum number of electrons in the first three shells?
5. Draw a diagram of a helium atom. What prediction can you make regarding the activity of this element with other elements?
6. Make a table of 10 elements, listing the following about each: (a) the number of protons in the nucleus, (b) the number of electrons outside the nucleus, and (c) the number of neutrons in the nucleus.
7. Write the formula for each compound: potassium sulfide, calcium hydroxide, ammonium sulfate, hydrogen phosphate, and copper(II) chloride.
8. Name the compounds represented by the following formulas: ZnS, $KClO_3$, HNO_3, NH_4OH, Na_2CO_3, and $Pb(C_2H_3O_2)_2$.
9. Sketch a diagram of the following atoms showing the number of protons and neutrons in the nucleus and the number of electrons in each of the

K, *L*, and *M* shells: aluminum, argon, carbon, fluorine, magnesium, nitrogen, and boron.
10. Explain two ways that atoms combine to form compounds. Give several examples of each.
11. From your knowledge of sodium and the Periodic Table, predict the activity of potassium.
12. Explain how the movement of atoms and molecules of solids, liquids, and gases is affected by a temperature increase.

D GASES OF THE AIR

The atmosphere surrounds the earth. Air is a common word used to mean the gases that make up our atmosphere. The atmosphere is an ocean of air surrounding the earth. It is not incorrect to speak of an "ocean of air" since the air is a *fluid* that surrounds and covers you completely, just as the ocean of water covers fish and other forms of life in it. Air is essential to our existence. We can get along without food or water for hours or even days, but we cannot live without the oxygen of the air for more than a few minutes.

Air is useful in many other ways. Scientists are finding that the atmosphere is an abundant source of raw materials from which many useful products are made.

Air is a mixture of many gases. As you have probably noticed, pure air is colorless, tasteless, and odorless. Air is a mixture primarily of *nitrogen* and

Gases of the Air (Percent by volume)	
Nitrogen (N_2)	78
Oxygen (O_2)	21
Noble gases	0.94
Carbon dioxide (CO_2)	0.04
Water vapor (H_2O)	varies

1-36. Recent developments in cutting metals involve using noble gases. (Union Carbide Corp., Linde Div.)

Oxygen compounds, such as sand, clay, and most rocks, make up about 50 percent of the earth's crust. All plant and animal tissues contain oxygen. Oxygen is 89% of the weight of water, and so, when you think of how much water there is on earth, you realize how abundant oxygen is.

Priestley's classic experiment. Joseph Priestley, an English scientist, is usually credited with the discovery of oxygen because he was the first sci-

oxygen, although other gases such as *argon, carbon dioxide,* and *water vapor* are present in very small amounts. Besides argon, other noble gases such as *neon, helium,* and *krypton* are also present in very small quantities. The stars are mostly *hydrogen,* and hydrogen is thinly scattered throughout the universe. So far as scientists have been able to determine, hydrogen accounts for about 76% of the total *mass* of the universe. However, there is only an insignificant trace of hydrogen in the earth's atmosphere.

Oxygen is our most abundant element. From the following table, notice that there is more nitrogen in the air than oxygen. But oxygen is actually more plentiful in the earth as a whole because it is found combined with many other elements in the earth's crust as compounds. Review the table at the top of page 13.

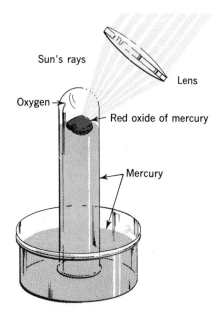

1-37. By concentrating the rays of the sun, Priestley separated oxygen from mercuric oxide, HgO.

entist to publish the results of his findings with this gas. Priestley prepared oxygen in 1774 by heating *red oxide of mercury,* or *mercuric oxide* (HgO). He used a glass lens to focus the sun's rays in order to heat a small sample of this compound.

He noticed that the mercuric oxide powder turned black as it became heated and then formed a small drop of mercury. As he stirred the mixture with a wooden stick, the stick, much to his surprise, burst into flame. Next he heated some of the HgO powder in a closed tube and collected the gas that came off, as shown in Fig. 1-37. A lighted candle burned much more brilliantly than usual in this gas.

Placing a mouse in the gas, Priestley observed that it scampered around at a livelier rate than normal. He

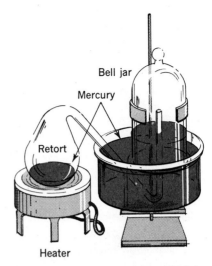

1-39. Lavoisier heated mercury (Hg) in air to produce mercuric oxide (HgO).

1-38. Lavoisier, a French scientist, performing his famous experiment in his laboratory. (NY Public Library)

breathed some of the gas himself and reported that his breath felt peculiarly light and easy for some time afterwards. He called this gas "good air," without realizing that this same gas (oxygen) was present in the air.

Lavoisier proved air contains oxygen. A few years later, Lavoisier (la-*vwah*-zee-ay), a French scientist, read of Priestley's experiments. Lavoisier thought that perhaps the gas which Priestley obtained might be in the air also. To prove this theory, Lavoisier conducted the following historical twelve-day experiment. (See Fig. 1-38.)

He heated mercury with air in a glass retort as shown in Fig. 1-39. A reddish powder began to gather on the surface of the mercury in the retort. After 12 days, no more red powder was formed and about one-fifth of the air in the apparatus disappeared. Mercury had risen in the bell jar to take the place of the air. The oxygen of the air had combined with the heated mercury, forming mercuric oxide.

Then Lavoisier heated the mercuric oxide to a higher temperature in a smaller retort. The mercuric oxide changed back to mercury, giving off a colorless gas. When he tested this gas, he found that substances burned vigorously in it, just as Priestley had previously discovered. Here, then, was the unmistakable proof that about ⅕ of the air is an active gas that unites chemically with substances when they burn. He named the gas *oxygen*.

Chemical equations must balance. The word equation for the above preparation of oxygen is written as follows

$$\text{mercuric oxide} \xrightarrow{\text{heat}} \text{mercury} + \text{oxygen}$$

By using symbols and formulas, we can write the chemical equation

$$\text{HgO} \xrightarrow{\text{heat}} \text{Hg} + \text{O}_2 \text{ (not balanced)}$$

From this equation, you see that one molecule of mercuric oxide forms one atom of mercury and one molecule of oxygen consisting of two atoms. From the law of conservation of matter, you recall that ordinary chemical changes cannot destroy or create atoms. Is there something wrong? Have we really created one additional atom of oxygen? If we actually weighed the substance of the left side of the equation and compared it with the total weight on the right side of the equation, we would find that there would be no increase or decrease in weight. What actually happened is shown in this *corrected* equation

$$2\text{HgO} \xrightarrow{\text{heat}} 2\text{Hg} + \text{O}_2$$

Now notice on the left side of the equation, we have *2 molecules of HgO*.

In other words, we have a total of 2 atoms of mercury and 2 atoms of oxygen. This is precisely the same number of mercury and oxygen atoms as on the right side of the equation.

In writing a correct chemical equation, numbers are written in *front* of the formula so that the correct number of atoms appears on both sides of the equation. This process is called *balancing an equation.* The smallest possible whole numbers are used to balance equations correctly.

Another method of preparing oxygen in the laboratory. You can also prepare oxygen by heating a mixture of approximately equal parts of *potassium chlorate* (KClO_3) and *manganese dioxide* (MnO_2), using the apparatus shown in Fig. 1-40. The word equation for this chemical change is

$$\text{potassium chlorate} \xrightarrow{\text{heat}} \text{potassium chloride} + \text{oxygen}$$

Using symbols and formulas, we may write the chemical equation as

$$\text{KClO}_3 \rightarrow \text{KCl} + \text{O}_2 \text{ (not balanced)}$$

We now see that there are 3 oxygen atoms on the left and 2 oxygen atoms on the right. To obtain the same number of oxygen atoms on both sides, we write

$$2\text{KClO}_3 \rightarrow \text{KCl} + 3\text{O}_2 \text{ (not balanced)}$$

Now we have 6 oxygen atoms on both sides. Let us examine the number of potassium (K) atoms. On the left we have 2 potassium atoms and on the right we have only 1 potassium atom. We now place the number 2 before the KCl so that the same number

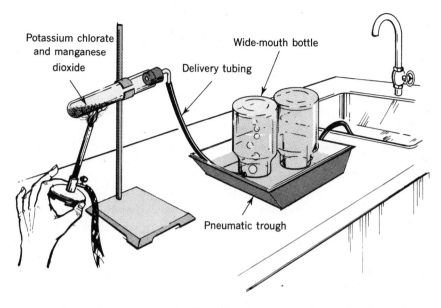

Potassium chlorate and manganese dioxide

Wide-mouth bottle

Delivery tubing

Pneumatic trough

1-40. Typical apparatus for the laboratory preparation and collection of oxygen, O_2.

of potassium atoms appears on both sides. Notice that this also balances the chlorine atoms. Our completely balanced equation is then written

$$2KClO_3 \xrightarrow{\text{heat}} 2KCl + 3O_2$$

You may wonder why *manganese dioxide* has not been included in this equation, although it was added to the potassium chlorate at the very start. The reason is that manganese dioxide *helps* the $KClO_3$ give off its oxygen more readily at lower temperatures. The manganese dioxide was not permanently changed and *did not become involved* in the reaction. Substances, such as manganese dioxide, which *speed up* chemical change but are not changed in the reaction, are called *catalysts* (*kat*-uh-lists). Some catalysts are used to *slow down* chemical changes. Catalysts are used widely in many modern chemical operations in industry.

Oxygen from liquid air. The two laboratory methods of preparing oxygen that you have just studied would not be practical to meet the industrial needs of oxygen. Oxygen for industry is usually prepared either by the electrolysis of water or by the evaporation of liquid air.

Air can be liquefied if it is greatly compressed at the same time that it is being cooled to a very low temperature ($-200°$ C). The liquid air that results consists largely of oxygen and nitrogen. Liquid nitrogen has a boiling point ($-196°$ C) about 13° lower than that of liquid oxygen ($-183°$ C). Hence, if the liquid air is allowed to stand, the nitrogen will soon boil away and leave nearly pure liquid oxygen.

Other gases are obtained also from liquid air as by-products. (Can you name them?)

Uses of oxygen. You may have seen trucks carrying steel cylinders of compressed oxygen. Oxygen is often given to hospital patients who have breathing difficulties. When flying above 10,000 feet, passengers and pilots depend on oxygen supplies. Since the air is too thin at that height to supply enough oxygen for regular breathing, modern planes have pressurized cabins to meet this need. Firemen and rescue squads may use gas masks with a tank to supply the necessary oxygen. Deep-sea divers and "skin-divers" are provided with compressed air tanks to insure an adequate supply of oxygen for breathing.

Oxygen is used with another gas, acetylene (ah-*set*-ih-leen), in a special torch that produces an intensely hot flame. This *oxy*acetylene torch is used to cut metals or weld pieces of metal together.

Today large amounts of oxygen are used in industry. All modern steel mills use many tons daily. A *blast furnace* that uses oxygen-enriched air can smelt much more iron ore. Steel is made from iron more rapidly by burning out the impurities with oxygen instead of air.

Our space program also demands great quantities of oxygen. The huge *liquid-fuel* rockets that launch satellites and space vehicles use *lox* or *l*iquefied *ox*ygen to burn the fuel.

What is oxidation? Modern chemistry really began when scientists discovered the important part that oxygen plays in the chemical changes occurring all around us. That is why Lavoisier is often called the "Father of Modern Chemistry." Progress in

chemistry and all other sciences has advanced by leaps and bounds since this discovery.

When a material such as coal, wood, or gasoline burns, it undergoes *oxidation*. This means that the atoms of carbon, hydrogen and other elements that make up these materials unite with the oxygen of the air to form new compounds. *Oxidation that takes place rapidly and produces heat and light is called rapid oxidation,* or combustion. Can you give several examples of rapid oxidation?

Ordinarily we depend on air to supply the necessary oxygen for the burning. However, by using purer oxygen we can make substances burn more vigorously.

Slow oxidation. The decay of dead plants and animals is another example of oxidation. Unlike burning, the process of decay results from a very slow chemical action and hence is called *slow oxidation.* Slow oxidation, like rapid oxidation, gives off heat. But the process is so slow, extending over a long period of time, that we do not notice it.

If you are familiar with wood fires, you know that partially decayed wood does not give off as much heat as good, fresh wood. This is because slow oxidation has already used much of the combustible material of the fuel.

The slow oxidation of decay disposes of dead leaves and other plant and animal matter. It changes them into useful materials that nourish growing plants. However, slow oxidation also produces harmful changes as well. The rusting of iron is an example of slow oxidation in which the iron unites with the oxygen of the air to form an *iron oxide,* commonly called *rust.*

Rusting of iron causes millions of dollars worth of damage every year. Various methods are used to prevent it. Steel tools are often maintained by coating them with a thin film of oil to prevent the oxygen from coming in direct contact with the metal. Steel bridges and water tanks are usually painted with a mixture of red lead and linseed oil, and sometimes given a coat of aluminum paint. Steel articles are sometimes plated with rust-proof materials such as tin, nickel, zinc, or chromium.

Some fires start by themselves. If you leave a pile of oily rags in a closed place, there is great danger that they may smolder, and then burst into flame. A fire that starts in this way is called

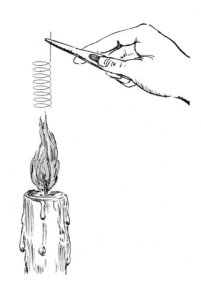

1-42. A copper spiral, when lowered into the candle flame, conducts heat away so rapidly that the flame is cooled below kindling temperature. As a result, the flame is extinguished.

spontaneous combustion. (*Spontaneous* means of its own accord, or by itself.) (See Fig. 1-41.)

The fire starts because the oil undergoes slow oxidation that results in giving off heat. In a confined space, the temperature slowly rises until the kindling temperature of the rags is reached and they burst into flame. *The lowest temperature at which a substance begins to burn is known as its kindling temperature.* (See Fig. 1-42.)

Nearly all industrial firms have a strict rule requiring all oily rags to be placed in covered metal containers. It is good to do the same thing at home. Cloths that have been used to polish furniture or wipe paint should be properly stored or disposed of.

Dust explosions. Many serious explosions have occurred in grain elevators, coal mines, starch mills, and other places where the air became filled with

1-41. Oily rags should be stored in closed metal containers to prevent the spreading of fires resulting from spontaneous combustion. (The Protectoseal Co.)

1-43. A dust explosion caused this fire in a grain elevator. (St. Louis Post Dispatch)

combustible dust. The rapid oxidation of these particles gives off heat, warming adjoining particles to their kindling temperatures. Combustion continues in this way from particle to particle very rapidly, causing a violent explosion. Coal mines and many industrial plants take precautions to keep the combustible dust from gathering in the air. (See Fig. 1-43.)

Nitrogen is a sluggish element. In contrast to oxygen, nitrogen is a rather inactive element. It does not combine readily with other elements. Like oxygen it has no odor, no taste, and no color. It does not dissolve readily in water, and cannot be oxidized easily. When nitrogen does react with another element, the union is usually not stable and the compound formed can be broken up easily.

Nitrogen compounds are present in all *protein* foods. Compounds of nitrogen are necessary for the growth of plants and animals, which explains why *fertilizers* contain nitrogen compounds. Large quantities of nitrogen compounds are made from the nitrogen of the air.

Common *explosives* such as gunpowder, dynamite, TNT (trinitrotoluene) and nitroglycerin are compounds of nitrogen. Their destructive power is due to the rapid breaking up of their molecules with the release of energy and the formation of rapidly expanding gases. (See Fig. 1-44.)

Carbon dioxide is necessary for plants. Carbon dioxide and water vapor are important compounds found in the air. Although carbon dioxide

1-44. Cold nitrogen vapor at −300° F is used for low temperature storage. (Union Carbide Corp., Linde Div.)

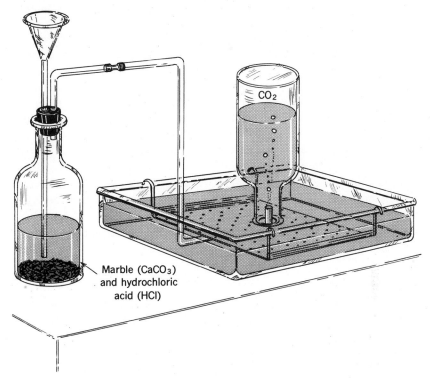

1-45. This apparatus is used for the laboratory preparation of carbon dioxide, CO_2. Why is the funnel tube used?

Marble ($CaCO_3$) and hydrochloric acid (HCl)

is in the air in very small quantities, it is necessary for green plants which must have carbon dioxide to grow.

The food-making process in green plants is known as *photosynthesis* (foe-toh-*sin*-theh-sis). In the presence of the green chemical *chlorophyll* (*kloh*-roh-fil) and sunlight, these plants use water from the soil and carbon dioxide from the air to make their food. Oxygen is then given off as waste.

Animals, including man, depend on plants for their food supply. They breathe the oxygen from the air and give off carbon dioxide as one of the products of food oxidation. Thus, the total carbon dioxide content of the air stays about the same.

In the laboratory, carbon dioxide can be prepared by adding hydrochloric acid (HCl) to pieces of marble. Marble is impure calcium carbonate ($CaCO_3$). Collect a bottle of carbon dioxide as shown in Fig. 1-45. Thrust a burning splint into the bottle and note that the flame goes out. Pour a bottle of the gas over a candle flame, just as you would pour water from a bottle and the flame goes out again. We conclude that carbon dioxide neither burns nor supports combustion. The equation for this preparation of carbon dioxide is

$$2HCl + CaCO_3 \rightarrow$$
$$CaCl_2 + H_2O + CO_2 \uparrow$$

The arrow (↑) indicates a gaseous product. If *limewater* ($Ca(OH)_2$) is added to a bottle of this gas and shaken, the limewater turns white. This is a common *test* used to detect the presence of carbon dioxide. Try blowing your breath through a soda straw into a bottle of limewater. Explain what happens.

The inert gases. Some of the inert gases in the air are *argon, helium,* and *neon. Argon* means "lazy," a name that correctly describes the activity of this element. *Helium* comes from the Greek word for *sun,* because this element was first detected in the sun a number of years before it was discovered on earth. *Neon* means *new.*

Electric light bulbs filled with argon can operate at a high temperature and give a very bright light. Helium is taken from gas wells in Kansas, Oklahoma, and Texas, and is useful for filling balloons because it is so light and will not burn. It is also used in welding metals and, when mixed with oxygen, in breathing tanks for deep-sea-diving. Liquefied helium is essential in modern scientific research.

Neon is widely used for advertising signs and for airplane beacon lights. A high voltage applied across a neon-

1-46. Hydrogen, H_2, may be prepared in the laboratory by the reaction between an acid and an active metal. Why is the funnel tube placed below the surface in the liquid?

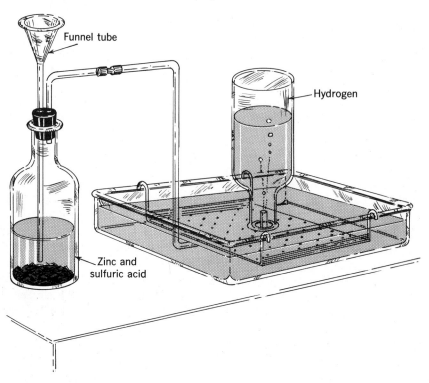

Funnel tube

Hydrogen

Zinc and sulfuric acid

filled glass tube causes the gas to glow with a familiar orange-red light. Mixtures of gases are used to produce varieties of colored lights. For example, argon mixed with mercury gives a bright blue color, helium gives a yellow color.

Hydrogen and its preparation. Hydrogen in *combined form* is found in all living things, in fuels, and in water. *Uncombined,* or *free,* hydrogen is encountered much less often. We have mentioned that hydrogen is only a trace element in the gas mixture we call air.

Hydrogen has the lowest density of all elements. Because of this, it has been used to fill balloons. However, it burns readily and is rather dangerous for such uses.

In the next section, we will learn that all acids contain a *replaceable* hydrogen. In most cases, it is easy to release the hydrogen from an acid by having an active metal such as zinc or iron substitute for it. In the laboratory, hydrogen is conveniently prepared by the reaction of *zinc* (Zn) with *sulfuric acid* (H_2SO_4). The equation for this reaction is

$$Zn + H_2SO_4 \rightarrow ZnSO_4 + H_2 \uparrow$$

zinc   sulfuric   zinc   hydrogen
metal   acid   sulfate   gas

The zinc sulfate is dissolved in the liquid that remains in the generator bottle as shown in Fig. 1-46. Hydrogen gas bubbles off and drives the water out of the collecting bottle. This laboratory procedure is called the *water displacement* method. Could you collect hydrogen in this manner if it were extremely soluble in water? Explain.

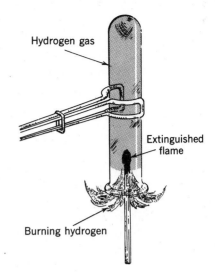

Hydrogen gas

Extinguished flame

Burning hydrogen

1-47. A burning splint is used to test for hydrogen gas. Notice the burning at the mouth of the bottle.

Properties of hydrogen. Let us open a bottle of hydrogen and hold a lighted candle to its mouth. If the bottle also contains some air there is a "pop" as the hydrogen burns rapidly, or explodes. If an open bottle of hydrogen is allowed to stand upright for a minute or two, nothing happens when a burning candle is brought near the mouth of the bottle because the hydrogen is so light it escapes into the air.

If a flaming splint is placed inside an inverted bottle of hydrogen, the flame goes out at the tip, but the gas burns at the mouth of the bottle. This is a rough test for hydrogen, and shows that while the gas itself burns, you cannot burn things in it. As hydrogen burns it unites with the oxygen of the air, forming water. (See Fig. 1-47.)

Hydrogen has many uses. The chemical industry uses large quantities of hydrogen. Industrial supplies are often obtained by the electrolysis of water. Large quantities of hydrogen are used in the making of ammonia (NH_3) and wood alcohol (CH_3OH).

When hydrogen is added to cotton-seed, coconut, or other oils, it combines chemically with them to form solid fats. Finely divided nickel is used as a catalyst to speed the process. We say that these oils are **hydrogenated** (hy-dro-jeh-nay-ted). Hydrogen also reacts with some petroleum compounds to produce more and better gasoline.

Atomic hydrogen torches are widely used in specialized welding and cutting work and are capable of producing extremely high temperatures. (See Fig. 1-48.) Partly because of this high burning temperature, liquid hydrogen is the newest fuel for rockets in the space age.

Air pollution. In many parts of the world, man has upset the oxygen-carbon dioxide balance that is necessary for the maintenance of life on this planet. He has encouraged the processes that use up oxygen and give off carbon dioxide and impurities. This he has done by burning vast quantities of fuel in industries, homes, and in automobiles. The dangers from air polluted by automobile exhaust gases and other fumes are becoming more and more threatening. Special filtering devices are now being installed on cars as a public health measure. By cutting down the forests, man has reduced the plant life that uses the carbon dioxide and gives off oxygen. Scientists are convinced that even slight changes in the carbon dioxide content of the at-

1-48. The temperature produced by this atomic hydrogen torch is estimated at 4,000° C. It is used for cutting and welding metals.

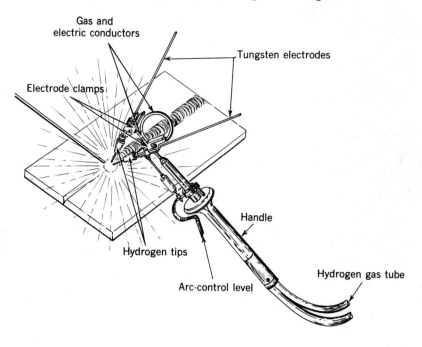

Gas and electric conductors

Tungsten electrodes

Electrode clamps

Handle

Hydrogen tips

Arc-control level

Hydrogen gas tube

mosphere could bring drastic changes in the world's climate.

A pollutant is a substance that contaminates such things as water, air, food, and other substances. A common air pollutant is *smog. Smog* is a mixture of fog with industrial gases, automobile exhaust gases, and smoke. It cuts down visibility and under some conditions produces substances that are harmful to plants and animals. In many cities today, the supplying of pure, smog-free air is becoming a very serious problem. As more of the world becomes industrialized, the problem becomes more acute.

Quick Quiz

1. Why do we say that air is a mixture?
2. Explain a convenient way of preparing oxygen in the laboratory.
3. What uses are made of nitrogen compounds?
4. How is carbon dioxide prepared in the laboratory? How is it tested?
5. How is hydrogen prepared in the laboratory? Industrially?
6. Why must a chemical equation be balanced?
7. How may oily rags cause spontaneous combustion?
8. What element would you expect to have chemical properties similar to oxygen? Potassium? Why? (See the Periodic Table.)
9. Copy the equations below on a separate sheet of paper and supply the numbers to balance the equations:

    a. $Na + HOH \rightarrow NaOH + H_2 \uparrow$
    b. $Mg + HCl \rightarrow MgCl_2 + H_2 \uparrow$
    c. $H_2 + Cl_2 \rightarrow HCl$
    d. $Mg + H_2O \rightarrow Mg(OH)_2 + H_2 \uparrow$
    e. $Cl_2 + NaBr \rightarrow NaCl + Br_2 \uparrow$
    f. $Na + Cl_2 \rightarrow NaCl$
    g. $NaCl + AgNO_3 \rightarrow AgCl + NaNO_3$

10. From the following word equations, write balanced chemical equations on a separate sheet of paper. (Refer to tables, pages 27 and 29.)

    a. zinc + hydrochloric acid →
    zinc chloride + hydrogen
    b. calcium oxide + water →
    calcium hydroxide
    c. iron (II) sulfide
    + hydrochloric acid →
    iron (II) chloride + hydrogen sulfide
    d. barium chloride
    + sulfuric acid →
    barium sulfate + hydrochloric acid
    e. potassium chloride
    + silver nitrate →
    potassium nitrate + silver chloride

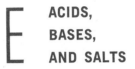

ACIDS, BASES, AND SALTS

Electrolytes. You can easily find out which solutions conduct an electric current by using the apparatus as shown in Fig. 1-49.

First, fill the beaker with pure (distilled) water and close the switch. Observe that the lamp does not light. This indicates that pure water does not provide a suitable path to complete the electric circuit. Now add a few drops of concentrated sulfuric acid to the water. The lamp now glows brightly showing that the solution now completes the electrical path. In other words, the solution conducts an electric current.

If certain other liquids such as solutions of ordinary salt (NaCl), hydrochloric acid (HCl), and sodium hydroxide (NaOH) are tested in the

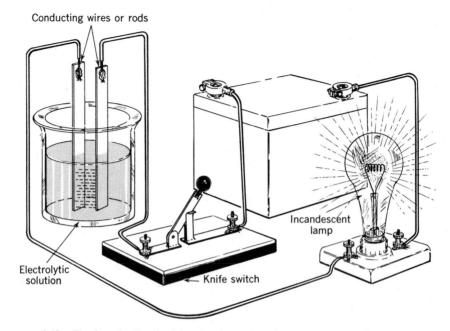

Conducting wires or rods

Electrolytic
solution

Knife switch

Incandescent
lamp

1-49. The ions in the liquid serve as an electric conductor causing the lamp to glow when the switch is closed.

1-50. Laboratory models of an ion "lattice" of a sodium chloride crystal. The open structure is on the left; a closed packing model is on the right.

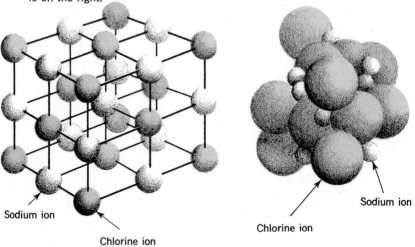

Sodium ion

Chlorine ion

Chlorine ion

Sodium ion

same manner, the lamp will glow brightly. Substances such as these, *that conduct an electric current when dissolved or melted, are called electrolytes* (eh-*lek*-tro-lites).

Solutions such as sugar, alcohol, and glycerin, do not conduct an electric current. These substances are called *non-electrolytes*. In this section, we shall be concerned with a large class of chemical compounds called *acids*, *bases*, and *salts*. These are *electrolytic substances* since their solutions conduct an electric current.

What are ions? It was mentioned in section C that the formula for sodium chloride (table salt) may be written as $Na^{+1}Cl^{-1}$. This means that it is an *ionic compound*, and its crystals are made up of an orderly assemblage of positive ions and negative ions. (See Fig. 1-50.) When the salt is dissolved in water (or melted), it *separates* into two kinds of *charged particles*, or *ions*.

$$Na^+Cl^- \rightarrow Na^+ + Cl^-$$
$$\text{(solid)} \qquad \text{(ions)}$$

The ions conduct the electric current through the solution in Fig. 1-49. In this case, we say that the sodium atom has lost the outermost electron in becoming a sodium ion (Na^+), while the chlorine atom has gained the electron making it a chloride ion (Cl^-). *Ions are atoms or groups of atoms that have lost or gained electrons.* Would you consider calcium chloride an ionic compound? Silver nitrate? Explain.

When substances break up in a water solution to form ions, they are said to be *ionized*. In non-electrolytes the particles *do not* ionize, and therefore they cannot conduct an electric current.

Acids. Acids are an important group of electrolytes. They have a sour or sharp taste in a dilute solution. You know how sour lemon juice tastes! This is caused by the *citric* (*sit*-rik) acid in the juice. Vinegar tastes sour because of the *acetic* (ah-*see*-tik) acid in it. Many foods turn sour when they spoil. This is because their starches and sugars break down to form acids. When milk gets sour, some of the milk sugar is changed to *lactic* (lak-tik) acid.

It is dangerous to taste unknown solutions in the laboratory to determine whether they are acids. Some chemicals will burn your tongue, and others are very poisonous. Therefore, it is necessary to have a more scientific method for identifying acid solutions.

If you dip a piece of *blue litmus* paper in hydrochloric acid, the paper

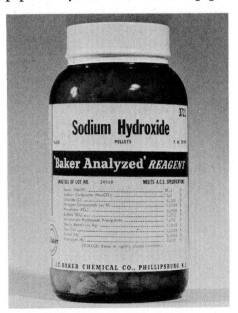

1-51. A typical chemical reagent bottle with a manufacturer's label showing information that is important to the chemist. (J. T. Baker Chemical Co.)

turns *red*. Other acids affect blue litmus similarly. *Litmus* is a plant dye that has the property of changing color when it comes in contact with acids. Substances like litmus are called *indicators* because they indicate the presence of certain ions.

Acids contain hydrogen. Acid bottles are labeled with formulas like those shown in the table below. Observe that all of these acids contain hydrogen. Hydrogen (H) always comes first in the formulas. If you place some zinc in an acid, hydrogen is given off as a gas. This is called *replaceable hydrogen*. Some acids like acetic and tartaric have additional hydrogen that is *not* replaceable. Notice in the table that the symbol for the replaceable hydrogen in the formula appears first.

---

*Names and Formulas
of Some Common Acids*

Sulfuric	H_2SO_4
Hydrochloric	HCl
Nitric	HNO_3
Carbonic	H_2CO_3
Boric	H_3BO_3
Phosphoric	H_3PO_4
Acetic	$HC_2H_3O_2$
Tartaric	$H_2C_4H_4O_6$

Acids form hydronium ions. Not all substances that contain hydrogen are acids. For example, water (H_2O), methane (CH_4), cane sugar ($C_{12}H_{22}O_{11}$), and ammonia (NH_3) have hydrogen in them but they are not acids. They do not turn blue litmus red. *A substance is an acid if it can release hydrogen ions (H^+) in a water solution.* The substances in the above table have the property of releasing hydrogen ions when in water and are called acids.

When we bubble hydrogen chloride (HCl) gas, a non-electrolyte, into water, we obtain a solution that turns blue litmus red. This solution is called hydrochloric acid (HCl). The following reaction appears to take place

$$HCl + H_2O \rightarrow H_2O \cdot H^+ + Cl^-$$

hydrogen chloride gas	*water*	*hydrogen ion united with water*	*chloride ion*

Notice that the hydrogen chloride reacts with water in a special way forming the $H_2O \cdot H^+$ ion and the chloride ion (Cl^-). Chemists sometimes write the $H_2O \cdot H^+$ ion as H_3O^+ and call it the **hydronium ion.** *The presence of the hydronium ions in the solution defines the substance as an acid.*

You will notice that water appears on both sides of the equation. For convenience, the above reaction is usually written as

$$HCl \rightarrow H^+ + Cl^-$$

However, it must be understood that *the H^+ ion is attached to a water molecule* (perhaps several molecules) becoming the hydronium ion. For simplicity, we shall use the term hydrogen ion (H^+) throughout the remainder of the text with the understanding that the H^+ ion in a water solution refers to the hydronium ion, $H_2O \cdot H^+$. This is the ion that turns blue litmus red. Study the diagram contained in Fig. 1-52 for important general properties of acids.

Acids corrode active metals. Put a few iron nails in a beaker with some dilute sulfuric acid. A gas that can be identified as hydrogen bubbles off.

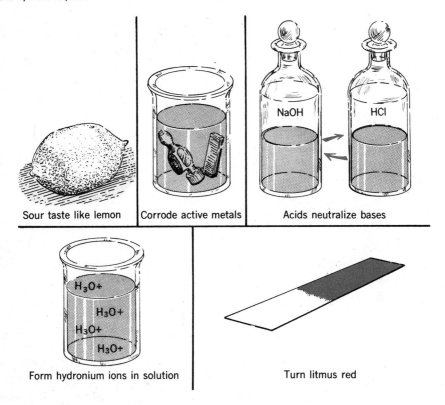

Sour taste like lemon | Corrode active metals | Acids neutralize bases

Form hydronium ions in solution | Turn litmus red

1-52. Five common properties of acids. Notice that the hydrogen ion, or proton, is attached to a water molecule ($H_2O \cdot H^+$ or H_3O^+).

The nails get thinner and thinner because the acid is *corrosive* and attacks or dissolves the metal. After some time, if there is enough acid, the nails disappear completely, and a green solution remains. We can write the equation for the reaction

$$Fe + H_2SO_4 \rightarrow FeSO_4 + H_2 \uparrow$$

Acids attack other active metals, such as zinc and magnesium, in the same manner

$$Zn + H_2SO_4 \rightarrow ZnSO_4 + H_2 \uparrow$$
$$Mg + 2HCl \rightarrow MgCl_2 + H_2 \uparrow$$

Strong and weak acids. Acids that ionize freely in water, forming many hydrogen ions, are called *strong* acids. Hydrochloric, nitric, and sulfuric are examples of common strong acids. These acids ionize completely, or nearly so, in water solution and provide a relative abundance of hydrogen ions.

Acetic, citric, and carbonic acids are common examples of *weak* acids. These acids furnish relatively few ions and are considered *slightly* ionized. Do not confuse the terms strong and weak with that of concentrated and dilute. It is possible to have a dilute solution

$$SO_3 + H_2O \rightarrow H_2SO_4$$

The process is more complex than indicated above, but these are the essential reactions.

Sulfuric acid has many uses. Thousands of commonly used finished products require sulfuric acid in their manufacture. Metals are "pickled" by dipping them in dilute sulfuric acid to remove the oxide coating before they are plated or enameled. Sulfuric acid is used in making chromium-plated bumpers on automobiles, as well as enameled sinks in our homes. (See Fig. 1-54.)

Sulfuric acid is used in the preparation of movie film. The liquid in an automobile storage battery is dilute sulfuric acid. Gasoline is treated with sulfuric acid to *dehydrate* it. Sulfuric acid is used in the manufacture of paints, plastics, rayon, and many other

1-53. Sulfur is used in making sulfuric acid. (E. I. du Pont de Nemours & Co., Inc.)

of a strong acid, hydrochloric acid, for example.

Commercial preparation of sulfuric acid. The amount of sulfuric acid used by a nation is a fair indication of how industrialized it is. Sulfuric acid is the most versatile and most widely used industrial chemical.

This chemical is made from water, sulfur, and oxygen. These materials are abundant and inexpensive, and so the acid is not very costly. First, sulfur is burned in air to form *sulfur dioxide* (SO_2)

$$S + O_2 \rightarrow SO_2 \uparrow$$

The sulfur dioxide is next changed to *sulfur trioxide* (SO_3) with the aid of a catalyst

$$2SO_2 + O_2 \rightarrow 2SO_3$$

The sulfur trioxide is then added to water to produce the *sulfuric acid*

1-54 Acids are widely used to remove the oxide coating on iron and steel in the "pickling" process. (Jones & Laughlin Steel Corp.)

1-55. Specially designed tank cars (top) and ocean barges discharge sulfuric acid for industrial use. (Allied Chemical Corp.)

articles in daily use. It is also used in the production of many other acids.

One of the major uses of sulfuric acid is in the making of *fertilizers*. The mineral called *rock phosphate* (calcium phosphate), which is quarried in large quantities in Florida and Tennessee, will not readily dissolve in the soil moisture. However, when it is treated with sulfuric acid, it becomes a *super-phosphate,* which dissolves readily for plant nutrition. This process makes important phosphate compounds available as a fertilizer for growing plants.

When ammonia gas is bubbled through sulfuric acid, *ammonium sulfate,* $(NH_4)_2SO_4$, is formed. This is widely used as a fertilizer because such soluble nitrogen compounds are also essential for plant growth. (See Fig. 1-56.)

1-56. Healthy crops will be produced when chemical fertilizers prepared with sulfuric acid are used. (Allied Chemical Corp.)

Some properties of sulfuric acid. Sulfuric acid is a colorless, oily liquid. It is nearly twice as dense as water. When it is diluted, it reacts rapidly with active metals like iron, zinc, and magnesium. The hot concentrated acid is a vigorous *oxidizing agent. An oxidizing agent is a substance that can give up oxygen to other substances.*

If a flat dish of concentrated sulfuric acid is left open in the air, its *volume increases.* This is because concentrated sulfuric acid *absorbs* moisture from the air, thereby diluting itself. Sulfuric acid takes hydrogen and oxygen from table sugar $(C_{12}H_{22}O_{11})$ in the proportion needed to form water leaving the carbon as a residue. (See Fig. 1-57.) A piece of wood or paper turns black for the same reason when placed in the acid. Can you think of a reason for this?

In each case, the sulfuric acid takes hydrogen and oxygen from these materials, leaving a black mass of carbon. *Substances that remove water from other substances are called dehydrating agents.* Sometimes, even a trace of moisture will spoil a chemical reaction, as in the making of smokeless gun powder. That is why this acid is often used as a dehydrating agent.

Caution is important in using sulfuric acid. You must always be careful when handling acids. For example, if you add concentrated sulfuric acid to water, it gives off considerable heat. In order to dissipate the heat more efficiently, *always add the acid slowly to the water, while stirring. Never add the water to the acid.* Otherwise, it is sure to spatter dangerously. This precaution should be taken for all strong, concentrated acids. Be sure to use a container that can withstand the heat

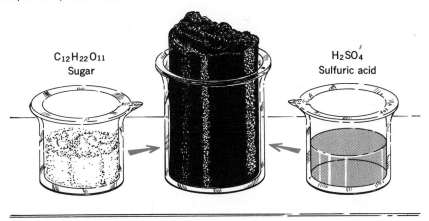

C₁₂H₂₂O₁₁ appears as $C_{12}H_{22}O_{11}$ Sugar

H_2SO_4 Sulfuric acid

1-57. Concentrated sulfuric acid removes the hydrogen and oxygen atoms from sugar, leaving a black carbon residue in the beaker.

given off. Concentrated sulfuric acid will burn your skin and, even when very dilute, will "eat" holes in your clothes.

Laboratory preparation and uses of hydrochloric acid. Hydrochloric acid is also an important common acid. It is made in the laboratory by heating ordinary table salt with sulfuric acid, as shown in Fig. 1-58. A choking gas, *hydrogen chloride,* is given off as one of the products. This extremely soluble and colorless gas reacts with water, as we learned earlier, to form hydrochloric acid.

Hydrochloric acid can be used in preparing hydrogen gas by reacting it with zinc or other active metals. You will recall that carbon dioxide gas, too, was prepared by adding this acid to marble chips.

Galvanized iron is made by coating sheet iron with melted zinc. Before the metal is dipped in the zinc, hydrochloric and sulfuric acids are used to remove the undesirable oxide coating

1-58. This diagram shows an apparatus for the laboratory preparation of hydrochloric acid. The heated salt and sulfuric acid react to form the hydrogen chloride gas. What precautions should be kept in mind when following this procedure?

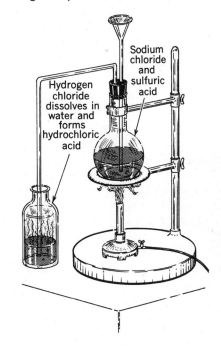

Sodium chloride and sulfuric acid

Hydrogen chloride dissolves in water and forms hydrochloric acid

found on the surface of the iron. Hydrochloric acid is also used in the cleaning of mortar from stone and brick. Impure hydrochloric acid is used commercially and is commonly called *muriatic* acid.

You may be surprised to learn that there is always acid in your stomach. The gastric juice of your stomach contains very dilute hydrochloric acid to assist in the digestion of food.

Nitric acid is very corrosive. Nitric acid (HNO_3) is both a strong acid and a strong oxidizing agent. It is unstable and breaks up easily, giving off its oxygen to other substances. Because of this, nitric acid reacts with less active metals like copper and silver, two metals with which concentrated hydrochloric acid will not react. In fact, concentrated nitric acid reacts with most metals, though platinum and gold are notable exceptions.

Preparation and uses of nitric acid. Nitric acid can be made in the laboratory by heating a mixture of sodium nitrate ($NaNO_3$) and concentrated sulfuric acid. The retort in Fig. 1-59 has a glass stopper because nitric acid is so corrosive it destroys cork or rubber.

Nitric acid is made commercially from relatively inexpensive raw materials: nitrogen, oxygen, and hydrogen. Where could you obtain these elements conveniently?

Nitric acid is used in making all common explosives. Among these are nitrocellulose, or smokeless gun powder, nitroglycerin, and dynamite. Still another is TNT, which is a high explosive used in making artillery shells. All of these explosives have unstable molecules that *decompose* and produce gaseous products with great force when they explode. Gun powder

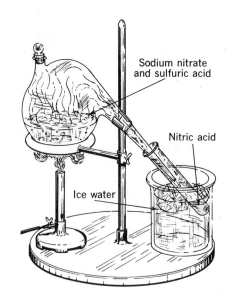

Sodium nitrate and sulfuric acid

Nitric acid

Ice water

1-59. In the laboratory preparation of nitric acid (HNO_3), sodium nitrate ($NaNO_3$) reacts with sulfuric acid (H_2SO_4).

is an older, less powerful explosive which contains potassium nitrate (KNO_3), carbon (C), in the form of charcoal, and sulfur (S).

Photographic film or cellulose nitrate is made from cotton fibers or wood pulp, and nitric acid. Nitric acid is used in making dyes and plastics. A mixture of nitric and hydrochloric acids, called *aqua regia,* is used to dissolve gold.

Care must be exercised in handling nitric acid. Nitric acid stains the skin yellow. It produces the same effect on any *protein*, and for that reason is used to identify protein substances. A drop of nitric acid can be added to a slice of hard-boiled egg white to demonstrate the presence of protein. The yellow color deepens to a bright orange when ammonia water is placed on the sample.

Hydroxides are bases. *Bases* are often considered as possessing the opposite properties of acids because one *neutralizes* the effect of the other, forming products that are neither *acidic* nor *basic*. The resulting products of *neutralization* are a salt and water.

Each base contains one or more *hydroxide radicals*, or *OH⁻* groups. When in a *water* solution, bases form hydroxide ions, for example,

$$NaOH \rightarrow Na^+ + OH^-$$

$$Ca(OH)_2 \rightarrow Ca^{++} + 2OH^-$$

A base is a substance that forms hydroxide ions when dissolved in water. The term *alkali* (*al*-ka-lie) refers to strong bases such as sodium or potassium hydroxides. The word *alkaline* describes substances having these basic properties.

In naming bases, you first name the metallic ion (such as sodium or calcium in the above equations), then follow it by the word "hydroxide." Thus, NaOH is called sodium hydroxide; $Ca(OH)_2$ is called calcium hydroxide. The symbol for the metal is written first in the formula as we have observed previously. One common base, ammonium hydroxide (NH_4OH), contains no metal. In this case, the ammonium radical (NH_4^+), acts like a metal.

Not all substances containing *OH* groups are bases. For example, methyl alcohol, commonly known as wood alcohol, has the formula CH_3OH. Since it *does not* ionize to form OH⁻ ions it is *not* a base. Common bases and their formulas are shown in the following table.

Some Common Bases and Their Formulas	
Sodium hydroxide	NaOH
Potassium hydroxide	KOH
Calcium hydroxide	$Ca(OH)_2$
Magnesium hydroxide	$Mg(OH)_2$
Aluminum hydroxide	$Al(OH)_3$
Ammonium hydroxide	NH_4OH
Iron(III) hydroxide	$Fe(OH)_3$

Strong and weak bases. Sodium and potassium hydroxides are very soluble in water, and are highly ionized in solution. Their solutions are strongly basic due to the high concentration of OH⁻ ions. These bases are said to be *strong* bases.

Ammonium hydroxide is a common example of a *weak* base because of the low concentration of OH⁻ ions. Calcium hydroxide is not very soluble in water. While its water solutions are completely ionized, it is only *moderately* basic because of the relatively low concentration of the OH⁻ ions. Most other common bases are relatively weak.

Properties of bases. Just as acids have a characteristic sour taste, we find that bases have a characteristic *bitter* taste in dilute solutions. Solutions of bases turn litmus paper from red to blue. Here is an easy way to remember these facts:

B — Base, Blue, Bitter

If you rubbed a drop of dilute sodium hydroxide solution between your fingers, you would detect its slippery feel. Sodium hydroxide attacks the skin at once because the solution is *caustic*. This means it attacks animal and plant materials. Besides the caustic action on the skin, strong bases destroy hair and wool, and are especially harmful to the eyes. Study Fig. 1-60.

Caustic soda, or sodium hydroxide, is commonly used when an inexpensive strong base is desired. Grocery stores sell it for household use under the name of *lye.* This caustic action is easily demonstrated.

Prepare half a beaker of 5% solution of sodium hydroxide (5 grams of solid NaOH dissolved in enough water to make 100 milliliters of solution). Heat the solution gently until it boils. Then add a piece of woolen and a piece of cotton cloth each about two inches square and stir with a glass rod. What

happens to the woolen cloth? Cotton is not destroyed by the hot alkali and remains in the beaker.

Preparation and uses of sodium hydroxide. One method of making sodium hydroxide is by the electrolysis of a water solution of table salt. The equation for the chemical change that takes place is

$$2NaCl + 2H_2O \rightarrow$$
$$2NaOH + H_2 \uparrow + Cl_2 \uparrow$$

Large factories with long rows of electrical cells are usually located in regions where the cost of electricity is low. One advantage of this method is that it makes valuable chlorine gas and hydrogen gas as by-products.

1-60. Five common properties of bases.

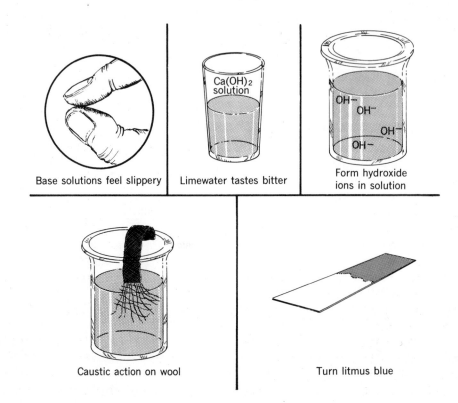

Base solutions feel slippery   Limewater tastes bitter   Form hydroxide ions in solution

Caustic action on wool   Turn litmus blue

In the home, sodium hydroxide is used to clean drain pipes that are clogged with grease. An important commercial use for sodium hydroxide, the making of soap, will be discussed in the next chapter. The largest users of sodium hydroxide are the manufacturers of rayon and cellophane, and refiners of gasoline and petroleum products.

Mercerized cotton is made by dipping the cloth into a sodium hydroxide solution while it is being stretched. This process gives the cloth a silky appearance and makes it somewhat stronger than ordinary cotton.

Ammonium hydroxide is a common base. Ammonia (NH_3) is a colorless gas with a pungent, penetrating odor. It is extremely soluble in water. Some of the ammonia actually reacts with the water to form ammonium hydroxide, which we learned previously, as shown in the following reaction

$$NH_3 + HOH \rightleftarrows NH_4^+ + OH^-$$

The double arrow ($\rightleftarrows$) in the equation shows that this is a dynamic, *reversible reaction*. This means that ammonia and water react to form ammonium and hydroxide ions, and that these ions react with each other to re-form ammonia and water in a continuous and simultaneous process. Many reactions in chemistry are reversible.

Calcium hydroxide is the least expensive base. We learned that calcium hydroxide is a moderately strong base. A water solution of this base is commonly called *limewater*. You may recall that limewater is used to detect the presence of carbon dioxide. As a moderate base, it is much less caustic than

sodium hydroxide because it is only slightly soluble in water.

Calcium hydroxide is used in large quantities for making building materials. It is also used for treating agricultural soils, for softening hard water, and for liberating ammonia from ammonium compounds. This base is used to remove hair from hides before they are converted to leather.

What are salts? When proper amounts of an acid and a base are mixed, each cancels the properties of the other. We call this process *neutralization*. The products formed are *salt* and *water*. The following is a general word equation of the neutralization reaction

$$acid + base \rightarrow salt + water$$

When solutions of hydrochloric acid and sodium hydroxide are mixed, we may conveniently write the reaction in the following manner

$$HCl + NaOH \rightarrow NaCl + HOH$$
acid   base   salt   water

Since the acid, base, and the salt—in water solution—are highly ionized, this equation is written more appropriately in an *ionic* form as

$$H^+ + Cl^- + Na^+ + OH^- \rightarrow$$
*hydrochloric   sodium
acid   hydroxide*

$$Na^+ + Cl^- + HOH$$
*sodium   water
chloride*

When the water is evaporated, white crystals of sodium chloride remain in the container. This salt is one of a very large class of compounds which are named *salts*. Chemists define a **salt** as *a compound composed of positive ions of a base and negative ions of an acid.*

Notice in the above reaction that sodium ions (Na^+) and chloride ions (Cl^-) appear on both sides of the equation. These ions actually take no part in the reaction. They are called "spectator" ions and merely remain dispersed in the solution. Hence, we may rewrite the last equation more simply as

$$H^+ + OH^- \rightarrow HOH$$

This equation indicates that the *neutralization reaction is essentially between the hydrogen ions of the acid and the hydroxide ions of the base.* Observe that the H^+ and OH^- ions lose their effect in the solution by forming an *un-ionized* compound, water. And when the water is evaporated, the solid salt material remains.

There are many compounds called salts. Sodium chloride is only one of the many thousands of known salts. The word "salt" has a broader meaning in chemistry than it has in everyday life. Since neutralization reactions between acids and bases produce salts, you can imagine how many different salts there may be by considering different combinations of acids and bases.

If potassium hydroxide and sulfuric acid are used, potassium sulfate (K_2SO_4) can be formed. Nitric acid with the same base produces potassium nitrate (KNO_3). We may express these reactions in chemical equations

$$2KOH + H_2SO_4 \rightarrow K_2SO_4 + 2HOH$$

$$KOH + HNO_3 \rightarrow KNO_3 + HOH$$

1-61. Salts and other chemical materials are sometimes found at or near the earth's surface. (Morton Salt Co.)

Potassium nitrate, called *saltpeter,* is used to make gun powder and fireworks. It is used also as a meat preservative in preparing corned beef, ham, and bacon.

Metals and nonmetals. Look at the formulas of the salts given above. Each one contains a *metal* such as sodium or potassium. All metals such as calcium, iron, zinc, mercury, lead, gold, copper, tin, and many others form salts.

Metals are a class of elements that show a luster and conduct heat and electricity. They usually have positive valence numbers, yielding positive ions, and form salts by combining with negative ions. Observe the location of these elements on the Periodic Table on page 607.

Notice also that each salt consists of *nonmetallic* ions such as sulfates, nitrates, or chlorides. *Nonmetallic elements* and radicals have negative valence numbers, form negative ions, and *are very poor conductors of heat and electricity*. Other nonmetallic ions include the oxides, carbonates, bicarbonates, sulfides, phosphates, and others. Observe again in the Periodic Table the location of nonmetallic *elements*.

You will find that salts as a group do not have special properties as a group. Some taste salty, some bitter. Many dissolve readily in water, others slightly, and still others not at all. Salts have varying colors, although most salts are white. They may be harmless, helpful, or poisonous. *Salts are compounds formed by the transfer of electrons. When dissolved in water, they ionize freely and conduct an electric current.*

Neutralization is an exact process. We have learned that neutralization consists essentially of the reaction

$$H^+ + OH^- \rightarrow HOH$$

From this, we see that one hydrogen ion combines with one hydroxide ion to form one molecule of water. If we have more H^+ than OH^-, our final solution would be *acidic*. If, on the other hand, we have more OH^- than H^+, our solution would test *basic*. So you see, an acid and a base will completely neutralize each other only when the same numbers of H^+ and OH^- are present in the solution.

No matter how small an amount of an acid or a base you use, there will always be many billions of ions in the reaction. Of course, you cannot count the ions, but you can use *indicators* to tell when you have added the right amount of acid or base in the neutralization process.

As you know, litmus turns red in the presence of hydrogen ions, and blue in the presence of hydroxide ions. Phenolphthalein (feen-ol-*thay*-leen) so-

lution, a colorless liquid, is another useful indicator. It turns pink in the presence of OH^- but remains colorless in neutral or acid solutions. *A neutral solution is one that is neither acidic nor basic.*

Making sodium chloride by neutralization. You can prepare ordinary table salt from hydrochloric acid and sodium hydroxide as mentioned previously. Burets, as shown in Fig. 1-62, are convenient for adding solution one drop at a time, but you can use a medicine dropper if burets are not available.

First dilute two milliliters of concentrated hydrochloric acid with enough water to make 100 milliliters of dilute acid. Then, add one gram of solid sodium hydroxide to 100 milli-

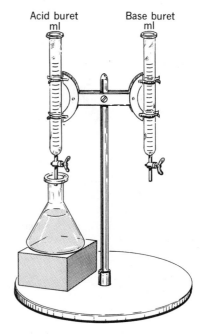

1-62. Neutralization experiments can be done quickly and accurately by using burets.

liters of water in another beaker. Stir the mixture until the sodium hydroxide is dissolved completely. Fill one buret with acid solution and the other with the alkali solution.

Run about 20 milliliters of the acid into a clean beaker or flask. Add a drop or two of phenolphthalein solution as the indicator. What color is the solution? A piece of white paper under the beaker will help you to detect any color changes. Now add sodium hydroxide from the alkali buret until the liquid in the beaker remains pink after stirring. Add the acid a drop at a time until the solution is once again colorless. One drop of the base should now turn the whole liquid pink. One drop of the acid should leave it faintly pink, or neutral.

When the solution is neutral, pour it into a dish and evaporate the liquid as shown in Fig. 1-63. To avoid spat-

Solution being evaporated

1-63. When proper quantities of an acid and a base are mixed and heated until all the liquid evaporates, a salt remains as a residue.

tering, be careful to use a low flame. Taste the solid remaining in the evaporating dish when it is cool. Do you recognize the flavor?

Other salts can be made similarly by using different acids or bases.

Common salt is abundant. Sodium chloride is found all over the world, much of it dissolved in the oceans. Ocean water is about 3 percent sodium chloride by weight. In one cubic foot of sea water there are almost 2 pounds of salt. If we took all the salt from the oceans, there would be enough to cover all land areas of the world about 500 feet deep. Some salt lakes, such as the Great Salt Lake and the Dead Sea, are much saltier than the oceans.

Underground salt deposits are found in many countries, too. These often contain other minerals besides sodium chloride, in about the same proportion as the minerals in ocean water. This suggests that these deposits were formed by the evaporation of sea water. Over a long period of time, changes in the earth's surface covered them. There are large salt deposits in Kansas, New York, Texas, Michigan, and Louisiana.

Salt from wells. Salt from sea water is sometimes obtained by letting the water evaporate in shallow bays or inlets. This method has been used since man first noticed salt crystals appearing in trapped pools of sea water. This method utilizes the sun's heat to evaporate the water. Rock salt is also mined like coal from underground deposits. (See Fig. 1-64.) It is a grayish rock and is used for such purposes as freezing ice cream, curing animal hides, and melting snow and ice on pavements.

1-64. Interior view of a salt mine (Morton Salt Co.)

However, much of our table salt comes from *salt wells*. A large pipe is driven down to the center of an underground salt deposit. Water is pumped down through the pipe to dissolve the salt. The salt solution comes back to the surface through a smaller pipe placed inside the larger one. (See Fig. 1-65.) This method of salt production is called "solution mining." Sulfur is mined in a similar fashion.

Salt must be purified. The salt solution that comes from the salt wells is carefully purified before it comes to your dinner table. First, it is allowed to settle, and then it is *filtered* to get rid of the suspended matter. It is not pure sodium chloride solution, however, because it still contains chlorides of calcium and magnesium.

These chlorides are more soluble in water than is sodium chloride. As

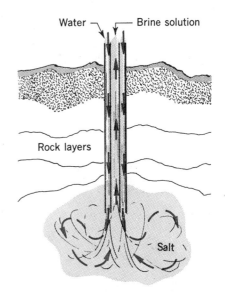

1-65. Water is forced down a salt well to dissolve the underground salt. The brine solution is then forced to the surface and water is removed, leaving pure salt.

the *brine*, or salt solution, is boiled down in evaporators, the table salt comes out of solution first. To make a good grade of salt, this crude salt is dissolved and the process is repeated.

Do you know that really pure sodium chloride does not get sticky in damp weather? It is the very small amounts of other chlorides in the table salt that cause the trouble. They pick up moisture from the air and make the salt sticky so that it will not pour easily.

You can purify salt in the laboratory. Dissolve about half a pound of crude salt in water in a large beaker. Then filter the solution as shown in Fig. 1-66. Evaporate the solution by boiling away the water until the salt begins to separate out. Now let the solution stand until it reaches room temperature. Pour off the liquid and observe the salt. Why is the filtering necessary?

Some uses of salt. At one time or another, many nations have used salt as a medium of exchange. This commodity was so valuable at one time that Roman soldiers were paid with it, hence the common expression, "worth his salt," and the word "salary."

Salt is essential in our diet. It is in solution in the body fluids such as blood, urine, and perspiration. In hot weather some people take salt tablets to replace the salt lost through perspiration. Usually we use more salt than we really need, simply because we like its taste.

If you look at a box of salt, you sometimes see the word "iodized salt" marked on the package. This means sodium or potassium iodide has been added to the salt in small amounts. This is done to protect people from

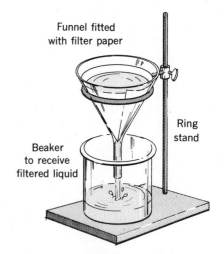

Funnel fitted with filter paper

Ring stand

Beaker to receive filtered liquid

1-66. Filtering separates the insoluble substances from a liquid.

the disease called *goiter*. A goiter is an enlargement of the thyroid gland, located in the neck, often caused by a shortage of iodine in the diet.

Salt is an important material in the production of many chemicals. Caustic soda, chlorine, hydrochloric acid, washing soda, and baking soda are some of the familiar chemicals made from sodium chloride. Salt is also used in processing foods to prevent decay by bacteria.

Sodium carbonate is an important salt. Sodium carbonate (Na_2CO_3) is a white powder often called *soda ash*. When dissolved in water, it forms a basic solution. Although not as caustic as sodium hydroxide, it makes a good grease solvent. Soda ash is also widely used as a raw material in making glass.

When sodium carbonate is allowed to *crystallize* from a water solution, large glassy crystals of *washing soda* are formed. These crystals have a formula, $Na_2CO_3 \cdot 10\,H_2O$. The water, which is not firmly bound to the sodium carbonate, is called *water of hydration*. The dot ($\cdot$) in the formula shows the water to be loosely connected. Many other crystals have water of hydration as part of the structure in the formation of a crystal. When the water molecules are driven off by heat, this crystal loses its structure and becomes a non-crystalline powder, Na_2CO_3. Other crystals, such as NaCl, KNO_3, and $KClO_3$, do not require the water of hydration to form crystals.

Sodium bicarbonate ($NaHCO_3$), called *baking soda*, is made commercially from solutions of sodium chloride and ammonium bicarbonate. All carbonates and bicarbonates give off carbon dioxide when mixed with an acid. For this reason, baking soda is used in baking powders, in some fire extinguishers, and in many household products. When sodium bicarbonate is heated in a furnace, the following reaction takes place

$$2NaHCO_3 \rightarrow Na_2CO_3 + H_2O + CO_2 \uparrow$$

This equation represents the commercial preparation of sodium carbonate from the sodium bicarbonate.

Some salt solutions are not neutral. After learning about neutralization, you might think that no salt solution would have an effect on litmus paper. However, some salts do not form neutral solutions. Many of them have an acidic or basic reaction in water. This is because some salts react with water to form an *excess* of either hydrogen or hydroxide ions. This means that the solution acts like an acid or a base depending on which kind of ion is in excess. This type of reaction is called *hydrolysis* and is the *reverse process of neutralization*.

Dissolve a little sodium carbonate (Na_2CO_3) in water and test it with litmus paper. The litmus turns blue, indicating an *excess* of hydroxide ions. Now dissolve some aluminum sulfate ($Al_2(SO_4)_3$) in water. This time the solution turns litmus red, indicating an *excess* of hydrogen ions.

Observe that sodium carbonate is the salt resulting from the reaction between a *strong base* (NaOH) and a *weak acid* (H_2CO_3). The strong base furnishes an *excess* of hydroxide ions over the *fewer* hydrogen ions furnished by the weak acid. Therefore, sodium carbonate in solution has basic properties.

Now let us examine aluminum sulfate. It is the result of a reaction between a *weak* base ($Al(OH)_3$) and a *strong* acid (H_2SO_4). The strong acid furnishes an *excess* of hydrogen ions over the *fewer* hydroxide ions furnished by the *weak* base. Hence, aluminum sulfate tests like an acid in water solution because of the excess of the hydrogen ions.

Some salts test neutral in water solutions. Potassium nitrate (KNO_3) is a salt that forms *neutral* solutions in water. In other words, red litmus will remain red and blue litmus will remain blue when tested in the solution.

This salt can be prepared by reacting potassium hydroxide and nitric acid.

$$KOH + HNO_3 \rightarrow KNO_3 + HOH$$

You recognize potassium hydroxide as a *strong* base, and nitric acid as a *strong* acid. Therefore, when potassium nitrate is dissolved in water, there is no excess of hydrogen ions or hydroxide ions. The solution is essentially neutral.

In general, a salt resulting from a strong acid and a strong base will form neutral solutions. The same is true of a salt obtained from a weak base and a weak acid.

What are crystals? Let a salt solution stand in an open dish until the water evaporates, and salt remains in the dish. Take a close look at the particles of salt. They have a regular shape or structure, with flat surfaces and straight edges. *Solids having or capable of having definite geometric form within their microstructures are called* **crystals.** Crystals of different substances have different shapes. Common table salt, for example, forms cube-shaped crystals as shown in Fig. 1-67.

The size of crystals depends largely upon the time it takes for them to form. The longer the time, the larger the crystals "grow." The shape of each crystal depends on the arrangement of the ions, atoms, or molecules in the crystal.

1-68. Copper(II) sulfate crystals ($CuSO_4 \cdot 5H_2O$) are six-sided. (B. M. Shaub)

Crystals of copper(II) sulfate ($CuSO_4$) are blue six-sided solids whose opposite sides are parallel. You can form these crystals by allowing a hot, concentrated solution of copper sulfate to cool. Then pour off the solution into another vessel and observe the crystals of copper sulfate that remain. (See Fig. 1-68.)

To make large copper(II) sulfate crystals, let the solution evaporate slowly for a week or two at room temperature. First, drop a very small nearly perfect crystal into this solution to serve as a "seed." The copper(II) sulfate deposits on the seed as the crystal grows in size. It is possible to obtain crystals weighing several pounds by this method. The complete formula for the copper(II) sulfate crystal is $CuSO_4 \cdot 5H_2O$. What would you expect to happen to this crystal if heated in a flame? Why?

The principal use of copper sulfate, commonly called *blue vitriol,* is in copper plating. It is also used in agricultural insecticides. Sometimes small amounts are added to city water reservoirs to destroy small plants that may give the water a bad taste.

1-67. Crystals consist of atoms arranged in orderly rows forming definite patterns. Table salt crystals (above) have a cubical shape. (Morton Salt Co.)

An alum is a double salt. Sometimes two salts will crystallize out of solution together and combine to form a *double salt*, such as *alum*.

If solutions of sodium sulfate and aluminum sulfate are mixed, crystals of *sodium alum* are obtained when the water evaporates. The crystal has eight sides, arranged like two pyramids with their bases together. The formula for this alum is $Na_2SO_4 \cdot Al_2(SO_4)_3 \cdot 24\,H_2O$. This is a long formula, but it is not really difficult to understand. It is simply sodium sulfate and aluminum sulfate, both crystallized with 24 molecules of water to form this double salt.

Maybe you have seen your father use a piece of alum to stop bleeding when he cuts himself shaving. Sometimes, alum is added to pickles to keep them from spoiling. Potassium aluminum sulfate is another alum found naturally, and dyers frequently use it to make dyes stick to cloth better. This alum is also used for fireproofing certain materials.

There are many different types of alums used both in industry and in the home. Some alums can be used in large quantities to acidify the soil for gardening in areas where the soil is too basic. Alums are also used in the purification of city water supplies, as well as in the manufacture of paper.

Quick Quiz

1. What is an electrolyte? Name four electrolytes and four non-electrolytes.
2. Explain why some liquids conduct an electric current and others do not.
3. What is an acid? Give four properties of acids.
4. How does the hydronium ion differ from the hydrogen ion?
5. What two substances are formed when dilute sulfuric acid reacts with iron? Write the equation for this reaction.
6. How is hydrochloric acid prepared in the laboratory? Describe the laboratory preparation for nitric acid.
7. What is a base? List four properties of strong bases.
8. What is the difference between a strong base and a weak one?
9. How would you test for a protein in the laboratory?
10. What important use is made of calcium hydroxide? Sodium hydroxide?
11. Write the balanced chemical equation for the reaction of sodium hydroxide and sulfuric acid. What general type of reaction is this?
12. Give two or three differences between a metal and a nonmetal. At which end of the Periodic Table would you expect to find metals? Nonmetals?
13. A dish of gasoline and a dish of concentrated sulfuric acid are weighed and left uncovered for several hours. They are then weighed again. What change in weight, if any, would you expect to occur in each? Explain your answer.
14. What is meant by hydrolysis?
15. Two products are obtained in the process of neutralization. What procedure would you use to separate these two products?
16. Each of the following salts can be dissolved in water. Write the formulas for each and predict whether each solution will be acidic, basic, or neutral. Give reasons for your answer.
    a. sodium sulfate
    b. potassium carbonate
    c. ammonium chloride
    d. ammonium acetate
    e. sodium nitrate
    f. aluminum nitrate

SUMMARY

Science concerns itself with the knowledge and understanding of all material things in the universe and their behavior under different conditions. Scientists construct models or theories to explain natural happenings.

Weight is the force of attraction of the earth for an object. This force decreases as the distance between the object and the earth increases. Rest mass is a measure of the quantity of matter. For normal velocities, mass of an object is practically constant.

Chemical reactions are expressed by chemical equations which tell what materials are used, in what proportions, and what is obtained in the reactions. While mixtures contain substances which vary in composition, compounds contain the same proportion by weight of the elements that compose them. The law of conservation of matter states that matter cannot be created or destroyed by ordinary chemical means. This law represents a useful model in balancing chemical equations.

Modern atomic theory explains how particles react to form new substances. By using valence numbers, predictions can be made as to what compounds are likely to be possible. Of course, all scientific statements are subject to rigorous tests by experimentation.

The kinetic theory states that the molecules of all matter are in constant motion, and that the higher the temperature of a substance, the faster its molecules move.

The molecules of acids, bases, and salts are formed by the transfer of electrons between atoms. These substances are called electrolytes, because they can conduct an electric current when dissolved or melted. Acids form hydrogen ions in a water solution. Bases ionize to form hydroxide ions in a water solution.

A salt is the substance other than water that is produced when an acid and a base react with each other. It consists of a metal or a metallic radical, and a nonmetal or nonmetallic radical. Some salts, when dissolved in water, react acidic or basic because of an excess of either hydrogen ions or hydroxide ions.

CHAPTER REVIEW

Vocabulary

Match the words in Column A with the *best* response in Column B. Do not write in your book.

Column A	Column B
1. meter	a. 39.37 inches
2. matter	b. measure of pull of the earth on an object
3. weight	c. supports combustion
4. chemical change	d. the burning of wood
5. density	e. concentrated sulfuric acid
6. oxygen	f. weight per unit volume

7. electrolysis
8. law of conservation of matter
9. law of definite proportions
10. proton
11. atomic number
12. valence number
13. diffusion
14. slow oxidation
15. catalyst
16. smog
17. ions
18. litmus
19. dehydrating agent
20. weak base

g. positively charged atomic particle
h. number of electrons in a neutral atom
i. mixing due to molecular motion
j. decay of wood
k. pollutant
l. decomposition of a substance into simpler substances by means of an electric current
m. every compound always has the same proportion by weight of elements that compose it
n. atoms that have lost or gained electrons
o. no matter is lost or gained in an ordinary chemical reaction
p. a measure of the combining power of elements with other elements
q. low concentration of OH^- ions
r. chemical indicator
s. anything that has weight and occupies space
t. substance that speeds up a chemical reaction

Questions: Group A

1. How are science and curiosity related?
2. The kilogram is a metric unit of mass. Sometimes scientists express the weight of objects in kilograms also. What is meant by a weight of one kilogram?
3. How does a lighted candle illustrate the three phases of matter?
4. List several chemical and physical properties of substances.
5. Explain how you would determine the density of a small irregular object.
6. Give the valence numbers of the following: calcium, oxygen, zinc, lead, barium, carbonate, and sulfate. Predict which of these are likely to combine with each other to form new substances.
7. Distinguish between atomic number and atomic mass.
8. Why is manganese dioxide used in the preparation of oxygen from potassium chlorate?
9. Compare the terms "oxidation," "slow oxidation," and "combustion."
10. List five properties of nitrogen gas.
11. What discovery did Priestley overlook when he prepared oxygen?
12. Why is it dangerous to use hydrogen in balloons? What other gas could you use?
13. How is table salt obtained commercially?
14. Explain how you would prove a piece of cloth was all wool.
15. What substances would you use to prepare sodium hydroxide? What are two by-products?
16. Explain the difference between a strong and weak acid.
17. What do we mean when we say that acids neutralize bases?
18. List three properties of salts.
19. When sodium carbonate is dissolved in water, is the resulting solution acidic or basic? Explain.

Questions: Group B

1. If you were given a flask of gas with no label, how would you test for oxygen? For hydrogen?
2. What does the formula for carbonic acid, H_2CO_3, tell you about its composition?
3. Write the chemical equation for the reaction of sodium chloride and silver nitrate solutions.
4. Explain the meaning of the law of definite proportions. Does it apply to mixtures? Explain.
5. How does the temperature affect the solubility of most solids? Of gases?
6. Explain why some elements have positive valence numbers and some negative.
7. Write the chemical formulas for the following compounds:
   a. aluminum hydroxide
   b. ammonium carbonate
   c. barium sulfate
   d. copper(II) oxide
   e. iron(III) hydroxide
   f. lead nitrate
   g. magnesium phosphate
   h. silver bromide
   i. sodium chlorate
   j. potassium hydroxide
8. Write the chemical names from the formulas:
   a. KNO_3
   b. $MgCl_2$
   c. $MgSO_4$
   d. $Ba(OH)_2$
   e. $Al_2(SO_4)_3$
   f. $NaC_2H_3O_2$
   g. $AgNO_3$
   h. $PbCO_3$
9. Explain how dust explosions occur.
10. When sodium carbonate crystals are heated, what change would you expect to take place?
11. When aluminum sulfate is dissolved in water, would you expect the solution to test acidic or basic? Explain.

Problems

1. How many liters are there in 4000 milliliters? Is this more or less than a gallon?
2. A measured distance is 3.5 kilometers. Express this distance in (a) meters, (b) centimeters, and (c) millimeters.
3. A steel rod is 25 cm long. Find its length in meters, millimeters, and kilometers.
4. A ton of coal weighs 2000 pounds. What is its weight in kilograms?
5. A metal bar is 12 feet long. What is its length in centimeters?
6. How many liters are there in 72 quarts?
7. Which is larger, a mile or 1500 meters? (Prove your answer.)
8. How many grams are there in 20 lb of sugar?
9. A boy is 5 ft 8 in. tall. What is his height in centimeters?
10. A rectangular box is 3.0 meters long, 2.3 meters wide, and 150 centimeters in depth. Find its volume in cubic meters (m^3).
11. The density of a piece of brass is 8.4 g/cm^3. If the weight of the brass is 500 grams, compute its volume.
12. A block of wood weighs 180 grams. It is 10 cm long, 6 cm wide, and 4 cm thick. What is its volume? Its density?

13. A material has a volume of 13 ft³. If its weight is 91 lb, compute its density.

14. It was found by experiment that 32 grams of sulfur combine chemically with 56 grams of iron to form 88 grams of iron sulfide. If 8 lb of iron are heated with 4 lb of sulfur, what will be left over? How much iron sulfide will be formed?

15. A sample of sea water contains 4% mineral salts. If you distill 5 lb of it, how many pounds of mineral salts would you have? Of water? What various salts would you expect to find in the residue?

16. An empty beaker weighs 100 grams. Salt solution is added until the total weight is 500 grams. The water is evaporated, leaving the salt. The beaker and salt now weigh 116 grams. (a) What did the salt solution weight? (b) What weight of salt was obtained? (c) What percentage of the solution was salt?

2 APPLYING CHEMISTRY

A WATER AND THE CHEMISTRY OF ITS TREATMENT

The abundance of water. Looking at a globe, you can see that oceans cover approximately three-quarters of the earth. This accounts for more than an estimated 300 million cubic miles of water. Tremendous quantities of water are also found in the form of water vapor, always present in the air, even over the deserts. About two-thirds of the weight of our bodies is water. Consequently, a person who weighs 150 pounds has about 100 pounds of water in his body. Vegetables and fruits such as cucumbers, tomatoes, celery, and lettuce, as well as other foods, actually contain more than 90 percent water.

Some properties of water. Pure water is a colorless, odorless, and tasteless liquid. We have seen that it exists in all three phases—solid, liquid, and gaseous. On the *Fahrenheit* thermometer, the kind in common use, water freezes at 32°. Under normal condi-

tions, water boils at 212°. On the *Celsius*, or centigrade scale, the one most widely used in science, water freezes at 0° and boils at 100°.

Experiments show that water expands as it freezes. When a closed tankful of water freezes, about 15 tons of force push on each square inch of the tank. Even a strong container filled with water may burst when freezing takes place, if it is tightly sealed. Water pipes and automobile engines often burst in winter when the water in them freezes.

Chemically, water is a very stable compound. It does not break up, or decompose, easily. It is our most important chemical solvent.

Underground water. Some of the water that falls as rain soaks into the ground and is called *ground water*. The ground becomes saturated with water, in much the same way that a sponge does. The upper surface of this underground water layer is called the *water table*. The depth of the water table in any region depends on the amount of rain that falls and the condition and nature of the ground. During a dry spell, the water table drops to lower levels, and many shallow wells go dry. (See Fig. 2-1.)

At even lower depths in many areas there are concentrations of underground water, which may be tapped by an *artesian well.* The artesian well is drilled through underground rock until a large enough water vein is reached. Water flows to the surface under its own pressure from some artesian wells, but must be mechanically pumped from other wells. (See Fig. 2-2.)

Pure water is not common. In spite of the great abundance of water, chemically pure water is not common. This is because water dissolves so many substances with which it comes in contact. Ordinarily, when we speak of pure water, we mean water that is suitable for drinking. Good drinking water is almost never pure in the chemical sense, but the impurities in it are harmless. Actually, water tastes better if some impurities remain in it.

Put a little drinking water in a watch glass. Let it evaporate by heating it over a beaker of boiling water, as shown in Fig. 2-3. Examine the watch glass carefully after all the

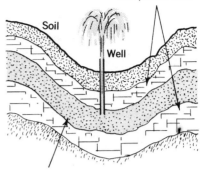

2-2. Pressure forces the water trapped between the non-porous layers of rock to the surface.

water has evaporated. You will find some solid material forming a layer on the watch glass. Now repeat this experiment, using a small sample of *distilled water.* You will find that no solids are left behind after evaporation.

The purest water in nature is rain water. However, as it drops from the clouds, it dissolves oxygen and other gases of the air. Bits of dust and bacteria floating in the atmosphere are also picked up. Even so, rain water

2-1. The presence of permanent bodies of water depends on the depth of the water table below the surface.

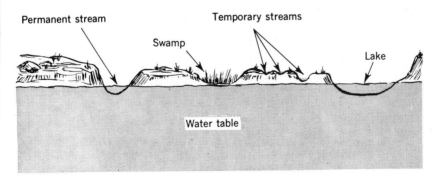

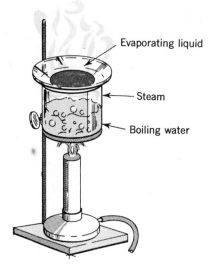

2-3. After the tap water evaporates, dissolved solids remain as a residue on the watch glass.

is relatively free of dissolved solids and is relatively pure.

However, as soon as rain water touches the ground, it dissolves minerals as well as impurities from plant and animal sources. These impurities often make water unfit for drinking and poor for laundry purposes.

Distillation purifies water. Chemists and pharmacists use distilled water for making up industrial and medicinal solutions. Distilled water is also used in automobile batteries.

Water is *distilled* by first boiling it in a vessel to form steam. The steam is then led through a tube that is surrounded by a stream of cold water. This condenses the steam into a liquid again. Dissolved solids that are not changed into gases remain in the distilling flask. By this process, we can prepare water that is quite free from dissolved solids. Impurities that evaporate easily, however, are not removed. Can you explain why?

Use the apparatus, shown in Fig. 2-4, for distilling liquids in the laboratory. Dissolve a spoonful of powdered copper(II) sulfate in 100 ml of warm water, and add this solution to the distilling flask. You will be starting with water that is not pure, as the blue color obviously indicates.

Next, heat the mixture to boiling and distill the liquid until a considerable amount of distilled water has been collected. Examine the distilled sample. *Distillation* separated the dissolved copper(II) sulfate from the water. This is shown by the fact that the distilled water sample is colorless.

Suspended matter in water. In addition to dissolved solids, flowing water contains *suspended* matter that will settle to the bottom if the water stands quietly. If you examine a glass container filled with almost any river water, you can observe the suspended material. The river may carry this mat-

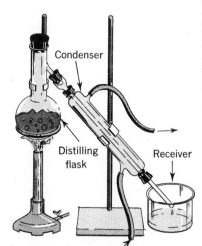

2-4. Laboratory distillation procedure involves evaporation of a liquid followed by condensation of the vapors.

ter for hundreds of miles. Some streams are very muddy because of the dirt and clay materials in suspension. This is especially noticeable following heavy rains in areas with much loose topsoil.

The Mississippi River carries tremendous amounts of suspended matter. As it reaches the Gulf of Mexico, the material is deposited, forming a triangle-shaped *delta* that extends for many miles into the Gulf of Mexico.

Suspended impurities in a river usually mean the loss of valuable *topsoil* from farm land. Until people apply adequate flood-control measures and conservation practices, rivers will continue to wash away valuable agricultural soils.

What is potable water? The distillation process purifies water. However, this laboratory method of purification of water is too expensive and impractical for large-scale usage at the present time. Water that has been boiled for about 10 minutes is usually safe to drink. While boiling the water does not remove dissolved impurities and suspended matter, it does kill harmful bacteria and renders it fit to drink. *Water that is fit to drink is called potable water.* It must be clear, colorless, pleasant-tasting, free of harmful bacteria, and fairly free of dissolved solids. Distilled water is pure, but it is not the best drinking water. Small amounts of mineral matter and air in the water improve its taste, whereas distilled water has a "flat" taste.

Organic and mineral matter in water. The impurities in untreated water are generally classified into two convenient groups: (1) matter in *solution,* and (2) matter in *suspension.* These two groups may be further sub-

2-5. Large amounts of matter in suspension and solution are picked up by water flowing in these rapids. (Leding from Monkmeyer)

divided to include in each: (a) *organic matter,* and (b) *inorganic* or *mineral matter.*

Animal and plant substances are classified as **organic matter.** Organic matter may be very harmful, depending on its nature and the amount contained in the water. What appear to be harmless bits of leaves or straw can be extremely dangerous because certain bacteria multiply rapidly on these materials.

Nonliving materials are considered **inorganic matter** and usually denote mineral compounds. Depending upon the composition of the soils and rock, different kinds of mineral matter are present in various streams and rivers. Some of these materials either become dissolved in the water or carried along by the water in suspension.

A stream flowing through a region where there is limestone, for example, will have calcium compounds in *solution* or in *suspension.* (See Fig. 2-5.)

Inorganic materials affect the taste of water. As a matter of fact, "mineral water" has long been used as a diet supplement.

Wells are a source of drinking water. Where you get drinking water depends on where you live. In rural areas, water is obtained from wells, springs, or streams.

Wells should be dug as far as possible from areas where contamination might make the water unfit for human use. Health authorities report that many farm wells are a menace to health because they are poorly located or improperly constructed. If the well is walled with loose stones, contaminated surface water may seep into the drinking supply.

Water supplies in cities. Rivers and lakes are the major source of drinking water in our country. They supply approximately 75 percent of the water used by cities and towns for drinking and by farmers for irrigation purposes. Water is industry's most important raw material.

Large cities use many millions of gallons of potable water daily. At the present time, our country consumes about 300 billion gallons of water per day and the rate is increasing rapidly. At the present time, the average family of five uses over 300,000 gallons of water yearly. It is estimated that by the end of the next decade, we will need double the present amount of fresh water to meet our daily needs. To meet our critical needs, the United States is experimenting with five demonstration plants across the nation, each using a different system for ob-

2-6. Colorado River water is lifted 291 feet into a series of aqueducts which transport it 654 miles across the State of California. (Steve Barrett)

taining fresh water from the ocean. In one of these plants, nuclear energy is used as the source of heat for the distillation of sea water into potable water.

Most of the water used by New York City comes from the Catskill Mountains about 100 miles away. It flows through long, underground pipes called **aqueducts.** Part of Los Angeles water supply comes from the Sierra Nevada Mountains, 250 miles away from the city. Some of the water comes through a huge aqueduct from the more distant Colorado River. Yet the needs of this rapidly growing area are so great that dams and aqueducts are now being built to bring water from the rivers of northern California, a distance of more than 500 miles away. (See Fig. 2-6.)

St. Louis and other large cities get their water from the Mississippi River.

This supply is first *filtered* and then *treated* with chemicals before it can be used.

Along the Great Lakes, cities have an almost unlimited supply of fresh water nearby. The water usually enters the *intake pipe* about 50 feet below the surface of the lake and approximately three miles from the shore. After *purification,* this water is fit for consumption.

The process of water purification. Water obtained directly from a river or lake should never be drunk because it is usually contaminated with organisms which may cause disease. Naturally, cities and towns purify water before it is used. To make water potable, sediment or suspended matter must be removed and harmful bacteria destroyed. This is usually accomplished through the following steps of water purification. (See Fig. 2-7.)

2-7. The basic steps in the purification of municipal drinking water are shown in the diagram below. What step is missing?

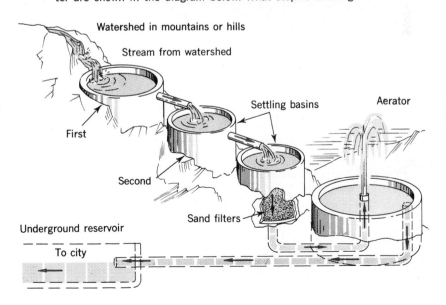

Watershed in mountains or hills

Stream from watershed

First

Second

Settling basins

Aerator

Sand filters

Underground reservoir

To city

1. Settling in first basin.

2. Settling in second basin after adding chemicals.

3. Filtration through sand and gravel.

4. Aeration to kill certain bacteria and improve taste.

5. Chlorination to kill additional harmful bacteria.

The settling process. The water is allowed to stand in a large pool or *settling basin* when it first comes from the stream, river, lake, or reservoir. The basin may cover more than an acre, forming a small pond. Here most of the heavy suspended materials and debris settles to the bottom.

The water is then fed into a second basin. Since very small particles suspended in water settle slowly, chemicals are used to speed up the settling process. Small quantities of *aluminum sulfate* ($Al_2(SO_4)_3$) and *calcium hydroxide* ($Ca(OH)_2$) are added to the water. These two chemicals react to form sticky precipitates of *aluminum hydroxide* ($Al(OH)_3$) and *calcium sulfate* ($CaSO_4$).

$$Al_2(SO_4)_3 + 3Ca(OH)_2 \rightarrow$$
$$2Al(OH)_3 \downarrow + 3CaSO_4 \downarrow$$

The arrows ($\downarrow$) indicate that the products are precipitates, or insoluble substances, that come out of the solution. Hence, the fine particles become coated with the precipitates and are made heavier, causing them to settle to the bottom rapidly. Some bacteria also become entangled in the precipitates. By this operation, much more of the suspended material and bacteria are removed in the second settling basin.

Settling is followed by filtration. The water is next filtered through layers of sand and gravel in containers, some of which are larger than your classroom. These filters are composed of a layer of sand about 5 feet thick that is placed above a layer of gravel. A layer of charcoal is often used between the sand and the gravel to remove coloring matter and foul-tasting substances.

Water from the second settling basin comes in at the top of the filter containers and seeps through the layers of sand, charcoal, and gravel. This process takes out the rest of the suspended material, as well as much of the remaining bacteria. The outlet for the filtered water is at the bottom of the huge container as shown in Fig. 2-8.

Aeration and chlorination. The filtered water is often sprayed into the air, much like a huge fountain. This process is called **aeration.** Oxygen of the air dissolves in the water and kills many types of bacteria that cannot sur-

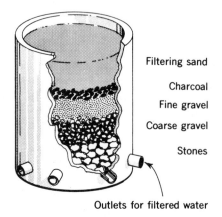

Filtering sand

Charcoal

Fine gravel

Coarse gravel

Stones

Outlets for filtered water

2-8. Diagram of a cross-section of a sand filter used in water purification. What is the purpose of the charcoal?

2-9. In the aeration process, oxygen of the air dissolves in drinking water, killing certain bacteria and improving the taste. (Annan Photo Features)

vive in the presence of great quantities of oxygen. Aeration also improves the taste of the water. (See Fig. 2-9.)

In the United States, *chlorination* is generally used to make sure that all harmful bacteria are destroyed before the water is fit for human consumption. A varying amount of *chlorine* is added to the water, depending upon the condition of the water and the season of the year. In the fall, more chlorine is used because more organic matter gets into the water. Can you see why?

Fluoridation. Many community water supplies are deficient in the *fluoride ion.* Under normal living conditions, fluorine is a trace element in our diet. To make up for this diet deficiency, fluoride salts are sometimes added to the water supply.

The American Dental Association confirmed the fact that no harmful effects are produced from water containing recommended amounts of fluoride salts. Studies by many sources have shown that *fluoridation* has been remarkably effective in reducing tooth decay. According to one report, the *fluoridation* of Baltimore's water supply has resulted in almost a 75 percent decline of tooth decay in 6-year-old children.

Many communities have hard water. Making water potable is but one problem. Many communities face still another major task. If you live in a section of the country where the water is *hard,* you are well aware of the difficulties it creates. *Hard water is water that precipitates, or curdles,* *soap.* The term "hard" means "it is hard to make suds with." Clothes may not be properly cleaned in hard water. Furthermore, the precipitate or *curd* that forms leaves a greasy film on the fabric and gives it a dingy appearance. Rain or distilled water is free of hardness, and is called **soft water.**

When water falls as rain, it dissolves a little of the carbon dioxide of the air. As the water soaks through the ground, it continues to dissolve more carbon dioxide from decaying roots and other plant materials. If this solution flows over limestone ($CaCO_3$), it reacts with it to form calcium bicarbonate ($Ca(HCO_3)_2$), some of which dissolves in the water, forming calcium ions (Ca^{++}) and bicarbonate ions (HCO_3^-).

$$CO_2 + H_2O + CaCO_3 \rightarrow$$
$$Ca(HCO_3)_2 \rightarrow Ca^{++} + 2HCO_3^-$$

It is essentially the calcium ions (Ca^{++}) in solution that cause the water to be hard. Soluble magnesium and iron salts also produce ions that cause hardness in water.

Why does soap curdle in hard water? We have mentioned that when soap is added to hard water, a curd forms. This sticky precipitate results from the reaction between the calcium ions in the water and the soap. As a result an insoluble calcium compound is formed. You recognize this curd as the greasy ring that is produced around the washbowl or bathtub.

To get a lasting lather with soap and hard water, all of the curd-forming ions must first be precipitated out of solution. Continuous adding of soap is required in order to do this. Obviously, this method of taking out the

undesirable ions is wasteful, and more desirable means of softening water have been developed.

Boiling softens water containing calcium bicarbonate. Calcium bicarbonate is a common salt causing hardness of water in many localities. Such hard water can be softened by boiling it, and allowing the precipitated mineral matter to settle. This is possible because calcium bicarbonate *decomposes* when heated, in accordance with the following equation

$$Ca(HCO_3)_2 \xrightarrow{\text{heat}} H_2O + CO_2 \uparrow + CaCO_3 \downarrow$$

The carbon dioxide gas is given off into the atmosphere, and the *insoluble* calcium carbonate ($CaCO_3$) settles to the bottom. The calcium carbonate does not affect the action of the soap because it does not dissolve to form the calcium ions. Boiling large amounts of water containing calcium bicarbonate to soften it is expensive and impractical for most purposes.

Certain chemicals are used to soften water. The calcium (or magnesium and iron) ions, which cause the hardness of water, can be removed from the water by adding *soda ash* (Na_2CO_3), *slaked lime* ($Ca(OH)_2$), or *borax* ($Na_2B_4O_7$). A typical reaction for the removal of the calcium ions using slaked lime is given as

$$Ca(HCO_3)_2 + Ca(OH)_2 \rightarrow$$
$$2H_2O + 2CaCO_3 \downarrow$$

The calcium ions in solution are *precipitated* as insoluble calcium carbonate which settles to the bottom of the container. Many communities and industries use slaked lime because it is a relatively inexpensive method of

2-10. Equal amounts of soap powder were added to the hard water (left) and the soft water (right). The hard water resisted sudsing and formed a sticky precipitate. (The Permutit Co.)

softening large quantities of hard water. Soda ash and borax are as effective and are more convenient for home use. (See Fig. 2-10.)

The ion-exchange method of softening water. Certain sodium compounds "exchange" their sodium ions for calcium ions. In this process, hard water containing calcium ions flows through a tank containing granules of a compound known as *sodium zeolite*. The calcium ions in the water replace the sodium ions of the zeolite as described in the reaction

$$Ca^{++} + Na_2 \text{ zeolite} \rightarrow$$
$$Ca \text{ zeolite} \downarrow + 2Na^+$$

The calcium ions have formed insoluble calcium zeolite which remains in the water-softening tank. The sodium ions that are set free in the process have no effect on the hardness of water.

When all of the sodium zeolite is used up, a concentrated solution of sodium chloride is added to the tank. The chemical reaction is then *reversed* and this changes the calcium zeolite back to sodium zeolite

$$2Na^+ + Ca \text{ zeolite} \rightarrow$$
$$Na_2 \text{ zeolite} + Ca^{++}$$

After the salt solution stays in the tank long enough to complete the reaction, the apparatus is ready to be used again. This method of water-softening is an example of *ion-exchange. It is the process of replacing an ion of one atom with that of another atom of like charge.* In the water-softening process, the calcium ions were replaced by the sodium ions, both ions being positively charged.

The zeolite-type softener is used in both homes and industries. The same zeolite may be used indefinitely, provided that salt is added at periodic intervals.

Some membranes and resins de-salt sea water. Ion-exchange is being used to process sea water for drinking purposes. Special *membranes* are now used to remove certain positive and negative ions from sea water. This process, in effect, removes salt compounds from ocean water and renders it potable.

In addition, certain *resins* are also available for removing ions from salt solutions. Special kits are carried on ocean liners so that sea water can be "de-mineralized" for drinking. Such devices in the chemical laboratory make it possible to produce water that is as pure as distilled water.

2-11. Over a long period of time, calcium carbonate scale, formed on the inside of these pipes, cuts down on the flow of steam. (Culligan, Inc.)

Hard water causes scale formation. Hard water may be no more than a nuisance at home, but it is a major problem in many industries. It is particularly troublesome when used in steam boilers and hot-water pipes. A crust, called *boiler scale*, is deposited inside boiler pipes, reducing the effective size of these pipes. This scale deposit usually consists of precipitated calcium carbonate. (See Fig. 2-11.)

These deposits insulate the boiler internally, causing a waste of fuel. For this reason, water-softening practices are vital to industry. Steam-electric generating plants must use carefully treated boiler water to minimize boiler scale; thus permitting a more efficient transfer of heat.

Textile and paper mills need an abundant source of soft water. Paper mills must have a supply of water free of iron compounds, which affect the color of the paper. Calcium and magnesium compounds in water react with the materials used, giving a smooth glossy surface. Obviously, removal of these compounds is a major concern to the paper industry. Soft water is necessary in textile mills to get exact shades of color uniformly distributed when dyeing yarn and cloth.

Many people in hard-water areas are using *soapless detergents*. They work well in both hard and soft waters. The major advantage of these cleaning agents is that they do not form an insoluble scum with the calcium ions of the hard water. Detergents will be discussed further in the next section.

Water pollution is an important community problem. Many communities are finding it increasingly difficult to get the quantity or quality of water needed for daily use. Abundant, clean water is necessary to promote good health. Many industries and agricultural areas need large amounts of suitable water. *Pollution* of existing water sources is making current water shortages even more drastic. We must protect our natural sources of water and find ways of reprocessing sea water.

About one-fourth of our municipalities still discharge their sewage into convenient streams and rivers without giving it any treatment whatsoever. Our country has developed into a nation of urban communities with nearly half of the population being concentrated in about 2 percent of the land surface. You can see why our water supply has become such a tremendous problem of concern to all citizens.

One logical way of having more water available is to save more water. In some cases, water can be used over and over again. Industrial waste water and sewage can be processed in order to *reclaim* fresh water.

Another problem of concern in our country is that of water pollution by certain detergents. Some detergents not only cause the foaming of water, but also resist the bacterial action necessary to break up sewage, upsetting the natural balance of animal and plant life. (See Fig. 2-12.) The culprit is the key chemical compound contained in many synthetic detergents called *alkyl benzene sulfonate, ABS* for short. This compound sometimes finds its way back to the drinking water supplies, rendering the water unsatisfactory for drinking purposes. Manufacturers of detergents have now found a way to break down this compound in waste water, or have replaced it by a new compound which can be broken down by bacterial action. The laws in some states require the use of detergents that are *bio-degradable*.

2-12. Foaming water appears in some cities where detergents contaminate the water supply. (Culligan, Inc.)

Quick Quiz

1. What do we usually mean by pure water? Why is rain water not entirely pure?
2. What is the difference between a solution and suspension? Which could you separate by filtering? Explain.
3. What is the difference between organic and inorganic matter? Give examples of each.
4. Why is organic matter harmful to health?
5. List five steps commonly used for purifying city water. Explain each.
6. What impurities cause hardness in water?
7. How do the calcium ions get into our water supply? Does this make it harmful to drink?
8. How does boiling the water containing calcium bicarbonate soften it?
9. Explain how the addition of slaked lime softens water containing calcium bicarbonate.
10. Why is the supply of water an important community problem? What is being done to increase the quality and quantity of our water supplies?

B CHEMISTRY OF THE HOME

Chemicals used in cleaning. Cleanliness is essential to good health. Of the several cleaning agents in the home, soap is the most common. Household chemicals used for cleaning also include scouring powders, soapless detergents, special purpose cleansers, and solvents.

Scouring powders loosen dirt by grinding or wearing it away. Solvents dissolve grease and are used frequently for *dry cleaning*.

We have learned that ammonia gas is very soluble in water and that some of the ammonia gas reacts with the water to form a weak base, *ammonium hydroxide*. This is called *household ammonia* or *ammonia water*. It has an important advantage over other bases. When it evaporates, it does not leave a solid residue. This base is a good household solvent for grease, although like all other bases, it harms painted surfaces.

Soap making. Place about two tablespoonfuls of lard in a beaker and add a 10 percent solution of sodium hydroxide or *lye*. Boil gently for about 15 minutes. One of the products formed is *soap*. The word equation for this reaction is

$$\text{fat} + \text{lye} \rightarrow \text{glycerin} + \text{soap}$$

To get the soap out of the mixture, let the above batch stand for a few minutes. Then add about a tablespoonful of table salt. The soap is insoluble in the salt water and will come to the top of the beaker. Skim the soap off the top and let it stand in molds until it hardens. Of course, the commercial soap that you buy in the store is perfumed. By beating air into the soap batch before it hardens, "floating" soap is obtained.

Fats are compounds of carbon, hydrogen, and oxygen. The most common basic fat for the manufacture of laundry soap is *tallow*, a by-product of the meat-packing industry. Oils used by manufacturers of toilet soap include coconut, palm, and olive. Soy bean, corn, castor and linseed oils are also used to a lesser extent. If *stearin*, a compound obtained from tallow, is reacted with sodium hydroxide, the soap making equation is

$$C_3H_5(C_{17}H_{35}CO_2)_3 + 3NaOH \rightarrow$$

fat   lye
(*stearin*)   (*sodium hydroxide*)

$$C_3H_5(OH)_3 + 3C_{17}H_{35}CO_2Na$$

glycerin   soap
                        (*sodium stearate*)

In the manufacture of some soaps, the *glycerin* remains in the soap. In the making of other soaps, the glycerin from the process is recovered as a by-product. Glycerin is used in the manufacture of cellophane, and in making printer's ink, medicines, lotions, and nitroglycerin explosives. (See Fig. 2-13.)

Aluminum, calcium, and potassium soaps are widely used in industry. Some of these are not soluble in water and are used in the manufacturing of special types of lubrication greases.

There are many kinds of soap. Inexpensive, brown *laundry soap* is made from low-grade fats. *Rosin* is frequently used in laundry soaps to increase the solubility and the lathering qualities of the soap. Sodium carbonate is used as a water softener in soaps for general household purposes. Sodium silicate is also added to soaps to increase their cleansing power.

2-13. Steam entering the bottom of a tank to superheat a kettle of soap. (Proctor & Gamble Co.)

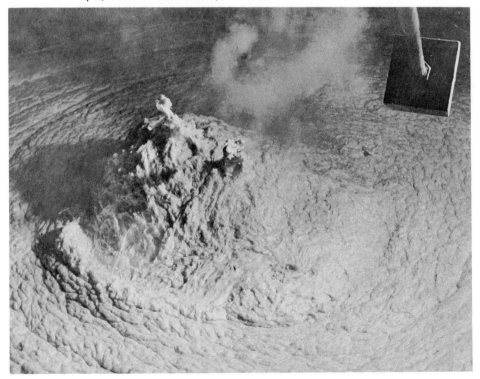

Soap makers are as careful as food manufacturers in protecting the quality of their products. *Toilet soaps* are made from higher-grade fat or oil. Large quantities of perfume are used to give refreshing fragrance to toilet soaps.

Deodorant soaps include small amounts of certain chemical substances that destroy the odor of perspiration or inhibit the perspiration process. *Scouring soaps* contain some **abrasive,** or gritty material, such as powdered sand or powdered pumice (a kind of volcanic rock), powdered soap, and sodium carbonate. The fine abrasives grind or wear away other substances and this makes them good for cleaning greasy pots and pans.

Scouring powders are rather active as *bases,* because many contain sodium carbonate or trisodium phosphate

which, upon the addition of water, *hydrolyzes* to give an abundance of hydroxide ions. These hydroxide ions provide the alkaline properties that make them effective in emulsifying grease. (See Fig. 2-14.)

How does soap clean? By using a soap solution, a thin film of soap is made to surround the greasy dirt particles. The soap molecule has a rather long structure. The "sodium end" of the molecule is water-soluble and tends to dissolve in the water, while the other end is oil-soluble and tends to dissolve in the oily covering of the dirt particle. Figure 2-15 shows the action of the soapy layer on the oily covering of the particle. After the oil-soluble end weakens the greasy film, the dirt particle is easily washed away by the water.

2-14. Soap manufacturers employ a freezing method to shape and harden the soap. The soap shown above leaving the freezing chamber is cut into bars and stacked. (Proctor & Gamble Co.)

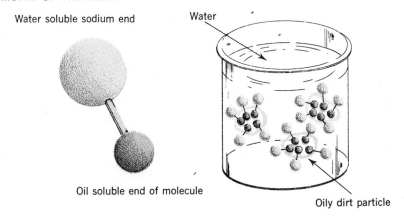

Water soluble sodium end   Water

Oil soluble end of molecule

Oily dirt particle

2-15. The oil-soluble end of the soap molecule prepares the way for the water-soluble sodium end to work away the dirt particles.

Soapless detergents. *A detergent is a substance that removes dirt.* Detergents include water, ordinary soaps, and *soapless* or synthetic detergents. *Soapless detergents* make water "wetter" by lessening the force of attraction between the water molecules. That is, they cause the water to spread through fibers of cloth more readily. This loosens the dirt. Soapless detergents work as well in hard water as they do in soft water. Most of them are by-products of petroleum research.

Dry cleaning. When a garment is dry cleaned, it is rinsed in a solvent other than water. Special dry-cleaning solvents are used by commercial cleaners. The use of these solvents avoids shrinking the garments and keeps the colors from running together.

Carbon tetrachloride (CCl_4) is a common example of a dry-cleaning solvent sometimes used around the home. This solvent dissolves the greasy film which locks the dirt particles in the garments. Many stains resistant to soaps and detergents are removed as the clothes are agitated in the solvent.

To test the superiority of carbon tetrachloride over water as a dry-cleaning solvent, try the following experiment: Take two small pieces of dirty cloth. Place one in a beaker of water. Squeeze the water through the cloth. You will observe that the water in the beaker remains fairly clean. Now place the second piece of cloth in a beaker containing a small amount of carbon tetrachloride. (**Caution:** *Carbon tetrachloride vapors are extremely harmful and contact with the skin can also be dangerous. Be sure to do this experiment in a well-ventilated room, and do not allow the liquid to touch your skin.*) Squeeze the solvent through the cloth and notice how dirty the liquid becomes. Remove both samples and dry. Observe the difference!

Gasoline is an important solvent, but it should never be used as a dry-cleaning agent because it is a *flammable* liquid and its vapors form an explosive mixture with oxygen of the air. So-called "cleaning solvent," a liquid much like kerosene, is less flam-

2-16. First the yeast causes the dough to rise, and then the heat of the baking produces the oven rise. (Wheat Flour Institute, Chicago)

mable, but should be used with proper precautions.

Leavening agents make bread rise. Centuries ago, housewives would let bread dough stand in the warm air for several hours before baking. During this time, the women would knead the dough several times over to assure a more thorough mixing of the ingredients. They knew that this practice was essential for the bread to "rise." They also learned to keep a lump of the dough to mix with the next batch of bread to obtain equally satisfactory results. Although they recognized the need for these practices, they did not know the reason for "rising."

Louis Pasteur's work was responsible for unlocking the mystery of this process. He found that while the dough was in warm air, tiny plant cells called *yeast* fell into it. These cells produced certain chemical substances called *enzymes* (*en*-zimes), or *organic catalysts*, that started a chemical reaction in the dough. The end result of this reaction, which is now known as *fermentation,* was the production of bubbles of carbon dioxide gas. Upon baking, the es-caping bubbles expanded in size, causing the dough likewise to expand or rise. *A substance that causes dough to rise is called a leavening agent.*

Action of enzymes in baking. The enzymes released by the yeast cells start the fermentation in the dough. When a housewife makes a batch of dough, she usually adds a little sugar to the flour. The yeast then provides an important enzyme, *zymase,* which converts the sugar to alcohol and carbon dioxide gas as shown in the following equation

$$C_6H_{12}O_6 \rightarrow 2C_2H_5OH + 2CO_2 \uparrow$$

Sugar　　　　grain alcohol　　carbon
(*glucose*)　　(*ethanol*)　　dioxide

The heat of baking drives off the alcohol from the finished bread. The nonpoisonous carbon dioxide gas causes the bread to be porous, palatable, and more easily digested. One disadvantage of this traditional method of baking is that it takes several hours for the dough to rise when yeast is used as a leavening agent. (See Fig. 2-16.)

Rapid-acting leavening agents. By using baking soda and an acid substance such as sour milk, which contains *lactic* acid, carbon dioxide is liberated quickly. After baking soda is mixed with flour and other dry ingredients, the sour milk is added. The lactic acid reacts with the baking soda, and carbon dioxide gas is released. Thus, the dough begins to rise.

A disadvantage of this process is that it becomes difficult to control the reaction, since sour milk varies in lactic acid content. Many housewives now use specially prepared *baking powders* for making baked goods.

Baking powders are leavening agents that contain mixtures of the following ingredients: (1) baking soda ($NaHCO_3$), as a source of carbon dioxide gas; (2) a substance producing an acid when water is added (calcium phosphate, cream of tartar, or sodium aluminum sulfate); and (3) corn starch to keep the mixture dry.

When water is added to the baking powder preparation, the acid substance forms hydrogen ions that react with the baking soda to produce the necessary carbon dioxide gas. Can you explain why manufacturers of baking powders pack their product in moisture-proof containers? (See Fig. 2-17.)

The advantage of baking powders lies in the fact that the reacting substances are contained in just the right proportions. On the market today we find "ready mixes" for baking breads and cakes. These products contain all the necessary ingredients, including the baking powder and the necessary directions for their baking.

Sources of drugs. Primitive people discovered by accident that some of the plants growing about them seemed to relieve pain, heal certain sores, or even cure diseases. These plants were the first *drugs*. **Drugs are chemicals that cure or prevent diseases or ease pain.** Some drugs still come from plants, such as *digitalis, morphine, belladona, cascara,* and *quinine.* Others are minerals such as magnesium sulfate, which is commonly known as *Epsom salts,* and milk of magnesia or magnesium hydroxide. Still other drugs, such as vaccines and various gland extracts, come from animal sources. But most drugs today come from chemical combinations developed in a laboratory.

Drugs are powerful friends. They deserve your understanding and intel-

2-17. Baking powder gives off carbon dioxide gas when water is added. (Fundamental Photographs)

ligent use. Some drugs are habit-forming. Others are poisonous and must be used with great care and only on the advice of your family physician.

Anesthetics and analgesics. *Anesthetics make a person insensitive to pain.* Physicians use *general anesthetics* to put a patient to sleep so that he does not feel the pain during an operation. The discovery of anesthesia ranks among the very greatest of all scientific discoveries for the alleviation of suffering. General anesthetics make the entire body insensitive to pain. Some of these are *cyclopropane, sodium pentothal, ether,* and *ethylene.* A *local anesthetic* such as *procaine* (*novocaine*) is now most widely used for minor surgical operations and for dental work. *Ethyl chloride,* when sprayed on the skin, acts as a local anesthetic. It evaporates very quickly, chilling that part of the body until it is numb and insensitive to pain. (See Fig. 2-18.)

2-18. Anesthetic is used during a surgical operation. (Squibb Div.-OLIN)

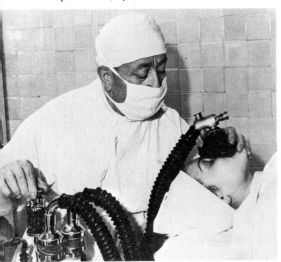

Drugs used to relieve pain are called analgesics (an-al-*gee*-zix). Perhaps the most common one is the sodium salt of *acetylsalicylic* (ah-*see*-tuhl-sal-ah-*sill*-ik) *acid,* or *aspirin.* Americans consume millions of pounds yearly of this important pain reliever. Physicians also prescribe various *narcotics* for the relief of serious pains. These are mainly plant extracts that are dangerously habit-forming.

Amphetamines ("bennies" or "pep pills"), *barbiturates, tranquilizers, and antihistamines* are other effective drugs that should not be taken except on your doctor's prescription. *Be sure to follow your physician's advice in the use of these potent drugs.*

What are sulfa drugs? We have long known that quinine, obtained from the bark of the *cinchona* (sin-*koh*-nuh) tree, has been used in curing certain fevers. Quinine enters the blood stream and kills the animal-like microbes that cause malaria. During World War II, our soldiers were given a synthetic drug called *atabrine* (*at*-uh-brin) in place of quinine. Atabrine is just as effective against malaria without causing certain undesirable "side effects" that are produced by quinine.

Since 1935 physicians found that certain organic sulfur compounds, called *sulfa drugs,* produced remarkable results in bringing certain diseases under control. Early in the history of these drugs it was found that they do not kill microorganisms but merely stop their multiplication. Once the bacteria stop multiplying, the body's natural defenses can soon overcome those microorganisms present. These drugs act by interfering with the ability of microorganisms to digest their own food. This gives the white corpuscles in the

2-19. A magnified view of penicillin mold as it appears in culture form. (Squibb Div.-OLIN)

body a better chance to attack and destroy the bacteria.

The first sulfa drug used was *sulfanilamide* (sul-fa-*nil*-uh-mide). There are now many other sulfa drugs used for fighting various infections. They are especially valuable for treating wounds, burns, certain types of pneumonia, "strep" throat, dysentery, venereal diseases, and blood-poisoning.

Penicillin was the first antibiotic. *Penicillin,* produced in 1929 by Dr. Alexander Fleming, was the first successful antibiotic. *Chemical substances obtained from certain molds and bacteria are antibiotics* (an-tih-by-*ott*-icks). Penicillin is a crystalline substance extracted from certain molds, similar to the mold which sometimes grows on bread in the summer, and is very effective against bacteria that cause local infections, certain types of pneumonia, and other bacterial inflammations. (See Fig. 2-19.)

The discovery of penicillin directed medical research into a new area. Soon other valuable antibiotics were discovered. For example, *streptomycin* (strep-toh-*my*-sin), which is effective against tuberculosis, peritonitis, and certain fevers; *chloromycin* (klor-oh-*my*-sin), used against typhoid and other fevers; *aureomycin* (aw-ree-oh-*my*-sin), which is effective against virus pneumonia and other virus diseases, and against some diseases of the intestinal tracts; *terramycin,* which acts as a growth stimulant for farm animals as well as an infection fighter; and *tetracycline* which is effective against a wide range of infections. Recently, many antibiotic drugs have been synthesized in laboratories. (See Fig. 2-20.)

A curious deficiency of penicillin is that bacteria tend to become resistant to it. After long use the drug may become ineffective. The same is true of other drugs, including the sulfa drugs. Sometimes, however, an infection which has become resistant to one drug may be treated by switching to another. The physician today can successfully combat many diseases that have afflicted man for centuries.

Cosmetics improve personal appearance. Cosmetics and beauty aids have been used throughout history. *Hydrated magnesium silicate,* or *talc,* is used in making most face and bath powders. This is mixed with calcium carbonate, to which may be added *kaolin* (basic substance in clay), for adhesion to the skin. Titanium dioxide and zinc oxide are used as white pig-

2-20. Huge fermentation tanks are used in the commercial preparation of antibiotics. (Merck & Co., Inc.)

ments. These materials are finely ground and thoroughly mixed. Some coloring matter and perfumes of various kinds are added also.

Rouge is essentially a face powder to which some red iron(III) oxide has been added. *Lipsticks* are mixtures of fat or wax with various dyes added.

Facial creams are mixtures of fats, waxes, and oils in water. Borax and other emulsifying agents are used to make the oils and water blend together as an emulsion. The oils used to make creams include olive oil, almond oil, and mineral oil. Beeswax and *spermaceti* (sper-muh-*set*-ee), a wax obtained from the sperm whale, are present in some *cold creams. Lanolin,* a grease from the wool of sheep, is an excellent skin softener, and is fre-

quently used in many creams and *lotions* and hair preparations. Many creams contain potassium soap for cleansing action. (See Fig. 2-21.)

Protecting your teeth. Proper use of a dentifrice helps to prevent tooth decay by inhibiting bacterial activity. You can prepare a good low-cost dentifrice by using one part by weight of baking soda, two parts of table salt, and a little precipitated chalk ($CaCO_3$), as a mild abrasive. Some flavoring and a small amount of soap powder or soapless detergent may be added.

Commercial dentifrices consist mainly of some mild abrasive such as precipitated chalk, some flavoring, and either soap or a soapless detergent.

Putting out fires. Every fire has three basic ingredients. The first is heat, which brings materials to kindling temperature. The second is combustibles, or fuel. The third is air containing oxygen to support the combustion. To extinguish a fire, take away any one of these.

Flooding a fire with sufficient water cuts off the oxygen supply, and also cools the burning substance below its kindling temperature. Sand is another simple material that can be used to cut off the supply of oxygen from a fire.

To control forest fires, firemen remove the fuel, either by maintaining "fire lanes" cleared of brush and trees, or by purposely burning off areas in front of the fire.

Water should not be used on oil fires because it may splatter the oily

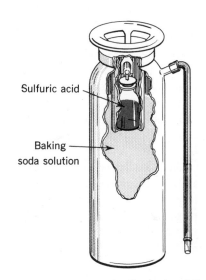

Sulfuric acid

Baking
soda solution

2-22. When a soda-acid fire extinguisher is inverted, the acid reacts with the baking soda solution to give off carbon dioxide.

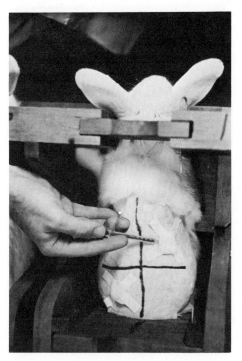

2-21. A cosmetic ingredient is applied to the clipped skin of a rabbit to determine signs of skin irritation. (FDA Photo)

substances about, thus spreading the fire. It is dangerous to use water near electrical wiring because impure water conducts an electric current. Therefore, water alone is not an ideal extinguishing material for every fire.

Soda-acid fire extinguisher. The soda-acid type extinguisher is the oldest chemical fire extinguisher and is still in common use today. It has a strong copper tank that is nearly full of a solution of *sodium bicarbonate*. Hanging inside from the top of the tank is a bottle of *sulfuric acid* with a loose stopper. (See Fig. 2-22.)

When the extinguisher is turned upside down, the stopper falls from the acid bottle. The sulfuric acid spills into the solution and reacts with it forming sodium sulfate, water, and carbon dioxide

$$H_2SO_4 + 2NaHCO_3 \rightarrow$$
$$Na_2SO_4 + 2H_2O + 2CO_2 \uparrow$$

The carbon dioxide comes off so fast that a high pressure develops in the tank. This pressure causes two things to happen: first, it forces a stream of water out the hose; and second, it causes some of the carbon dioxide to dissolve in the liquid. The liquid helps put out the fire by cooling the burning material. When the liquid comes in contact with the fire, the carbon dioxide comes out of solution, forming a heavy gaseous blanket. This blanket helps exclude the oxygen from the fire. Can you see why this stream of liquid is more effective than plain water?

This extinguisher has its disadvantages, too. The liquid from a soda-acid extinguisher always contains some sulfuric acid that has not reacted with the baking soda. This could cause damage to clothing and home furnishings. As a result, other extinguishers are more desirable for home use.

If this type is used around electric wiring, it is likely that a bad shock may be transmitted to the user because the liquid is an *electrolyte*. The soda-acid extinguisher is ineffective for oil or gasoline fires. The stream of water tends to sink below the blazing oil (Why?), thus causing the fire to spread. Its size and weight also make it inconvenient to use, and once started, there is no way of stopping the chemical action.

Carbon tetrachloride extinguishers are convenient. The CCl_4-type extinguishers have a pump and container that holds about a quart of the chemical, the same compound that is used for dry cleaning in the home. It is a *volatile* liquid, *one that evaporates very easily*. If you spray it around a fire, it forms vapors that are about five

times as dense as air. These heavy vapors settle around the burning material and shut off its supply of oxygen. This extinguisher is easy to handle but must be used in well ventilated places, because the vapor is very poisonous.

Carbon tetrachloride is a nonconductor and is especially useful for electrical fires. However, it will dissolve many materials that it touches. This type of extinguisher is being replaced by one containing safer chemicals, such as *monoammonium phosphate,* an effective "fire-stopper" that also forms a fire-resistant coating on material surfaces.

Foam extinguishers are effective for oil fires. The foam extinguisher makes a lather that effectively blankets burning material. The foamy substance is a mixture of *aluminum hydroxide* and *carbon dioxide*. An extract of licorice root makes the foam a lasting one with tough bubbles. Foam extinguishers are not generally used around the house because the foam will damage upholstery, rugs, and other home furnishings. They are effective for fighting oil fires.

The liquid CO_2 fire extinguisher produces "snow." Carbon dioxide extinguishers have a strong steel cylinder that holds liquid carbon dioxide under great pressure. When you open the valve, carbon dioxide rushes out through a cone-shaped nozzle. The cooling effect of the sudden expansion changes most of the escaping gas into carbon dioxide "snow." (See Fig. 2-23.)

This snow has a temperature of about $-110°$ F, and is so cold that it lowers the temperature of the burning material below its kindling point. The heat of the fire causes the snow to change to heavy CO_2 gas that excludes oxygen from the fire. The liquid

2-23. A liquid CO_2 fire extinguisher is effective against oil fires. (Walter Kidde & Co., Inc.)

CO_2 extinguisher is effective against blazing oil and electrical-wiring fires. The carbon dioxide gas soon diffuses and does not harm home furnishings.

Can you list some of the defects of each type of fire extinguisher mentioned? What would be some characteristics of an "ideal" fire extinguisher?

Quick Quiz

1. Write the word equation for the making of soap. What ingredients are placed in soap to give it desired characteristics?
2. Why must the right amount of lye be used in soap making?
3. What are synthetic detergents? Explain how they remove dirt.
4. What is the danger in using carbon tetrachloride for dry cleaning? What precautions are necessary? Why should gasoline never be used for dry cleaning?
5. Name and explain the action of three important ingredients of baking powder.
6. Why is baking powder worthless after standing in an open container for a long time?
7. How does ethyl chloride act as a local anesthetic?
8. What are the chief ingredients in face powder? In lipstick? In facial cream?
9. List some advantages and some disadvantages of the soda-acid type of fire extinguisher. The carbon tetrachloride type.

C MATERIALS FOR BUILDING

Calcium carbonate is widely and abundantly distributed. In this section we shall concern ourselves chiefly with the chemistry and uses of limestone as a building material. We have learned that *limestone* is essentially calcium carbonate. *Marble, calcite, and precipitated chalk* are other forms of calcium carbonate which may be familiar to you. Ordinary blackboard chalk contains a great deal of calcium carbonate with clay-like material mixed in.

To prepare precipitated chalk, mix together solutions of sodium carbonate (Na_2CO_3) and calcium chloride ($CaCl_2$). The white precipitate formed is calcium carbonate

$$Na_2CO_3 + CaCl_2 \rightarrow 2NaCl + CaCO_3 \downarrow$$

Except for special purposes, calcium carbonate is not prepared by this method. It is abundantly found in many parts of the country and sometimes entire mountains are masses of limestone. (See Fig. 2-24.)

Calcium chloride is a by-product of certain industrial processes. It is used in solution as a refrigerant. This salt takes up moisture readily from the air and is often used as a *drying agent,* and to lay dust on dirt roads. (See Fig. 2-25.)

Lime makes a moderately strong base. *Calcium oxide* (CaO), usually called *lime*, reacts with water to form calcium hydroxide. This is the least

2-24. These complex limestone formations are found in the Luray Caverns in Virginia. (Luray Caverns, Va.)

2-25. Dust on an unpaved road is sometimes controlled by the use of calcium chloride, a material that becomes moist by absorbing water vapor from the air. (Allied Chemical Corp.)

expensive of all bases, and builders use enormous quantities of it for making mortar and plaster. Industries use calcium hydroxide when they need large quantities of a low-cost base, just as sulfuric acid is used when a strong, relatively inexpensive acid is required. Calcium hydroxide, which is often called *slaked lime* or *hydrated lime,* has many commercial uses other than in building. A clear solution of it is called *limewater.*

The word "lime" is often misused. "Lime" is a word used to describe several different things, although it really means *calcium oxide.* Other names for calcium oxide that are sometimes used include *quicklime* and *unslaked lime.* There is a tendency to use the word "lime" when referring to almost any calcium compound. For example, it is often said that our bones

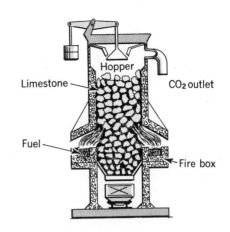

2-27. Lime (CaO) is made by heating limestone ($CaCO_3$) in a kiln.

contain lime. Actually, the bones of the human skeleton contain the compound *calcium phosphate.*

Quicklime is a white solid that reacts violently with water. If you add a little water to a lump of quicklime, the lime breaks up, gives off heat, and acts as though it were "alive." This is why it is called "quick," an old-fashioned word meaning "alive." The quicklime unites with water according to the reaction

$$CaO + H_2O \rightarrow Ca(OH)_2$$

How lime is made. Essentially, the making of lime involves the process of heating limestone in a special kind of furnace called a *kiln.* Limestone from the quarry is run through huge crushers to break it into the proper size. The crushed limestone is then dumped into the top of the kiln, as shown in Fig. 2-27. Heat from a fuel burned near the bottom converts the calcium carbonate into calcium oxide and carbon dioxide

2-26. Limestone is removed from this quarry in huge blocks. (Bureau of Mines, US Dept. of the Interior)

$$CaCO_3 \xrightarrow{\triangle} CaO + CO_2 \uparrow$$

Usually, the carbon dioxide is released into the atmosphere. The calcium oxide is recovered and placed in packages for commercial use.

Lime is packed in airtight containers and stored in a dry place. Otherwise, as explained earlier, it will absorb moisture from the air and form calcium hydroxide. Lime that has been in contact with the carbon dioxide of the air is changed back to calcium carbonate again, the reverse of the kiln reaction just described

2-28. Plaster is chiefly a mixture of slaked lime, sand, and water. (Plastering Industries)

$$CaO + CO_2 \rightarrow CaCO_3$$

Mortar and plaster. A pasty mixture made with one part slaked lime, three or four parts sand, and water forms lime *mortar*. You may have seen masons spread mortar on bricks as they build a wall. The mortar soon sets to a hard mass.

The process by which mortar sets to a rock-like mass is not fully understood. It is believed some of the hydrated lime reacts slowly with the sand (SiO_2) to form calcium silicate ($CaSiO_3$)

$$Ca(OH)_2 + SiO_2 \rightarrow CaSiO_3 + H_2O$$

In addition to the above process, the carbon dioxide of the air slowly unites with some of the hydrated lime to form limestone

$$Ca(OH)_2 + CO_2 \rightarrow CaCO_3 + H_2O$$

Putting *plaster* on the walls or ceiling of buildings is really a twofold process. First, an undercoat is applied consisting essentially of mortar to which hair or shredded fiber is added as a binder, making it hold together until it has hardened. Then a second or finish coat, which is a mixture of calcium hydroxide, water, and a powder called *plaster of Paris*, is applied over the undercoat. The finish coat dries quickly, with a smooth, hard surface. (See Fig. 2-28.)

Plaster of Paris. *Gypsum* (*jip*-sum) is a mineral that occurs in large deposits in some of our western states. It is composed of crystallized calcium sulfate ($CaSO_4 \cdot 2H_2O$). When gypsum is heated, it loses part of its water of hydration, and leaves a fine, white powder, called **plaster of Paris.**

Plaster of Paris forms a paste when water is added. This hardens or "sets" in a few minutes. During the "setting," water of hydration combines with the plaster of Paris and forms hard, crystallized gypsum again. When you use plaster of Paris, you must work fast or the paste will set before you are ready. Obviously, plaster of Paris should be stored in moisture-proof containers.

How cement is manufactured. Cement is made primarily from two abundant raw materials, *limestone* and *clay*. These materials are inexpensive and widely distributed. However, it takes a great deal of fuel, power, and heavy machinery to make cement.

First, pulverized limestone and clay are mixed together in proper proportions. Then the mixture is dumped in

2-29. A rotary cement kiln, 450 feet long and 12 feet in diameter (top). Notice the clinker formed in the interior of one such kiln (bottom). (Portland Cement Assoc.)

the upper end of a slowly revolving *cement kiln.* The mixture finally melts into lumps about the size of peas, called *clinker.* After the clinker cools, it is ground into a fine powder. The finer the powder, the harder the *concrete* that is made from the cement. Powdered gypsum is often added to make the cement set a little slower.

The cement kiln is a remarkable machine. Kilns are mounted with a little tilt, so that the raw materials will tumble slowly to the bottom as the kiln turns. Such kilns are the world's largest single piece of revolving machinery. (See Fig. 2-29.)

Fuel oil or powdered coal blown in at the lower end of the kiln is burned to supply just enough heat to begin to melt the mixture. The clinkers drop out of the lower end and are then placed in machines that do the grinding.

Concrete is made from cement. The most important use of cement is in the making of *concrete.* By mixing cement, sand, gravel, and water together in proper proportions, **concrete** is produced. When a very strong concrete is required for special purposes, additional cement is added to the mixture.

Concrete is poured into forms that hold it in place until it hardens. After two or three days of setting, it becomes firm. The hardening is due to crystal formation in the concrete. The crystals lock together and make a very hard artificial stone. For many purposes, steel rods or mesh are placed in the forms before the concrete is poured. This gives a stronger product called *reinforced concrete.* (See Fig. 2-30.)

2-30. Workman placing steel mesh on this road construction in order to reinforce the concrete slab. (Portland Cement Assoc.)

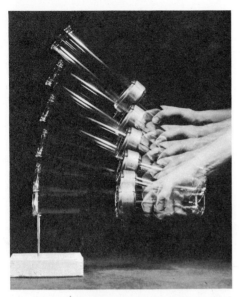

2-31. Modern glass is an important engineering material, the properties of which can be controlled and varied. (Corning Glass Works)

Clay is used to make bricks. Bricks were used in prehistoric times. Originally they were blocks of clay, baked in the sun. Today much harder bricks are made by heating them to high temperature in a furnace.

Brickmaking begins with the sifting of dried clay and mixing it with water to form a stiff paste. The soft blocks are then molded and dried for a few days. Finally, they are "burned" in a kiln. The temperature and duration of firing depend upon the hardness desired and the kind of clay used to make the bricks.

Common bricks and tiles are baked at relatively low temperatures, while higher temperatures produce a glassy type of brick. Different and varying amounts of substances in the clay produce bricks of various colors. Red brick, for example, is due to the iron compounds in the clay.

Clay is also used in making *pottery*. A paste of clay is first fashioned into various objects, then *fired* until it becomes hard and porous. *China-ware* and *porcelain* contain a white clay called *kaolin*, mixed with powdered *quartz*, and a mineral called *feldspar*.

How glass is made. The Egyptians made glass centuries before the Christian era. However, only within the past 75 years have we learned to develop many varieties and to explore its versatility. Most **glass** is made by melting together *limestone* ($CaCO_3$), *soda ash* (Na_2CO_3), and *sand* (SiO_2). This process yields almost 90 percent of all glass used in the home such as drinking glasses, bottles, and window panes. Broken scrap glass, called *cullet*, is often added to the batch. The addition of scrap glass causes the raw materials to melt at a lower temperature, and provides an economical way of utilizing glass that otherwise would be wasted. (See Fig. 2-31.)

The raw materials for a batch of glass are mixed in the right propor-

2-32. A batch of raw materials is being fed into the glass-making furnace. (Libbey-Owens-Ford Glass Co.)

tions and dumped into a tank furnace as shown in Fig. 2-32. The furnace resembles a small rectangular swimming pool, except that it is very hot and filled with melted glass. Some furnaces hold as much as 1200 tons of glass.

As in a swimming pool, one end is shallow and the other deep. As the raw materials melt, they move slowly toward the deep end.

The temperature in the furnace at the hottest part is about 2800° F. At this temperature, glass is a pasty liquid having a consistency like molasses. It takes about a week for the raw materials to move from the shallow end of the furnace to the deep end. During this time, bubbles of carbon dioxide gas escape from the glass, and some of the raw materials gradually change into a mixture of *silicates*

2-33. A ribbon of plate glass that has just come out of the annealing oven. (Libbey-Owens-Ford Glass Co.)

$$CaCO_3 + SiO_2 \rightarrow CaSiO_3 + CO_2 \uparrow$$
$$Na_2CO_3 + SiO_2 \rightarrow Na_2SiO_3 + CO_2 \uparrow$$

We see from these equations that ordinary glass is essentially a mixture of calcium and sodium silicate.

The molten glass then moves from the tank to various glass-forming machines. From the machines, the glass objects are carried to *annealing* ovens where gradual cooling takes place. This process helps remove strains in the glass caused by uneven cooling of the objects.

Perhaps you have seen bubbles in cheap glass bottles. These are carbon dioxide flaws which indicate that the glass was not heated long enough to drive off all the gas. This type of glass cannot be used for making lenses or other optical instruments.

Window glass. To make window glass, a machine dips a horizontal iron rod into the furnace. The rod is lifted straight up, and melted glass clings to it, forming a sheet of glass.

The thickness of the sheet is controlled by regulating the speed of the rising rod, and by keeping the glass in the furnace at the proper temperature. After the glass cools, the edges are trimmed to make rectangular sheets of the desired size. (See Fig. 2-33.)

There are many kinds of glass. Some glass is manufactured with substantial amounts of lead oxide and potash (potassium carbonate) in it. This kind of glass is most often used for making expensive tableware and decorative pieces. It is also used for making *lenses* for eyeglasses, cameras, microscopes, telescopes, and other optical instruments.

Certain kinds of glass will withstand sudden changes in temperature without breaking or cracking. Your mother may have *Pyrex* baking dishes at home. *Pyrex* glass expands much less than ordinary glass when heated. It is made with a small amount of *boric oxide* in it to give it the desired properties. *Vycor* is a relatively new glass that withstands sudden heating and cooling even better than Pyrex. (See Fig. 2-34.)

Glass bricks form useful building materials. They are hollow, and the air space inside acts as a good heat insulator. They are designed so that "soft" light can be transmitted, and yet a person cannot see through them.

One of the most highly specialized types of glass is one containing silver halide (salt) crystals that "tint" in a strong light and clear up quickly when the light diminishes. Can you think of some uses for this type of glass?

Vehicles use safety glass. Before we had *shatterproof glass*, people riding in autos were apt to be seriously injured or killed by flying pieces of glass, even in low-speed collisions. All automobiles now have "safety glass" in all windows. This glass does not shatter. It breaks when it is hit hard, but the pieces are held firmly together.

Shatterproof glass is made by inserting a transparent plastic between two sheets of glass. It is then subjected to high temperature and pressure in order to bond the materials together to form a single clear sheet. Thus, the passengers in buses, trains, and autos are protected from flying glass fragments.

Glass may be colored in various ways. If a glassmaker wants a clear,

2-34. Samples of Pyroceram glass-ceramic materials are being developed in the workshop (left) in preparation for heat-resistant missile nose cones (right). (Corning Glass Works)

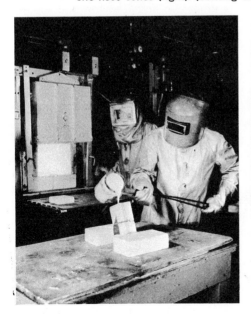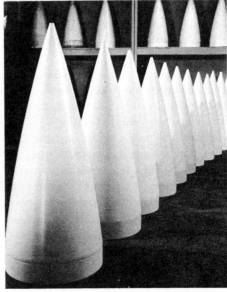

2-35. Hand glass blowing is still used to form much specialized glassware. (Corning Glass Works)

Waterglass dissolves in water. By melting together sand and soda ash in a tank furnace, *waterglass* (Na_2SiO_3) is produced. When cooled, it looks like ordinary glass. However, when heated with water, it forms a thick sirupy solution. In this form, waterglass is used for fireproofing various materials as well as a filler for soaps, as a sizing for paper, and as an adhesive in the manufacture of wallboards and corrugated paper boards for cartons.

Limestone is used in agriculture. Farmers spread pulverized limestone on their fields in order to "sweeten the soil." This means that limestone *neutralizes* the acids in the soil. In certain areas acids may accumulate in the ground after crops have grown in it for several years. In some parts of the country, the soil contains enough natural limestone so that it is not necessary to introduce additional supplies into the ground. Many farmers use calcium hydroxide instead of limestone because it acts faster. Quicklime is much too active to be used for this purpose. (See Fig. 2-36.)

colorless glass, he has to use pure ingredients. Traces of iron oxide in the sand will give the glass a pale green color. Manufacturers use this type of glass for making such things as inexpensive bottles for general purposes. However, would milk appear appetizing in a green bottle?

Cobalt impurities give glass a blue tint, while chromium compounds make glass deep green. Red glass can be made by using finely divided gold or selenium. Selenium glass is used for the red stop signals in traffic lights.

Most of our glass is machine-made. Bottle-making machines imitate the process used by the glassblower. (See Fig. 2-35.) These machines have a great many pipes that dip into the melted glass. Then compressed air blows the glass. This process can turn out thousands of bottles an hour.

2-36. Excess soil acidity is neutralized by lime. (USDA)

What are the ingredients in paint?
To make a white paint, try the following experiment. Take about 3 or 4 grams of zinc oxide and add linseed oil, a few drops at a time, until you have made a white thick paste. Now to about 10–15 ml of linseed oil in another beaker add about a half gram of manganese dioxide. Let the oil and manganese dioxide come to a boil. After this mixture has cooled for several minutes, filter out any solid particles. Next add the white paste to the filtered solution and mix thoroughly. You may then wish to thin the paint by adding a little turpentine.

From the above exercise, you can see that an *oil* paint is basically a mixture of the following types of ingredients: (1) a *drying oil* such as *linseed oil* to act as a binder and as the principal liquid to absorb oxygen of the air as it dries; (2) a *pigment* such as zinc oxide to give body and "hiding" power, and color to the paint; (3) a *thinner* such as turpentine to make the paint spread easier; and (4) a *drying agent* such as manganese dioxide to act as a catalyst to speed up the drying process.

Drying oils absorb oxygen. Oils used as drying oils in paints absorb oxygen of the air and become elastic solid. The rubber-like coating that is on the surface of an open can of paint that has been standing for a long time is a good example of this. Common drying agents include *linseed oil* pressed from ripe flaxseeds, *tung oil* from the nut of the China tung trees, and *soybean oil* from soybeans. Other oils used come from seeds of *castor,* *safflower, sunflower,* and *hemp.* Oils from cottonseed and coconut are also used as binders in paints.

The strained liquid just as it is pressed from the flaxseed is called *raw linseed oil.* It takes up oxygen slowly. If the raw oil is heated with oxides of lead or manganese, the product is "boiled" oil which has the important property of drying faster. Most paints contain some boiled oil so that it will not dry too slowly.

Tung oil is used especially for high-grade paints because it forms a harder film than linseed oil does. Soybean oil is often used in making interior paints because it does not turn as yellow upon drying as does linseed oil.

Pigments must cover well. When we spread paint on a wood surface, we expect to hide the grain of the wood. The thinner we can spread it and still have the paint cover, the better the paint. Paint pigments are usually a mixture of several substances. Three of the best *white* pigments are *white lead,* one of the oldest pigments; *zinc oxide,* obtained from zinc ore; and *titanium dioxide,* one of the best of the commercially available white pigments. *Lithopone* is another white pigment made from zinc sulfide and barium sulfate.

For colored paints, small amounts of colored substances are added to the white pigments. For example, *cadmium sulfide* or *lead chromate* makes paint yellow; *ferric ferrocyanide* gives paint a deep blue color; *chromic oxide,* a green color; *lampblack,* a form of carbon, gives paint a black or grayish color; and red *lead oxide,* a red color.

Thinners and drying agents. *Turpentine* comes from the pine trees of our southern forests. It is a volatile liquid that is added to paint as a *thinner.* Thinning allows the paint to get into the pores of the wood easily,

2-37. Paint protects industrial equipment from weathering and makes it attractive. (E. I. du Pont de Nemours & Co., Inc.)

2-38. Paints are tested and evaluated under all weather conditions in this outdoor laboratory. (E. I. du Pont de Nemours & Co., Inc.)

and it is usually added to the first coat. The paint for the finish coat has very little turpentine added to it since thinner "kills the gloss."

Some thinners such as *mineral spirits, benzene, naphtha,* and *xylene* are derived from petroleum products.

Most paints contain certain catalysts that promote faster drying of paint. Driers are metallic compounds which are soluble in oil. Many of them are known as metallic soaps. The most widely used metallic driers are compounds of lead, cobalt, and manganese. Too much drying agent causes the paint to "crack" upon drying. (See Fig. 2-37.)

Varnish, enamel, and lacquer. *Varnish* is made by boiling certain gum-like materials, called *resins,* in oils. No pigment is included so that it is

transparent and does not hide the grain of the wood. Today, synthetic resins such as *Bakelite* are widely used.

Enamels are made by adding pigments to varnish. Enamel costs more than ordinary paints, but offers a higher gloss, and usually a harder surface.

Lacquers are solutions of resins that dry to form a hard, shiny surface. Although paint hardens by taking in oxygen of the air, lacquers dry by evaporation of the solvent. The drying rate of lacquers depends upon the type of solvent used. Some lacquers dry so rapidly that you cannot put them on with a brush. They must be applied by using a mechanical sprayer. (See Fig. 2-38.)

Water-thinned paints. For many years man has used various water-mixed paints. **Whitewash,** a suspension of calcium hydroxide and water, was tinted and sold under various names for painting interior house walls. Later, a water-mixed paint using *casein* from milk was developed. Casein is little used in paints today.

In recent years, *water-thinned paints,* those in which the thinner is water, are commonly used. They dry rapidly, have little odor, and the finish has a low gloss. When the binder substance in the water-thinned paints is a synthetic resin emulsion, the paints are called *latex paints.* These paints have good covering properties, and form easily-cleaned satin-like surfaces.

Modern paints are made of many ingredients from plants, animal matter, and minerals from all over the world.

Quick Quiz

1. What names are used for the compound CaO? How is CaO made?
2. How is slaked lime made?
3. Give two reasons for storing lime in air-tight containers.
4. How is mortar made? Plaster?
5. Explain the difference between concrete and cement.
6. List the three materials used in the making of ordinary glass.
7. What is the cause of the bubble-like flaws in some glass?
8. Explain how glass is made. Name three different kinds of glass?
9. What are the raw materials for the making of glass to be used in optical instruments?
10. Name four types of ingredients usually present in ordinary house paint.
11. What is the purpose of using drying oils in paint? Name three drying oils.
12. Name four pigments and the color produced by each.

D RUBBER AND PLASTICS

Natural rubber. In the United States alone, over 40,000 different rubber products are manufactured from this versatile material. It is said that Columbus, fascinated when he found natives in the New World playing games with balls made of raw rubber, brought back samples of it to Queen Isabella.

While the rubber tree grows wild in the Amazon Valley of South America, it is also cultivated on plantations there and in Southeast Asia. It takes 5 to 7 years before a tree is large enough to tap. A warm climate and from 70 to 100 inches of rainfall per year are needed for its proper growth and development.

A sap, called *latex,* drips from man-made V-shaped cuts in the trunk of the rubber tree as shown in Fig. 2-39. It

2-39. A native tapper makes a thin cut on the rubber tree to obtain the latex. (United Nations)

is a milky fluid that contains about 35% rubber. About one ounce of latex a day is obtained from a tree.

The rubber in the latex appears as small particles dispersed in the liquid somewhat like butterfat in cow's milk. When the latex is collected, it is first strained as shown in Fig. 2-40 to remove some of the suspended matter. Next it passes into *coagulating* tanks, where *acetic acid* is added in order to coagulate the rubber into a mass. The mass of rubber is then made into sheets, smoked, dried, and baled. It is now ready to be shipped as raw natural rubber. Over 90 percent of the world's supply of *natural* rubber comes from Southeast Asia.

Rubber is a hydrocarbon. The simplest formula for rubber is $(C_5H_8)_x$. This compound is called a *hydrocar-*

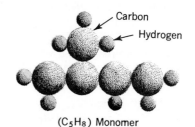

(C_5H_8) Monomer

(C_5H_8)—(C_5H_8)—(C_5H_8)$_x$ Polymers

2-41. Rubber monomers link together to form polymers.

2-40. Latex from the rubber tree is strained to remove impurities as it is poured into coagulating tanks. (National Rubber Bureau)

bon because it contains *only* hydrogen and carbon. However, this formula does not explain how the carbon and hydrogen are combined in the molecule.

The "X" in the formula represents a number that may be as high as 400,000. This means that rubber molecules are giants compared with simple molecules like H_2O, FeS, and $CaCO_3$. Chemists called the C_5H_8 unit a *monomer* (*mon*-oh-mer), or a single unit of the whole molecule. When many monomers link together, they form a giant molecule called a *polymer* (*pol*-ih-mer) —meaning *many units*. Natural rubber is a polymer of C_5H_8. (See Fig. 2-41.)

With the aid of the electron microscope, chemists have seen and examined some of these giant molecules. Almost all plastics are examples of polymers.

Sulfur improves the properties of raw rubber. Crude rubber is tough and sticky, and lacks strength and elasticity. In 1839, Charles Goodyear discovered a way to make rubber less sticky, more elastic, and better suited for the many uses of rubber products.

By heating small quantities of sulfur with the crude rubber, he developed a product that was more resistant to hard wear. This process, called *vulcanization,* launched the modern rubber industry that now supplies articles for thousands of purposes.

The properties of vulcanized rubber depend upon the amount of sulfur added. Automobile tires and rubber bands usually contain about 4 percent sulfur, while hard rubber contains a much higher percentage. The sulfur combines with the polymer chains to form rubber with more desirable properties. Sunlight, wide temperature changes, and petroleum products are harmful to natural rubber.

Other substances are used in making rubber articles. Used or *reclaimed* rubber from automobile tires is usually added to the batch of new rubber. This process lowers the cost, and produces better-wearing rubber. Rubber goods made largely from reclaimed rubber are of low quality.

Organic catalysts, called *accelerators,* are added to rubber in order to speed up the vulcanization process. Other organic substances or *antioxidants* are also added to prevent the rubber from getting too stiff and brittle.

Automobile tires contain large amounts of *carbon black*. This "filler" increases the ability of the rubber used for tires to give extra mileage. In less expensive rubber goods, clay is also used as a filler. Zinc oxide is sometimes added to produce white rubber.

Automobile tires. About 75 percent of the rubber used in the United States each year goes into the production of automobile tires. In fact there are some 600 rubber parts in an automobile.

Strong cotton, rayon, or nylon cords are embedded in soft rubber for reinforcement of the tire. Steel wires, called *beads,* are embedded in the rims of the tire. This makes the edges rigid so that the tire holds firmly to the wheel.

Tires are usually built up to "four ply" or "six ply" on hollow steel drums. The *ply* refers to the number of layers. Each layer is applied in sequence, with the tread layer applied last. Finally, the tire carcass is placed in a mold as shown in Fig. 2-42, and heated or "vulcanized."

Foam rubber. Thousands of tiny air bubbles in foam rubber make it good for upholstering material and for many other purposes. Blocks of foam rubber, covered with leather, cloth, or sheet

2-42. This worker is removing a vulcanized automobile tire from its mold. (Goodyear)

plastic, make excellent cushions because they hold their shapes well even after continued use. Many mattresses, for example, are thick blocks of foam rubber, covered with cotton cloth.

One method of making foam rubber is to add *ammonium carbonate* to the batch of raw rubber. Ammonium carbonate changes into gaseous ammonia, carbon dioxide, and water vapor when heated.

$$(NH_4)_2CO_3 \rightarrow 2NH_3 \uparrow + CO_2 \uparrow + H_2O \uparrow$$

The vulcanization process produces the heat necessary to decompose the ammonium carbonate into gaseous products that blow up the dough-like mass of rubber.

Another method of making foam rubber consists of whipping air into the latex much as cream is whipped for strawberry shortcake. During vulcanization, the trapped air expands and inflates the mass into foam rubber. (See Fig. 2-43.)

Synthetic rubber. In 1931 *neoprene*, a man-made rubber, appeared on the market. The important raw material for making neoprene is a hydrocarbon called *acetylene*. Oils and greases, which destroy natural rubber, have little effect on neoprene. Hence, this synthetic rubber is useful for gasoline-pump hoses, gaskets, tank linings, and many other items in common use. More than 70 percent of our rubber in use today in the United States is synthetic or man-made.

Several kinds of synthetic rubbers are now being manufactured. Of these, the most popular general-purpose rubber is made from two hydrocarbons, *butadiene* (byoo-tuh-*dy*-een) and *styrene* (*sty*-reen). Butadiene is a colorless, almost odorless liquid which is the by-product of petroleum refining. And styrene is a colorless liquid captured either in the manufacture of coke or as another petroleum refining by-product. When these two ingredients are mixed in the presence of soapsuds, liquid latex results. The rubber is then

2-43. Air is whipped into latex to produce foam rubber which is used for making cushions or mattresses. (US Rubber Co.)

2-44. These specially designed rubber tires are used as fuel tanks. Each tire holds 500 gallons of fuel. (Goodyear)

coagulated, washed, dried, and baled for shipping.

"Stereo" rubbers. Recently, a completely new class of synthetic rubbers, called "stereo" rubbers has been created. The most extraordinary feature of this development is that the molecule of the stereo rubber is identical to that of tree-grown rubber. The raw material for its production is petroleum.

This rubber can now be used to replace natural rubber in certain critical applications such as bus, truck, and aircraft tires where greater elasticity and high heat-resistant properties are necessary. This group of rubbers is expected to supplant natural rubber in increasing amounts. (See Fig. 2-45.) In fact *Natsyn,* a combination of the first syllables of *"nat*ural" and *"syn*thetic," is a commercial rubber that can be used in any application which calls for natural rubber.

Many plastics are high polymers. We have seen that monomers can be linked together to form very large molecules called polymers. The term *plastic,* as used by chemists, refers to substances having giant molecules. Natural rubber $(C_5H_8)x$ qualifies as one example. When the molecular weight of the polymer is extremely high, the substance is often called a *high polymer.* Many plastics are high polymers.

In 1868 John W. Hyatt, trying to find a substitute for ivory for billiard balls, treated *cellulose nitrate* with *camphor.* This produced the synthetic plastic called **celluloid.** The appearance of celluloid articles for popular use marked the beginning of our modern plastic industry.

Some 40 years later, a second major step forward was undertaken. At that time, Dr. Leo Baekeland experimented with the combination of *phenol* and *formaldehyde* and developed the first *phenolic* plastic given the trademark, *Bakelite,* coined from his name.

Today the plastic industry is one of the few billion-dollar industries in the United States. The growing use of plastics in almost every phase of our society is attributed to their desirable physical properties: wide variety of colors, light weight, ease of mass-production, and low cost.

Two general classifications of the plastics family. Synthetic plastics occupy two main groups, *thermoplastic* and *thermosetting.* Those that are **thermoplastic** can be softened and shaped by gentle heating, and then harden when cooled, no matter how often this process is repeated. **Thermosetting** plastics take their permanent shape when heat and pressure are applied during the manufacturing process and reheating will not soften these materials. Most plastic eyeglass frames

2-45. Research scientists discuss a reaction in the preparation of a new man-made rubber. (Goodyear)

serve as good examples of thermoplastic articles. They can be heated and shaped to fit the wearer. Many portable television cabinets and outer cases of telephones are articles made from thermosetting plastics.

Whether a plastic is thermoplastic or thermosetting depends on the kind of chemical reaction that occurs when it is made. Thermoplastic materials *polymerize* in the way that rubber does. That is, molecules link to other similar molecules to form a large chain cluster. Thermosetting plastics are the product of a reaction in which water is set free. In both of these reactions, *giant molecules* are formed.

How are thermosetting articles made? Thermosetting plastics are sold by manufacturers in the form of *molding powders*. The finished articles are made from the powder by a **compression molding**. As shown in Fig. 2-46, the powder is forced into a shaped metal mold called a **die**. By using a mold, many identical articles can be manufactured. Wood that has been ground into a fine powder is often mixed with the plastic molding powder

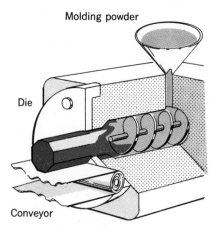

2-47. Thermoplastic materials can be shaped into various forms by extrusion molding.

in order to make the finished product stronger.

Carefully measured quantities of the molding powder are put between the heated die in the powerful press. When the press closes, the molding powder changes under the heat and pressure to a plastic that takes the shape of the die. After a given time, the press opens and out comes the finished product.

Thermoplastic articles. Thermoplastic materials are shaped into rods, tubes, and sheets by a process called **extrusion**. The dry powder material is first loaded into a hopper. A rotating screw feeds the material into a heated chamber, like the one shown in Fig. 2-47. The material softens and is forced out through a die onto a conveyor belt where it is cooled either by blowers or by immersion in water. The extrusion process is similar to that of squeezing toothpaste out of a tube.

Another method by which thermoplastic articles are made is by **injec-**

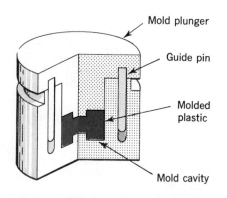

2-46. A compression mold can stamp out many identical plastic articles.

tion molding, as shown in Fig. 2-48. In this process, a plunger forces the plastic powder through a heated chamber, where it becomes soft. At the end of the heating chamber there is a small opening into a closed mold through which the liquid plastic enters. As soon as the material cools to a solid, the finished article is taken from the mold.

Plasticizers and accelerators. Various substances, called *plasticizers,* are often added to the plastic batch before it is molded. This makes molding easier and increases the hardness of the final product. *Camphor* and *castor oil* have long been used as plasticizers. Lubricants, such as wax, are also added to plastic materials in order to free the finished article from the mold easily.

Other substances, called *accelerators,* are also added to the batch to speed up the *polymerization* process. These substances include *zinc chloride, calcium oxide,* and *oxalic acid.* Various pigments are added to the plastic materials to color the articles.

Cellulose plastics. We have seen that cellulose nitrate and camphor were first used in the making of celluloid. Cellulose nitrate is prepared by treating cotton with a mixture of nitric and sulfuric acids. This is then dissolved in a mixture of alcohol and *ether.* The cellulose nitrate is left as a jelly-like mass when the solvent evaporates. The camphor is then added as a plasticizer. The result is celluloid. Among the many things that are made from this plastic are fountain-pen barrels and photographic film. Its use as a com-

2-48. An injection molding compresses and shapes a measured amount of thermoplastic materials.

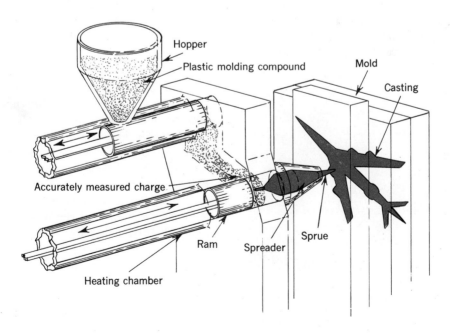

mon material, however, is limited because this plastic burns readily.

Another plastic in the same family is *cellulose acetate*. It is produced when acetic acid is used instead of nitric acid in the above reactions. Although similar to cellulose nitrate, cellulose acetate does not burn the way the nitrate does. For this reason it is used for "safety" film for motion pictures. Other varieties of cellulose acetate are used in vacuum cleaner parts, combs, toys, spectacle frames, and lamp shades. The plastics which compose this group are thermoplastic.

Vinyl and acrylic plastics are widely used thermoplastics. All *vinyl* (*vye*-nil) plastics are tough and strong. The flexible types can be bent back and forth without weakening or tearing. They resist chemicals and water; they also resist heat and cold. Familiar items

2-49. This tough plastic sheet has unusual strength. (E. I. du Pont de Nemours & Co., Inc.)

such as raincoats, shower curtains, phonograph records, floor and wall coverings, and belts are made from this family of plastics.

Another widely used family is the *acrylics* (uh-*kril*-icks). These plastics, called "Lucite" or "Plexiglass," are important because of their transparency to light. They are used as airplane canopies and windows, TV and camera-viewing lenses, dentures, salad bowls, surgical instruments, skylights, outdoor signs, and costume jewelry. Acrylics withstand exposure to weather. However, they are softer than glass and are easily scratched.

Polyethylenes are flexible. *Ethylene* (C_2H_4) polymerizes to produce *polyethylene* plastic. This thermoplastic is tough, waxy, moisture-proof, and resists reaction with most solvents. It is familiar as the material for ice-cube trays, moisture-proof bags for freezing foods, rigid and squeezable bottles, tumblers, dishes, and many other unbreakable articles. (See Fig. 2-50.) This plastic can be cooled to $-100°$ F without becoming stiff and brittle. It has excellent insulating properties.

Families of thermosetting plastics. The important families of thermosetting plastics are *phenolics, melamine, polyesters,* and *epoxies*. Bakelite is a phenolic plastic and is considered by the industry to be the "work horse" of the group. *Phenolics* are strong and hard. They do not readily absorb water and other chemicals and hence retain their luster, strength, and rigidity. Automobile distributor-heads and insulation, washing-machine agitators, and telephone cases are some of the things that are made from this group of plastics. However, some members of this family, such as Bakelite, are dark in

2-50. Two examples of widely differing uses of plastics. The electrical cables (left) are protected by polyethylene jackets, while the body of the car is made of a thermoplastic material, Royalex. (Left: Union Carbide Corp., Plastics Div.; Right: US Rubber Co.)

color and the number of shades obtained by adding pigments is limited.

The familiar colorful dinnerware can be fashioned from *melamine* plastics. Smartly-styled handles for kitchen utensils, as well as buttons and hearing aid cases are usually made from melamine plastics. These give a glossy surface, and are scratch-resistant, heat-resistant, and very resistant to mechanical shock.

A plastic used to impregnate cloth, paper, and mats of glass fibers may be one of a family called *polyesters.* Polyesters are highly resistant to most solvents, acids, bases, and salts. They offer a low water absorption rate, and excellent weathering qualities.

Certain plastics are used to bond firmly metals, ceramics, glass, and other plastics. *Epoxy* resins are often used for this purpose. Epoxies are employed

most commonly in castings, coatings, and adhesive-bonding applications. (See Fig. 2-51.)

2-51. A single worker is capable of carrying 300 feet of plastic pipe, a task that would be unlikely with usual metal pipes. (US Rubber Co.)

BASIC PLASTIC GROUPINGS

Name	Type	Properties and Uses
acrylic ("Lucite")	thermoplastic	Withstands weather exposure; dentures, combs, lenses, lamp bases, windows.
alkyd	thermosetting	Excellent heat resistance; molding materials, enamels, lacquers, paints.
amino (urea, melamine)	thermosetting	Wide range of colors, glossy surface; electric insulators, housings for computing machines, dinnerware.
casein	thermosetting	Product of the protein from milk. Strong, takes brilliant polish; buttons, buckles, novelty-counter items.
cellulosic (cellulose, acetate and nitrates)	thermoplastic	Among the toughest plastics; safety film, transparent wrappings, toys.
epoxy	thermosetting	Chemical-resistant, strong; bonding of materials, castings, printed circuits.
fluorocarbon (Teflon)	thermoplastic	Low coefficient of friction, high corrosion and temperature resistance; valve seats, cooking utensils, gaskets, insulation for high voltage.
phenolic (Bakelite)	thermosetting	Strong, hard, and durable; radio and television cabinets, telephone cases.
polyamide (nylon)	thermoplastic	Long-wearing, resistant to temperature extremes; washers, brush bristles, gears, fishing lines, cloth.
polyethylene	thermoplastic	Strong and flexible; ice-cube trays, moisture-proof bags, squeezable bottles, dishes.
polyesters	thermosetting	Highly resistant to most solvents, form hard surfaces; impregnate cloth or mats of paper, fibers, glass, pipe, luggage, jewelry casts.
polystyrene	thermoplastic	Clear, good insulation, not affected by water; tiles, blocks, instrument panels, kitchen items, battery cases.
silicone	thermosetting	High heat stability, water-repellent, and weather-resistant; insulation for motor and generator coils, grease, polish, coatings.
vinyl	thermoplastic	Strong and tough, and wide range of colors; raincoats, curtains, floor covering, belts, garden hose.

What are laminated plastics? Thermosetting plastics are used to make many *laminated* articles, meaning that they are built in *layers* or *plates*. Sheets of cotton cloth or paper are dipped in Bakelite varnish, and are piled on one another to any desired thickness. The layers are put in a press, and heat and high pressure applied. This makes a very hard, tough sheet of material.

Laminated plastics are used for making gears, table tops, electronic panels, and light-weight airplane propellers, as well as many other items.

Looking ahead in plastics. A new *fluorocarbon* plastic, called "Teflon," has been on the market for some time now. This plastic, sometimes called an "anti-adhesive" product, has virtually no friction with other surfaces and feels something like a wet bar of soap. It resists high temperatures and also swift temperature changes from subzero to past boiling.

Foods cooked in frying pans coated with Teflon can be removed from the pan without sticking, even though no fat or cooking oil is used. By adding certain reinforcements, we now use Teflon to make long-lasting, self-lubricating piston rings for compressors. Auto bearings, bushings and ball joints are now being made with this new material, and car manufacturers look forward to the day when automobiles and other similar machinery will require no lubrication. Surgeons are using this "miracle" plastic to replace sections of veins and arteries.

Industrial interest in the *polyurethane* (poly-*your*-eh-thane) family has grown rapidly in recent years. This plastic grouping is made in increasing quantities from fairly inexpensive ma-

terials. One type of polyurethane forms a rubber-like foam and is superior to foam rubber in many ways. It is lighter in weight and can be stitched, laundered and dry-cleaned. These plastics resist heat and light that harm natural rubber. (See Fig. 2-52.)

Other varieties of this type of plastic are used for industrial adhesives and paint bases. Still another type shows great promise as a substitute for use in automobile tires that may last over 100,000 miles. Our future cars may not carry a spare tire, any more than they now carry a spare carburetor or battery.

2-52. The eggs in this special Vinyl film package will survive an 80-foot drop. (Union Carbide Corp., Plastics Div.)

Quick Quiz

1. How is latex processed to obtain crude rubber?
2. Why are accelerators and antioxidants added to rubber?
3. What environmental conditions are necessary for the proper growth of rubber trees?
4. Why is the vulcanization process so important?
5. In what respect is neoprene better than natural rubber?
6. What raw materials are used to make synthetic rubber?
7. What is the most important fact about "stereo" rubber?
8. What were the first plastics used? What properties do they have?
9. Explain the difference between thermosetting and thermoplastic. How could you tell whether a plastic article was thermoplastic?
10. Tell how a plastic article is made by compression molding.
11. How is celluloid made? What is its major disadvantage?
12. What are some uses of the casein plastics? Silicone?
13. What type of plastic would you recommend for (a) a computing machine housing? (b) garden hose? (c) false teeth? (d) frying and baking pans? (e) squeezable bottles? (f) dinnerware? (g) radio and TV cabinets?

E TEXTILES

Wool fibers provide warmth. Wool is a natural elastic fiber that comes from the fleece of the sheep, llama, alpaca, goat, or camel. The curly, kinky hairs of these animals mat together, trapping a good deal of "dead air." This property makes wool the ideal cold-weather fiber because it serves as an excellent insulator, preventing the loss of body heat.

The quality of wool is based upon the length of fiber, fineness, luster, and texture. Wool that comes from the shoulders, sides, and backs of animals is best. Fibers from the chest and belly of the animal are too coarse, while those from the legs are too short.

At the woolen mills, skilled sorters separate the fleeces into groups of different qualities. The highest quality woolen goods have a very large percentage of the longest fibers. "All wool" appearing on the label of a garment is no indication of the quality of the wool it is made of, since it does not indicate what kind of fibers make up the garment.

Quality of wool. Federal law requires that labels on clothing reveal the percentage of wool and other fibers mixed into the goods. Wool that has never been woven into cloth before is called *new* or *virgin wool.* But all wool is not new! Scraps of woolen cloth are sometimes shredded by machines into fibers again. This process yields an inferior wool that must be labeled *reprocessed wool.*

Woolen rags from worn clothing can be reworked into fibers again also. This kind of wool is labeled *reused ʹvool.* Reprocessed and reused wools do not wear as well as virgin wool with its greater fiber length.

Properties of wool. If you look at wool fibers through a microscope, you will observe that they have tiny, scale-like plates. (See Fig. 2-53.) These plates overlap each other like shingles

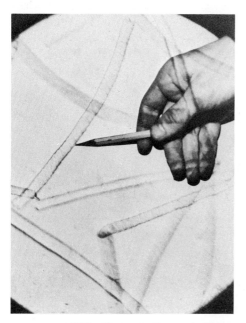 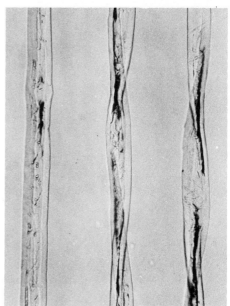

2-53. Compare the scale-like appearance of the wool fiber (left) with the smoother and twisted cotton fiber (right) as viewed under a microscope. (Left: Wool Bureau; Right: Institute of Textile Technology)

on a roof. The scale-like fibers hook onto each other, causing wool to mat together. The fibers of wool tend to spring back into their original shape after you bend or fold them. This is why your woolen clothes hold their shape better than do cotton, rayon, or linen garments.

Wool is composed of carbon, hydrogen, oxygen, nitrogen, and sulfur, the basic elements in all *protein* compounds. Strong bases, such as solutions of sodium or potassium hydroxide, dissolve wool. Wool burns poorly, with an unpleasant odor, forming a black charred mass.

Heat weakens woolen fibers and so hot irons should not be used on woolen cloth. Hot water causes wool to shrink.

Thus, cool water and a mild soap should be used to wash woolen materials.

How woolen cloth is made. Wool as it comes from an animal is quite dirty and greasy. It is washed with soap and a mild alkali in warm water to remove the grime, and then goes to the *carding* machine, where the tangled mass is spread into a flimsy, web-like sheet. Carding machines have large revolving drums covered with short, projecting steel teeth that comb the wool into a flat web.

Next, the web is rolled into a loose strand called a *rove*. The rove is then drawn into thinner strands and twisted into *yarn* by *spinning machines*. Yarn may be dyed before it is woven into

2-54. An oil emulsion is sprayed on a wool blend to lubricate the fibers. (Wool Bureau)

2-55. Cotton is shipped to the manufacturers in 500-lb bales. (Burlington Industries, Inc.)

cloth, or it may be dyed after the cloth is made. (See Fig. 2-54.)

Cotton is a high polymer. Cotton fibers are nearly pure cellulose, having the formula $(C_6H_{10}O_5)_x$. The "X" in this giant molecule is not known but believed to represent a number that is perhaps as high as 500,000. Body moisture is readily absorbed by cotton fibers and lost through evaporation. Cotton is also a very poor conductor of heat. These properties make cotton garments suitable for summer wear.

Under the microscope, as shown in Fig. 2-53, cotton fibers look much like flattened, twisted tubes quite unlike the appearance of wool. Alkalis do not harm cotton as they do wool, but acids do. Can you suggest a way to determine the percentage of wool contained in a sample of mixed wool and cotton cloth?

Perspiration produces a weak acid reaction on contact with cotton that weakens the fiber. This is one reason why cotton clothing wears out in places where perspiration is most active. Cotton burns readily, leaving almost no ash.

The cotton belt. The so-called "cotton belt," the region where our cotton is grown, includes eighteen of our southern states stretching from Virginia to California. Cotton plants are grown from seeds that are planted each year. The mature cotton fibers may be from ¾ of an inch to 2½ inches long. Longer fibers are best because they spin better and make a stronger yarn.

Some of the finest cotton in the world is Sea Island cotton, which is grown along the Atlantic seaboard of our southern states. It has fibers from 1½ to 2½ inches long. The shortest fibers are used in the manufacture of rayon, explosive nitrocellulose, and plastics.

Cotton seeds are processed to produce oil for cooking and making oleomargarine. The solid that remains makes a protein-rich feed for cattle, or flour for low-starch diets.

Processing cotton into cloth. Cotton arrives at the mills in large bales as shown in Fig. 2-55. A machine called a *picker* rips the cotton from the bale into a fluffy mass. The cotton then goes to the carding machine where it is changed to a flat web-like sheet. Combing then removes the short fibers.

The loose strands, or roves, are then spun into cotton yarn by a process of drawing and twisting. Large looms then weave the yarn into materials for clothing manufacture. (See Fig. 2-56.)

Garments made from cotton tend to shrink when they are first washed. In order to prevent shrinking, a process called *sanforizing* is employed. *Sanforizing* subjects the cloth to steam while the cloth is stretched. This treatment "pre-shrinks" the finished cloth before it is made into a garment.

In order to make cotton cloth glossy and stronger, cotton fibers are sometimes *mercerized*. In this process, cotton is stretched and dipped into a concentrated solution of sodium hydroxide where the fibers swell, become rounded, more lustrous, and stronger.

Specially treated cotton fibers have the "wash-and-wear" or wrinkle-proof properties of synthetic, or man-made, fibers. In wash-and-wear cottons, the natural fibers are treated with basic solutions of special resins. This process allows the fibers to spring back into place after being deformed. Some of these fibers resist water and stain. Clothing made from such treated cot-

2-56. Automatic looms are used to weave intricate patterns into cloth. (Burlington Industries, Inc.)

ton requires infrequent laundering and maintains a freshly pressed appearance.

The nature of silk. Like wool, silk comes from an animal. The *cocoons* of the mulberry silkworm provide the source. The caterpillars, or *larvae*, feed on mulberry leaves and then spin cocoons as protective coverings while they undergo a period of transformation to the *moth* stage.

Silk is secreted as a liquid from tiny glands below the mouth of the caterpillar. The fluid changes into a solid upon contact with the air, forming a strand of silk. The caterpillar winds this strand around itself in a continuous fiber that may be thousands of feet long, thus forming the cocoon.

After about three weeks, the insect, if left undisturbed, bores a hole in one end of the cocoon and comes out as a moth. However, silk from these punctured cocoons is of little value. Steam or hot air is used to kill the insect before it emerges from the cocoon.

Silk· is a luxury fiber. After the cocoons are treated with heat to soften the gummy material on the outside, the fibers are untangled. Fibers from several cocoons are joined to form a single strand of silk. This process is time-consuming, for as many as 3000 cocoons are needed to produce a pound of raw silk. For this reason, silk is more expensive than any of the other natural fibers.

The silk fibers are very fine, about 1/2500 inch in diameter, and remarkably strong, elastic, and *resilient;* that is, it springs back after being folded or stretched. A silk rope is as strong as a steel cable of equal weight. The fiber is free from joints or scales, which makes silk smooth to the touch. Alkalis and acids damage or even destroy this fiber.

Linen comes from the flax plant. Linen is the oldest fiber known to man, dating back some 10,000 years.

The *flax* plant provides us with two main products, *linen* fiber and *flaxseed.* If linen fiber is desired from the crop, the plant is pulled up by the roots before the seeds mature. When flaxseed is the desired product, the plant is allowed to mature, but the fibers are no longer good for linen.

After the flax plants are pulled up for making linen, they· are spread in the sun to dry. They have a thin covering of bark that must be removed. Linen fibers are about 2 to 3 feet long, very soft, lustrous, and yellow in color. These fibers are much stronger than cotton, and tend to lie parallel. Like cotton, linen is nearly pure cellulose and has similar chemical properties.

Linen cloth is manufactured in a manner similar to that of cotton. *Spinning* is done to draw and twist the fibers. The cloth is then woven from the spun yarn on *looms.* As our most permanent natural fiber, linen outwears cotton and wool. Unlike cotton, linen fibers shed no lint, making them ideal for use as dish towels. Linen has excellent water-absorbing properties. However, since linen fibers lack the resiliency found in other fibers, linen garments wrinkle quite easily.

Paper is made from cellulose. The principal raw materials for making paper are wood pulp and short cotton and linen fibers. To make paper, the fibers of cellulose in the raw materials are separated from one another by *chopping, shredding,* and *beating.*

The shredded fibers are mixed with a great deal of water to form a thin "soup." This soup is forced out of a narrow horizontal slit and drops onto a vibrating wire screen. As the water drains through the horizontal screen, the fibers become tangled together in a matted sheet. These sheets pass between heavy felt-covered rollers that squeeze out the remaining water, and then through other steam-heated rollers that iron the surface to a smooth finish.

Of course, there are many refinements in this process that are used to produce paper of special quality. However, all paper is essentially a tangled mass of cellulose fibers. (See Fig. 2-57.)

Various types of· paper. When crude sheets of tangled fibers from logs of poplar, spruce, and certain kinds of pine are formed, the product is called *mechanical pulp.* Newspapers are printed on bleached mechanical

2-57. Most of our ordinary paper comes from spruce, poplar, and certain kinds of pine. (Courtesy AFPI)

pulp because it is cheap and abundant. (See Fig. 2-58.)

"Kraft" paper, made from our southern pines, is one kind of paper made from *chemical pulp*. **Chemical pulp** is made from wood chips which are *digested*, or boiled under pressure. *Kraft* is a Swedish word meaning "strength," a property which is necessary for paper to be used in making cartons, bags, and ordinary wrapping paper.

Cotton and linen rags are beaten into the pulp to make the highest quality paper. In fact, United States currency is printed on rag paper that has colored silk and nylon fibers added for strength and to make the task of counterfeiting a more difficult one.

A glossy surface is obtained on paper by adding rosin, alum, casein, or gelatin to the surface. White paper is produced by means of a bleaching process.

Parchment paper is given a hard, transparent finish by running it through a tank of sulfuric acid, and then washing off the acid quickly. *Waxed paper*

is made by passing paper through a vat of melted paraffin. Tar and asphalt are used in making some *roofing papers*.

Asbestos is a mineral fiber. *Asbestos* is a silky, fibrous form of *hydrated magnesium silicate*. This mineral can be

2-58. Newsprint is wound into rolls containing about five miles of paper. (Courtesy AFPI)

2-59. Asbestos is a mineral fiber used for making fire-proof materials. (Johns-Manville, Asbestos Fibre Div.)

spun into threads and woven into cloth. Asbestos fibers are firepoof, and unaffected by most common acids. You can see why asbestos materials are used as insulation for hot water and steam pipes, fireproof clothing, and brake linings for automobiles. (See Fig. 2-59.)

When a blast of high-pressure steam is directed against molten glass under proper conditions, *glass wool* is obtained. This fluffy mass of very fine fibers may be spun into yarn and woven into **fiber-glass** cloth. Glass wool does not rot or burn, and is verminproof. It makes an excellent heat insulator for refrigerators.

Synthetic or man-made fibers. Synthetic fibers are made by forcing suitable liquids through tiny holes in a metal plate and allowing them to harden. By using different liquids in the process, a great variety of fibers can be produced.

The metal plates are made of gold or platinum alloy because these metals are not affected by most chemicals. These plates, called **spinnerets,** are about the size of a thimble and have from 10 to 150 tiny holes in them, depending upon the desired size of the strand.

Large mills have hundreds of these spinnerets arranged in long rows. Each spinneret hole may produce as much as five feet of filament per second.

Most rayon is produced by the viscose process. Cellulose obtained from wood pulp or from short cotton fibers is the raw material used for making *rayon.* In the *viscose* process, the cellulose is changed to *cellulose xanthate* by treating it first with sodium hydroxide, and then with carbon disulfide (CS_2). The cellulose xanthate is then dissolved in a sodium hydroxide solution to form a viscose solution. The solution is then forced through spinnerets into a bath of dilute sulfuric acid. The acid re-converts the viscose solution into a filament of cellulose.

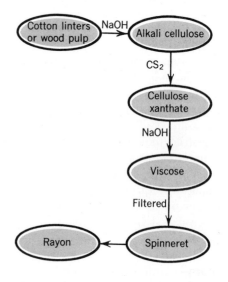

2-60. Steps involved in making of viscose rayon yarn.

2-61. Viscose, derived from cellulose, is forced through the spinneret into a dilute acid bath. This causes the fluid to harden, forming rayon. (American Viscose Corp.)

Several strands of filaments are gathered together, passed over rollers, and collected in a *spinning pot*. The pot revolves at high speed, twisting the filaments slightly, forming *viscose rayon* yarn. (See Fig. 2-60 and Fig. 2-61.) About 80 percent of all the rayon manufactured in this country is made by this process.

During the manufacture of viscose rayon, the cellulose is changed to a liquid and is then re-converted into a solid. Rayons produced in this way are said to be *regenerated* cellulose. *Cellophane* is also made from cellulose. Cotton linters are used in a process similar to that for making viscose rayon, except that the solution is extruded through a narrow slit instead of a spinneret. When the viscose is solidified into transparent sheets by passing through an acid bath, **cellophane** is produced.

Cuprammonium process. Another method of making rayon is called the *cuprammonium* process. You can make a sample of rayon by this method in the laboratory.

In a beaker, dissolve a small amount of copper(II) sulfate in a small amount of ammonium hydroxide. Now stir into this solution small shreds of paper cleaning tissues (cellulose). The liquid becomes thick and syrupy as you add more paper to it. Draw some of this liquid into a medicine dropper and squirt it into a 5 percent solution of sulfuric acid. The resulting tube of hardened material is rayon made by the cuprammonium process. Of course, at the mill the fiber is forced through a spinneret and is further stretched to produce very fine yarn, called *Bemberg* rayon.

Viscose and cuprammonium rayons lose considerable strength when wet. Perspiration gradually weakens these fibers.

Cellulose acetate fibers. *Cellulose acetate* produces fibers that wrinkle and shrink less than the rayons made by either the viscose or cuprammonium process. The reaction between pure cellulose and concentrated acetic acid is the basis for this process. When the reaction is complete, the batch is added to water, causing cellulose acetate to separate out as solid flakes. These flakes are dissolved in *acetone* and squirted through spinnerets into a tube. Fibers formed in this way are dried by evaporation of the acetone.

Cellulose acetate fibers when made into cloth display two important disadvantages. A very hot pressing iron destroys the fibers, and some dry-cleaning solvents dissolve them.

Nylon fibers. Coal, air, and water are the basic raw materials used in making *nylon*. **Nylon** is the result of *polymerization*, the joining together of small molecules into larger ones. (See Fig. 2-62.) The polymer is squirted

2-62. Polymerization—the linking together of small molecules into large ones—takes place in these tanks in the making of nylon. (E. I. du Pont de Nemours & Co., Inc.)

through spinneret holes to form nylon filament. The filaments are stretched to about four times their original length. This stretching causes the molecules to line up, providing nylon with increased strength and elasticity. The elasticity of nylon has made it popular for making hosiery and other wearing apparel.

This versatile fiber is lustrous, transparent, and even stronger than silk. It is easily washed, resists mildew, and is not affected by water or dry-cleaning solvents. Nylon fiber does not readily absorb water, a property which allows it to dry quickly. It is used in making clothing, upholstering materials, bristles for brushes, faucet washers, gears, tumblers, and numerous other items in common use.

Other man-made fibers. You have probably heard of name like Vinyon, Saran, and Velon. Acrilan, Orlon, Dynel, Dacron, and Aralac are other synthetic fibers used by man to make fabrics with specialized uses. *Vicara* is a fiber made from a protein from corn. It can be easily blended with other fibers and processed into garments. (See Fig. 2-63.)

What chemicals will bleach cloth? All natural fibers have a tinge of yellow in them. If snow-white yarns are desired, the process of *bleaching* is employed. As you know, sunlight is effective for the bleaching of dampened cotton and linen fabrics. On the other hand, sunlight tends to "yellow" the animal fibers such as silk and wool. Synthetic fibers such as nylon, Vinyon, Saran, and others do not require bleaching.

Chlorine is the most effective chemical for bleaching cotton and rayon. It cannot be used to bleach wool and

2-63. Strands of a new "wonder" fiber of exceptional durability are made from a gas called propylene. (Humble Oil & Refining Co.)

silk, however, because it destroys them. For wool and silk, *sulfur dioxide* or *hydrogen peroxide* are used. A solution of *sodium hypochlorite* ("*Clorox*," or "*Purex*") is used for home bleaching of cotton materials.

Chlorine is an active element. *Chlorine* is a poisonous, greenish-yellow gas with a choking vapor. It unites with many metals and with hydrogen. Chlorine reacts slowly with water, uniting with the hydrogen and setting oxygen free. This liberated oxygen then reacts with some dyes in the fabric, causing a loss of color. As shown in the following equations, *it is the oxygen that does the actual bleaching of the cloth*

1. $2Cl_2 + 2H_2O \rightarrow 4HCl + O_2 \uparrow$

2. oxygen $+$ dye in the fabric $\rightarrow$ colorless compound

Making chlorine and using it as a bleach. You can make chlorine gas in the laboratory by adding an acid to *chloride of lime* ($Ca(ClO)Cl$), which is often called *bleaching powder*.

Put a spoonful of bleaching powder in a tall glass cylinder, and pour in 10 ml of concentrated hydrochloric acid. The greenish-yellow chlorine gas is set free immediately. *Use extreme caution when handling chlorine as it is very poisonous. Be sure to have your room well ventilated!*

Now lower strips of wet, colored cotton cloth into the gas in the cylinder. Cover the container and leave the strips in the chlorine for about 45 minutes, and then examine them. It is essential that the cloth be wet for bleaching to take place. Why?

After the cloth has been bleached, thoroughly rinse to remove all traces

2-64. The apple peel on the left is being slowly bleached white by sulfurous acid. (Fundamental Photographs)

of the chemical. Otherwise, the chemical action will continue and will decompose the cloth.

Sulfur dioxide as a bleach. Sulfur dioxide is a dense, colorless, choking gas. We can make some of this gas by burning a little sulfur in a glass cylinder.

Put a wet piece of apple peel in the glass container with the gas. Do the same with dried apricots that have been soaked in water. Now examine them after about 20 minutes and note any changes in color. (See Fig. 2-64.)

Sulfur dioxide gas unites with water to form *sulfurous acid* (H_2SO_3), a very weak acid. The molecules of sulfurous acid readily unite with atoms of oxygen to form sulfuric acid. The sulfurous acid converts some colored compounds in materials to colorless compounds by *removing* oxygen atoms. *Observe that sulfurous acid bleaches by removing oxygen,* while chlorine bleaches by *adding* oxygen.

Sulfur dioxide is a milder bleach than chlorine. It is used widely for bleaching wool, silk, paper, and straw. White wool sweaters and white silk cloth often yellow with age because sulfur dioxide bleaching is not permanent. The oxygen of the air finally restores the original color.

It is interesting to note that because of the use of sulfur compounds in the paper industry, most books and documents printed in the past fifty years are deteriorating at a rapid rate; if prompt measures are not taken, practically no printed record of this period in history will survive.

Hydrogen peroxide. Hydrogen peroxide is prepared commercially by passing an electric current through cold, dilute sulfuric acid. It is an unstable liquid that decomposes readily, forming water and oxygen

$$2H_2O_2 \rightarrow 2H_2O + O_2 \uparrow$$

The oxygen that is set free can *decolorize* some materials. Besides wool and silk, hydrogen peroxide is used to bleach paper, feathers, and hair. Aside from bleaching, hydrogen peroxide is used for many other purposes. Mild solutions are used as antiseptics, while concentrated solutions are used as a source of oxygen for burning rocket fuels.

What is the nature of dyes? All dyes are complex compounds. Formerly, we obtained most of them from roots, barks, leaves, flowers, and berries. Today, most dyes are made from a few synthetic compounds by a series of complex chemical changes.

The chemist has learned how to build up molecules of bright-colored substances, duplicating some of the changes that go on in nature. Over 5,000 synthetic dyes have been pro-

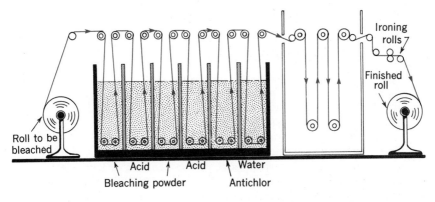

2-65. The commercial bleaching of cotton goods is a continuous process.

duced. The chemist has also learned how to combine minerals with these dyes to produce many shades of color. These minerals make some dyes *fast*. A *fast dye* is one that clings to the fabric, does not lose its color, or wash away easily.

Coal tar is the raw material for most dyes. Coal tar is a black, sticky liquid obtained as a by-product from the coke ovens. Coal tar itself does not contain dyes. However, a colorless liquid, called *benzene,* can be extracted from it. Benzene is then used to make another colorless liquid, called *aniline. Aniline* is the starting point for making many synthetic dyes

coal tar → benzene → aniline

→ aniline dye

Direct, acid, and mordant dyes. If fiber takes and holds the dye with little assistance, the dye is called a *direct dye.* Direct dyes can be used for all natural fibers. Common salt added to the dye bath causes the dye to leave the solution and attach to the cloth. In general, animal fibers are easier to dye than plant fibers.

To give bright colors with silk and wool, *acid dyes* are sometimes used. These dyes do not cling to linen and cotton. Fabrics that have been dyed with acid dyes must not be washed with alkalis because the dye can be removed from the cloth.

Some dyes will not cling to cotton unless a chemical, called a *mordant,* is used first. The *mordant* forms a precipitate within the cotton fibers. The cloth is then immersed in the dye bath, and the precipitate unites with the dye, forming a fast color. Dyers often use different mordants with the same dye to produce a variety of shades. *Aluminum hydroxide* is widely used as a mordant.

Removing stains from textiles. When you want to get a stain out of a garment, you should first know the kind of stain it is and the kind of cloth. A little experimenting may be necessary. Soap and water are effective in removing a great variety of stains. However, certain stains require solvents other than soap solutions. Other stains require a degree of careful bleaching.

REMOVAL OF STAINS FROM CLOTHING

Stain	Type of Cleaner
acids	ammonia; rinse with water
alkalis	vinegar; rinse with water
blood	cold water and salt or soap and cold water
coffee	boiling water
fruit juices	water
grass	alcohol; wash with soap and water
grease	carbon tetrachloride, benzene, or kerosene
ink, iron rust	detergent and water, oxalic acid, or lemon juice
lipstick, rouge	glycerin, or soap and water
paint (oil)	turpentine or mineral spirits

In all cases, you must be careful to use an agent that will not injure the fabric. For example, you may recall that some dry-cleaning solvents destroy cellulose acetate fiber. Bleaches containing chlorine will ruin wool and silk. Dilute acids must be washed out of cotton and linen because they weaken the fabric. Bleaches may not only remove the stain, but they may bleach the dye out of the cloth!

The table above contains information on the removal of some common stains from many kinds of cloth.

Quick Quiz

1. Why is the label "all wool" no guarantee of quality?
2. Explain what happens to wool blankets when they are washed in hot water, or with an alkaline soap.
3. What elements make up cellulose? Why is cotton considered a high polymer?
4. Explain how silk is produced from the silkworm. Why is silk considered an expensive fiber?
5. How is linen obtained from the flax plant?
6. What products are made from cotton seeds?
7. What material is used in making newsprint?
8. How is cotton mercerized? Sanforized?
9. Why is linen cloth desired for use as dish towels?
10. What are the basic raw materials for making nylon? List five properties of nylon.
11. Name five properties of chlorine gas. Explain how you would prepare a small quantity of it. What precautions would you take in the preparation of chlorine gas?
12. Is it the chlorine that actually bleaches cotton? Explain.
13. Explain how hydrogen peroxide is used as a bleach. Sulfur dioxide.

PETROLEUM

The origin of petroleum is not completely known. The word "petroleum" is derived from the Latin "petra" meaning *rock* and *"oleum"* meaning *oil*. The use of petroleum was recorded very early in history. Certain primitive people worshipped "sacred" fires resulting from seepages of oil and natural gas. In fact the Chinese used petroleum as a fuel as early as 200 B.C. (See Fig. 2-66.)

One theory concerning the origin of petroleum is that it is a product of *marine* life buried in sediments millions of years ago. Scientists believe that bacterial action on marine organisms is the source of petroleum. Heat and pressure through the ages helped the chemical action, producing petroleum and natural gas in layers of *sedimentary* rock. A covering of nonporous rock usually keeps the oil deposit and gas from escaping to the surface.

Petroleum, sometimes called *crude oil*, is an important liquid material occurring in the earth's crust. It is a slippery, odorous mixture made up of many thousands of compounds. It consists mostly of hydrocarbons, but also contains compounds of oxygen, nitrogen, and sulfur. Crude oil is seldom used as it comes directly from the ground, but is separated into a great variety of products by *refining.*

Many people heat their homes with fuel oil extracted from petroleum. Lubricating oils, petroleum jelly, and paraffin wax are only a few of the thousands of products obtained from petroleum. Asphalt, gasoline, kerosene, tar, and carbon are also important products of the refining process.

Petroleum is our principal source of energy. Oil and natural gas together provide about ¾ of the total U.S. energy supply. California, Oklahoma, Louisiana and Texas produce almost 70% of our petroleum. Approximately one-half

2-66. Petroleum was popular as an ointment and was used for other medicinal purposes before it was widely used as a fuel. (Standard Oil Co. (NJ))

of the world's petroleum comes from wells in the United States. The richest deposits yet discovered in the world are located in Saudi Arabia, Iran, Iraq, and other Middle East countries. Canada, Mexico, and Venezuela also have rich oil deposits.

Great quantities of oil deposits are also located in several offshore areas in the continental shelf. These regions will undoubtedly be an important source of oil in the future.

Petroleum is obtained from wells. The first oil well, 69 feet deep, was dug by Col. Edwin L. Drake in 1859 near Titusville, Pennsylvania. The well produced only a few barrels of oil a day for many years.

Not all drilling operations are successful. The cost of locating and drilling a well depends partly upon how deep it is going to be. It is not unusual to spend over a half-million dollars for drilling a deep oil well. The dry holes, or *dusters,* are a total financial loss. The deepest well, so far, is in Texas. It was drilled to a depth of over 25,000 feet, at a cost of about 3 million dollars, but proved to be a dry hole. The deepest producing oil well is in Louisiana, approximately 20,000 feet deep.

Petroleum, natural gas, and salt water commonly saturate the *oil-bearing* sands under domes of cap rock, as shown in Fig. 2-67. When a drill moves into the oil-bearing sands, the pressure of the natural gas may force the oil upward towards the surface. As the pressure of the natural gas decreases, the oil must be obtained by pumping operations.

Crude petroleum must be sent from the well to the refinery to be separated into numerous by-products. A network

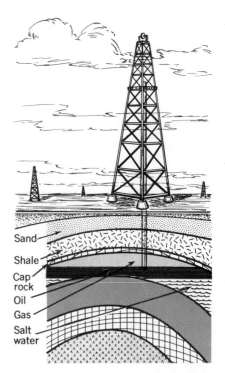

Sand
Shale
Cap rock
Oil
Gas
Salt water

2-67. Crude oil, natural gas, and salt water saturate the oil-bearing sands under a dome of cap rock.

of underground *pipelines* carries the oil to the refinery or to a port where it is loaded on ocean-going tankers. Pumping stations, located at 10- to 60-mile intervals, force the crude oil through the pipelines to refineries that often are thousands of miles away. Pipelines also carry refined gasoline, fuel oil, and natural gas. Branch lines connect different oil fields with main lines, forming a huge underground transportation system.

Searching for oil deposits. It is difficult to tell just where the dome-like oil formations are located. However, by using an instrument called a **seismograph** (*size*-mo-graf), and using man-made "earthquakes" to determine the

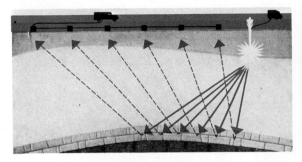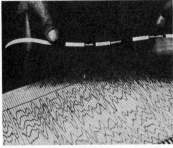

2-68. Waves from an explosion are reflected from the rock layer (left) to provide data on magnetic tapes (right) to furnish information for locating oil. (Standard Oil Co. (NJ))

nature of the reflections of shock waves from underground rock layers, much useful information is obtained. (See Fig. 2-68.) The *magnetometer*, an instrument used to measure slight variations in the earth's magnetism, and the *gravity meter* (Fig. 2-69) are other important devices used by the scientists in locating areas where oil is likely to be found. The odds are at least 8 to 1 against finding oil in spite of these investigations.

Oil wells are usually drilled by the use of *rotary bits*. A heavy bit is fastened to a length of steel pipe. (See Fig. 2-70.) Bit tips are usually made of diamond or very hard steel. The pipe is then fastened to a circular drill table. An engine supplies the power to rotate the table, pipe, and bit. New lengths of pipe are attached to the main shaft as the bit bores its way underground. Each time that a worn-out bit must be replaced, the entire shaft

2-69. A geophysicist uses a gravity meter for determining the location and density of rock materials. Slight variations in gravitational force provide a clue to the nature of underground formations. (American Petroleum Institute)

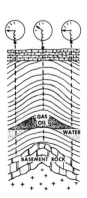

2-70. A new drill bit is being placed on the shaft of an oil-drilling rig. (Standard Oil Co. (NJ))

must be raised and removed from the hole. (See Fig. 2-71.)

During the drilling, a soupy mud is continuously pumped through the pipes to furnish pressure to flush out the cuttings. This suspension also serves as a coolant and lubricant for the drill. When the drill reaches the oil dome,

2-71. Examination of cores of rock obtained from drilling shows characteristics of materials found at various depths. (American Petroleum Institute)

the oil may be forced out by the pressure of the trapped gases as a "gusher." In order to prevent the loss of large quantities of oil resulting from a gusher, a "Christmas-tree" of valves for controlling the flow of crude oil is finally placed in position after the towering drilling rig is removed. (See Fig. 2-72.)

The alkane series. You may recall that the simplest carbon compounds are the *hydrocarbons,* which contain only carbon and hydrogen. Before we study the refining of crude oil, we must learn about classes of compounds that make up petroleum. The number of known hydrocarbon compounds runs into the tens of thousands, and new ones are being prepared and identified all the time. Fortunately, chemists have found it possible to classify these compounds into various *series.*

The simplest and most abundant series of hydrocarbons is called the *alkane* (*al*-kayne) series. The first member of this series is the gas *methane* (CH_4). Methane, or *marsh gas,* is the main constituent of natural gas. Natural gas usually, but not always, exists in deposits of crude oil.

The next member of the alkane series is *ethane* (C_2H_6), followed by *propane* (C_3H_8) and *butane* (C_4H_{10}). From these four compounds in the alkane series, can you see how the formula of each member differs from the previous one of the series?

The table below lists some of the common members of the alkane series. Notice that each compound differs from the next by CH_2. The general formula for determining successive compounds in this series is given by C_nH_{2n+2}. The first compound, methane, starts with $n = 1$.

2-72. The "Christmas tree" is a series of valves and taps designed to control the flow of crude oil from a well. (Humble Oil & Refining Co.)

THE ALKANE SERIES

Name	Formula	Phase at Room Temperature
methane	CH_4	gas
ethane	C_2H_6	gas
propane	C_3H_8	gas
butane	C_4H_{10}	gas
pentane	C_5H_{12}	liquid
hexane	C_6H_{14}	liquid
heptane	C_7H_{16}	liquid
octane	C_8H_{18}	liquid
nonane	C_9H_{20}	liquid
decane	$C_{10}H_{22}$	liquid
* * * *		
eicosane	$C_{20}H_{42}$	solid
* * * *		
hexacontane	$C_{60}H_{122}$	solid

Notice that the name of each member ends in *-ane.*

The maximum value of "n" is not known. However, there are some members of this series that have values of "n" of over 1,000. Many members of the alkane series, together with many other hydrocarbons, are found in petroleum. You can see that crude oil is a complex chemical mixture!

Structural formulas. In many compounds, the atoms may be arranged as a molecule in several different ways. For this reason, various carbon compounds may have the same chemical formula. To avoid confusion, chemists often show how the atoms are arranged in a molecule by using a *structural formula*. For example, the structural formula or atomic arrangement for each of the first four members of the alkane series are:

$$
\begin{array}{cc}
\begin{array}{c}
\quad\; H \\
\quad\; | \\
H - C - H \\
\quad\; | \\
\quad\; H
\end{array}
&
\begin{array}{c}
\; H \quad\; H \\
\; | \quad\;\; | \\
H - C - C - H \\
\; | \quad\;\; | \\
\; H \quad\; H
\end{array}
\end{array}
$$

methane, CH_4 *ethane,* C_2H_6

$$
\begin{array}{c}
\; H \quad\; H \quad\; H \\
\; | \quad\;\; | \quad\;\; | \\
H - C - C - C - H \\
\; | \quad\;\; | \quad\;\; | \\
\; H \quad\; H \quad\; H
\end{array}
$$

propane, C_3H_8

$$
\begin{array}{c}
\; H \quad\; H \quad\; H \quad\; H \\
\; | \quad\;\; | \quad\;\; | \quad\;\; | \\
H - C - C - C - C - H \\
\; | \quad\;\; | \quad\;\; | \quad\;\; | \\
\; H \quad\; H \quad\; H \quad\; H
\end{array}
$$

butane, C_4H_{10}

The dash ($-$) in the above formulas indicates that an outer electron of carbon atom is *paired* with the electron of the hydrogen atom or another carbon atom. The pairing of electrons between atoms, as indicated by the dash, is called a chemical **bond.** In other words, hydrogen and carbon atoms form molecules by the sharing of electrons. Observe from the structural formulas that each carbon atom is surrounded by four bonds. This is because each carbon atom has four outer electrons that are shared with hydrogen or other carbon atoms. A laboratory model of the methane molecule is sometimes represented as shown in Fig. 2-73.

Straight-chain and branched-chain compounds. In some hydrocarbons, the carbon atoms are linked or bonded together in long, *straight chains.* These are illustrated by the structural formulas for propane and butane shown above. Many hydrocarbon compounds form side chains, or *branched chains,* that have carbon atoms attached to the main string of carbon atoms. Butane (C_4H_{10}) may have its carbon atoms attached in a straight chain, or one of the carbon atoms may form a branched chain by attaching to the middle carbon atom:

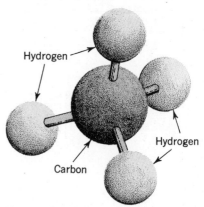

2-73. A laboratory model of the methane molecule (CH_4) shows how its atoms are bonded together.

$$H - \overset{\displaystyle H}{\underset{\displaystyle H}{C}} - \overset{\displaystyle H}{\underset{\displaystyle H}{C}} - \overset{\displaystyle H}{\underset{\displaystyle H}{C}} - \overset{\displaystyle H}{\underset{\displaystyle H}{C}} - H$$

straight chain, normal butane

$$H - \overset{\displaystyle H}{\underset{\displaystyle H}{C}} - \overset{\displaystyle H}{\underset{\displaystyle |}{C}} - \overset{\displaystyle H}{\underset{\displaystyle H}{C}} - H$$
$$H - \overset{\displaystyle}{\underset{\displaystyle H}{C}} - H$$

branched chain, iso-butane

Although both of the above compounds have the same chemical formula, C_4H_{10}, they are different compounds. The branched-chain compound is called *iso-butane* and has different

properties from that of the *normal* straight-chain butane. This is due entirely to the different *arrangement* of the atoms forming the molecule. *Isomers are compounds whose molecules have the same number and kind of atoms but in a different arrangement.* While most chemical and physical properties of isomers are similar, there are significant differences because of the variations in molecular structure.

Isomers are plentiful. The more carbon atoms a hydrocarbon molecule has, the more isomers it is likely to have. Butane has only one isomer, but pentane (C_5H_{12}) has three isometric forms. Can you write the possible structural formulas for the three isomers of pentane? Octane (C_8H_{18}) can have 18 different isomers.

Octane is one of the important hydrocarbons in gasoline. The amount and kind of isomers in gasoline affect its quality. For example, gasoline containing branched-chain hydrocarbons burns smoother than gasoline with mostly straight-chain compounds.

Other series of hydrocarbons. In the alkane series carbon atoms are connected by only *single* bonds. The *alkene* (*al*-keen) series is composed of straight-chain or branched-chain compounds in which two carbon atoms in the molecule are connected by two bonds (indicated by two dashes, =). This means that two outer electrons of one carbon atom are paired with two outer electrons of another carbon atom to form a *double bond*. The first member of this series of hydrocarbons is *ethene* (C_2H_4). The structural formula of ethene is

$$\begin{array}{ccc} H & & H \\ \diagdown & & \diagup \\ & C = C & \\ \diagup & & \diagdown \\ H & & H \end{array}$$

The names of the members of the alkene series are derived from the names of the alkane series with the same number of carbon atoms by merely substituting the suffix *-ene* for the suffix *-ane*. For example, eth*ane* is the alk*ane* with two carbon atoms, and so the alk*ene* with two carbon atoms is named eth*ene*.

Sometimes two carbon atoms in the molecule may be connected by three dashes (≡) to represent a *triple bond*. Can you suggest what this means? This kind of bonding gives rise to still another series, called the **alkynes.** *Ethyne,* commonly called *acetylene,* (C_2H_2), is the first member of this series. It has the structural formula

$$H - C \equiv C - H$$

Another series of hydrocarbons, of which benzene (C_6H_6) is the first member, is called the **aromatic** series.

Molecules of compounds in this series form a structure in which the ends of the chain of carbon atoms are linked together forming a closed ring. These are referred to as ring *compounds*. Benzene, a ring compound that is typical of this group, is one of the many by-products in the making of coke. The structural formula for the benzene ring is

$$\begin{array}{c} H \\ | \\ C \\ \diagup \diagdown\!\!\!\!\backslash \\ H - C \qquad C - H \\ \| \qquad | \\ H - C \qquad C - H \\ \diagdown\!\!\!\!\slash \diagup \\ C \\ | \\ H \end{array}$$

Ring compounds also may have side chains, thus producing tremendous numbers of different hydrocarbons. Observe from the above formula that double bonds exist between every other carbon atom in the ring. However, each carbon atom is still satisfied by having four bonds around it.

Fractional distillation. Although petroleum contains thousands of different hydrocarbon compounds, refiners do not have to separate every individual compound.

Gasoline, for example, is a complicated mixture consisting of significant amounts of *pentanes* through the *nonanes* of the alkane series as well as other hydrocarbons. *Gasoline* does not have a fixed boiling temperature. It boils within a certain temperature range. *Kerosene,* containing other hydrocarbons, boils at a higher temperature range than the gasoline mixture. *Fuel oil* boils at a still higher temperature range. Light, medium, and heavy lubricating oils are hydrocarbon mixtures with still higher boiling temperature ranges. *Greases, petroleum jelly, asphalt, paraffin,* and *petroleum coke* are products obtained near or at the end of the heating. These products are solids at room temperature.

A single compound has a definite boiling temperature at a particular atmospheric pressure. Alcohol boils at 78° C and a mixture of alcohol and water starts to boil at 78° C. The temperature then gradually rises to 100° C as the boiling continues. Hence, this mixture does not have a fixed boiling point, but ranges between 78° C and 100° C.

When the petroleum mixture boils, the liquids with the lowest boiling temperature ranges distill off first. *The process of separating a mixture of liquids having different boiling points*

is called fractional distillation. The refining of petroleum into various fractions of hydrocarbons with properties suitable for certain uses is accomplished by this important process.

Petroleum refining. The separation of the crude oil into its various components is accomplished industrially by the use of a special distillation apparatus. This equipment is divided into three main parts; a *pipe still,* a *fractionating tower,* and a *condenser.* (See Fig. 2-74.)

First, the petroleum is heated under pressure in a special furnace, called a pipe still, to about 700°–800° F. The pressure in the tubes keeps the crude oil from vaporizing. The hot petroleum goes from the pipe still to the bottom of a tall fractionating tower. Here the pressure is released and the liquid vaporizes.

2-74. The basic components of the fractional distillation process of petroleum refining. Can you explain how the different products are separated?

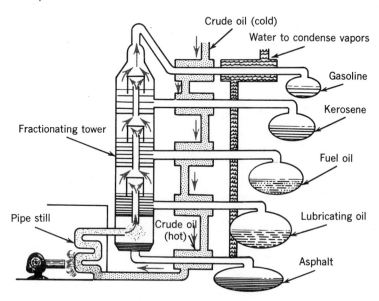

The vapors then go up the tower, which may be more than 100 feet tall. Those hydrocarbons that have a high boiling temperature range are easily condensed to liquids in the lower part of the tower. The ones that have a lower boiling temperature range, like those in gasoline, continue to move up the tower as a vapor. The condenser cools the vapors to liquids. Shelves collect the condensed liquids within the tower. Then they are drained off into separate storage tanks as shown in Fig. 2-74. The table below shows the boiling ranges of the various petroleum fractions.

To obtain a better separation, each of the liquids obtained in the table below is redistilled. Further, each liquid is chemically treated to remove objectionable impurities. (See Fig. 2-75.)

Major products from petroleum. We have seen that in the refining process, the fraction of petroleum having the highest boiling temperature remains in the bottom of the tower. This residue may be burned as *fuel*, processed into *asphalt*, or used in the production of

2-75. Photograph showing an exterior view of a battery of fractionating towers of a refinery. (Humble Oil & Refining Co.)

petroleum coke. Petroleum jelly ("Vasoline"), used in making ointments, and *paraffin wax*, used in making candles and waxed paper, are solids obtained

PETROLEUM FRACTIONS *

Number of carbon atoms	Boiling temperature range	Name of product	Principal use
1 to 5	Below 40° C	gas	fuel
6 to 10	40° to 180° C	gasoline	fuel
11 to 12	180° to 230° C	kerosene	fuel, cracking stock
13 to 17	230° to 300° C	light gas oil	diesel fuel, cracking stock
18 to 25	300° to 405° C	heavy gas oil	lubricant stock
26 to 60	405° to 515° C	residue	wax, residual oil, asphalt

* (Page 10, *Chemistry and Petroleum,* American Petroleum Institute, New York)

2-76. Asphalt, a by-product of petroleum refining, is widely used as a surface for roads. (Courtesy of American Bitumen & Asphalt Co.)

from the refining process. (See Fig. 2-76.)

Lubricating oils are obtained from the middle and lower fractions of certain crude oils. Some automobile lubricating oils have detergents added to them to help keep the automobile engines clean. *Greases* are usually made with lubricating oils and certain soaps. Some greases contain graphite, and are used on bearings that are not easily lubricated by oil.

Fuel oils are used in tremendous quantities for heating, for household oil burners, and aboard ships. The fuel used in diesel engines, called *diesel-ene*, resembles fuel oil in composition and in boiling temperature. Diesel engines run best on straight-chain hydrocarbons. *Kerosene* is an important fuel used for oil stoves, and as an illuminant for oil lamps. A kerosene-type fuel is

also used in some types of jet aircraft and rockets.

Benzene, dry cleaning "solvent," and *naphtha* are volatile mixtures used largely for special-purpose solvents.

The principal product of petroleum refining is *gasoline*. Billions of gallons of this important product are produced each year in the United States alone. A single barrel of crude oil can yield 30 gallons of "straight-run" gasoline.

In addition to the above products obtained directly from petroleum, there are many thousands of compounds and mixtures that have their source in petroleum and natural gas. Among them are plastics, synthetic rubber, drugs, explosives, alcohols, synthetic detergents, and dyes.

Properties of gasoline. Good gasoline should have the following characteristics:

1. It should vaporize quickly so that the engine will start promptly, especially in cold weather. However, if the gasoline is too volatile, much of it is lost by evaporation.

2. The gasoline should not have many high-boiling-point compounds that might form carbon residues in the engine cylinders.

3. It should be free of gummy materials that would make the engine valves stick.

4. It should burn smoothly in the engine without "knocking."

Sometimes the mixture of gasoline and air burns too rapidly in the engine. Instead of a smooth power stroke, the pistons in the cylinder of the engine get sharp hammer-like blows, resulting in lost power and possible damage to the engine. This is called "knocking."

Modern automobile engines compress the air-gas mixture to about ⅛ or 1/10 of their original volume. This brings the air and gas particles very close together. The more that the engine compresses the mixture before firing, the greater is the amount of power produced. However, too much compression can cause the gasoline vapor to burn unevenly, producing the knocking described above.

Straight-chain hydrocarbons produce knocking in gasoline engines while branched-chain and ring hydrocarbons perform much better under high compression.

Knocking may be prevented by using a fuel that has less tendency to knock, and by adding certain catalysts to the gasoline. The catalyst that is most widely used for this purpose is *tetraethyl* (tet-ruh-*eth*-il) *lead*. This compound slows down the rate of

burning of the fuel and improves the anti-knock qualities of the gasoline. Much of the gasoline sold today contains tetraethyl lead and is known as *ethyl gasoline.*

The octane rating of gasoline. Engineers have arbitrarily established a system of comparing the knocking characteristics of a fuel. The ability of a gasoline to resist knocking is expressed by a *number* called the **octane rating.** The higher the octane number, the better the gasoline resists knocking.

One of the isomers of octane with three branched chains has excellent anti-knock qualities. This *iso-octane* hydrocarbon is used as a standard, and is assigned a rating of 100. Normal straight-chain *heptane* knocks very badly in high-compression engines and is given a rating of zero. Various test mixtures of these two compounds are then used as a *standard* by which gasoline may be compared.

For example, a mixture of 95 percent iso-octane and 5 percent normal heptane solution is assigned an *octane number* of 95. Any gasoline that has the same anti-knock quality of this standard test mixture is assigned an octane rating of 95. This gasoline makes an excellent fuel for automobiles. Airplanes and some automobiles use 100-octane gasoline, which means that the fuel performs as well as pure iso-octane.

Some hydrocarbon mixtures resist knocking even better than pure iso-octane and have an octane rating above 100. *Toluene,* for example, is used in aviation gasoline to boost its octane rating.

Getting more and better gasoline to meet our needs. Petroleum chemists have responded to meet the increasing demand for more and better gasoline. They have developed processes for increasing the yield of gasoline from crude oil. A process, called *catalytic cracking*, breaks up large hydrocarbon molecules (see table page 137), such as the ones found in fuel oil, into smaller molecules, such as those of gasoline. This process involves heating the oil under an increase in pressure and in the presence of catalysts. The selection of the catalyst depends upon the nature of the chemical changes desired.

You may recall that *polymerization* involves a process by which small molecules are linked together to form larger ones. This process is the opposite of that of cracking. Simple molecules such as those of gaseous hydrocarbons are combined to make molecules of proper size and structure for the making of gasoline. Gasoline made by the polymerization process is *polygasoline.*

Alkylation (al-keh-*lay*-shun) is one of the important processes for producing high-quality compounds for aviation gasoline. This widely-used method produces larger molecules by the reaction of simpler alkanes with certain alkenes. By careful control, the gasoline produced is rich in branched-chain compounds that possess a very high octane rating.

Almost all gasoline today is obtained directly or indirectly from petroleum. However, a synthetic gasoline can be made from other raw materials such as coal, coal tar, or alcohol. This source might become of importance in those countries that have little or no crude oil resources.

Quick Quiz

1. Discuss a theory of the origin of petroleum. What kinds of compounds are found in crude oil?
2. What three instruments assist the scientist in the location of oil deposits?
3. How are oil wells drilled? In what way is crude oil transported to the refineries?
4. Explain the structural difference between the alkanes and alkenes.
5. Do straight-chain or branched-chain compounds make better gasoline?
6. Write the structural formula for straight-chain pentane. What does this formula tell us?
7. Name and explain the action of the three main parts of the distillation apparatus in a refinery.
8. Name six major products obtained directly from the distillation of petroleum, listing each product in order of increasing boiling point temperature.
9. What four properties should a good gasoline have?
10. What causes a gasoline engine to knock?
11. What is the advantage of ethyl gasoline? What special compound does it contain?
12. Name and explain three ways for increasing the yield of gasoline.

SUMMARY

Potable water is clear, colorless, pleasing to taste, and free of harmful bacteria. Community water supplies are purified by (1) first settling, (2) second settling after chemicals are added, (3) filtration through sand and gravel, (4) aeration, and (5) chlorination.

Hard water precipitates soap because of the calcium, magnesium, or iron ions in the water. Water containing calcium bicarbonate can be softened by boiling. Chemicals such as soda ash, slaked lime, and borax are used to soften water. The ion-exchange process makes use of sodium zeolite as a water softener. Hard water causes a scale of calcium carbonate to form inside steam pipes. Soapless detergents clean well both in hard and soft water.

The most common type of household cleanser is soap. It is made by boiling fat or vegetable oil with a solution of sodium hydroxide. Glycerin is an important by-product in the making of soap. Soapless detergents lessen the force of attraction between the molecules of water, permitting them to spread through the fibers, thus removing the dirt.

Lime is made by heating limestone in a kiln. It is used primarily for making mortar and plaster, as well as for many purposes requiring a cheap, moderately-strong base.

Cement is made by heating a mixture of limestone and clay, followed by fine grinding. Ordinary glass is made by melting together sand, soda ash, and limestone. Oil paint is a mixture of drying oil, a pigment, a thinner, and a small amount of drying agent.

Natural rubber molecules are giant molecules composed of hydrogen and carbon. Raw rubber is sticky, but when vulcanized with sulfur it loses its stickiness and becomes more elastic.

Plastics are high polymers that can be formed or molded into desired shapes. Thermoplastic and thermosetting are two basic groups into which plastics are divided.

Wool, cotton, linen, and silk are important natural fibers obtained from plant and animal sources. Synthetic fibers are made by squirting suitable liquids through tiny holes in a metal plate called a spinneret.

Chlorine, a poisonous, greenish-yellow gas, is the most common chemical used for bleaching plant fibers. Sulfur dioxide and hydrogen peroxide are used to bleach wool and other animal fibers.

Petroleum is an oily liquid, usually found deep underground. Fractional distillation of petroleum yields naphtha, fuel oil, kerosene, gasoline, and lubricating oils. Lubricating grease, asphalt, petroleum jelly, and petroleum coke are other products made from petroleum.

CHAPTER REVIEW

Vocabulary

Match the words in Column A with the *best* response in Column B. Do not write in your book.

Column A	Column B
1. distillation	a. first member of alkane series
2. calcium ions	b. single molecule or single unit of a polymer
3. detergent	c. can be softened by heating

 4. leavening agent
 5. antibiotic
 6. lime
 7. kiln
 8. mortar
 9. cement
10. glass
11. latex
12. monomer
13. thermoplastic
14. cotton
15. sanforizing
16. sulfur dioxide
17. methane
18. chemical bond
19. tetraethyl lead
20. catalytic cracking

d. prepared by heating calcium carbonate
e. material made from limestone and clay
f. material made from lime, sand, and water
g. bleaching agent
h. material made from sand, soda ash, and limestone
i. furnace for making such things as lime, cement,
and bricks
j. one source of hard water
k. substance that causes dough to rise
l. subjecting cotton cloth to steam while it is
stretched
m. substance obtained from rubber trees
n. compound to slow down rate of burning of
gasoline
o. cellulose
p. substance that removes dirt
q. chemical substance obtained from certain molds
and bacteria
r. process of evaporating a liquid, then condensing the vapors in a separate container
s. process of breaking up of large molecules into
smaller ones
t. one pair of shared electrons linking two atoms
together

Questions: Group A

1. What chemicals are used to settle suspended particles in water? Explain.
2. Explain the difference between potable and hard water.
3. What is ammonia water? What advantage does it have as a cleaner?
4. Describe three ways of putting out a fire.
5. Explain how the soda-acid fire extinguisher works.
6. Show by using two chemical equations what happens to lime when it
is left uncovered in a container for a long time.
7. Describe the making of cement.
8. List three pigments used in white paint.
9. Discuss the properties of "Teflon." What are some of the uses for it?
10. Explain why wool is a good insulator of heat.
11. Can any dye of suitable color be used for cotton? Explain.
12. How would you remove a coffee stain? Grease? Paint?
13. Explain why the oil sometimes "gushes" from newly-drilled oil wells.
What is done to prevent this from happening?
14. What is meant by a triple bond?
15. Describe what happens in a fractionating tower.
16. How is the octane rating of a gasoline determined?

Questions: Group B

1. How can you precipitate the calcium ions from hard water? Why is it advisable to remove these ions from solution?
2. How does sodium zeolite soften water by the ion-exchange method? How is the zeolite renewed?
3. Explain the cleansing action of a water solution of soap.
4. How does a carbon tetrachloride fire extinguisher put out a flame?
5. What two chemical reactions cause mortar to set?
6. Explain the difference between the drying action of ordinary oil paint and that of lacquer.
7. What are some advantages of polyurethane plastics?
8. Explain how thermoplastic articles are manufactured.
9. Why are plasticizers added to the batch in making plastics?
10. Name three common types of rayon. Explain how each is made.
11. What is the difference between the bleaching action of chlorine and that of sulfur dioxide?
12. Explain the action of a mordant in dyeing of cotton cloth.
13. Explain the difference between the structure of the alkene series of hydrocarbons with that of the alkyne series.
14. The general formula for the alkene hydrocarbon series is C_nH_{2n}. Starting with $n = 2$, write the chemical formulas for the first five members of this series.

3 METALLURGY AND METALS

A METALLURGY OF IRON

What is metallurgy? Think of the many objects you see and use every day that make use of metals such as iron, aluminum, or copper. Can you imagine a world without these metals? It would be difficult to find suitable substitutes for them. Some metals like gold, silver, and platinum are found in the earth's crust in a free or *native* state. A **native metal** is one that is found in nature *uncombined* chemically with another element. Although they are sometimes mixed with rock, native metals may be separated by physical means discussed earlier in the text. Most metals such as iron, aluminum, and zinc are found chemically combined with other elements and must be separated from their *ores* by chemical means. An **ore** is a rock or mineral from which a metal can be obtained *profitably*. This does not mean that any piece of rock is an ore, even though it may contain some useful metal. Only those minerals from which we can

obtain profitable amounts of metal are classed as ores.

The science of taking useful metals from their ores, refining them, and preparing them for use is called metallurgy. The actual industrial process involved in obtaining a metal from its ore, however, is called **smelting**.

Common ores of iron. Most ores are compounds of metals. For example, the chief and most abundant ore of iron is a reddish-brown substance called *hematite* (*hem*-uh-tite), Fe_2O_3. For many years the chief supply of hematite came from the Lake Superior region. Today we import the ore from huge deposits in Quebec, Labrador, and South America. Iron ore is mined in nearly half of the states of our country. (See Fig. 3-1.)

In addition to the high-grade hematite deposits there is also in the Lake Superior region an abundance of low-grade ore called *taconite*. This ore is becoming increasingly important in the production of iron and steel as higher grade ores are used up.

Limonite ($Fe_2O_3 \cdot 3H_2O$), *magnetite* (Fe_3O_4), and *siderite* ($FeCO_3$) are less important sources of iron. *Iron*

3-1. Open iron ore pits like those near Lake Superior supply about 65 percent of our needs. (American Iron and Steel Institute)

pyrites (FeS_2), sometimes called "fool's gold," is the sulfide of iron sometimes used in the making of iron and also in the production of sulfuric acid. Magnetite is so named because it is magnetized. That is, it will attract iron filings like an ordinary magnet. Vast supplies of iron ores are essential because steel, which is made from iron, is the very backbone of modern industry. If the present rate of consumption continues, it is estimated that the high-grade iron ore reserves around the Lake Superior region will be exhausted by the end of this decade.

The extraction of iron from hematite. A chunk of hematite does not look like iron nor does it have many properties characteristic of iron. The formula, Fe_2O_3, shows that oxygen is chemically combined with the iron in the ore. To get rid of this oxygen, the ore must be heated with a *reducing agent* in a blast furnace. A *reducing agent is a substance that removes oxygen from a compound.*

Coke, which is essentially a high-carbon (C) fuel, is used to reduce the iron oxide to iron. The coke, when burned with the oxygen of the air, is converted to carbon dioxide, and then to *carbon monoxide* (CO). The carbon monoxide acts as the reducing agent in removing the oxygen from the ore, Fe_2O_3. The following equations summarize essentially what takes place in the process of separating iron from hematite:

Step 1. Burning of coke.

$$C + O_2 \rightarrow CO_2 \uparrow$$

Step 2. Formation of carbon monoxide from carbon dioxide and coke.

$$CO_2 + C \rightarrow 2CO \uparrow$$

Step 3. The carbon monoxide formed acts as the reducing agent that takes away the oxygen of the ore, leaving metallic iron,

$$Fe_2O_3 + 3CO \rightarrow 2Fe + 3CO_2 \uparrow$$

The carbon dioxide formed as one of the products in Step 3 reacts with coke to form more carbon monoxide.

If hematite were *pure* iron oxide, it would be fairly easy to separate the iron. However, the ore always contains varying amounts of impurities.

The most common impurity in the hematite ore is sand. Sand often contains *silica* (*silicon dioxide*, SiO_2). Fortunately, silica reacts with limestone at high temperatures to form *calcium silicate* ($CaSiO_3$) and carbon dioxide. The easily melted calcium silicate is a waste product called *slag,*

$$CaCO_3 + SiO_2 \rightarrow CaSiO_3 + CO_2 \uparrow$$
(limestone)   (sand)   (slag)   (carbon dioxide)

Large quantities of limestone are included with the ore and coke to bring about the above reaction in the blast furnace. At high temperatures, the slag is liquid and drops to the bottom of the furnace. Because of its relatively low density, the slag floats on the surface of the liquid iron which also collects at the bottom of the furnace.

3-2. A large steelmaking plant in Pennsylvania, showing six heating stoves between two blast furnaces. (US Steel Corp.)

3-3. Coke to be used in the blast furnace is dropped from the oven into a special car. (US Steel Corp.)

The blast furnace. In order to bring about the chemical reactions necessary for the making of iron on a large scale, the *blast furnace* is used. (See Fig. 3-2.) The coke, limestone, and iron ore are fed into the top of this giant structure by means of small self-emptying skip cars which run up on a long incline as shown in Fig. 3-2. The mixture of coke, limestone, and iron ore is called the *charge.* (See Fig. 3-3.)

For a one-day period, a modern blast furnace is fed an average of 2000 tons of ore, 1000 tons of coke, 500 tons of limestone, and about 4000 tons of air, from which oxygen is obtained for the burning of coke. The furnace runs continuously, often two or three years, seven days a week, until it has to be shut down for major repairs.

A blast furnace is about 100 feet high and 30 feet in diameter. It is made of steel, lined with *firebrick* to resist high internal temperatures. Cir-

cling the lower part of the furnace is a large pipe that supplies the blast furnace with hot air, which in turn supplies the oxygen needed. (See Fig. 3-4.)

Near the bottom are *tapping holes* for drawing off the melted iron and slag. These holes are plugged with a wad of wet clay. It becomes so hot around the base of the furnace that the clay bakes hard at once, sealing the opening.

Huge stoves heat the air. Giant stoves located near the blast furnace heat the air before it is forced through the blast furnace. They are filled with firebrick stacked in an open checkerboard fashion so that the air can pass through. Hot exhaust gases from the top of the furnace are led to the bottom of the stove and make the firebrick red-hot. The exhaust gases are then diverted to another stove while fresh air is brought in through the hot stove. The air becomes *preheated* before it is sent to the bottom of the blast furnace. (Can you see the reason why?) Several stoves are in use at the same time. Some are preheating the air while others are being heated up.

Today many steel mills are using huge quantities of pure oxygen, or oxygen-enriched air, to improve and speed up the steel-making process and thus increase the output. Large plants for preparing oxygen from liquid air are built near iron and steel mills for this reason.

Coal is changed to coke by heating the coal in special ovens. The facilities for this process are also located near the steel mills.

Tapping the furnace for the liquid iron. Approximately every six hours

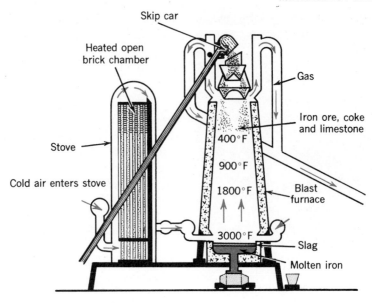

Skip car

Heated open
brick chamber

Gas

Stove

Iron ore, coke
and limestone

400°F

900°F

Cold air enters stove

1800°F

Blast
furnace

3000°F

Slag

Molten iron

3-4. Cross-sectional diagram of a blast furnace and a stove.

the molten iron is run into a large ladle. The clay plug is broken with a long crowbar, to let out the hot liquid. Sparks fly in all directions. When most of the iron is drained off,

3-5. Molten iron poured from the blast furnace to be further refined in the Bessemer converter, open hearth, or electric furnaces. (US Steel Corp.)

the hole is plugged again with clay. The molten slag is drawn off separately.

The reaction in a blast furnace is a very efficient chemical operation. Almost everything that comes from the furnace has valuable uses. Some of the slag is used in making insulating material and cement. The "waste" heat from the furnace is used to warm the air blast, and its waste gases are burned as fuel. Even the escaping dust is captured and processed for use as a fertilizer. (See Fig. 3-5.)

Pig iron. The stream of molten iron from the blast furnace may be allowed to run along sand-lined gutters to sand molds. It cools there and forms blocks called *pigs*. *Pig iron* is the product of the blast furnace. It contains about 92 to 94 percent iron, and also carbon, manganese, phosphorus, silicon, and sulfur as impurities. This iron is used for making pipes, radiators, stoves, and other castings not usually subjected to sudden shock and great stress.

The molten iron from the blast furnace may be run also into giant ladles that hold many tons. An overhead crane then carries these ladles to steel-making furnaces such as the *Bessemer converter*, the *open hearth*, or the *electric*. When the ladle arrives at a particular furnace, powerful hoists tilt it. The molten iron, at a temperature as high as 3000° F or above, pours out into the furnace that will process the iron into *steel*.

The Bessemer converter produces steel quickly. The conversion of the output from the blast furnace to steel is esssentially one of purification.

To make steel by the Bessemer method, molten iron from the blast furnace is poured into a large egg-shaped container called a *Bessemer converter.* This converter, which may hold 15 to 20 tons of iron, is made of steel with a thick lining of silica or limestone. It is mounted on pivots so it can be tilted; and has a double bottom, one of which is perforated with half-inch air holes. No fuel is needed because the chemical reaction between oxygen and the iron's impurities is so violent that the temperature is raised by this process.

A blast of air, or oxygen, is forced through the holes in the false bottom and through the molten iron. The blast burns out carbon and other impurities and sends a flame rushing from the mouth of the converter. When most of the impurities are burned away, the flame diminishes. An experienced op-

3-6. A Bessemer furnace produces steel by forcing air through the bottom of the molten pig iron batch. (American Iron and Steel Institute)

erator can tell from the appearance of the flame when all the impurities have been burned out by the air blast. It takes about 15 to 20 minutes to complete the process. (See Fig. 3-6.)

After the impurities are removed, a weighed quantity of carbon and manganese steel is mixed into the batch. The finished steel is then ready for pouring into blocks called *ingots.*

The Bessemer reaction occurs so rapidly that there is little time available to have a chemist test the steel during the process. Therefore, it is not easy to regulate the percentage of carbon and other elements exactly. Thus, steel from different batches is often not uniform in quality. The slower open hearth process, which yields a better quality steel, is more widely used in our country today.

The open hearth process. *Open hearth* furnaces are large brick structures lined with firebrick. They hold a shallow pool of molten iron 30 to 80 feet in length, 12 to 15 feet in width, about 2 feet in depth. Besides liquid iron from the blast furnace, the charge includes scrap steel. Old machinery, pipes, automobile parts, and other steel items sometimes constitute 50 percent of the charge. Iron ore and limestone are also often added.

Open hearth furnaces are heated by burning a blast of preheated gas or oil. The roof of the furnace reflects the heat down on the melted steel. (See Fig. 3-7.) Although it takes about 8 to 12 hours to make a batch of steel in the open hearth furnace, 100 tons or more are made at a time. During the process, a chemist can test samples

3-7. In the open hearth furnace, hot brick checkers pre-heat the fuels.

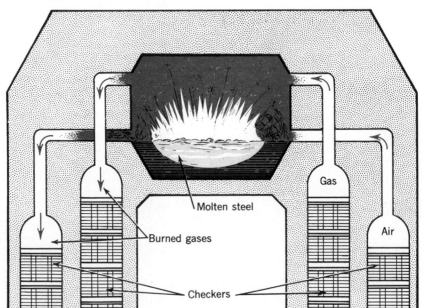

3-8. Ingots are the first solid form that steel takes in its manufacture. Giant tongs lift the mold from the ingots. (American Iron and Steel Institute)

3-9. Electric furnace is tipped to pour a batch of molten iron into ladle. The pipe-like rods on top of the furnace are carbon electrodes. (American Iron and Steel Institute)

at frequent intervals to insure a more consistent quality of steel. When the percentage of carbon is right, the furnace is tapped.

The steel empties into ladles big enough to hold the entire contents of the furnace. It is then poured into molds where it cools into ingots. (See Fig. 3-8.) About 90 percent of our steel is made by the open hearth process.

The electric furnace. In the production of high-grade steels, the electric furnace is used. It is a large steel container, lined with silica or limestone, with a removable cover. Carbon rods about 10 feet long serve as electrodes to carry a very large current through the molten iron charge. The heat from the electric current keeps the charge in a molten state throughout the entire process. Materials are then added to the furnace to produce a carefully controlled batch of steel.

Impurities go into the slag, and the furnace tilts for tapping of the molten steel into ladles from which ingots are made. Scrap iron and steel are also used in the electric furnace as part of the charge.

Electric furnaces produce up to 25 tons of steel per batch in 4 to 6 hours. High-grade steel for fine quality tools, automobile and airplane parts, and other objects are usually produced by this process. (See Fig. 3-9.)

Processing steel from the ingots. The liquid steel from the furnace runs into a big ladle, which is carried by an overhead crane to a row of cast-iron molds five or more feet high and twenty or more inches square. The liquid steel is poured into these molds, which rest on a steel plate that acts as the bottom of the molds.

When the steel solidifies, the crane removes the cast-iron mold, leaving a hot-steel ingot. Because the ingots cool quickly on the surface and slowly through the center, they must be placed in "soaking pits" where the steel is brought to uniform *rolling* temperature throughout the entire mass.

The white-hot steel is ready to be squeezed into various shapes under strong pressure, much like the shaping of clay in your hands. The hot steel is passed between powerful rolls, which work somewhat like an old-fashioned clothes wringer. Various slabs and I-beams, railroad rails, and other specified shapes are produced this way.

Some ingots are shaped by huge hammers and are then machined into

3-10. Powerful rollers position the hot steel for "squeezing" into a more workable shape. (US Steel Corp.)

crankshafts, propeller shafts, and other structural rods, bars, plates, and pipes. Steel slabs are rolled into thin sheets that are used in making such items as automobile bodies, refrigerators, and stoves. (See Fig. 3-10.)

What is steel? One important difference between steel and iron is that *steel contains a small but carefully regulated percentage of carbon.* Steels may also contain small but regulated amounts of other metals, added to give the finished steel certain desired characteristics and properties. Impurities like sulfur, silicon, and phosphorus are removed from the iron in the steel-making process.

The amount of carbon in steel varies from about 0.05 to 2.0 percent. If the percentage of carbon is low, the product is a very soft steel. The purest form of iron used commercially is *wrought iron,* which contains less than 0.1 percent carbon. It is used for making ornamental furniture, wire, and chains.

Steel with a high percentage of carbon is very brittle and hard. However, the hardness of steel depends not only on the amount of carbon present but also on how the carbon is united with the iron as determined by *tempering.*

Tempering affects the quality of steel. When a high-carbon steel is suddenly cooled, it becomes very hard. For most purposes, steel made this way would be too hard and brittle for commercial use. To obtain the right degree of hardness, the steel is heated again to a specific temperature. The higher the reheating temperature, the softer the finished steel becomes. The temperature is varied depending on the type of steel desired. After heating, the steel may be put into water or oil to cool suddenly. *The heating of steel, followed by rapid or slow cooling to produce the degree of hardness desired, is called* **tempering.**

Quick Quiz

1. What is meant by smelting? Metallurgy?
2. What is meant by a "native" metal? List three metals found chemically combined with other elements. List three metals usually found free in nature.
3. Are all metal-bearing rocks ores? Explain.
4. Name three important ores of iron.
5. Explain by means of chemical equations how pig iron is produced in a blast furnace.
6. What is the difference between the composition of iron and steel?
7. Describe the steel-making process in a Bessemer converter.
8. How is the slag removed from the molten steel in a furnace? Of what use is it?
9. Explain the purpose of the stoves in a blast furnace operation.
10. Why are liquid-air plants and coke ovens sometimes located near steel mills?
11. What happens to steel after the molds are removed from the ingots? Why?

B METALLURGY OF OTHER COMMON METALS

Roasting of ore. The method of smelting an ore to set free its metal depends on whether it is an oxide, a sulfide, a carbonate, or some other compound. We have learned that hematite is reduced by the carbon monoxide formed by burning coke. This carbon monoxide removes the oxygen from the iron oxide ore, leaving the metal. The oxide ores of other common metals are reduced in this manner.

Some metals occur as sulfide ores. Before a metal can be obtained from a sulfide ore, the sulfide is usually converted to an oxide. Then it can be reduced with carbon as indicated in the above paragraph. *Many sulfide compounds can be converted to oxides by heating the ore in air, a process called* **roasting.** Zinc is an example of a metal that is obtained from its common ore by this method. The ore, chiefly zinc sulfide (ZnS), is first roasted to produce zinc oxide (ZnO), which is then *reduced* to produce the metal. Lead is another metal that is commonly obtained from its sulfide ore in the roasting process.

More active metals such as sodium, magnesium, and aluminum are obtained commercially by *electrolysis.* Sodium is produced from fused sodium chloride, and magnesium from magnesium chloride ($MgCl_2$), contained in abundance in sea water. Aluminum is obtained from molten aluminum oxide.

Aluminum compounds are abundant. Aluminum is the most abundant metal in the earth's crust. Its compounds are found in clay and in many rocks. *Metallurgists* are studying the possibility of obtaining aluminum from ordinary clay, but at the present time, no profitable method has been devised. Men have used clay for thousands of years without realizing that a useful silvery metal was hidden in it. In spite of its abundance, metallic aluminum has been in use for only a little over 100 years.

The reason why aluminum remained undiscovered for such a long time is that it forms very stable compounds, not easily reduced. When first produced, metallic aluminum was so expensive that jewelry was made from it. In fact, Napoleon had aluminum knives, forks, and spoons which he used in place of gold and silver for special occasions. As late as 1852, aluminum commanded a price of more than a hundred dollars a pound. Today a pound of aluminum costs only slightly more than 20 cents. (See Fig. 3-11.)

The Hall process of obtaining aluminum. Aluminum is produced for commercial markets by passing an electric current through melted aluminum oxide (Al_2O_3). This oxide is the main compound in an ore called *bauxite*

3-11. The Crown Jewels of the aluminum industry are represented by the small globules on the left. These were the first nuggets prepared by Charles Martin Hall. (Aluminum Company of America)

(*bawks*-ite), most of which is mined in Arkansas, Dutch Guiana, and Jamaica. The impurities in the ore must first be removed in order to obtain pure aluminum oxide, called *alumina*. Alumina has the appearance of refined table sugar. To produce 1 pound of aluminum, about 4 pounds of bauxite are generally required.

In 1886, Charles Martin Hall, an American, discovered a practical method for separating aluminum from its oxide ore. He found that aluminum oxide dissolves in melted *cryolite* (*kry-oh-lyte*), a mineral mined in Greenland. When this mineral is heated to about 1800° F, it melts and forms a liquid that conducts electricity. When an electric current is passed through a solution of alumina and cryolite, metallic aluminum is deposited at the *negative* terminal, or **cathode,** of the electrolytic cell. Oxygen is set free at the *positive* terminal, or **anode.** (See Fig. 3-12.) The equation for the electrolysis reaction is

$$2Al_2O_3 \xrightarrow{\text{elect.}} 4Al + 3O_2 \uparrow$$

Aluminum plants must be located in areas where large quantities of low-cost electric energy is available.

Some properties of aluminum. Aluminum is a silvery metal, somewhat soft, and only about one-third as dense as iron. A thin almost invisible layer of oxide forms on its surface when exposed to air. This oxide forms a protective coating and prevents the metal underneath from any further oxidation.

Hydrochloric and sulfuric acids corrode aluminum rapidly, but nitric acid does not. Sodium hydroxide and other strong alkalis attack aluminum. That is the reason why you should not use

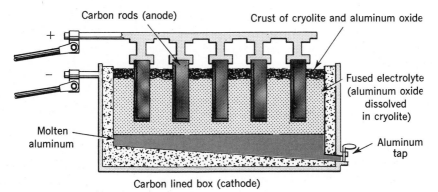

Carbon rods (anode) Crust of cryolite and aluminum oxide

Fused electrolyte (aluminum oxide dissolved in cryolite)

Molten aluminum

Aluminum tap

Carbon lined box (cathode)

3-12. Aluminum is produced commercially from purified oxide ores in molten cryolite (sodium aluminum fluoride) by electrolysis.

a strong *basic* cleaning powder on aluminum cooking utensils.

Aluminum is a good conductor of heat and is used widely for cooking utensils. Aluminum melts at 1220 F. Since kitchen stoves can produce temperatures much higher than this, you should not let a thin aluminum pan of water boil dry.

Aluminum ranks next to copper as a conductor of electricity. However, aluminum is much lighter than copper and so is used to some extent in electric power lines.

Aluminum has many uses. Because it is light-weight, attractive, and long-wearing, it has a great many uses. Aluminum can be made into thin sheets, or foil. Foil is used in the walls and ceilings of many homes to reduce the escape of heat in winter or the entrance of heat in summer. It is also widely used for wrapping foods. Certain airplane and automotive parts are made from aluminum Powdered aluminum is often used in paints because it reflects *radiant* energy. Rubies, sapphires, emeralds, and garnets are aluminum compounds valued as gems. (See Fig. 3-13.)

The greatest user of aluminum is the construction industry. Aluminum shingles, sidings, pipes, window frames, and roofs are a few examples of the

3-13. Homes are often insulated with aluminum foil. (Reynolds Metals Co.)

many building products on the market. Mixed with other metals such as magnesium, aluminum forms strong, lightweight alloys. Airplanes and modern trains make much use of these materials. At the present time, the United States produces about two million tons of aluminum yearly, about half of the world's supply of this important metal.

The mining of copper as a native metal. Copper, one of the first metals used by man, is frequently found as a *native* metal. Free copper is still found in Egypt, and probably was more plentiful there thousands of years ago. Scientists have found copper dishes dating back to 4000 B.C.

In this country, though commercial deposits of copper exist in 28 of the 50 states, about 95 percent of the deposits are concentrated in Michigan, Arizona, Utah, Montana, Nevada, and New Mexico. The largest known deposits of native copper ore are in Michigan. Many thousands of tons of copper have already been taken from these mines, some of which are about a mile deep.

The native copper ore from the mine contains varied rock substances. This ore is first crushed to a coarse powder by heavy weights made of hardened steel.

The native copper is then separated by a stream of water that washes away the lighter rock particles from the heavier copper metal. This operation, called *concentrating*, increases the percentage of copper in the ore batch.

The concentrated ore is then mixed with coke and limestone and dumped into a small blast furnace. The limestone unites with the silica impurities to form slag, in the same way that slag is formed during the smelting of iron.

3-14. In the flotation process, copper ore is mixed with certain oils and agitated. Particles of copper sulfide collect in the froth of bubbles and are floated off. (Copper & Brass Research Association)

The burning coke melts the copper, which collects in a pool at the bottom of the furnace. The molten copper is drawn off and cast into large plates. It is then further refined by electrolysis for commercial use.

The smelting of other copper ores. Besides native copper the principal ores of copper are *chalcopyrite* (kal-koh-*pie*-rite) ($CuFeS_2$), *chalcocite* (*kal*-koh-site) (Cu_2S), *bornite* (Cu_3FeS_3), for the sulfide ores; while *cuprite* (*coo*-prite) (Cu_2O), *malachite* ($Cu_2(OH)_2CO_3$), and *azurite* ($Cu_3(OH)_2(CO_3)_2$) are representative *oxide* and *carbonate* ores. It is believed that about half the world's copper resources are in the form of chalcopyrite.

The following steps describe basically the smelting process of chalcocite (Cu_2S), a sulfide of copper.

(1) The *ore-flotation* process is used to separate the copper(I) sulfide from the rock material. In this process, pul-

verized ore, water, and cheap oil are mixed in huge tanks. When air is blown through the tanks, *froth* collects on top. The particles of the ore cling to the air bubbles on top, while the rock material settles to the bottom. Then the froth and copper(I) sulfide are skimmed off into other tanks to be further processed. (See Fig. 3-14.)

(2) *Roasting the ore.* The concentrated copper(I) sulfide ore is then heated in air. This process essentially converts most of the copper(I) sulfide to copper(I) oxide. The ore is then heated with limestone, which removes the silica as slag. The slag floats on top of the molten copper oxide-sulfide mixture. Newly developed techniques involve the use of oxygen-enriched air in the roasting process.

(3) *Reduction of the mixture to metallic copper.* Air is blown through the molten mixture in a furnace sim-ilar to the Bessemer converter in the steel-making process. The copper(I) oxide reacts with the copper(I) sulfide to form metallic copper and sulfur dioxide gas according to the equation,

$$Cu_2S + 2Cu_2O \rightarrow 6Cu + SO_2 \uparrow$$

As the molten copper cools into slabs, the escaping gases give the metal a *blistered* appearance. Because of this, the impure copper (98.5–99.5% Cu) is commonly called *blister copper.* (See Fig. 3-15.)

Electrolytic refining of copper. The final step in preparing copper for the market is the electrolytic *refining* process. Impurities in crude copper make it a poor conductor of electricity. Since copper is mainly used for electrical conductors, it must be further refined to a higher degree of purity.

3-15. Blister copper is being poured from a giant converter. (Copper Development Assoc., Inc.)

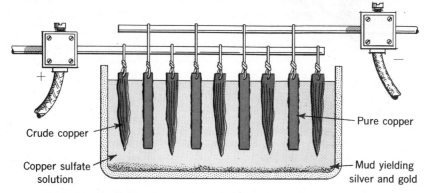

3-16. Crude copper is refined by electrolysis. The muddy residue yields gold and silver.

Native as well as crude copper is refined by electrolysis as shown in Fig. 3-16. The *electrolytic cell* is a tank of copper(II) sulfate solution containing some sulfuric acid to make it conducting. The *anodes* are slabs of relatively impure copper, and thin sheets of pure copper serve as *cathodes* for the final refining process.

When the electric current passes through the solution, the copper ions (Cu^{++}) in the solution are attracted to the cathode terminals, where they plate out as pure copper (Cu). The impure copper anodes supply fresh copper ions for the solution. Chemists write such reactions as follows:

At the cathodes ($-$):
$$Cu^{++} + 2 \text{ electrons} \rightarrow Cu$$

At the anodes ($+$):
$$Cu - 2 \text{ electrons} \rightarrow Cu^{++}$$

As this plating process continues, the anodes gradually get thinner as the atoms of copper go into the solution as copper ions. Meanwhile, the cathodes get thicker as the copper ions from the solution are deposited as pure copper. Electrolytic copper is over 99.9 percent pure. The impurities from the anodes drop to the bottom of the tank as a muddy deposit that often contains gold and silver as a valuable by-product. (See Fig. 3-17.)

Properties of copper. Copper is a reddish metal that is usually covered with a brownish coat of tarnish. If you

3-17. Pure copper is used to make electrical conductors. (Life Magazine)

rub off the tarnish with sandpaper, you will see the red color of pure copper. Copper is softer and denser than iron, and has a lower melting temperature.

When copper is exposed to the weather, it becomes covered with a green coating of copper carbonate or copper(II) sulfate. This coating protects the copper underneath from further *corrosion.* You may have noticed this green coating on copper roofs and the trim of public buildings.

Copper is not an active metal. Hydrochloric and sulfuric acids do not attack it readily, but nitric acid does. All soluble compounds of copper are poisonous.

Copper is used extensively. Most of our copper is used for making electrical wires and other electrical conductors. Copper is also used for making water pipes and special roofing. Some of the common *alloys,* discussed in section D of this chapter, such as

bronze and brass, contain copper. Most nations use some copper in their coinage.

The most important copper compound is copper(II) sulfate, commonly called *blue vitriol.* Several important uses of this salt include the making of agricultural spray known as *Bordeaux* mixture, the killing of algae in reservoirs, and the making of other copper compounds. (See Fig. 3-19.)

Tin is found as an oxide. Tin was employed centuries ago in the making of bronze, an alloy of copper and tin. The principal ore from which tin is obtained is *cassiterite,* essentially SnO_2. The ore is usually concentrated by *ore-flotation* process prior to shipment to the smelters. The metal is then obtained from its oxide ore by *reduction* with coke as indicated in the following equation,

$$SnO_2 + 2C \rightarrow Sn + 2CO \uparrow$$

3-18. This automatic electroplating tank is depositing copper on printed wiring boards. Notice the thick copper anodes. (Copper Development Assoc., Inc.)

3-19. Copper is used to prepare electrotypes for printing purposes. (International Association of Electrotypers & Stereotypers, Inc.)

The world's supply of tin today comes mainly from Malaysia, Indonesia, and Bolivia. Small amounts of tin ore are mined in the Black Hills of South Dakota, and some tin has been discovered in Alaska. Although the United States is the world's largest user and refiner of tin, we are almost entirely dependent upon foreign sources for this important metal.

Properties and uses of tin. Pure tin is a silvery, rather soft metal, and has a lower density than copper and iron. It melts at about 232° C (450° F), which is lower than most metals.

Air, water, and most dilute acids do not affect tin, although concentrated strong acids will attack it. It is not affected by weak acids present in foods, and so is a very useful material for lining food containers. The chief use of tin is in *tin plate*, from which "tin cans"

are made. The thin layer of tin on sheets of soft steel protects the steel from corrosion. (See Fig. 3-20.)

Tin plate is made by first dipping sheets of soft steel into a tank of acid to dissolve the oxide coating. (This process is called "pickling.") Then the sheets are put into a tank of melted tin. A shiny coating of tin clings to the "clean" surface of the metal.

In order to further protect the can's contents from possible chemical action, a yellowish enamel is baked onto the sheets of tin plate before the cans are manufactured.

How long will foods in tin cans keep? Food in tin cans will keep indefinitely without spoiling as long as nothing happens to the can to make it leak. There are recorded instances of food still being edible after being packed in cans for 40 to 50 years.

3-20. Tin plate is carefully examined for flaws by inspectors. Of what use is this material? (US Steel Corp.)

Where is lead mined? Lead sulfide (PbS), or *galena,* is the principal ore of lead. Missouri, Idaho, Utah, Mexico, and British Columbia are the largest producers of the ore.

It is fairly easy to extract lead from galena. The ore is concentrated by flotation. It is then roasted to convert the lead sulfide to lead oxide.

The roasted ore is next heated in a blast furnace with coke and limestone. The coke provides the fuel and the carbon for the reduction of the oxide into the metal. The limestone reacts with silica, present as an impurity, and forms the slag.

Properties of lead. The expression "heavy as lead" tells you that this metal has a high density. A cubic foot of lead weighs over 700 pounds.

Lead is a silvery metal, although a freshly cut surface soon takes on a dull gray coating of tarnish. This coating sticks firmly to the metal and protects the metal underneath from further chemical action. Lead is so soft you can scratch it with your fingernail. It can be rolled into thin sheets of foil, pulled apart, bent and cut without difficulty. Lead has a low melting point, 327° C (620° F).

Since all soluble lead compounds are poisonous and accumulate in the body, lead is not used for food containers.

Uses of lead. In ancient Rome, lead was used for making water pipes. In fact, our modern word "plumber" is derived from the Latin word "plumbum," meaning lead. Water and air have little effect upon lead, making it ideal for use in plumbing and for covering telephone and electric cables. Lead shields are used extensively to stop the deadly radiations from X rays and radioactive materials.

3-21. Lead is used in the porcelain-enameled panels on the exterior of the Chase National Bank building in New York. (Sam Falk for The Chase Manhattan Bank)

About 30 percent of our total lead output is used in making car batteries. *White lead,* used in manufacturing of house paints, is made from metallic lead. *Red lead,* an oxide of lead, is used as an undercoat on steel beams to keep them from rusting. Lead compounds are added to gasoline to reduce "knocking" in engines. (See Fig. 3-21.)

Zinc is always found as a compound. Zinc is too active a metal to occur in its native state. The principal ore of zinc, sometimes called *zinc blende,* is zinc sulfide (ZnS). The metal is obtained from its sulfide ore by roasting, followed as usual by reduction of the oxide with carbon. High-purity zinc may be obtained from its oxides by electrolysis, for use in making alloys. (See Fig. 3-22.)

The United States is the largest producer of zinc in the world. The largest zinc-producing area is a section about 15 miles square that lies partially in Oklahoma, Kansas, and Missouri. New Jersey, Montana, Colorado, and Arkansas also produce considerable amounts of this metal.

What are some properties and uses of zinc? Zinc is a bluish-white metal almost as dense as iron. A dull coating of tarnish usually sticks firmly to the surface and protects the rest of the metal. Bars of zinc are crystalline and brittle. However, if zinc is heated to about 150° C (300° F), it gets soft and can be rolled into sheets. Rolled zinc stays soft after it cools. Most pure zinc in use today is in the form of zinc sheet.

All of the common acids react with zinc. You will recall that we used zinc to obtain hydrogen from sulfuric acid. Zinc burns, combining with the oxygen of the air to form *zinc oxide*. Zinc oxide is used in medicine, chiefly in the form of ointments.

Large quantities of zinc are used for making *galvanized iron*. This process protects the iron by covering it with a thin coating of zinc. The iron is first cleaned by pickling in an acid bath. It is then coated with zinc by dipping it into molten zinc or by electroplating. All soluble salts of zinc are poisonous, so acid foods must not be stored in galvanized iron containers. (See Fig. 3-23.)

Industry uses many other metals. *Nickel* is used for toughening steel, in nickel plating, and for making important alloys. Nickel is also used as a

3-22. The negative terminals of high-quality zinc deposits are being lifted from the electrolytic cell by a worker. (Anaconda)

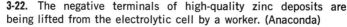

3-23. Galvanized steel used in air-conditioning and heating-duct work. (Bethlehem Steel Corp.)

catalyst for hardening oils into solids. *Cobalt,* like nickel, is used for making many important alloys. *Tungsten* is used in making valuable steel alloys. A carbide of tungsten is mixed with cobalt to make *carboloy.* This is one of the hardest materials manufactured, and is used in high-speed cutting tools. *Mercury,* often called *quicksilver,* is an unusual metal because it is a liquid at room temperature. It is 13.6 times as dense as water. Mercury is used in mercury-vapor lamps and in many scientific instruments such as thermometers and barometers. The chief ore of mercury is *cinnabar,* which is mercury(II) sulfide (HgS).

Cadmium is used for plating iron and steel objects such as screws and bolts. Rods of cadmium are also used as control rods for nuclear reactors. Cadmium is becoming increasingly important industrially because of its low coefficient of friction and resistance to fatigue.

Tantalum is like lead in many ways. It is very resistant to corrosion by many chemicals. Tantalum is now being used for many industrial purposes as a substitute for platinum because it is so much cheaper. Surgeons use plates of this metal to repair bone fractures.

Titanium is one of the wonder metals of the space age. It is used in making combustion chambers for rockets and jet aircraft. Titanium metal is remarkably strong, lightweight, and able to withstand high temperatures without corrosion or loss of strength.

The table below shows some principal uses of other important metals.

SOME USES OF OTHER METALS

Beryllium	Springs; windows for X-ray tubes
Germanium	Transistors
Lithium	Ceramics and drugs; H-bomb
Selenium	Photoelectric cells; rectifiers
Silicon	Solar batteries; transistors
Vanadium	Tough steel alloys; catalysts
Zirconium	Nuclear reactors

Quick Quiz

1. What is meant by roasting an ore? Why is this process undertaken?
2. How are many active metals obtained from their metallic ores?
3. How could you demonstrate that aluminum tarnishes?
4. What contribution did Charles Martin Hall make to chemistry? Explain his process.
5. Why should you not use strong cleaning powders on aluminum pans?
6. Explain how native copper is separated from rock that is mixed with it.

7. Explain briefly how copper is obtained from its sulfide ore. Give reasons for each step in the process.
8. Does copper corrode? Explain.
9. Why must native and crude copper be refined to a high degree of purity?
10. What is blue vitriol? What are three uses for it?
11. What is the principal ore of tin and where is tin ore found?
12. What properties of lead make it suitable for plumbing?
13. What is the principal ore of zinc? Name four uses for zinc.
14. Complete the blanks in the following reactions on a separate sheet of paper. Do not write in your book.

(a) $Zn^{++} + 2$ electrons $\rightarrow$ _____
(b) Pb _____ electrons $\rightarrow Pb^{++}$
(c) $2Cl^- $ _____ electrons $\rightarrow Cl_2$
(d) _____ $- 1$ electron $\rightarrow Na^+$
(e) $K^+ + 1$ electron $\rightarrow$ _____
(f) Mn^{++++} _____ electrons $\rightarrow Mn^{++}$

C PRECIOUS METALS

What are precious metals? Precious metals are those that are useful but scarce and costly. You are familiar with the most common precious metals, *silver, gold,* and *platinum.* Others not so well known are *palladium, osmium, iridium,* and *rhodium.* Other less common metals have specialized but important uses.

Sources of silver. Silver is found as a native metal, in the form of silver sulfide (Ag_2S) called *argentite,* and the chloride ore (AgCl) called *horn silver.* Most commercial silver, however,

is obtained from the copper, lead, and zinc ores. Large amounts of silver are produced from the deposits of muddy impurities in the electrolytic refining of copper.

When this mud is treated with concentrated sulfuric acid, silver sulfate (Ag_2SO_4) is formed. This reaction separates the silver from the gold that is also present because sulfuric acid does not react with gold. The silver is then obtained from the silver sulfate solution by introducing strips of scrap copper. The pure silver is deposited on the copper strips, as indicated in the equation

$$Ag_2SO_4 + Cu \rightarrow CuSO_4 + 2Ag \downarrow$$

The silver is then melted into carefully weighed bars called *bullion.* (See Fig. 3-24.)

3-24. Silver bullion is stored in huge vaults for safekeeping. (Eastman Kodak)

3-25. Silver is obtained during the refining of crude lead by the Parkes process. (American Smelting and Refining Co.)

Mexico is the largest silver-producing country, followed by the United States and Canada. Utah, Montana, Idaho, Arizona, Nevada, and Colorado have valuable silver mines.

The Parkes process. Silver is often found as an impurity in crude lead. To obtain the silver from lead, the mixture is melted in a large kettle to which a small amount of zinc is added. The molten zinc dissolves the silver. The zinc, being insoluble in molten lead, floats on top and the zinc-silver mixture is scraped off. Then the zinc is vaporized by heating, freeing the silver. This method, known as the *Parkes process*, is illustrated in Fig. 3-25.

Properties of silver. Silver is a soft metal that shines with a beautiful luster. It is the *best* known conductor of heat and electricity, but is too expensive a metal to use for electric wiring or for cooking utensils.

Strong bases and most acids do not affect silver. However, concentrated nitric and sulfuric acids react with it. Although silver does not oxidize in air, you have seen how silver tarnishes and turns brown or even black. Sulfur compounds present in such foods as mustard and eggs, and fumes of sulfur in polluted air, will cause silverware to tarnish. This tarnish is a coating of *silver sulfide*, produced by the reaction of silver with sulfur compounds.

How is silver plate made? Much silver is used in jewelry and other ornaments. The best table silver is solid *sterling*, but a large amount of silverware is *plated*. An electric current is used to put a coating of silver on a cheaper metal by electrolysis.

For this process, bars of pure silver are used as *anodes*. The objects to be plated are the *cathodes*. Both are suspended in a conducting solution of sodium silver cyanide (*sigh-uh-nide*). The silver from the bar goes into the solution as *silver ions* (Ag^+), which are attracted to the cathode and deposit out on the objects as metallic silver (Ag). The equations for this reaction are

At the cathode ($-$):
$$Ag^+ + 1\ electron \rightarrow Ag$$

At the anode ($+$):
$$Ag - 1\ electron \rightarrow Ag^+$$

In other words, the silver is transferred from the anode bars of silver to the cathode objects to be plated. The concentration of the silver ions in the solution remains about the same during the entire process.

Much silver is used in coinage. Pure silver is too soft for most industrial and commercial purposes. To make it harder, it is mixed with copper. *Sterling silver,* for example, has 92.5 percent silver and 7.5 percent copper, a proportion fixed by law for this material. Our silver coins, a principal use of silver, contain large amounts of copper and other hardening metals.

An important silver compound, *silver nitrate* ($AgNO_3$), is sometimes used to sear wounds and bites. A few drops of a very dilute solution of silver nitrate are placed in the eyes of new-born infants to prevent an infection that may cause blindness.

Silver compounds are sensitive to light. Photography is based on the fact that light can change silver compounds to metallic silver. *Silver bromide* (AgBr), for example, is especially sensitive to light. To observe this, add some silver nitrate solution to a solution of sodium bromide (NaBr) in a beaker. A yellowish-white precipitate of silver bromide forms at once.

$$AgNO_3 + NaBr \rightarrow NaNO_3 + AgBr \downarrow$$

Now hold the beaker in the sunlight for a minute or two, and notice that the precipitate turns dark. The black substance observed is made up of small particles of finely-divided silver. The action of the light on the AgBr causes some of the silver ions to be changed to silver.

How are photographs made? Photographic film and printing paper are coated with a mixture of light-sensitive silver bromide and gelatin.

The first thing you do to make a photograph is to "expose" the film. Light is passed through the camera lens for a brief interval of time. The light forms an image on the film and starts to change the silver ions to silver, as observed in the above experiment.

In the darkroom, the exposed film is passed through a solution called a *developer.* The developing solution *continues* the chemical reaction already started by the light, producing black, powdered silver on the film only where the light struck the film during the exposure.

When the process has gone far enough to show the details of the picture, the action of the developer is stopped by passing the film through a

3-26. When exposed film is treated with a reducing agent, black silver particles are formed on negative (left). The positive or print (right) is prepared from the developed negative.

solution called a *fixer*. This solution is sodium thiosulfate (*thigh*-oh-*sul*-fate), commonly called "hypo." The fixing solution dissolves any unchanged silver bromide from the film leaving the black metallic silver deposit. After the film is thoroughly washed and dried, a *photographic negative* is obtained, which is insensitive to light. (See Fig. 3-26.)

To obtain a *photographic positive*, or *print*, the negative is placed over a sheet of photographic printing paper in a darkroom. The sensitized film on the printing paper is exposed to light for a brief time interval. The paper is

then *developed*, *fixed*, and *washed* in a darkroom just as the negative was. This gives a positive print that appears like the original scene. Many science students find photography a very fascinating hobby.

Gold is widely distributed. Gold occurs chiefly as a native metal, being rarely found in compounds. Although gold usually occurs as tiny grains, it is sometimes found in chunks or *nuggets*. (See Fig. 3-27.)

The major problem associated with obtaining gold from its widely-distributed deposits is that of cost. For example, a thousand tons of sea water

3-27. Nugget of gold which came from a river in California weighs about 10 ounces. (Bureau of Mines, U.S. Dept. of the Interior)

has a little over one cent's worth of gold in it. However, it would cost several dollars to recover this tiny amount of gold.

Each of the continents of the world has rich deposits of gold. South Africa produces the most gold, with the Soviet Union, Canada, United States, and Australia following in order. South Dakota, Utah, Alaska, and California are the largest producers of gold in the United States. The United States accounts for about 10 percent of the total gold production of the world.

Gold is malleable. Gold has several unusual properties. It is a very soft metal and is probably the most *malleable* (*mal*-ee-ah-b'l) of all metals. *Malleability* is the property of a metal which enables it to be hammered or rolled into thin sheets. Gold can be hammered so thin that several hundred sheets placed one on top of an-

other would equal only the thickness of this page. This metal can also be drawn into very fine wires for special purposes. It is an excellent conductor of heat and electricity.

The density of gold is nearly twenty times that of water. It melts at about 1100° C (2000° F), forming a bluish-green liquid. Gold does not unite with oxygen at any temperature, nor is it affected by water or any single common acid. This accounts for the fact that gold jewelry keeps its luster. *Aqua regia,* a mixture of nitric and hydrochloric acids, will dissolve the metal.

Mercury dissolves gold very readily, forming gold *amalgam.* If you are working around mercury in the laboratory, you should remove your gold jewelry to keep it from being contaminated by the mercury.

Uses of gold. Formerly, gold was used for making coins. Since the United States went off the gold standard in 1933, no gold coins have been minted in this country. "White gold," used for jewelry, is gold mixed with silver or platinum.

The proportion of gold in a substance is commonly expressed in **carats.** Pure gold is considered to be 24 carats. Gold jewelry, for example, that is 18-carat (18K) contains 18/24 gold and 6/24 of other metals, usually copper or silver. Although more expensive, 18-carat gold will not wear as well as 14-carat gold because it is softer.

Considerable amounts of *gold leaf,* made by hammering pure gold, are used for gold lettering on book bindings, architectural decorations, fine chinaware, and for signs on store and office windows.

Most of the gold in the world is stored in bank vaults as it represents a standard of commodity value in world commerce. Our government stores its gold reserves in well-guarded vaults at Fort Knox, Kentucky. The price of our gold is set by Federal law at $35 an ounce.

Platinum. Like gold, platinum occurs as a native metal in grains and small nuggets. Some platinum comes as a by-product from the refining of copper and nickel. The United States, Canada, Russia, and South Africa are large producers of the metal.

Platinum is widely used for making jewelry. Finely-divided platinum adsorbs large quantities of gases, especially hydrogen, giving off heat. Platinum is an important catalyst in several industrial processes, such as the manufacture of sulfuric acid and the oxidation of ammonia (NH_3) to nitric acid.

Conductors made of platinum are used extensively in electronic research. The United States is the largest user of platinum in the world.

Newer developments in the use of precious metals. As you have learned, modern industry requires large quantities of metals that were formerly scarce and rare. This is particularly true of the electronic, nuclear, aviation, and aerospace industries. Today the electronics industry alone uses more of the precious metals than jewelers do. A common practice is to plate conductors with silver to obtain a low electrical resistance contact with other elements in a circuit. The silver is protected from tarnishing by applying a thin coating of *rhodium,* only a few thousandths of an inch thick, which prevents oxidation of the silver.

3-28. Streams of water wash away dirt and rock particles leaving the denser gold grains in the sluice. (Bureau of Mines, U.S. Dept. of the Interior)

1. What is a precious metal? List five precious metals.
2. List three sources of silver. Where is silver mined?
3. How is silver obtained from the muddy impurities in the refining of copper?
4. Explain what causes silver to tarnish.
5. Why are silver and gold often alloyed with other metals?
6. What compound of silver is especially sensitive to light?
7. How is silver plated on another metal?
8. Explain the steps you would take in the preparation of a photographic negative. A photographic positive.
9. In what areas are rich deposits of gold found?
10. A gold bracelet weighing 50 grams is marked 14K. Compute the grams of pure gold in the bracelet.
11. The density of platinum is 21.4 g/cm³. Compute the weight of 1000 cm³ of platinum.

D METALLIC ALLOYS

Most metals are not pure. Many metallic articles are made mostly of mixtures of metals, not pure metals. Very pure copper must be used for conducting electricity efficiently. Even the presence of less than 0.5 percent impurity in copper will cut down its electrical conductivity by about 50 percent. Pots and pans are made of almost pure aluminum. But with these two important exceptions, few metal objects in common use are made of pure metals. We use tailor-made mixtures of metals that have properties especially desired for particular purposes. Besides, the obtaining of *pure* metals from the ore is a costly process and one that is not usually necessary.

Hundreds of different metallic mixtures are used, but in this section we shall study only a few of the more important ones.

What is an alloy? *A material composed of two or more metals that are melted together is called an* **alloy.** Over 36 metallic elements are used in making hundreds of alloys. Different alloys are obtained from the same elements by using them in different proportions.

There are several ways in which metals may be distributed in an alloy. Sometimes one metal dissolves in another when they are melted together. If this metal stays dissolved, it forms a *solid solution* when cooled. Copper and zinc mix in all proportions, like the mixing of alcohol and water. However, only a limited amount of zinc will mix with lead to form an alloy. If more than the required amount of zinc is added, the excess will form a layer on top. *Most common alloys are solid solutions.*

Sometimes metals form *metallic compounds* which do not combine in accordance with the common scheme of valence numbers discussed earlier in the text. These alloys may have such unusual formulas as Cu_5Zn_8, Na_4Pb, or Al_2Cu.

Still another class of alloys is the *metallic mixtures.* In this class of alloys, crystals of one material are scattered throughout the mass, somewhat like raisins in a cake. Related alloys

3-29. The cast iron automobile block (left) is very heavy while a much lighter block made of aluminum alloy can do the same job. (General Motors)

of this class may have a considerable range of properties. Steels are notable examples of alloys in this general classification.

Some metals will not alloy with certain other metals. For example, copper will not alloy very easily with iron. However, copper forms some of our most widely used alloys when mixed with tin and zinc.

General properties of alloys. The properties of alloys are usually quite different from the properties of the basic metals that they contain. For one thing, an alloy is usually *harder* than the metals that compose it. For example, brass, which is composed of zinc and copper, is harder than either of these metals.

Alloys are usually *poorer* conductors of heat and electricity than the pure metals. We have already mentioned how impurities in copper greatly reduce its electrical conductivity.

Further, the melting temperature of an alloy is usually *lower* than that of any of its component metals. Many other properties of metals are altered in alloys. These include color, elasticity, expansion by heat, and magnetic properties. Microscopic examination of the smooth surface of alloys reveals a good deal about the distribution of the metals in the alloy. (See Fig. 3-30.)

Bronze was the first alloy. An alloy of copper and tin, called *bronze*, was probably discovered accidentally centuries ago when someone melted

3-30. Alloying metals such as titanium, tungsten, and chromium enable missiles and jets to withstand very high temperatures. (US Dept. of Defense)

copper that happened to have tin in it as an impurity. The bronze alloy that resulted was harder and more durable than either copper or tin. At any rate, we do know that more than 3000 years ago people sought tin to make bronze utensils.

Our one-cent coin is not made of pure copper but of bronze with a small amount of zinc. Bronze *bearings* are used in the rotating parts of electric motors. Bronze is an enduring metal that corrodes only on the surface. You may recall seeing bronze memorial tablets and statues in public places. The Statue of Liberty in New York City harbor is one such example.

Brass takes a high polish. Another widely used alloy is **brass,** an alloy of copper and zinc. It is a bright yellow metal that readily tarnishes on the surface. It must be polished frequently or coated with lacquer to keep it shiny.

Brass hardware is used on ships, and also around the home. It is commonly used for metal objects exposed to the weather. Foods affect brass, and so it cannot be used for cooking utensils, but it does make long-lasting water pipes.

Babbitt metal is used for bearings. You have probably heard someone talk about "burning out a bearing" in his car. A bearing is usually a hollow metal cylinder that allows turning parts to rub against each other with the minimum of friction. (See Fig. 3-31.) An alloy called *babbitt* metal is often used for such bearings. It is an alloy of tin,

3-31. Automobile bearings are made of babbitt metal to reduce friction. (Clevite Corp.)

copper, and antimony. The friction between this alloy and steel is much less than that of steel against steel. Babbitt bearings are used on the crankshaft of automobile engines.

Airplanes, rockets, and space vehicles must use light-weight materials. A metal must be strong and light for it to be considered in the making of bodies and parts for air-borne vehicles. Every pound of weight saved in construction means another pound of *payload* that the airplane or space vehicle can carry.

Aluminum has a density about one-third that of steel. But it has too little *tensile strength,* or ability to withstand a stretching force, to use as a pure metal in making air-borne structures. The problems involved in designing materials to withstand high temperatures will be discussed later in the text.

Magnesium is even lighter than aluminum, but this metal also is not strong enough to be used alone. However, combinations of aluminum, magnesium, and small amounts of copper and manganese make a light but strong alloy, called *duralumin* (doo-*rahl*-yuh-min), suitable for various parts.

Alclad is an aluminum alloy that is coated with pure aluminum. It is used in seaplanes because sea water does not affect the aluminum coating. Wheelbarrows, garden tools, and ladders made of aluminum-magnesium alloys are widely used.

Alloys of nickel and antimony. Nickel alloys have a wide variety of industrial applications. Just as pennies are not pure copper, neither are "nickels" made of pure nickel. The alloy of our five-cent coin has 75 percent copper and only 25 percent nickel.

Nickel and copper containing small amounts of iron and manganese form an alloy called *monel* (moh-*nel*) *metal*. Monel metal wears well, is strong, and is not attacked by dilute acids. It is used in making ice cream cabinets, sinks, drainboards, functional trimmings in cafeterias, and for other purposes requiring a metal that does not tarnish easily.

Lead melts easily, and melts still more easily if a little tin is mixed with it. In addition, such an alloy *shrinks* when it hardens. However, if about 15 percent antimony is added to this lead-tin mixture, the alloy *expands* when it solidifies. This makes *type metal* that forms very sharp clear-cut letters as it cools. (See Fig. 3-32.)

Wood's metal melts in hot water. You may be surprised to learn of an alloy that melts easily in hot water.

3-32. This line of type metal is an alloy of antimony, tin, and lead. (Mergenthaler Linotype Co.)

3-33. Wood's metal, a low-melting alloy, is used in sprinklers that work automatically when a fire occurs in a building. (Courtesy of Grinnell Co., Inc.)

This silvery-looking alloy, composed of *bismuth, cadmium, tin,* and *lead,* is called *Wood's metal.* It melts at 70° C (158° F), which is lower than the boiling temperature of water.

You can make this alloy in the following manner. In a crucible heat 20 grams of bismuth, 10 grams of lead, 5 grams of tin, and 5 grams of cadmium. Stir with an iron wire until the mixture is melted. Then pour the molten mixture into a mold to harden. Observe what happens when this alloy is placed in hot water. From the weights you used, could you calculate the percentage of each ingredient in your sample alloy?

Wood's metal is used in making special plugs for automatic fire sprinkling systems. A fire soon gives off enough heat to melt the metal plugs

in these sprinklers, releasing streams of water. (See Fig. 3-33.)

Other alloys. Plumbers use a lead-tin alloy called *solder* (*sah*-der). Solder melts easily and is used to join two pieces of metal together.

Nichrome is an alloy of nickel, chromium, iron, and manganese. It has a high electrical resistance and so gets very hot when current passes through it. It is used as a heating element in devices such as electric irons and toasters. Can you think of an important reason why copper and silver would not be used in heating elements of electric devices?

A magnetic alloy, called *alnico*, is composed of *al*uminum, *ni*ckel, *co*balt, and iron. Alnico is used extensively for making powerful permanent magnets used in telephones, loudspeakers, hearing aids, and scores of other devices.

An alloy consisting of silver, tin, cadmium, and mercury is used by dentists in filling teeth. When freshly prepared, it is soft enough to be pressed into the tooth cavity, and it hardens in a very short time.

Simple steel is an iron alloy. Do not confuse *alloy steels* with the simple steels containing only carbon. The *alloy steels* have other metals added to them while the *simple steels* are iron-carbon *mixtures.* We have seen that the amount of carbon in steel varies between 0.05 percent to about 2.0 percent depending on whether a soft or a hard steel is desired. Steel that contains no other elements is often called **carbon steel** to distinguish it from the various other steel alloys. The table on page 175 shows the carbon content and uses for several types of carbon steels. (See Fig. 3-34.)

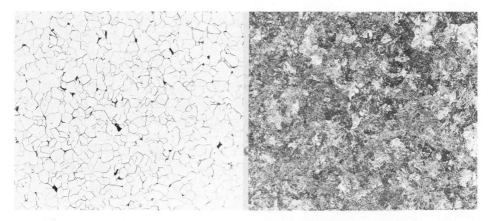

3-34. Steel varies according to the amount of carbon it contains. Photomicrograph on left shows steel containing 0.07 percent carbon. On the right, the sample of steel contains 0.70 percent carbon. (Inland Steel)

Alloy steels. If 2 percent to 4 percent chromium is added to steel, the new steel has great hardness. This *chromium steel* is used for making safes, bank vaults, special tools, and armor plate.

Steel containing about 15 percent manganese is extraordinarily hard and very resistant to wear. Hence, *manganese steel* is used for making railroad-track curves and switches which must take greater shocks than straight sections of track. Jaws of power shovels, grinding machines, rock crushers, and plow points are also made from this kind of alloy steel.

Nickel steels resist penetration and shock. *Molybdenum* (moh-*lib*-dehnum) is a hard, silvery element that has a very high melting point. It makes steel hard and tough. *Molybdenum steel* is used for boilers and valves that operate at a high temperature, for crackshafts of diesel engines, and for automobile axles.

An alloy of low-carbon steel containing about 15 percent or more of chromium is known as *stainless steel*. As you would guess from its name, stainless steel does not rust easily even when attacked by food acids. However, it is a poor conductor of heat, so cook-

Type of Steel	Amount of Carbon	Uses
low-carbon	0.05 to 0.3%	Steel is malleable and can be welded; sheet steel, bridge beams, wire, structural work, and boiler plate.
medium-carbon	0.3 to 0.8%	Piston rods, rails, axles, and projectiles.
high-carbon	0.8 to 2.0%	Lathe tools, axes, drills, springs, and knives.

3-35. Durability and ease of maintenance makes stainless steel an ideal material for industrial tanks. (Eastern Stainless Steel Corp.)

ing pots made from stainless steel are usually coated with copper on the bottom. Why? (See Fig. 3-35.)

New alloys for new uses. New and improved alloys are constantly being developed. For example, improved alloys are being made by melting the metals in a vacuum furnace. The need for materials designed to withstand the heat of exhaust gases of rocket and jet engines, and the heat produced by friction on the metal skin coverings of high-speed missiles and planes, demands the development of new alloys. Atomic-energy furnaces, or reactors, require special alloys, and research in this field is very extensive.

Quick Quiz

1. Why are alloys often used instead of the pure metals?
2. What was the first alloy known to man? How did this probably come about?
3. Name three general classes of alloys.
4. Why do we never use brass pots and pans for cooking?
5. What is monel metal used for? Wood's metal?
6. What metals are used to make solder?
7. Why does type-metal contain antimony?
8. Explain the difference between carbon steel and alloy steel.
9. Name two elements that are added to steel to make it hard and tough.

SUMMARY

Hematite is the principal ore of iron. To obtain the metal, the iron ore, coke, and limestone are fed into a blast furnace. Carbon monoxide from the burning coke reduces the iron oxide of the ore to iron. Limestone unites with the silica impurities to form slag. A blast furnace uses hundreds of tons of charge every day, and its operation is a continuous process.

There are three principal processes by which steel is produced. The Bessemer process burns out the impurities in iron to make steel, but the quality is not very uniform. The open hearth process is widely used and produces batches of good steel in 8 to 12 hours. The electric furnace makes smaller batches of fine-quality steel.

Before a metal can be obtained from a sulfide ore, it is first heated or "roasted" in air, in order to convert the sulfide into an oxide. The oxide can then be reduced with carbon to obtain the metal. Aluminum is extracted from bauxite by means of electrolysis. It is a lustrous, soft metal, about one-third as dense as iron. Active metals such as calcium, sodium, and magnesium are also obtained commercially by electrolysis.

Copper is found both as a native metal and in compounds. Concentrated native copper ore is smelted in a blast furnace, much as iron is. It is finally refined by electrolysis. Some copper is obtained from low-grade sulfide ores by the processes of flotation, roasting, reduction, and refining. The most important commercial use of copper is in the electrical industry.

Silver, a soft lustrous metal, is the best conductor of heat and electricity. Sterling silver has 92.5 percent silver and 7.5 percent copper. Silver reacts with sulfur compounds to form a dark tarnish of silver sulfide. Silver salts are used in photography.

An alloy is a material composed of two or more metals melted together. Some metals mix together in solid solutions, others form metallic compounds, and still others form metallic mixtures. Alloys are used instead of pure metals because they have more desirable characteristics.

All steels are alloys of iron and carbon. Other metals are added to make alloy steels that are harder, tougher, more elastic, or rust-proof, shock-proof, or heat-proof.

CHAPTER REVIEW

Vocabulary

Match the words in Column A with the *best* response in Column B. Do not write in your book.

Column A	Column B
1. native metal	a. process of removing oxygen from oxide ores
2. ore	b. solvent for gold
3. smelting	c. alloy of copper and zinc
4. reducing agent	d. carbon monoxide
5. slag	e. oxide ore of aluminum
6. steel	f. the heating of a sulfide ore in air to convert it
7. tempering	into an oxide
8. roasting	g. property of a metal which enables it to be hammered or rolled into thin sheets
9. bauxite	
10. anode	h. ability of a metal to withstand a stretching force
11. ore-flotation	i. light-sensitive salt
12. reduction	j. metal which is found free in the earth's crust, not combined with another element
13. galena	
14. silver bromide	k. process used to separate certain ores from worthless rock by preferential wetting action
15. malleability	

16. aqua regia
17. alloy
18. bronze
19. brass
20. tensile strength

l. heat treatment of steel
m. mineral from which a metal can be obtained profitably
n. waste product from the smelting of ores -
o. material usually composed of two or more metals
   melted together
p. positive terminal of an electrolytic cell
q. iron containing a carefully regulated amount of
   carbon
r. alloy of copper and tin
s. sulfide ore of lead
t. process of obtaining metals from their ores

Questions: Group A

1. Where in the United States is hematite found in large quantities?
2. Describe the operations of a blast furnace.
3. Explain how a batch of steel is made by the open hearth process. Why is this steel of higher quality than that obtained from a Bessemer converter?
4. How is wrought iron different from steel? What use is made of wrought iron on the commercial market?
5. What is the effect of sudden cooling on hot steel?
6. Why is aluminum not found as a native element?
7. List three important uses for pure copper. What properties of copper make it suitable as an important industrial metal?
8. What are the principal sulfide ores of copper? Oxide and carbonate ores? Where are large deposits of copper ores found?
9. Why is galvanized iron such a useful product? How is it made?
10. Explain the action of a photographic developer. The fixer. Why is the washing step necessary?
11. How is gold leaf made? What are three uses for it?
12. List four steel alloys. What is the essential chemical composition of each? What are several uses of each steel alloy named?
13. What is alnico made of? What are some uses for it?

Questions: Group B

1. Explain why the action of the blast furnace is a good example of an efficient chemical operation.
2. Explain how silica is removed in the steelmaking process.
3. What are some properties of high-carbon steel?
4. Describe how the flotation process is used for concentrating copper sulfide ore.

5. What important generalization can you make concerning all soluble copper, lead, and zinc salts? What precautions would you follow in placing food in containers made of these materials?

6. Are the tarnish coatings on copper, lead, and zinc desirable or undesirable? Explain.

7. Would you expect to find a zinc-lead alloy for sale? Explain.

8. Explain how silver is removed from crude lead in the Parkes process.

9. How would you separate a mixture of gold and silver?

10. List three general properties of alloys which differ from those of the pure metals from which the alloys are made.

11. Why is bronze or babbitt used for bearings?

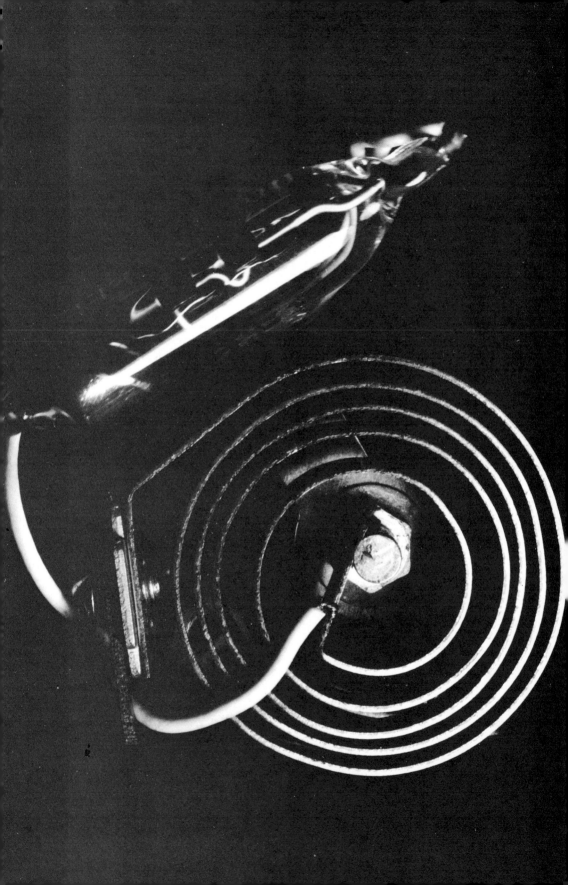

MECHANICS AND MOLECULAR ENERGY

4 MECHANICS AND ENERGY

A FORCE AND MACHINES

The idea of force. In Chapter 1 we defined force as a push or a pull. In this chapter we shall study the nature of forces and relate them to our understanding of machines and to our study of energy.

There are many kinds of force. For example, a moving object exerts a *pushing force* against anything it hits. Think of a fast ball hitting a catcher's mitt, or a bowling ball hitting the pins! Moving objects can also exert a *pulling force*. When a cowboy ropes a running steer, the animal exerts a pulling force against the rope as it is brought to a halt. Meanwhile, the cowboy is also exerting a pulling force against the other end of the rope.

Some combinations of forces just balance each other, and the object upon which they act remains stationary. An unbalanced force acting on an object will increase or decrease its speed or change the direction of motion. Forces may also act so as to change the shape or size of objects.

Frictional forces. The push or pull that is required to keep a box sliding at constant speed along a level floor is a measure of the friction between the box and the floor. The rougher the surface and the heavier the box, the greater will be the *force of friction*. In other words, there is a force which opposes the motion. *Resistance to motion, caused by one surface rubbing against another, is called* **friction.** (See Fig. 4-1.)

4-1. To move the sled, the football player must overcome the friction between the sled and the ground. Why is the coach standing on the sled? (UPI)

Friction can be reduced by smoothing and polishing the surfaces of contact, by lubricating surfaces with grease or oil, or by *rolling* instead of *sliding*. Hence, ball-bearings or roller-bearings are used in such machines as bicycles and automobiles.

Sometimes, of course, we want to increase the frictional forces. When turning a corner, we want plenty of friction between our tires and the road. For a fast stop we also want a lot of friction between the brake linings and the brake drums. Did you know that we could not walk without friction? Can you explain why?

Another kind of friction opposes the motion of an object through a *fluid*, a term used to mean liquids and gases. Examples of fluid friction are wind resistance that acts against your speeding automobile, and the water resistance that slows down your boat when your motor fails or when you stop rowing. The property of a fluid that causes frictional forces when objects move through a fluid is called its *viscosity*. Liquids that pour slowly, such as heavy oils, have a high viscosity.

Gravity is a common force. We have already seen that gravity is the force that pulls objects vertically downward toward the center of the earth, and that the weight of an object is the measure of the earth's gravitational pull upon that object. The more mass that an object has, the more it weighs. For example, a two-cubic-foot block of steel has twice the mass of a one-cubic-foot block, and hence weighs twice as much at the same location on the earth. If someone weighs twice as much as you, his body actually has twice as much material as yours does. You may recall that the farther an ob-

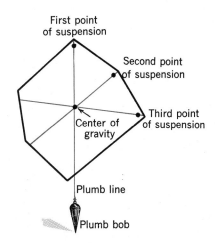

4-2. From this diagram, can you explain how to experimentally determine the center of gravity of a thin, irregular metal plate of uniform thickness? How could you check it?

ject is from the center of the earth, the less it weighs. How is the mass of an object affected by its distance from the center of the earth?

Our muscles are under a constant tension as they resist the pull of gravity on every part of our body. This gives us a feeling of stability and security. When a condition of "weightlessness" exists, as for example when an astronaut is circling the earth in a space capsule, this tension is no longer there.

If an object is supported at its *center of gravity*, it remains in balance when it is placed in any position. *The center of gravity of an object is that point at which all of its weight may be regarded as concentrated.* For uniform objects such as spheres, cubes, and rods, the center of gravity coincides with the geometrical center. (See Fig. 4-2.)

Force is a vector quantity. We cannot completely describe a force by its *magnitude* (amount) alone. To say

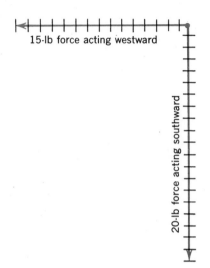

4-3. These two vectors represent two forces acting simultaneously upon the same point at right angles to each other. Using the scale above can you draw, on a separate sheet of paper, a vector of 5 pounds acting northeast?

that a force of 10 pounds acts on an object is not enough. We must know its *direction* as well. We always assume that the force of gravity acts vertically downward. Force is said to be a *vector.* A vector is defined as a quantity which has magnitude and direction. Vector quantities may be represented by an *arrow,* drawn to a convenient scale. The *head* of the arrow indicates the direction of the vector, and the *length* of the arrow, according to some scale, represents the magnitude of the vector.

Suppose we wish to draw a vector to represent a force of 10 pounds acting in an eastward direction. We select a convenient scale, say 1 inch equals 2 lb, and draw a line 5 inches long on a sheet of paper with the arrowhead pointing toward the right, indicating an eastward direction. The

tail of the arrow indicates the point of application of the force. Study Fig. 4-3 to see how a vector of 15 lb acting westward is drawn with one of 20 lb acting southward.

Constructing a force diagram. It is possible to combine the effects of two or more vectors acting simultaneously on a point to give the single *resultant* vector that produces the same effect. This resultant can actually be substituted for the original vectors, and will produce the same effect.

In Fig. 4-4 you see two strings pulling on a spring scale fastened to the top of a board. The strings are pulled at an angle of 90° to each other. Other spring scales show that the pull along **OA** is 6 lb, while the pull along **OB** is 8 lb.

To find the *combined effect* of both pulls, we need to construct a *force diagram* making use of vectors. You may decide to represent the 6-lb pull by making vector **OD** 6 inches long, with a scale of 1 lb equals 1 inch.

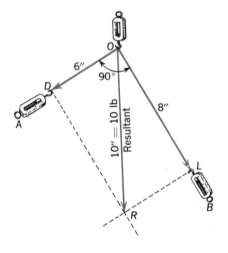

4-4. When the above vectors are added, 6 lb plus 8 lb equals 10 lb.

OL is now made 8 inches in length to represent the 8-lb pull. Now carefully construct a parallelogram on your drawing by making the opposite sides parallel. The *diagonal OR* of the parallelogram is then measured, and the reading of 10 inches on your drawing represents a resultant force of 10 lb, according to the scale used. The spring balance at **O** should read 10 lb also. In other words, the resultant of 10 pounds has the same effect as, and may be used as a substitute for, the 6-lb and 8-lb pulls at 90° to each other. In order to determine the direction, a *protractor* can be used to find angle **DOR** or angle **LOR**.

Visualize the forces acting on a corner post of a wire fence. What might happen to the corner fence post if it were pulled too hard by wires at right angles to each other? Where should a supporting wire be placed to prevent this?

SAMPLE PROBLEM

If *each* wire exerts a 50-lb pull at 90° to each other on a corner fence post, calculate the magnitude and direction of the resultant force.

SOLUTION:

Step 1. By scaled vector diagram. Select a convenient scale, such as 1 cm equals 10 lb. On a sheet of paper, lay out two vectors 5 cm in length, at a 90° angle to each other. Complete the construction of a parallelogram and measure the diagonal. It should be slightly over 7 cm long, representing a force of a little more than 70 lb. A protractor shows that the angle made by this resultant with each force vector is about 45°.

Step 2. By computation. Since the forces act at right angles to each other, the mag-

nitude of this vector can be computed from geometry. The diagonal, or resultant, is the hypotenuse of a right-triangle, and is found by the following formula:

$$(\text{resultant})^2 = (\text{side})^2 + (\text{side})^2$$
$$R^2 \quad = \quad 50^2 + 50^2$$
$$R^2 \quad = \quad 5000$$
$$R \quad = \sqrt{5000} = 70.7 \text{ lb}$$

You can always determine the magnitude and direction of the resultant of any two forces by constructing a force diagram. Can you suggest a method of determining the resultant force for three forces acting simultaneously in a plane on the same point?

Law of moments. As a child, you learned how to balance with a friend on a seesaw. You soon realized that two factors were important: (1) how much you weighed, and (2) how far from the *fulcrum,* or point of support, you sat. A 50-lb child can balance a 100-lb boy by sitting *twice* as far from the fulcrum.

In Fig. 4-5 observe that the product of the force (weight) on the left and the distance from the fulcrum is 200 lb × 2 ft = 400 lb-ft. This *product of a force and the perpendicular distance from the fulcrum is called the moment of force or torque.* The torque to the left of the fulcrum tends to turn the rod in *counterclockwise* motion.

Obviously, if a seesaw is to balance, an *equal clockwise* torque must be present. A force of 100 lb placed at 4 ft to the right of the fulcrum will provide a torque of 400 lb-ft. The rod, or lever, will then be balanced.

If we have two people on the left side of the seesaw, each one's weight times his distance from the fulcrum makes a separate counterclockwise

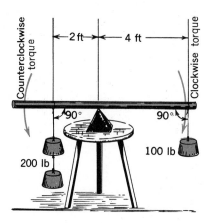

4-5. To prevent rotation on this lever the clockwise moment must equal the counterclockwise moment. Where is the center of gravity of this rod? What effect does it have on producing rotation?

torque. By adding these counterclockwise torques we can compute the total clockwise torque we need on the right side of the seesaw to balance it.

From this illustration and from many similar experiments, we are able to deduce the *law of moments,* which states that in order to prevent rotation of a body or change in rotation, *the sum of the clockwise moments, or torques, about any axis must be equal to the sum of the counterclockwise moments, or torques.*

SAMPLE PROBLEM

A weight of 500 g hangs from a uniform lever 20 cm to the right of its mid-point fulcrum. At the left is a 250-g weight 20 cm from the fulcrum, and a 100-g weight 50 cm from the fulcrum. Is the rod balanced? Explain.

SOLUTION:

Step 1. Be sure to draw a sketch from the data above and indicate the forces and torques involved.

Step 2. Clockwise torque:

500 g × 20 cm = 10,000 g-cm

Step 3. Counterclockwise torques:

250 g × 20 cm = 5,000 g-cm
100 g × 50 cm = 5,000 g-cm
Total   10,000 g-cm

Since the clockwise torque equals the sum of the counterclockwise torques, the lever is balanced. You may wish to check your conclusion in the science laboratory by using a meter stick as a lever with the fulcrum at its mid-point, and known weights.

What are parallel forces? Forces that act either in the same or in opposite direction are called *parallel forces.* A force that pushes straight up, and another force that acts straight down make a pair of parallel forces. The forces shown in Fig. 4-6 are parallel

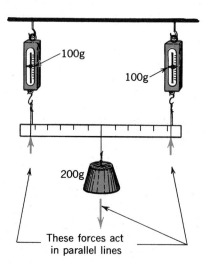

4-6. Parallel forces act either in the same or opposite directions. Notice that the sum of the upward acting forces (100 g + 100 g) equals the downward force (200 g).

forces and we shall make an important engineering application using this concept:

Suppose a 100-ft bridge has a span that weighs 50 tons. Two piers support it as shown in Fig. 4-7. A 5-ton truck, a 20-ton truck, and the weight of the bridge itself make up the load on the two piers. You can see that the two piers must support this entire load by pushing upward. Since the downward forces total 75 tons, the upward forces must also total 75 tons or the bridge will collapse.

If one pier holds 40 tons, the other must push up with a force of 35 tons. This will be the case if the 5-ton truck is 40 ft from the left end, and the 20-ton truck is 65 ft from the same end. You can see why this is so if you think of the bridge as a lever, with one pier acting as the fulcrum, and the other

pier exerting an upward force providing a torque about this same fulcrum. You can then use the law of moments to convince yourself that the sum of the clockwise torques equals the sum of the counterclockwise torques for the bridge to be in equilibrium.

Machines. It is common practice for people to call a simple device, such as a knife or a screwdriver, a *tool*. Possibly, you may think of a machine as being more complicated, such as a typewriter, a bicycle, or a lathe. In science, however, there is no distinction between machines and tools. A knife and a screwdriver are as much machines as are bicycles.

Any device that changes the amount, speed, or direction of a force can be called a machine. Let us discuss each of these three effects. If you pull gently on the rope of a *block and*

4-7. The piers of the bridge must sustain the downward force due to the load and the weight of the bridge. Which pier supports the most weight?

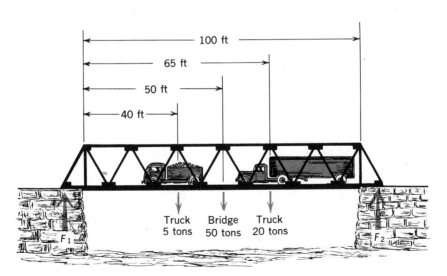

100 ft

65 ft

50 ft

40 ft

Truck 5 tons Bridge 50 tons Truck 20 tons

F_1 F_2

tackle, you can make it lift a heavy weight. Here the *magnitude,* or the amount, of force is changed. When a low speed is applied to the crank of a hand-operated egg beater, the blades turn at a higher rate of *speed* through a set of gears. By pushing *down* on one end of a crowbar, you can pry *up* an object at the other end. In this example, you are changing the *direction* of the force.

You can think of many other situations where machines make work easier. For example, do you get more force, or speed, or a change in direction, or a combination of these, when you (a) push down on a bicycle pedal; (b) press down on the brake pedal of an automobile; (c) push down on the handle of an automobile jack when hoisting a car?

Compound machines. Of all the different machines man has invented, only a few are classed as simple machines. By using specific combinations of simple machines, man has created thousands of compound machines.

Simple machines include the *lever, pulley, inclined plane, wedge, screw,* and *wheel-and-axle.* Not all of these are really different machines. The screw and wedge are just forms of the inclined plane. The wheel-and-axle is really a kind of lever. Gear wheels and hydraulic devices are other simple machines.

A typewriter and an automobile are good examples of a device that is made up of many simple machines. *A compound machine consists of a combination of two or more simple machines.*

The lever. We have seen that a *lever* is essentially a rigid bar that is free to turn about a point where it is supported, like a seesaw. We can ap-

ply the law of moments and parallel forces to all kinds of levers. Let us apply them to the loaded wheelbarrow as shown in Fig. 4-8, which may be considered a form of lever.

The load **W** is placed so that the center of gravity of the wheelbarrow and load combined is 2 ft from the fulcrum **F**. How much *effort* force, **E**, must you exert upward at the handles in order to lift it?

Let's examine the torques about **F** of the parallel forces acting *on* the wheelbarrow. The clockwise torque produced by **W** is equal to 200 lb × 2 ft = 400 lb-ft. The force of effort **E** needed to overcome **W** can be determined by using the fact that the counterclockwise torque of **E** about the same fulcrum is $E \times 5$ ft, and equating the two torques: $5\,E = 400$ lb-ft, or $E = 80$ lb.

With your elbow on the table, raise this book in your hand. You have just used your forearm as a lever. Levers are so common in life that we do not realize how often we use them. Things like shovels, brooms, scissors, nutcrackers, piano keys, and can openers are types of levers.

Mechanical advantage. For any machine, if we divide the weight **W** lifted by the effort **E**, we obtain a number called the *actual mechanical advantage* (**AMA**). This number tells us just how much a machine multiplies the force we put into it. In the above case, W/E equals 200 lb/80 lb = 2.5. This number means that an applied force of 1 lb can counterbalance a force of 2.5 lb.

The mechanical advantage of a machine is sometimes expressed as the ratio of two *distances.* If we divide the distance the effort moves by the distance the weight or resistance moves,

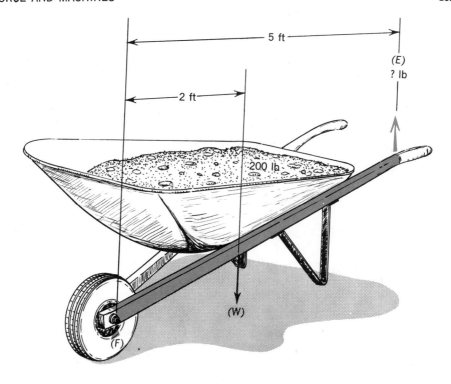

4-8. The wheelbarrow is a machine that may be considered to act as a lever.

we obtain a number called the *ideal mechanical advantage* (**IMA**). This value neglects the effect of friction in the machine. It tells you how many times the machine would multiply the force if there were no friction. Since friction is present in all machines, the **AMA** is always less than **IMA**.

A single pulley changes the direction of a force. A single pulley is a grooved wheel, mounted in a frame or *block*, so that it can turn on its axis. It is much easier to use a mounted (fixed) pulley at the top of a flagpole than to climb the pole to raise the flag. If the flag weighs 10 lb, you still have to pull with a force of 10 lb on the rope plus a small additional force needed to overcome friction in the pulley. With a single *fixed* pulley there is no gain in force or in distance. However, we have changed the direction of the applied force, making it more convenient for us.

A single *movable* pulley is shown in Fig. 4-9. Here the effort *E* acts upward. In this case the direction of the force is not changed. However, a force of 1 lb can lift a weight *W* of 2 lb if friction is neglected. Notice the comparison between the two pulley systems in the diagram.

What do we gain by using a block and tackle? Piano movers may use a block and tackle to raise a piano to a second-story window. Although a small

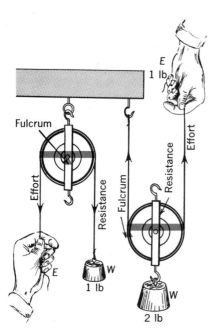

4-9. The mechanical advantage of the single fixed pulley is one (left). Using the law of moments, how does this mechanical advantage compare with that of the movable pulley (right)?

piano may weigh about 400 lb, one man can raise it easily by pulling down on the rope.

A block and tackle is a system of pulleys that is used to raise a heavy weight with a relatively small force. In the pulley system of Fig. 4-10, the weight W is the load we want to raise. Of course, the lower, movable block weighs a few pounds, too, and is really part of the load raised. Note that W hangs from four strands of rope. The total upward force must equal the total downward force of 400 lb. Hence, each of the four strands must support 100 lb. Therefore, the tension, or pull, on the rope, E, must be 100 lb. If friction is considered in this case, a pull of a little over 100 lb will be required

to raise the load of 400 lb on this system.

It is easy to find the ideal mechanical advantage of a block and tackle. All you have to do is to count the *number* of ropes which support the *movable* pulley block. Since there are four ropes that support this block, the IMA is four.

Now if we assume that a force of 125 lb must be applied to actually raise the 400-lb weight, the actual mechanical advantage is 400 lb ÷ 125 lb, or 3.2. Since, when there is no motion, the tension on each rope is 100 lb, you can see that the force of 25 lb is used in overcoming friction caused by the motion.

Input and output work. In science, *work* is the product of force and the distance through which the force acts. While we shall discuss this concept more fully later in this chapter, we need to have some understanding of work in its application to machines.

Machines never give something for nothing. You may be able to lift 400 lb with a block and tackle by exerting a 125-lb pull. But you will soon discover that for every foot that you raise the weight W, you have to pull the effort E through a distance of 4 feet. In other words, what you gain in force, you must lose in distance. The machine makes it more convenient for us but it *does not* do the job with less work. In any machine that makes lifting or moving easier, the smaller effort must be used over a greater distance. This is merely a confirmation of the law of conservation of energy studied earlier in the text.

Work is done only when something is caused to move over a specific distance. The work that is put into the machine is called *input work.* It is equal to the effort *E* times the distance that the effort moves. In case of the block and tackle arrangement above, the input work is 125 lb × 4 ft = 500 ft-lb.

The work that we get out of the machine is called *output work.* It is equal to the weight, or load to be lifted, times the distance that the weight is moved. Here the output work is equal to 400 lb × 1 ft = 400 ft-lb. You can see that we have wasted 100 ft-lb of work (500 ft-lb − 400 ft-lb), or energy, in overcoming friction. Of course, if there were no friction, the input work would be equal to the output work.

All machines waste energy. From our experiences and from scientific experiments, we learn that no machine

works without friction, and friction wastes some energy. The energy used to overcome friction produces heat.

We have seen, therefore, that our block and tackle machine does not operate with perfect *efficiency.* In fact, no machine does. To determine the efficiency of any machine, we compute the ratio of the useful work we get *from* the machine to the work we put *into* it.

$$\text{Efficiency} = \frac{\text{output work}}{\text{input work}} = \frac{\text{AMA}}{\text{IMA}}$$

In this example, the efficiency is 400 ft-lb/500 ft-lb = 4/5, or 80 percent. You can see that if we had a machine having an efficiency of 100 percent, the input work would be equal to the output work, and also the AMA would

4-10. A pulley system consisting of a block and tackle multiplies the force many times.

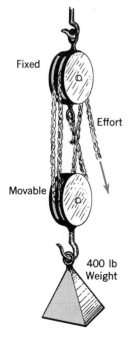

Fixed

Effort

Movable

400 lb
Weight

be equal to the IMA. Of course, a well-lubricated machine wastes less energy and has a higher efficiency than one that is not lubricated.

The wheel-and-axle is a lever. Have you ever tried to open a door with your fingers by turning the rod when the doorknob was missing? If you have, you can appreciate how a doorknob acts as a wheel-and-axle and makes the job easier. The steering wheel of an automobile is another good example. Just a little effort on the rim of the steering wheel is enough to change the direction of the front wheels of the car. The screwdriver and the brace-and-bit are other common examples of the *wheel-and-axle*. From the above examples, you can see that the "wheel" and the "axle" are of different radii and are rigidly connected to each other, so that they move as one piece.

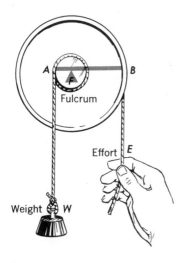

4-11. Observe that the wheel-and-axle is equivalent to a lever with unequal distances from the fulcrum.

From a study of Fig. 4-11 and the law of moments, we see that $W \times AF$ is equal to $E \times BF$. Hence, the actual mechanical advantage of this machine is $W/E = BF/AF$. You know that if frictional forces are neglected, the ideal mechanical advantage and the actual mechanical advantage are equal. Therefore, the ideal mechanical advantage of the wheel-and-axle is simply the ratio of the radius of the wheel to the radius of the axle. We can make the ideal mechanical advantage as great as we wish by using a very large wheel coupled with a very small axle.

The inclined plane. The *inclined plane* is another machine that is often used to lift heavy objects.

Examine Fig. 4-12. Here a force of 25 lb, neglecting friction, is enough to roll a 100-lb load up the plank. Therefore, the actual mechanical advantage, $W/E = 100$ lb/25 lb $= 4$. But also note that we have to use a plank 8 ft long in order to raise our load a vertical distance of 2 ft. Again we see that the 4-time gain in *force* is obtained only by a loss of 4 times in *distance*. In other words, if we raise the weight W a vertical height of 2 ft, our 25-lb effort must move a distance of 8 feet. Can you calculate the input work? The output work?

The ideal mechanical advantage of an inclined plane may be obtained by dividing the length of the plank by its height above the ground, 8 ft/2 ft $= 4$. Of course, when frictional forces are considered, effort E must be greater than 25 lb.

If a road rises 4 ft in a stretch of 100 ft, then it is an inclined plane with an ideal mechanical advantage of 100 ft/4 ft $= 25$. This means that the engine must exert a force equal to 1/25

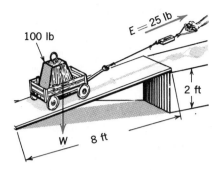

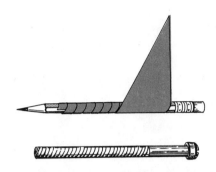

4-12. How can you increase the mechanical advantage of the inclined plane?

4-13. The screw is equivalent to an inclined plane wound on a cylinder.

of the car's weight to climb the grade. This is in addition to the force needed to drive the car on a level road.

A wedge is an inclined plane. It is easy to split a log with a thin *wedge* if we hit the wedge with a heavy hammer. While we speak of a wedge as a simple machine, it is actually only an inclined plane. The thinner the wedge, the easier it is to drive it into a log. This is because it has a higher mechanical advantage.

Wedges operate with a very low efficiency because much of the effort is used up in friction. A knife is a wedge. The sharper the knife, the less our effort becomes in cutting.

The jackscrew raises heavy objects with little effort. It would be hard to lift one end of a car without the help of a machine. Some automobile jacks are examples of the simple machine called the *screw*. From a study of Fig. 4-13, you can see that the screw is essentially an inclined plane wrapped in a spiral around a cylinder.

Cut a piece of paper into a long, right-angle triangle and then wrap it around a pencil. Is this not just like a screw? We get a large mechanical ad-

vantage by using a screw or bolt that has many threads to the inch. This is equivalent to an inclined plane that is very long compared to its height.

The wood screw, threaded bolt, and the bench-vise are applications of the screw that have large mechanical advantages. However, there is so much friction to overcome that the screw has a very low efficiency.

Perpetual-motion machines. The perpetual-motion machine is defined as a machine that will do work with no fuel, or energy input. Of course, no such machine can exist! But it has been a "pipedream" of the ages, and there are always clever quacks trying to dupe the ignorant with devices that are supposed to operate with no fuel. This is a variation of the "something for nothing" philosophy.

The law of conservation of energy is confirmed by the fact that you cannot get more work out of a machine than you put into it. All experimental evidence confirms this far-reaching conservation law. Actually, because of friction between the moving parts of a machine, the output work is always less than the input work.

4-14. The escalator is an example of a moving inclined plane. (Brooks from Monkmeyer)

This does not mean that we can expect no improvement in the efficiency of our machines. Nevertheless, machines which transfer energy (work) will continue to be less than 100 percent efficient.

Be careful not to confuse the perpetual-motion machine with *perpetual motion*.

Quick Quiz

1. Explain how you would find the resultant of two forces, one a force of 20 lb acting east and the other of 5 lb acting on the same point in the same direction. What would be the resultant if they acted in opposite directions?

2. On a separate sheet of paper, draw a force diagram with data contained in Fig. 4-3 and determine the resultant. With a protractor, determine its angular direction from one of the given forces.

3. What are three purposes of a simple machine?

4. What is meant by the actual mechanical advantage of a machine? Efficiency?

5. How do you find the ideal mechanical advantage of a pulley system? Inclined plane? Wheel-and-axle?

6. Explain how torque differs from work, since both are products of force and distance.

7. Discuss what data you would take and what computations you would make to determine the efficiency of a pulley system.

8. How does friction affect the efficiency of a machine?

9. Of the machines discussed in this section, which do you think is the most efficient? Least efficient? Why?

10. Is the making of a perpetual-motion machine a sound idea? Explain.

B MOTION

Force and motion. In our last section we related the idea of force to machines and to the work (energy) transfer that is brought about as a result of motion. Machines do not create energy; they are merely devices which transfer energy. And with frictional forces always present, there is always some loss of energy which we cannot recapture to do useful work.

4-15. The inertia of the coin enables us to flick the card from beneath it as the coin drops into the glass.

In this section we are going to explore the *effect* of force on *motion*. The idea that force can change motion is a valuable one in science because it allows us to *predict* the kind of motion that occurs in a given situation. As we have seen previously, our conclusions as to the behavior of matter must stand the test of close scrutiny of controlled experimentation in the science laboratory.

Newton's first law of motion. Many of the important advances made in the physical sciences during the past 250 years were due to the pioneering work of such scientists as Galileo and Newton. By formulating the famous *three laws of motion,* Newton clarified many points of confusion regarding force and motion. The *first law of motion* states that if an object is at rest, it tends to remain at rest, and if it is moving, it tends to keep on moving at the same speed and in the same direction. Newton gave the name **inertia** *to this tendency of all matter not to change its motion.* You can test the *reasonableness* of this law from the following examples. (See Fig. 4-15.)

If you are standing in the aisle of a bus as it starts suddenly, you tend to fall backward because the inertia of your body has a tendency to keep you where you were (at rest) as your feet move forward with the movement of the bus. Later on, if the moving bus stops suddenly, you tend to move forward because your body continues in a forward motion while the bus stops. Both situations are examples of Newton's first law.

Scientists use the property of inertia as a way of measuring mass. The weight of an object changes as you take it to different places in the universe. However, its inertia and, hence its rest mass, always remains the same. On the moon, an object weighs about one-sixth as much as it does on earth, but its inertia and mass remain unchanged.

If there is too little road friction as your car rounds a curve, it will skid. Because of its inertia, it tends to continue moving straight ahead and skids off the curving road. Do you think it would act the same way when rounding a similar curve on the moon? Would it have the same rest mass and inertia on the moon? Would it weigh the same? Would there be as much friction?

Velocity and acceleration. It is common for "velocity" to be used interchangeably with "speed." Actually, speed and velocity have separate meanings. The *speed* of an object indicates how fast it is moving, and how far the object will travel in a given time interval. It tells us nothing about the direction in which the object is moving.

The term **velocity** includes the *direction* in which the object is moving, as well as its speed. You can now see that velocity is a *vector*, having both magnitude (speed) and direction. And we can make diagrams composed of *velocity vectors* just as we can draw *force vectors*. Therefore, a *change in velocity* could refer to either a change in speed or in direction, or both. We say that the motion of a body is *uniform* when its velocity is *constant*. An automobile going 60 miles/hour along a straight, level road is an example of uniform motion. If the automobile changes its speed or its direction, the velocity is no longer constant, and the motion is no longer uniform.

Only under very unusual circumstances can an automobile be driven at constant velocity. When we change the velocity of an automobile, we accelerate it. You may accelerate your car from 20 mph (miles per hour) to 30 mph by stepping on the gas pedal. That is, you ordinarily think of acceleration as an increase in speed. *But acceleration is any change of motion, either speeding up or slowing down, or changing direction.* You accelerate your car when you round a curve at a steady speed of 30 mph, because you are continuously changing your direc-

tion. **Acceleration** *is also a vector quantity; it is defined as a change in velocity per unit of time.*

SAMPLE PROBLEM

An automobile moving on a straight, level road goes from 35 mph gradually to 45 mph in 5 seconds. What is its acceleration?

SOLUTION:

Step 1. From the definition of acceleration, we may write the formula,

$$a = \frac{v_f - v_i}{t}$$

where a is the acceleration, v_f is the *final* velocity, v_i is the *initial* velocity, and t is the elapsed time.

Step 2. Substituting the data contained in the problem in the above formula,

$$a = \frac{45 \text{ mph} - 35 \text{ mph}}{5 \text{ sec}}$$
$$= 2 \text{ mph/sec}$$

Newton's second law of motion. You have learned about three physical quantities: force, mass, and acceleration. It was Newton who first showed that these quantities are *related* to one another. Experiments show that the amount of acceleration produced depends upon the amount of force applied to an object. If a baseball pitcher wants to throw a fast ball, he must exert a large force on the ball. That is, to give it a greater acceleration, he must apply a greater force.

In a drag-race, cars accelerate from a standing start and try to reach the highest possible speed during a quarter-mile run. No car can win a drag-race unless it has a powerful engine to exert the large force required to give maximum acceleration.

4-16. A powerful engine in a light chassis accelerates easily. (Hot Rod Magazine)

It is easy to see that acceleration is in some way related to the mass of an object. The more mass an object has, the greater the inertia. And, the greater the mass or inertia, the less acceleration you will get from a given force. In other words, a 10-lb force gives a greater acceleration to a baseball than to a bowling ball.

For example, if a car is to win a drag-race, it must not only have a powerful engine but also a fairly lightweight body with little inertia. (See Fig. 4-16.) The same engine in a truck would be a sluggish combination!

We may summarize our statements above by stating that *the acceleration of a body is directly proportional to the net force acting on the body and inversely proportional to its mass*. This is a statement of Newton's second law of motion. Stated as a formula, we have

$$a = k(F/m)$$

where k is a proportionality constant the value of which depends upon the *units* that are used.

Observe that in the above statement of Newton's second law, the term "net" force must be used to determine the acceleration of a body. No matter how hard you push against a stationary locomotive, you cannot accelerate it. Your pushing force is completely neutralized by the frictional forces, and so no *net* or unbalanced force is left to produce the acceleration of the locomotive. Study the data contained in Fig. 4-17. To cause a body to accel-

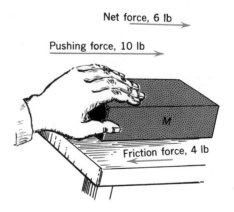

4-17. Acceleration that is produced is proportional to the net force acting on mass M.

erate, we must first overcome the force of friction. Then any additional force will cause it to accelerate. Notice that a net force does not cause motion. It causes *change* in motion, or acceleration.

How quickly can you stop your car? When you apply the brakes of your car, the force of friction acts to slow it down. You can call this kind of acceleration "deceleration," or *negative acceleration.* The information in Fig. 4-18 gives some average values for stopping distance under normal road conditions. Distance traveled during the "reaction time" needed for you to apply your brakes is not included in these figures.

The weight of your car affects the force required to stop it. If your car is twice as heavy as another car, it has twice the mass and needs twice the force to stop it under similar situations. This means more powerful brakes are needed or else the car will travel much farther before it stops.

Notice in the diagram that if the speed is doubled, four times the stopping distance is needed. At 60 mph you are going three times as fast as at 20 mph and it takes nine times the distance to stop (9×22 ft $= 198$ ft). Remember this when you are tempted to drive too fast or too close!

What is Newton's third law? Suppose you place a heavy book on the table. The weight of the book is a *downward* force on the table, and the table top exerts an *upward* and equal force on the book. There is no net force acting on the book, hence the book does not move.

If this does not seem clear to you, imagine that you tried to support the book on a stretched sheet of very thin tissue paper. The paper is too weak to push up on the book with a force equal to the book's weight. Thus, there *will be* a net downward force, and the book will break the paper as it starts to accelerate toward the floor.

In walking across the classroom, you exert a force against the floor with your feet, while the floor exerts an equal and opposite force (friction) against your feet. (See Fig. 4-19.)

4-18. When you apply the brakes on your car going 20 mph, it moves about 22 feet before stopping.

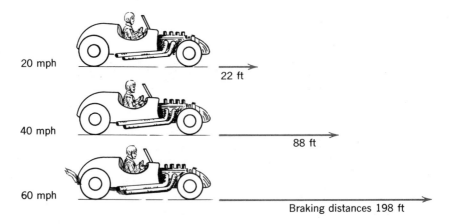

20 mph

22 ft

40 mph

88 ft

60 mph

Braking distances 198 ft

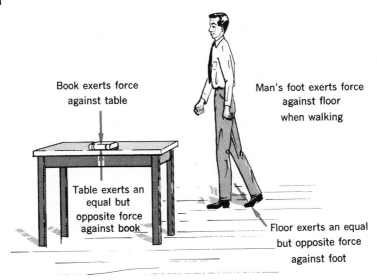

Book exerts force
against table

Man's foot exerts force
against floor
when walking

Table exerts an
equal but
opposite force
against book

Floor exerts an equal
but opposite force
against foot

4-19. Action and reaction are force pairs that apply to two bodies. How can motion occur if action and reaction are equal and opposite?

Imagine that you are standing on a frictionless surface. What would happen when you walk forward? Why?

Observe that in both situations, *two* separate objects are involved in each pair of forces. In the first case, the objects are the book and the table; in the second, the objects are the feet and the floor. In these examples, we may call one force *action* and the equal and opposite force *reaction*. *When one object exerts a force on a second object (action), the second object exerts an equal and opposite force upon the first (reaction).* This is a statement of **Newton's third law** of motion, often called the law of *interaction*.

Momentum. Ever since the early days of jet propulsion, many of you have heard the phrase "action and reaction." Let us suppose that a man and a boy are standing facing each other on a pair of roller skates as shown in Fig. 4-20. They shove each other, and

each moves away from the other in opposite directions. Because the mass of the boy is less than that of the man, the boy moves away with a greater velocity. In this example, if a 75-lb boy shoves a 225-lb man so that the man goes backwards at a velocity of 1 ft/second, the boy will move off in the opposite direction at a velocity of 3 ft/sec. Notice that the product of the mass and the velocity of the boy is exactly equal and opposite the product of the mass and the velocity of the man. This quantity of motion is called *momentum. The momentum of a body is the product of its mass and velocity* ($M \times V$).

Why does a gun kick? The sharp recoil when a gun is fired is another good example of an application of Newton's law of motion. This time the action and reaction are between the bullet and the gun. The rapidly expanding gas in the exploding shell

4-20. In the above situation, the momentum (action) of the boy is equal and opposite to the momentum of the man (reaction).

pushes equally on each, thus giving the bullet momentum in one direction and the gun equal momentum in the other. In other words, the momentum of the bullet $(M_b \times V_b)$ equals the momentum of the gun $(M_g \times V_g)$. If any three of these four quantities are known, we can determine the fourth.

SAMPLE PROBLEM

A gun having a mass of 5000 g fires a 5-gram-mass bullet at a speed of 1000 meters/sec. Find the recoil velocity of the gun.

SOLUTION:

Step 1. Substitute the given quantities in the equation,

$$M_g \times V_g = M_b \times V_b$$

$M_g = 5000 \text{ g};\ M_b = 5 \text{ g}$

$V_g = \quad ?\quad ;\ V_b = 1000 \text{ m/sec}$

$(5000 \text{ g}) \times V_g = (5 \text{ g}) \times (1000 \text{ m/sec})$

Step 2. Solve for V_g in this equation.

$$V_g = \frac{(5 \text{ g}) \times (1000 \text{ m/sec})}{(5000 \text{ g})}$$

$$= 1 \text{ m/sec}$$

Conservation of momentum. In our examples we have considered momentum in one dimension, in a straight line. This was done for simplicity. Momentum, like force, velocity, and acceleration, is a vector quantity. The direction of momentum of an object is the same as the direction of the velocity of the object. Scientists draw *mo-*

mentum vector diagrams in much the same manner that you have constructed force vector diagrams.

Let us reconsider our gun-firing problem above. Since the gun and the bullet were at rest with respect to each other *before* the shot was fired, the total momentum of the gun and the bullet was zero. This was so because the velocity of each was zero, and the mass times zero equals zero. Now consider the situation *after* firing the shot. If we arbitrarily call the momentum of the bullet *positive,* and the recoil momentum *negative,* the total momentum after firing adds up to zero. In other words, the *total* momentum is the same (zero) both before and after the shell exploded. This example illustrates the law of *conservation of momentum.* This law is one of the great cornerstones of science.

Other examples of momentum changes. The propulsion of jet planes and rockets is an illustration of Newton's third law. Remember that action and reaction must take place between two *different* masses. The jet plane or rocket itself is one mass, and the exhaust gas fired from the rear is the other mass. Think of the rocket as a gun firing bullets (high-speed molecules), and the forward thrust it receives as being like the recoil of a gun. At present the only known way of powering or controlling space flight is by this reaction principle. (See Fig. 4-21.)

When you row a boat, the oars give a mass of water some momentum toward the rear. The reaction gives your boat an equal forward momentum. If you leap for shore from the front of a rowboat, the boat will be kicked back with as much momentum

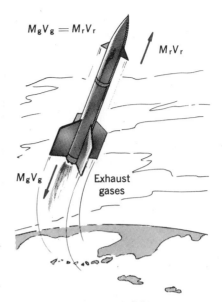

4-21. When the conservation of momentum is considered, the momentum of the gas (M_gV_g) equals the momentum gained by the rocket (M_rV_r).

as your body develops going forward. If you are using a lightweight boat, you are apt to land in the water! Would you experience the same fate if you were to leap for shore from a large ship? Why?

The rotary water sprinkler furnishes another good example of the reaction principle. The jet of water comes from the nozzle with a certain momentum, and hence the nozzle is given the same "kick" in the opposite direction. The spinning nozzle sprays the water in a circular pattern. (See Fig. 4-22.)

The law of gravitation. Sir Isaac Newton, the brilliant English scientist, made many important discoveries during the 17th century. One great contribution was that of the *law of universal gravitation,* in which Newton concluded that *every mass in the universe exerts a force of attraction on*

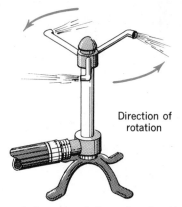

Direction of rotation

4-22. If the rate of flow of water through the nozzle were to increase, what would happen to the speed of the sprinkler head?

every other mass. The "weight" of objects near the earth is just one example of this force between bodies that acts in a similar manner throughout the whole universe.

This important generalization further concludes that *the greater the masses, the greater the force between them.* For example, if the earth had twice its present mass, but the same size, everything on it would weigh twice as much. A 1000-lb mass on the surface of the earth is attracted toward the center of the earth by twice as much force as a 500-lb mass.

Further, *the closer the two masses are to each other, the greater is the gravitational force between them.* Experiments show that the *force varies inversely as the square of the distance between the centers of the masses.* This means that if the distance is reduced to *half* as much, the force then becomes *four* times as great. If the two masses are only one-third as far apart, the force is 9 times as great.

Right now you are about 4000 miles from the center of the earth. At 4000

miles above the surface, you would be twice as far from its center, hence, would weigh one-fourth as much as you do now. Study Fig. 4-23.

Can you predict whether the man's weight would increase or decrease if a hole were bored into the earth toward the center to a depth of 1000 miles and the man placed in this hole? Explain. Would his mass increase or decrease?

Everything weighs a little more at the poles than it does at the equator. One reason for this is that the earth is slightly flattened at the poles. Hence, objects at the poles are closer to the center and weigh more.

Force fields. A mass such as the earth or sun produces a gravitational *field* in the space around it. This field, in turn, exerts a force on all masses located within it. Each field can be imagined as a set of vectors showing both magnitude and direction of forces acting on objects in the field. This field is strong near the central mass and rapidly weakens at greater distances from the centers, in accordance with the law of universal gravitation. All masses in the universe are affected by the fields of all other masses in the universe.

The moon does not fly away from the earth as it swings through space because it is "caught" in the gravitational field of the earth. Similarly, the earth is held in its orbit around the sun because the tremendous gravitational field of the sun extends far out into space. A rocket is not free of the earth until it has entered another field that is stronger than that of the earth.

Gravitation, like other forces, is mutual. That is, the pull between two masses is the same in each direction. For example, not only does the earth attract the moon but the moon also attracts the earth. This mutual attraction accounts for the tides, about which you will learn in a later chapter.

Fields are also produced by electricity and by magnetism. Scientists find that the concept of fields is a fruitful model that is used extensively in their work.

4-23. The weight (force) of a man decreases as his distance from the center of the earth increases.

Objects near the earth fall with uniform acceleration. Galileo, the great Italian scientist, was one of the first to experiment with falling objects. He made measurements on the time it took for a metal ball to roll down a groove cut into a sloping plank. He found that the ball gained a definite amount of *additional* speed each second that it rolled. In other words, the ball was *uniformly accelerated* as it rolled toward the ground.

With improved equipment, scientists have accurately studied the motion of objects as they fall freely, straight down toward the ground. By the *end* of the first second, objects have picked up a speed of 32 ft/sec. At the *end* of two seconds, they fall at a speed of 64 ft/sec. From this information, you can calculate the acceleration produced. Hence, *the acceleration of a freely falling object is 32 ft/sec per second.* What is the speed of a falling object at the end of three seconds? Four seconds?

This acceleration, caused by the gravitational field of the earth, is called *one g.* For objects near the earth's surface, g equals 32 ft/sec per second. An acceleration of 5 g's, therefore, means a change in velocity of 160 ft/sec per second (5 × 32).

At the start of its fall, an object has a speed of zero. After falling for one second, its speed is 32 ft/sec. Therefore, the *average speed* during the *first* second of fall must be (0 + 32 ft/sec) ÷ 2, or 16 ft/sec. (How do you find the average of two test grades of 70 and 90?) Because the object moved at an average speed of 16 ft/sec for one second, it must have fallen 16 feet. If the object falls for two seconds, its final velocity will be 64 ft/sec (It gains 32 ft/sec each second). The average between its initial speed (0) and its final speed (64) is $(0 + 64) \div 2 = 32$ ft/sec. If an object travels at an average speed of 32 ft/sec for 2 seconds, it will go a distance of (2×32), or 64 ft. Notice that an object falls four times as far in two seconds as it does in one second $(64 \text{ ft} \div 16 \text{ ft} = 4)$. Notice also that when the time is doubled (2 sec instead of 1 sec), the distance covered is the *square* of the time change. That is, the distance becomes 2^2, or 4 times as much (64 ft instead of 16 ft).

Galileo observed that this was a general rule. That is, if the time of fall is tripled (3x), the distance covered will be 3^2, or 9 times as much. From his experiments, he derived the law that the distance covered in uniformly accelerated motion depends on the *square of the time* of fall. Hence, to find how far an object will fall, we square the number of seconds that it falls and multiply this by 16. The *general* formula for this motion is

$$s = \frac{1}{2}at^2$$

where s is the space or distance covered, a is the acceleration, and t the time of fall.

SAMPLE PROBLEM

An object starts from rest and falls freely under the force of gravity. (a) What is its velocity at the end of 5 seconds? (b) What is its average velocity during the fall? (c) What distance has it fallen during this time?

SOLUTION: (a)

Step 1. Given: acceleration due to the force of gravity is 32 ft/sec/second; initial velocity is 0, time is 5 seconds, and $v_f = ?$

Step 2. The above quantities are related by the formula,

$$a = \frac{v_f - v_i}{t}$$

Step 3. Substituting given quantities and solving for v_f,

$$32 \text{ ft/sec/sec} = \frac{v_f - 0}{5 \text{ sec}}$$
$$v_f = 160 \text{ ft/sec}$$

SOLUTION: (b)
Step 1. Given:

$$v_f = 160 \text{ ft/sec}, \ v_i = 0.$$

Step 2. Average velocity is

$$v_a = \frac{v_f + v_i}{2}$$

Step 3. Substituting,

$$v_a = \frac{160 \text{ ft/sec} + 0 \text{ ft/sec}}{2}$$
$$= 80 \text{ ft/sec}$$

SOLUTION: (c)
Step 1. Use the general formula for distance,

$$s = \frac{1}{2}at^2$$

Step 2. Substitute known or given values,

$$s = \frac{1}{2} \times (32 \text{ ft/sec/sec}) \times (5 \text{ sec})^2$$
$$= 400 \text{ ft}$$

Air resistance. You may have noticed that all things do not fall at the same speed. A pillow certainly falls more slowly than a stone. The reason, of course, is that *air resistance* (friction) slows down the bulky pillow more than it does the stone.

In solving the sample problem above, we have neglected the effect of air friction on the falling object in order to simplify our calculations. Hence, our results are only approximately correct. In a vacuum, there is no air and therefore no air resistance

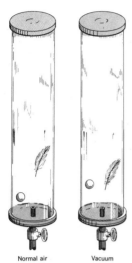

Normal air   Vacuum

4-24. In a vacuum, a feather and a steel ball fall with the same velocity.

to slow down some objects more than others. Figure 4-24 demonstrates that in a vacuum falling objects accelerate at the same rate.

If a parachutist jumps from a high-flying plane and delays opening his parachute, he rapidly picks up speed as he falls. But the faster he falls, the greater the air friction becomes. Eventually, the upward force of the air against him becomes equal to the downward force of gravity; that is, equal to his own weight. Now there is no *unbalanced* force acting on him and so, there is no further acceleration. He then continues to fall at a constant velocity which is called **terminal velocity.** (See Fig. 4-25.) This speed may be as great as 150 mph, depending on his bulkiness. An open parachute simply increases the wind resistance on the system, so that a parachutist reaches his terminal velocity more rapidly, at a lower and safer speed.

Centripetal and centrifugal forces. In order to whirl a stone around on the

4-25. When the opposing forces of gravity and wind resistance (friction) are equal, the parachutist's speed of fall does not change. (US Dept. of Defense)

end of a string, you must keep pulling on the string. (See Fig. 4-26.) This *inward* pull must be applied in order to pull the stone from its normal straight-line motion. This force is called **centripetal** (sen-*trip*-ih-tul) *force.* The amount of centripetal force that is needed depends on the mass of the stone, its speed of travel, and the radius of the circle.

$$F = \frac{m \cdot v^2}{r}$$

The *outward* pull that you feel the whirling stone exert on you is called

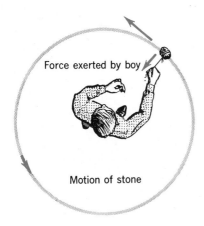

4-26. A force must be exerted inward to keep the stone moving in a circular path. What happens if the string breaks? Why?

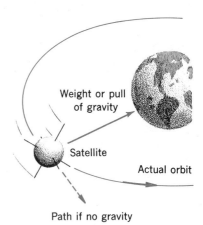

4-27. The gravitational force between earth and satellite provides centripetal force that keeps the satellite from flying into space.

the **centrifugal** (sen-*trif*-you-gal) **force.** This force is the result of the stone's inertia, since a body in motion tends to continue in motion in a straight line. Centrifugal force is simply the *inertial* reaction of the stone to being pulled out of the straight-line path. If the string breaks, you are no longer exerting an inward, or centripetal force. The centrifugal force disappears at the same instant and the stone resumes its straight-line motion in the direction in which it was moving when the string broke.

Hence, centrifugal force is always precisely equal and opposite to the centripetal force. Since it is only the inertial reaction to centripetal force, it appears and disappears when centripetal force appears and disappears.

The orbits of satellites. Our moon, a natural satellite, and *artificial satellites* circle the earth like the stone on the end of the string. What *pulls* them into their orbits? Why doesn't their inertia cause them to fly off into space in a straight line? The answer is that

the earth's gravitational field furnishes the centripetal, or inward-acting force that continually pulls them into a curved path. (See Fig. 4-27.)

No matter what the satellite speed is, there is a certain distance from the earth where the gravitational pull is suitable for maintaining it in an orbit. A satellite close to the earth's surface must be going at high speed, or else the strong pull of gravity will curve it too sharply and it will fall to the earth. The earth pulls more gently on a distant satellite, curving it less from its straight-line tendency. Hence, it moves more slowly in a large orbit, far from the earth. For example, the moon travels at only 2200 miles per hour at a distance of 240,000 miles.

Spinning produces interesting effects. The earth and other planets bulge at their equators because of their spin. The equator is about 13 miles farther away from the earth's center than the poles are. This is one reason why objects weigh less at the equator as we have seen previously. There is still another reason for this. As the earth spins, the inertia of objects tends to "throw" them off the earth, especially at the equator. In fact, if the earth rotated about 17 times as fast as it now does, loose objects at the equator would leave the earth and go into orbit!

When a grindstone spins too fast, it may fly apart. The cement that holds the grains together is no longer strong enough to supply the centripetal force needed to pull them into a curved path.

A device that separates substances by spinning them at high speeds is called a *centrifuge* (*sen*-trih-fewj). It may be used to separate a liquid from a solid, as in a "spin-dry" washing machine. Solids such as sugar are washed and partly dried by being centrifuged. Sometimes a centrifuge is used to separate mixtures of liquids. For example, by spinning whole milk in a cream separator, we separate the less dense cream from the skim milk. In testing samples of blood, petroleum, and other liquids, centrifuging is a routine laboratory procedure.

The recent development of very high-speed machines, called *ultra-centrifuges,* has increased their usefulness. One kind of centrifuge has attained a speed of 2,500,000 revolutions per minute. (See Fig. 4-28.)

4-28. The pilot enters the gondola on the rotor arm of a giant human centrifuge which will subject him to conditions of stress similar to those he will encounter in rocket flight. The technician in the control room controls the speed of the centrifuge and records the pilot's body reactions. (US Dept. of Defense)

Quick Quiz

1. Give two reasons why things weigh more at the poles than at the equator.
2. Why would you weigh less on the moon than on the earth?
3. What is universal gravitation?
4. Define inertia and give three examples.
5. What is acceleration? What causes it?
6. State Newton's second law of motion. Give an example.
7. What is momentum? What is the momentum of an object at rest?
8. If you double the net force acting on an object, how is its acceleration affected?
9. How much *extra* speed do falling bodies pick up each second?
10. If you drive four times as fast, what happens to the distance needed for stopping your car?
11. What happens to the acceleration if the mass is tripled while the force remains the same?
12. Would the acceleration of a falling object 100 miles above the earth's surface be more or less than 32 ft/sec per second? Explain.
13. What three factors determine the magnitude of the centripetal force acting on a rotating body?
14. Newton's third law of motion involves two objects and two forces. Explain what this means in terms of action and reaction.

C BEHAVIOR OF MATTER

What is elasticity? In previous sections we have seen how the concepts of force and energy are related to describing the operation of machines, and how forces cause change in the motion of matter or have a tendency to do so. We have learned that force, velocity, acceleration, and momentum are vector quantities. In this section we shall continue our study of the behavior of matter under the influence of forces.

When the opposite ends of a spiral steel spring are pulled apart, the applied force makes the spring longer. If the force is increased, the spring stretches farther. When the force is released, the spring snaps back to its original position. The property of matter that enables it to *return to its original shape* after being distorted by a force is called **elasticity.**

If the spring is stretched too far, it will *not* come back to its original position. At this point the material is permanently distorted. We say that it has stretched beyond its **elastic limit.** *Up to the elastic limit,* the steel spring returns to its original shape when the force is removed. Beyond this limit, it does not.

Because steel is almost perfectly elastic, it returns to its original position when the stretching force is removed. Experiments show that steel is even better than rubber in this respect. Steel is also more elastic than rubber in that it takes more force to *distort* steel, and the steel pulls back to its original shape with more force. However, rubber is more **resilient** (ree-zil-ih-yent) than steel. That is, it can be stretched *farther* without going beyond its elastic limit.

On the other hand, substances like putty or molding clay are *inelastic.* They do not regain their original shape when a distorting force is removed.

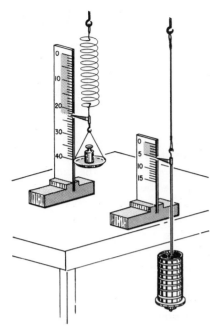

Total weight, W, on spring, grams	Length, L, total stretch of spring, centimeters
0	0.0
100	1.5
200	3.0
300	4.5
400	6.0
500	8.1
600	10.7

4-29. Equal weights added to the spring (left) cause it to stretch by equal amounts. If weights stretch the wire (right) to its elastic limit, the pointer will not return to zero when weights are removed.

Spring scales make use of the elastic properties of matter. Kitchen and bathroom scales make use of the elasticity of coiled steel springs. When a spiral spring is suspended by one end and a small weight is hung from the other, the spring will increase in length by a certain amount. When another equal weight is added, the total stretch of the spring is doubled. When still another equal weight is added, the total stretch becomes three times the original stretch, and so on. Study Fig. 4-29 and table of experimental data at the top of this page.

Observe from the table that during the early part of the experiment, the increase in length is the same for every 100 grams added to the end of the spring. However, the 500-g and 600-g weights exceeded the elastic limit of the spring. When the weights were removed the spring did not return to its original position, and the spring became *permanently* distorted. The *data* provided by the table can be summarized more conveniently in the graph shown in Fig. 4-30.

The elastic property of solids applies to other forces than stretching and to other objects and materials than springs. It describes the *compression* of bridge piles, the *bending* of steel building beams, and the *twisting* of drive shafts.

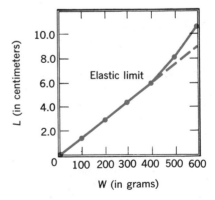

4-30. The spring does not stretch with regularity beyond the elastic limit.

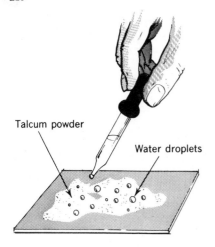

Talcum powder

Water droplets

4-31. Cohesion causes the water to form spherical droplets.

What is cohesion? Dust some talc on a piece of paper. Then drop a little water on the powder with a medicine dropper. The water forms small droplets, that do not wet the paper. The attraction of the water molecules for each other draws them together in a ball. (See Fig. 4-31.)

This tendency of similar molecules to cling to one another is called cohesion (co-*hee*-zhun). The strength of a steel wire, for example, is due to the great force of cohesion that is exerted between its adjacent molecules.

When you drop mercury on a table top, it forms spherical droplets because of the great cohesive force existing between the molecules of mercury. The force of cohesion between liquid molecules is not nearly as great as the cohesion in solids. But it does, nevertheless, account for some interesting properties in liquids.

Adhesion is a force also. Glue and paste display *adhesion* when they stick to wood or paper. *The attraction be-*

tween unlike molecules of two substances for each other is described as adhesion. You can really feel the force of adhesion when you pull an adhesive bandage off your skin.

When you take your hands out of water, some of the water clings to your skin by adhesion. Yet if you put your finger into mercury, no mercury clings to it. This is because the force of attraction between the molecules of mercury (cohesion) is greater than the force of attraction between the mercury and your skin (adhesion).

Surface tension. Cohesion between molecules on the surface of a liquid produces an interesting effect. Since molecules *within* the liquid are attracted by other molecules equally in *all* directions, they undergo no net pull. But the molecules at the surface are attracted only by the molecules *below* and *at the sides,* as shown by the force vectors in Fig. 4-32. This combined effect produces a drawing together of the molecules at the surface of the liquid, causing the liquid to act as if it has a thin elastic surface "film." We call this effect *surface tension.*

To illustrate this effect, carefully pour water into a glass until the liquid rises above the rim. If you continue

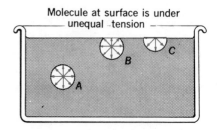

Molecule at surface is under unequal tension

4-32. The unbalanced downward force on the molecules near the liquid surface causes surface tension.

Capillary tubes

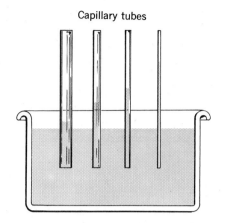

Mercury is depressed

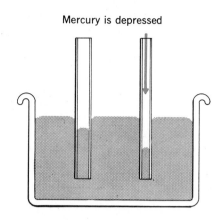

4-33. The height of the water in the capillary tubes of smaller diameter is greater. Adhesion and surface tension produce the concave surface.

4-34. The level of mercury in the tubes is below that of the outside surface. Why is the mercury surface in the tubes convex?

to add water, the surface tension is finally overcome and the thin elastic "film" will break, allowing the water to overflow.

Mercury shows this property even more strikingly, and it may pile up as much as a quarter of an inch before it runs over the edge of the container.

Capillary action. Have you ever wondered why blotting paper soaks up ink, or a bath towel soaks up water? Have you ever observed the rising of water in hollow tubes of small diameter? It does this by *capillary action.* The word *capillary* comes from the Latin word for "hair," and capillary action occurs in fine hair-like tubes.

When one end of an open glass tube of very small inner diameter is dipped into water, water rises a considerable distance in the tube. The forces of *adhesion* and *surface tension* are both acting in capillary action.

The height of the water in the capillary tubes depends upon the diameter. The smaller the diameter of the tube, the higher the water rises. (See Fig. 4-33.) Many other liquids are similar to water in this respect.

Some liquids, such as mercury, have much stronger cohesion than adhesion. This is illustrated by the fact that these liquids do not "wet" the surface of glass. The surface tension of the mercury now depresses its level in a capillary tube *below* the level of the mercury outside the tube. (See Fig. 4-34.)

Surface tension and capillary action occur all around us. Capillary action aids in lifting water in plants by bringing ground water up into the roots, and by lifting the sap to the stem and leaves.

If the soil is tightly packed, much of the moisture comes to the surface by capillary action and is evaporated. Soil around plants that is loosely packed will experience less capillary action (because the spaces within it are larger), and hence moisture is held in the ground longer.

You can illustrate this by covering one end of a lump of sugar with a little powdered sugar. When the lower end is dipped slightly into ink, you can see the ink rise in the lump, but it is stopped or slowed down when it reaches the loose powdered sugar on top of the lump. The loose particles reduce the capillary action.

We have seen that soapless cleaners are efficient because they lower the surface tension of water. The lower surface tension permits water to spread out better, penetrating underneath the dirt and grease, making cleaning easier. Even towels absorb water from our bodies by capillary action.

What is pressure? You find it much easier to cut meat with a sharp knife than with the side of your fork. Even though you apply the same *force* in both cases, the *pressure* applied on the

meat by the knife is much greater than that applied by the fork. The knife edge has much less area pressing on the meat than does the side of the fork. *The force acting upon a unit area of surface is called* **pressure.** To obtain the pressure against any sur-face, we *divide the force by the area* upon which the force acts. Study the following sample problem.

SAMPLE PROBLEM

A rectangular block of wood that weighs 3600 grams is placed on a table as shown in Fig. 4-35. Find the pressure exerted on the table top when the block is placed in each position: **A, B,** and **C.**

SOLUTION:

Case A. The area of the surface of the brick in contact with the table is,

$$(10 \text{ cm}) \times (20 \text{ cm}) = 200 \text{ cm}^2$$

4-35. The pressure on the table depends on the position of the blocks. In each position the force (weight) is the same but the pressure varies.

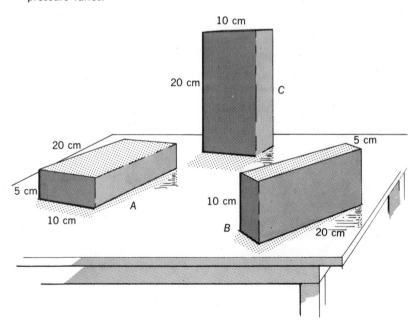

Since pressure is force acting on a unit area, we substitute our values given,

$$Pressure = \frac{force}{area} = \frac{3600 \text{ g}}{200 \text{ cm}^2}$$
$$= 18 \text{ g/cm}^2$$

Case B. The area of contact is

$$(5 \text{ cm}) \times (20 \text{ cm}) = 100 \text{ cm}^2$$

Therefore, the pressure is

$$\frac{3600 \text{ g}}{100 \text{ cm}^2} = 36 \text{ g/cm}^2$$

Case C. The area of contact is

$$(5 \text{ cm}) \times (10 \text{ cm}) = 50 \text{ cm}^2$$

The pressure now becomes,

$$\frac{3600 \text{ g}}{50 \text{ cm}^2} = 72 \text{ g/cm}^2$$

Observe in the above problem that although the weight or force against the table top, remains the *same* in each position, the *pressure* becomes four times as much in position **C** as in position **A**. You can readily see that the pressure can be increased by *increasing* the force applied or by *decreasing* the area of contact.

Liquids also exert pressure. Just as air pushes down on the surface of the ground because of its weight, water also pushes down on the bottom of a river bed or a water tank. Since water is denser than air, it exerts a greater pressure.

Many communities have water tanks or standpipes to provide needed pressure for the water supply system. Let us see how we can find the pressure of water for any depth of the liquid. Suppose that a city has a cylindrical standpipe 100 ft high with a bottom that is 500 ft² in area. This means that the tank holds $(500 \text{ ft}^2) \times (100 \text{ ft}) = 50,000 \text{ ft}^3$ of water.

The density of fresh water is experimentally determined to be 62.4 lb/ft³. Therefore, the water in the tank will weigh $(50,000 \text{ ft}^3) \times (62.4 \text{ lb/ft}^3)$, or 3,120,000 lb. Of course, this weight of water, or force, is distributed evenly over the entire bottom. Since the circular bottom has an area of 500 ft², the pressure on the bottom is force/area, or $(3,120,000 \text{ lb}) \div (500 \text{ ft}^2) = 6240 \text{ lb/ft}^2$. This means that *each square foot* on the bottom of the 100-ft-high tower has a force of 6240 lb pressing upon it.

We can also calculate the pressure exerted by a liquid by a method that is more convenient than that used in the above example. The *pressure* exerted by liquids is merely the product of its *height* and its *density*. Since the tank in our example contained a vertical water column 100 ft high, the pressure at the bottom is determined as follows: *pressure = height × density* = 100 ft × 62.4 lb/ft³ = 6240 lb/ft². This is precisely the value we obtained before.

What is the pressure in pounds per square inch (lb/in.²) in our problem above? You will remember that there are 144 square inches (in.²) in one square foot (ft²).

SAMPLE PROBLEM

A column of water is 25 ft high. What is the pressure of the water at the bottom of the column?

SOLUTION:

Step 1. **Pressure = height × density**

Step 2. Substituting known and given values,

$$Pressure = (25 \text{ ft}) \times (62.4 \text{ lb/ft}^3)$$
$$= 1560 \text{ lb/ft}^2$$

There are 144 in.² in 1 ft². If we want to find the pressure in lb/in.², we could write,

$$\frac{1560 \text{ lb}}{1 \text{ ft}^2} = \frac{1560 \text{ lb}}{144 \text{ in.}^2} = 10.8 \text{ lb/in.}^2$$

SAMPLE PROBLEM

A column of mercury is 10 cm high. What is the pressure of the mercury on the bottom of the column? The density of mercury is 13.6 g/cm³.

SOLUTION:

Step 1. **Pressure = height × density**

Step 2. Substituting known data,

Pressure = (10 cm) × (13.6 g/cm³)
= 136 g/cm²

How does the pressure of the mercury compare with the pressure exerted by a column of water of the same height? How many times denser than water is mercury?

A standpipe or water tank is usually constructed on top of a hill in order to take advantage of the greater height of the liquid column. For the same reason, the tank is kept almost full at all times.

The pressure at any particular tap or faucet in the community depends on the *difference* between the height of the water surface in the standpipe and the faucet. The lower down in the building the faucet is located, the higher is the pressure that it has. A faucet in the basement of a building delivers water with more force than one located on the top floor.

Pressure acts in all directions. Liquids do not push only against the bottom of a tank. Their molecules slide

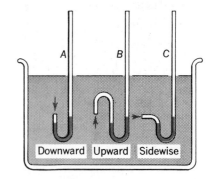

Downward   Upward   Sidewise

4-36. For a given depth, the pressure is the same in all directions.

over one another quite easily. Pressure against the molecules below the surface of a liquid is distributed to nearby molecules *equally* in all directions. (Study Fig. 4-36.)

If you pull the plug out of a small hole in the side of a barrel filled with water, the water will spurt out due to a sideward pressure. The downward pressure of the water above the outlet causes the sidewise pressure, and is equal to it. The sideward pressure is equal to the downward pressure at any point. Sides of deep tanks are made extra strong near the bottom because of this.

If you push the bottom of a drinking glass down into water, you will feel the upward push of the water against the bottom of the glass. The deeper you push it, the greater the upward force the water exerts on it.

Liquid pressure is independent of the shape of the vessel. Figure 4-37 shows four various-shaped vessels connected by a horizontal pipe, and the whole apparatus filled with water. The water illustrates the old saying, "water seeks its own level." Let us see why this is so.

Water level the same in each vessel

4-37. The pressure at the bottom of each vessel is independent of the shape of the vessel.

In general liquid flow in a horizontal pipe is due to *difference in pressure,* the flow always being from a point of high pressure to that of low pressure. Since the liquid is not flowing along the horizontal tube, the pressure must be the same throughout its length.

Observe that the vertical height of the water in each vessel is the same. This means that the pressure in the tube under each vessel must also be the same. You have already learned that the pressure depends on the depth of the liquid. If the water level in one vessel were lower than in the others, the pressure below would be less also. Water would then flow from the other vessels through the horizontal pipe towards this spot of low pressure. The water would be forced up in the vessel above this point until all levels were equal.

Pressure on dams. Before building a dam, engineers calculate the total force of water that will press against its face. To do this, they compute the pressure half-way down from the surface, called *average pressure.* This average pressure multiplied by the area

of the whole face of the dam gives the total force exerted against it by the water.

Curiously enough, the length of the lake backed up by the dam has no effect on this force. That is, the force is the same whether the lake is 100 miles long or only 1 mile long. The push against the dam depends only on the size of the dam and the depth of water at the face of the dam.

Of course, dams and other structures are always built so that they are strong enough to resist a force several times greater than that expected. *The ratio between the force that a structure can withstand to the force that is expected is called the factor of safety.* For example, if a dam is five times as strong as the calculations require it to be, we say that the factor of safety is five.

What is Pascal's law? We have seen that an increase in depth increases the pressure of a liquid in an open vessel. Let us now consider the effect of extra pressure applied to a liquid in a *confined* space.

You may have experienced how easy it is to smash a liquid-filled jug by striking a sharp blow on the stopper. The principle that explains this was discovered over 300 years ago by the French scientist, Pascal. *Pascal's law states that pressure applied to a confined fluid acts equally in all directions.* Let us investigate this generalization further.

When you apply a pressure of 10 lb/in.² to the stopper of the confined liquid shown in Fig. 4-38, *each* square inch of the jug is pushed out with an *added* force of 10 lb. If the area of the surface of the jug is 250 in.², a force of 250 in.² × 10 lb/in.², or 2500 lb, pushes outward on its inner surface. This force is great enough to shatter the glass jug.

Hydraulic devices are applications of Pascal's law. The word *hydraulic* refers to any device that operates by applying pressure to a liquid, just as *pneumatic* (nu-*mat*-ik) devices are operated by a compressed gas. Hydraulic and pneumatic machines have multiplied man's strength tremendously.

For example, a hydraulic press has two pistons. The pressure, or force acting on each square inch, is the *same* for both pistons. However, one piston is much larger than the other. Therefore, the *total force* acting on the larger piston will be much greater than that acting on the smaller piston. This is so because the total force is equal to the *area* times the pressure.

If the smaller piston shown in Fig. 4-39 has an area of 1 in.^{2}, and the other an area of 100 in.^{2}, a downward force of 1 lb on the smaller piston produces an upward force of 100 lb (1 lb/in.^{2} × 100 in.^{2} = 100 lb) on the larger piston. Now if you apply a 100 lb push to the smaller piston, you will then obtain a force of 10,000 lb (100 lb/in.^{2} × 100 in.^{2}) against the larger one. In other words, with this device you can support a force of 10,000 lb by exerting a force of 100 lb. What is the mechanical advantage of this machine? Would the kind of liquid used—water, oil, or alcohol—make any difference?

SAMPLE PROBLEM

In a hydraulic press, the smaller piston has an area of 0.5 in.^{2} and the larger one an area of 80 in.^{2} What force must be

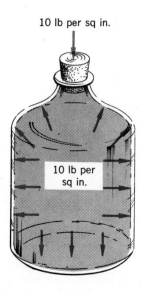

10 lb per sq in.

10 lb per sq in.

4-38. A pressure of 10 lb/in.^{2} applied to the stopper of a jug filled with a liquid causes an additional force of 10 lb to act on every square inch of the jug.

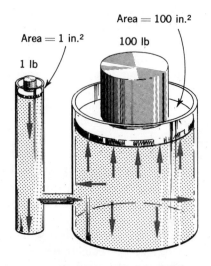

Area = 100 in.^{2}

Area = 1 in.^{2} 100 lb

1 lb

4-39. A one-pound weight placed on the small piston (left) having a cross-sectional area of 1 in.^{2} will support a one-hundred-pound weight when placed on the large piston with a cross-sectional area of 100 in.^{2}

applied to the small piston to balance a force of 2400 lb acting on the larger one?

SOLUTION:

Step 1. Since the pressure equals force divided by the area, the pressure on the larger piston is,

$$= \frac{2400 \text{ lb}}{80 \text{ in.}^2}$$

$$= 30 \text{ lb/in.}^2$$

According to *Pascal's law*, this is also the pressure on the small piston.

Step 2. The area of the small piston is 0.5 in.² and the pressure is 30 lb/in.² Therefore,

$$\textbf{\textit{Force}} = \textbf{\textit{area}} \times \textbf{\textit{pressure}}$$
$$= 0.5 \text{ in.}^2 \times 30 \text{ lb/in.}^2$$
$$= 15 \text{ lb}$$

Notice that a force of 15 lb acting on a piston having an area of 0.5 in.² will balance a force of 2400 lb acting on an area of 80 in.²

Hydraulic machines are used in many industries where huge forces are required. These include hydraulic presses for baling cotton, extracting oils from seeds, shaping automobile bodies (Fig. 4-40), punching holes in steel plates and molding articles from plastics. Hydraulic brakes on automobiles and airplanes, automobile lifts used in service stations, and barber chairs are other applications of Pascal's principle.

Fluids push up on objects immersed in them. When a piece of cork is dropped into water, it quickly bobs up to the surface. Some upward force must have pushed it to the surface. *This upward force that fluids exert on objects immersed in them is called buoyancy.* Remember that by fluids, we mean both liquids and gases.

4-40. The hydraulic press is used in forming automobile bodies. (American Iron and Steel Institute)

You have probably noticed that it is easier to lift a heavy object when it is under water than when it is in the air. This is due to the buoyant force exerted by the water, as you can see by doing the following experiment.

Weigh a glass stopper or some other small, dense object on a platform balance. Then tie a cord around it and hang it under the balance so that it is under water. (See Fig. 4-41.) Weigh the object again while it is in the water. Suppose that the object weighs 100 grams in air, but only 75 grams when submerged in water. By subtracting, you can readily see that its *apparent* loss of weight, or buoyant force, is 25 grams.

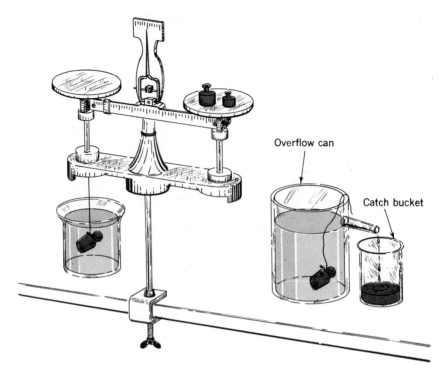

4-41. The apparent loss of weight of the glass stopper (left) is equal to the weight of an equal volume of water (right).

Next, lower the same object carefully into an overflow can that is brimful of water. The overflow goes into the catch bucket. If you know the weight of the empty catch bucket, and you weigh it again with the water overflow, you can find the weight of water that was displaced by the object. If this experiment is done carefully, you will find that 25 grams of water is displaced. From many such experiments, we conclude that *the apparent loss of weight of the object is equal to the weight of liquid displaced.*

Similar experiments were performed by the Greek scientist Archimedes (ahr-kih-*mee*-deez) more than 2000 years ago. He discovered the now famous law which is called Archimedes'

principle—"an object immersed in a fluid is pushed up with a force that equals the weight of the displaced fluid." Buoyancy is the name we give to the force that pushes an object up and makes it *seem* to lose weight in the fluid.

Why do some objects float in a liquid? Archimedes' principle applies to objects that float in a fluid as well as to objects that sink. If you push a wooden block under water and then let go, it bobs up to the surface and floats. This is because the buoyant force on the submerged block is *greater* than the weight of the block, and the net force acts on the block to move it *upward* to the surface. If you do the same experiment with a piece of iron of the same size, it sinks to the bottom. In this case, although the buoyant force is as much as before, it is less than the weight of the iron, and the net force is in a *downward* direction. *Hence, an object floats in a liquid only if its weight is less than that of an equal volume of the liquid, and sinks if it weighs more.* In other words, if the density of the object is less than that of the liquid, it floats; if the density of the object is greater than that of the liquid, it sinks.

When you put equal-sized cubes of balsa, cork, maple, and ice in water, they all float. (See Fig. 4-42.) Notice, however, that some cubes have greater amounts above the water than others. The greater the density of the floating object, the more liquid must be displaced, and the deeper it sinks in the liquid. *A floating object sinks deep enough to displace a weight of liquid equal to its own weight.*

Let us check the last statement by a simple demonstration. Weigh a wooden block on a platform balance. Then lower it into an overflow can, as shown in the previous experiment. Next weigh the water that overflows in the catch bucket. Note that *the weight of the block is equal to the weight of the water that overflows.* Can you explain what would happen to a block if its density were the same as the liquid it was placed in?

We may repeat the above experiment using a less dense liquid such as kerosene or alcohol. The block sinks deeper in a liquid of lower density. Remember that the weight of the displaced liquid must equal the weight of the block. Of course, it takes more of the lighter liquid to equal the weight of the block.

4-42. The weight of the liquid displaced is equal to the weight of the object in each of the samples.

Balloons and submarines are applications of Archimedes' principle. A balloon rises in the atmosphere if the weight of the air displaced by the balloon is greater than the balloon's weight. This then provides a net upward force causing the balloon to ascend. Hence, balloons are filled with a light gas such as hydrogen or helium. A balloon rises by throwing out *ballast.* It descends by letting out gas, or by compressing the gas in a container, thus reducing its *size.* When a balloon becomes smaller in size, it displaces less air and the buoyancy decreases.

A submarine dives by taking in sea water, becoming heavier. It rises by blowing out the water, becoming lighter. We say that a ship has a displacement of 40,000 tons, meaning that it weighs 40,000 tons, and, when floating, displaces an amount of water equal to 40,000 tons.

Specific gravity. The number that indicates the weight of a substance compared with the weight of an equal volume of water is known as the *specific gravity* of the substance. In other words, *specific gravity is the weight of an object divided by the weight of an equal volume of water.* This figure tells us how many times *denser* a substance is than water.

Specific gravities of substances are determined experimentally in the laboratory. The table below gives the specific gravities of some common substances.

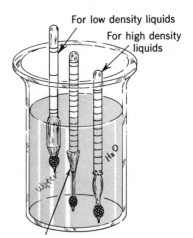

For low density liquids

For high density liquids

H_2O

For low or high density liquids

4-43. Hydrometers are used to measure the specific gravities of liquids.

TABLE OF SPECIFIC GRAVITIES

Butter	0.87	Human body	1.07
Copper	8.9	Ice	0.92
Cork	0.25	Lead	11.3
Diamond	3.5	Mercury	13.6
Gasoline	0.7	Wood (oak)	0.85
Gold	19.3	Wood (pine)	0.5

Can you use the information contained in the above table to determine which substances will float in water? Sink in water? Give reasons for your answers.

The easiest way to find the specific gravity of a liquid is to use a floating device called a **hydrometer** (hy-*drom*-uh-ter). Hydrometers are hollow glass instruments weighted at the lower end so that they float upright. They sink until they displace their own weight of the liquid. Hence, they sink deeper in liquids of lesser density. You read the specific gravity directly from the scale on the stem of the hydrometer. (See. Fig. 4-43.)

Many industries, such as those producing gasolines, salts, sugars, and soaps make constant use of specific gravity determinations for quality control purposes. The chemist may use it to help identify a substance or to de-

termine its purity. Service station workers use hydrometers to check the concentration of anti-freeze in the radiators of cars and of the sulfuric acid in the storage cells of automobile batteries. Physicians often test the specific gravity of body fluids.

Air pressure. We mentioned that we live at the bottom of an ocean of air, made up of a mixture of gases. A cubic foot of air weighs little, only about 1.25 ounces. However, the air in an average classroom weighs several hundred pounds. Because of its huge volume, the total weight of the whole atmosphere is many billions of tons. This weight of air exerts a pressure of 14.7 lb/in.² at sea level. And it will support a column of mercury 760 mm high. To investigate the fact that air exerts pressure, let us do the following experiment in the laboratory.

Tie a thin rubber membrane over a glass bell jar that has an opening at the bottom for a tube from a vacuum pump. As the air is pumped out of the jar, the rubber is forced by the pressure of the atmosphere farther and farther down into the glass. This pressure may be great enough to break the membrane.

At the start, the upward pressure of the air in the glass balances the downward pressure of the air above the membrane. But when we remove the air inside the vessel, there is less pressure under the membrane and the atmosphere pushes the upper surface. This principle explains your ability to drink through a soda straw, as shown in Fig. 4-44.

Barometers measure air pressure. We measure atmospheric pressure by means of an instrument called a *barometer*. An Italian scientist, Torricelli, devised a barometer over 300 years ago.

He took a glass tube about 3 feet long, closed one end, and filled it with mercury. He put his thumb over the open end and turned the tube over

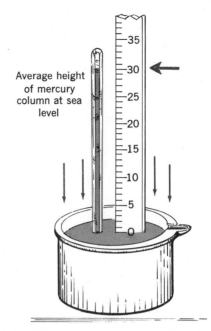

4-45. The average pressure of the atmosphere at sea level can support a column of mercury 30 inches high.

4-44. When you reduce the air pressure within the straw by the action of your cheeks and lips, the higher air pressure outside then forces the liquid up through the straw into your mouth.

so that its open end dipped below the surface of some mercury in a dish. When he took his thumb away, mercury ran out of the tube until the mercury stood at a height of 760 mm, or about 30 inches. (See Fig. 4-45.)

The pressure of the atmosphere on the surface of the mercury in the dish is enough to support the weight of this column of mercury. If it were not so, the mercury would run out of the tube. The mercury column exerts a pressure that is equal to the pressure of the atmosphere at a particular location.

If we do this experiment on a high mountain top, the column of mercury will be less than 760 mm high. A mountain top is not as deep in the ocean of air as a valley is, and there is less air above to push down on it.

The atmospheric pressure varies from day to day at the same location.

Pressure changes bring about weather conditions that we shall study later in the text.

A relationship exists between the pressure of a gas and its volume. Let us examine a relationship between the pressure and the volume of a confined gas. Suppose a gas is placed in a cylinder with a movable piston as shown in Fig. 4-46. Let us call the original volume occupied by the gas, V_1, and its corresponding pressure, P_1. When the pressure on the piston is *increased* to a new pressure, P_2, its new volume is *decreased* to a value, V_2. If we continued this investigation, we would obtain a set of readings such as that shown in the table below.

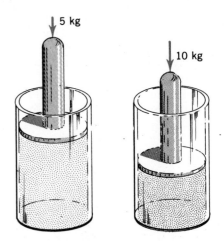

4-46. The volume of a gas decreases as the pressure increases, providing the temperature remains the same. How does the increase in pressure affect the density of the gas?

Pressure P ($lb/in.^2$)	Volume V (ft^3)	Pressure × Volume $P \times V$ = constant
15	12	180
30	6	180
45	4	180
60	3	180
90	2	180
180	1	180

Numerous experiments with confined gases have shown that *for any gas the pressure multiplied by its corresponding volume is a constant, providing the temperature remains unchanged.* This may be expressed by the following formula,

$$P_1 \times V_1 = P_2 \times V_2$$

This relationship allows us to calculate any of the above quantities providing the other three quantities are known or can be determined. This relationship was discovered many years ago by Robert Boyle, a British scientist, and is called **Boyle's law.** A graph of the above table may be useful for many purposes and is plotted as Fig. 4-47.

SAMPLE PROBLEM

When 300 in.³ of a gas under a pressure of 15 lb/in.² is compressed to a volume of 20 in.³, what will be its new pressure? Assume no change in temperature.

SOLUTION:

Step 1. Given:

$$P_1 = 15 \text{ lb/in.}^2$$
$$V_1 = 300 \text{ in.}^3$$
$$P_2 = ?$$
$$V_2 = 20 \text{ in.}^3$$

Step 2. From Boyle's law,

$$P_1 \times V_1 = P_2 \times V_2, \text{ or}$$
$$P_2 = \frac{P_1 \times V_1}{V_2}$$

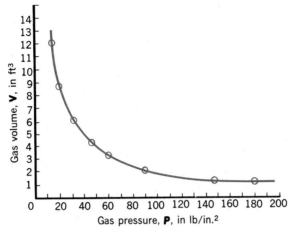

4-47. Graph showing a plot of data contained on page 222. When the pressure is 110 lb/in.², what is the volume of this sample of gas?

Step 3. Substituting,

$$P_2 = \frac{15 \text{ lb/in.}^2 \times 300 \text{ in.}^3}{20 \text{ in.}^3}$$

$$= 225 \text{ lb/in.}^2$$

You can see that when a particular mass of gas is subjected to greater and greater pressures, its molecules are crowded closer and closer together, decreasing the volume. What effect does the increase in pressure have on the *density* of the gas in the cylinder?

Quick Quiz

1. How does the resiliency of steel compare with that of rubber?
2. What is elasticity? Is all matter elastic? Explain.
3. Cohesion and adhesion are forces between molecules. What is the difference between them?
4. Why does mercury not "wet" your finger?
5. Explain why it is possible for a needle or a razor blade to float on a water surface even though the density of steel is much greater than that of water.
6. How does the height of water vary with the diameter of a capillary tube?
7. What happens to mercury in a capillary tube?
8. Is the pressure at the bottom of a tank filled with gasoline as great as if the tank were filled with water? Why?
9. How could you show that there is a sideward pressure against the inside of a barrel filled with a liquid?
10. How can a small force on one piston of a hydraulic press produce such a large force on the other piston?
11. Why does a piece of iron float in mercury? Why does a piece of iron sink in water?
12. Does Archimedes' principle apply both to gases and liquids? Give examples.
13. What is a convenient way of finding the specific gravity of a liquid?
14. Why doesn't the mercury run out of the open lower end of a barometer tube?
15. Does Boyle's law apply to liquids as well as gases? Explain.

D WORK, POWER, AND ENERGY

The meaning of work. The idea of *work* was introduced previously when we considered the use of machines to transfer energy. In this section we shall explore this concept further.

The term *work* has a somewhat more restricted meaning in science than it does in everyday life. In a scientific sense, **work is the result of a force moving an object a certain distance.** For example, when you lift a one-pound weight vertically a distance of one foot, you do one foot-pound of work. (See Fig. 4-48.) Thus, raising a ten-pound weight one foot in a similar manner would require ten foot-pounds of work. Further, when you raise the same ten pounds a distance of ten feet, you would do one hundred foot-pounds of work. *Work is determined by mul-* tiplying *the force by the distance through which the force acts,* or

$$W = f \times d$$

where **W** is the work accomplished, **f** is the force applied, and **d** is the distance the object moves under the influence of this force. It is important to remember that the force used must be in the *direction of motion.* We do no work when a force acts perpendicular to the direction of motion. By this definition, observe that if the force acting upon an object does not move it, *no work is done.* This would be the case if you pushed against a strong brick wall and no motion resulted.

It takes work to raise water to a high reservoir. This water, in turn, by dropping through a large pipe, can do work by turning the blades of a water wheel or *turbine.* In this manner mechanical energy or work can be transformed into electrical energy. Thus, when a million pounds of water 100 ft above a water wheel is allowed to fall, the water can do 100 million foot-pounds of work, part of which can be converted to electrical energy. *Work is essentially a measure of energy transfer.*

SAMPLE PROBLEM

A trunk weighing 150 lb rests on a floor. How much work is done when it requires a horizontal force of 45 lb to drag the trunk a distance of 20 ft? (See Fig. 4-49.)

SOLUTION:

Step 1. Remember that only the force acting in the same direction that the trunk moves can be used in calculating the work. Hence,

Work = force × distance

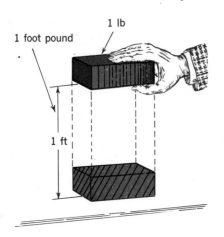

4-48. The foot-pound (ft-lb) is a unit of work. It is the work done in overcoming a resistance of one pound through a distance of one foot.

Step 2. Substituting,

$$Work = 45 \text{ lb} \times 20 \text{ ft}$$
$$= 900 \text{ ft-lb}$$

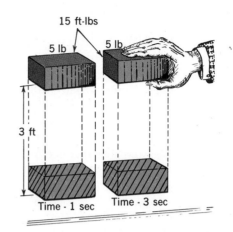

What would be the work done if the trunk were lifted vertically a distance of 20 ft?

What is power? The amount of work done on an object does not tell us how long it takes to do the job. For example, we do the *same* amount of work in dragging the trunk 20 feet whether it takes us 10 seconds, one minute, or one day to complete the task.

The rate at which work is done is called power. The greater the amount of work to be done in a given time, the greater the power required. When 100 ft-lb of work is done in 5 seconds, the power is 100 ft-lb ÷ 5 seconds, or 20 ft-lb/sec. On the other hand, if the same work is accomplished in 25 seconds, the power required is now 4 ft-lb/sec. (See Fig. 4-50.)

We see that power depends on three factors: (1) the force applied, (2) the distance through which the

4-50. It takes more power to do 15 ft-lbs of work in one second than it does in three seconds.

force acts, and (3) the time required. In formula form we have,

$$Power = \frac{f \times d}{t}$$

You have heard the term *horsepower* used frequently in connection with the ratings of engines. *One horsepower is equal to 550 ft-lb of work done in one second.* If an engine is

4-49. A force of 45 pounds moves this 150-lb trunk a distance of 20 feet. How much work is done?

Work = distance × force
Work done = 900 ft-lb

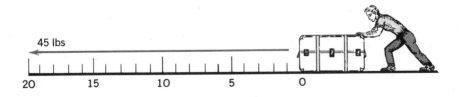

rated at *two* horsepower, it is capable of doing 1100 ft-lb of work in one second (2×550). At this rate, how many foot-pounds per minute are equivalent to one horsepower?

Other units of power that are used frequently are the *watt* and the *kilowatt*. One horsepower equals 746 watts or 0.746 kilowatt (since 1 kw = 1000 w). It is useful to remember that one horsepower equals about ¾ kilowatt. For example, a 250-watt light bulb uses about ⅓ horsepower.

SAMPLE PROBLEM

A horizontal force of 110 lb is required to move an object across the floor a distance of 20 ft in 8 seconds. (a) What is the work done; (b) the power required; (c) the horsepower; and (d) the kilowatt requirement?

SOLUTION:

(a) **Work** = **force** × **distance**
$$= 110 \text{ lb} \times 20 \text{ ft}$$
$$= 2200 \text{ ft-lb}$$

(b) **Power** $= \dfrac{work}{time}$

$$= \dfrac{2200 \text{ ft-lb}}{8 \text{ sec}}$$

$$= 275 \text{ ft-lb/sec}$$

(c) One horsepower equals 550 ft-lb/sec. Therefore, 275 ft-lb/sec equals 275/550, or 0.5 horsepower.

(d) Since one horsepower equals 0.75 kilowatt, 0.5 horsepower equals 0.5×0.75, or 0.375 kilowatt.

Falling water provides energy. You may have seen water pouring over the top of a dam or a spillway. Do you know that the water that spills over the dam or goes through the spillway does not do any useful work? Only the water that turns the turbine wheels provides the work.

In colonial days, water power was used to turn the millstones that ground the grain into flour. Dams held back the water and made mill ponds. Water was led from the pond through a trough to a water wheel. The turning water wheel performed the necessary work to grind the grain.

Large volumes of falling water can provide tremendous amounts of energy. This energy may be used to generate electricity which, in turn, does work. At Niagara Falls, for example, part of the water goes over the falls and part of it is channeled off to run the turbines.

From points above the falls, some of the water is directed through a large channel around the falls to a basin located at the top of the gorge. Next, the water drops about 200 ft through large pipes, called *penstocks*, to the water turbines, as shown in Fig. 4-51. These turbines are modern versions of old-fashioned water wheels. They are located at the foot of the slope, just above the level of the water in the river below the falls.

Turbines develop much energy. The fixed blades in the turbine case direct the water from the penstocks against the movable blades of the *turbine rotor* at the proper angles to insure the greatest amount of impact. The shaft of the turbine is coupled to the rotor of an *electric generator*. (See Fig. 4-52.) The huge turbines at Niagara Falls each develop about 70,000 horsepower. Such power, obtained from falling water, is called *hydroelectric power*.

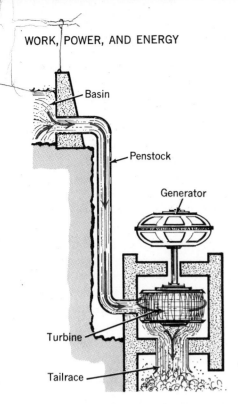

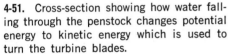

4-51. Cross-section showing how water falling through the penstock changes potential energy to kinetic energy which is used to turn the turbine blades.

4-52. A 500-ton rotor of a turbine generator is shown being lowered into position in the Niagara Power Project. (Westinghouse)

Electric power is generated on both the American and Canadian sides of Niagara Falls. The cost of electric power in this region is low because it was not necessary to build an expensive dam to do the job.

Dams are designed for various purposes. Dams are designed and built for many reasons. Whenever feasible many purposes are served by one dam. The following are the major purposes considered in building a dam at a particular location: (1) the *control of floods* below the dam; (2) *irrigation* of agricultural lands in areas of low rainfall; (3) the control of soil *erosion*; (4) the development of *hydroelectric power* for homes and industries in the area; (5) the improvement of *navigation* fa-

cilities; (6) the *supply of fresh water* for cities and towns; and (7) recreation and the preservation of wildlife. Although very costly, dams are worthwhile, especially when they serve more than one purpose. Large cities must have enough water, and a dam may be necessary to hold back water in a reservoir to meet the year-round needs of the community.

Many cities in river valleys have severe floods when the rainfall is excessive or when excessive winter snow melts in the springtime. Dams help control these rivers and prevent the flooding of many areas below the dam by holding back some of the water and allowing for a slower rate of discharge. Artificial lakes created by dams often provide excellent recreational facilities for nearby communities.

Millions of acres of unused land would grow food if adequately irrigated. Dams help to provide large volumes of water for the timely irrigation of such "wasted" land areas.

Dam construction requires many skills. The design and the building of a large dam is a huge project requiring many skills and extending over several years. Engineers make a survey of the site before construction of a dam. Geologists make a study of the rock formation and assist the engineers in determining a suitable site for the dam. Special cost and feasibility studies are also undertaken by teams of scientists and economists.

Survey teams bore down to the bedrock, for the dam must be anchored on solid rock under the river bed. Otherwise, the water pressure at the base would cause the water to seep under the dam. Lands for the lakesite must also be purchased, and special roads must be constructed. Often whole communities must be relocated.

Water of the stream or river must first be channeled away from the construction site. In the construction of Hoover Dam, long tunnels were drilled through the canyon walls. A small temporary dam diverted the river through these tunnels while the dam was built.

When the river bed was exposed, workers dug a trench across it right down to the bedrock and were ready to begin construction. Many engineering and scientific problems were met and solved before Hoover Dam was completed. Lake Mead, behind Hoover Dam, is 115 miles long. It is the largest artificial lake—by volume—in the world. (See Fig. 4-53.)

Materials for building dams. Today, our highest dams are made of concrete. They may be arched in a curve as shown in Fig. 4-53, or they may have a straight wall across the river as shown in Fig. 4-54. Some multiple-arch dams have been constructed when the span across the river gap was especially long.

Arched dams are stronger than straight-wall dams. This fact is illustrated by bending a piece of light cardboard into a curve. When you press against the convex side of the card with your finger, you will notice that it does not "give" as easily as a straight piece of cardboard. Why do you suppose the outside curve of arch dams is always pointed upstream?

Some dams are made of earth with a concrete core to add strength, as shown in Fig. 4-55. These dams are called *earth-fill* dams. Observe in the

4-53. Hoover Dam, on the Colorado River between Arizona and Nevada, is 726 feet high, the highest dam in the western hemisphere. It is of multiple-arch design. (Bureau of Reclamation, Dept. of the Interior)

diagram that dams are wider at the base than at the top. There are two main reasons for this: it makes them more *stable,* and it provides added strength for the increased pressure acting at the base of the dam. The maximum water pressure at the base of Hoover Dam is 45,000 lb/ft².

Grand Coulee Dam is the largest. Most of the world's largest concrete dams have been constructed in the United States. The Grand Coulee Dam in the State of Washington is one of the biggest single structures made by man. This dam harnesses the Columbia River and has a fivefold purpose: (1) irrigation, (2) flood control, (3) hydroelectric power, (4) improvement of navigation and streamflow regulation, and (5) recreation. The 22-million-ton Grand Coulee Dam as shown in Fig. 4-54 is a "gravity dam"; that is, it depends upon its weight alone to prevent water pressure on its upstream face from tipping it over, or causing it to slide downstream.

Aswan High Dam, across the Nile River in Africa, is scheduled to be completed in 1970. The dam, over two miles long at the top, will produce more hydroelectric power than Grand Coulee. The lake backed up behind the dam is expected to be about 300 miles long and 16 miles wide in places. This engineering masterpiece will be capable of storing an entire year's flow of the Nile and holding sufficient irrigation water to compensate for three successive years of drought.

What is potential energy? Mechanical energy can be stored and called upon for later use. The water held back by a dam, for example, is capable of doing work on the turbines as it falls through the penstocks. Similarly, as the

4-54. Grand Coulee Dam on the Columbia River is a multiple-purpose dam. The turbines are at the foot of the panels at each end of the dam. (Bureau of Reclamation, Dept. of the Interior)

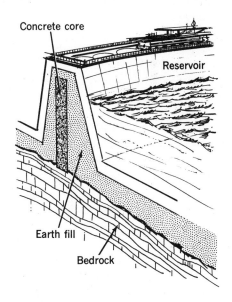

4-55. Diagram of a cross-section of an earth dam showing a concrete core. Why is the dam thicker at the bottom?

wound-up mainspring of a clock un-coils, the stored or *potential energy* in the spring is released and does work on the gears of the clock.

When we raise a heavy object from the floor to the table, we do work *on* the object. This object now has poten-tial energy because it is capable of doing work on some other object as it falls to the floor. The potential energy acquired by a body equals the work done on the body to place it in posi-tion. (See Fig. 4-56.)

We can calculate the work done on an object against the force of gravity by multiplying its *weight* (force) by the *height* (distance) of the object above some convenient reference level. *Potential energy is stored energy, or energy that an object has because of its position or condition.* From our defini-tion, we can see that a stick of dyna-mite has potential energy because it can do work as it explodes. A lump of coal has potential energy because it can give off heat, a form of energy. In other words, *chemical energy* is a form of potential energy.

SAMPLE PROBLEM

What is the potential energy of a block which weighs 55 lb, when placed on a ladder 10 feet from the ground?

SOLUTION:

Step 1.

  Potential energy = weight × height

Step 2. Substituting given values in the above formula,

  Potential energy = 55 lb × 10 ft
  = 550 ft-lb

120 ft-lb of potential energy

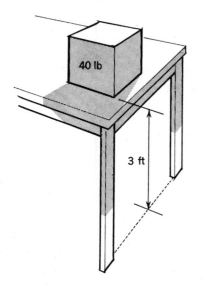

4-56. The 40-lb block raised 3 ft above the floor acquires 120 ft-lb of potential energy. How much kinetic energy does the block have in this position?

A second type of mechanical energy is *kinetic energy*. A moving automo-bile, or a speeding rifle bullet are ex-amples of bodies having **kinetic energy,** or *energy of motion*.

What does kinetic energy depend upon? Let us suppose that we have two automobiles moving in a straight line down the road. If the speeds of the two automobiles are the same, the car hav-ing the *greater mass* has the *greater amount of kinetic energy*. This is so be-cause the heavier car is capable of do-ing more work. If this car hits a parked car, for example, it can push it farther. We say, therefore, that at identical speeds the object with the greater mass has the greater amount of kinetic en-ergy because it is capable of doing more work.

Now let us suppose that two automobiles having the same mass are moving in a straight line down the road. The car moving at the *greater speed* will have the *greater amount of kinetic energy*. As a matter of fact, the kinetic energy rises rapidly as the speed increases, varying as the *square* of its speed. For example, at 3 times the speed, a car has 9 times as much kinetic energy. You can now see that *the kinetic energy of an object depends upon its mass and also on the square of its speed.*

The following formula is used to find the kinetic energy of a body.

$$\textit{Kinetic energy} = \frac{w \times v^2}{2 \times g}$$

If *w* is the weight of the object in pounds, *v* the speed in ft/sec, and *g* the acceleration due to gravity or 32 ft/sec per second, the kinetic energy will be expressed in foot-pounds.

SAMPLE PROBLEM

Find the kinetic energy of a bullet weighing 0.15 lb if its speed of flight is 2000 ft/sec.

SOLUTION:

Step 1.

$$\textit{Kinetic energy} = \frac{(\text{weight}) \times (\text{speed})^2}{2 \times g}$$

Step 2. Substituting,

$$\textit{Kinetic energy} = \frac{(0.15 \text{ lb}) \times (2000 \text{ ft/sec})^2}{2 \times 32 \text{ ft/sec}^2}$$
$$= 9375 \text{ ft-lb}$$

Energy can be changed from one kind to another. We have seen that water behind a dam contains potential energy because of its height above the downstream portion of the river. As this water falls down the penstocks, it increases its speed, thus gaining in kinetic energy. When the water hits the bottom, its potential energy has been changed to kinetic energy. The water is moving with high speed as it strikes the turbine blades.

Suppose a boy throws a ball vertically into the air. He has given it high speed, and hence kinetic energy. The speed gets less and less as the ball travels upward. Finally the ball reaches its highest point in the air and its speed is zero. Since there is no motion at this instant, its kinetic energy is zero. But at this point all of the kinetic energy of motion of the ball has become potential energy of elevation. As the ball falls, the potential energy due to its height above the ground is changed back to kinetic energy. The ball then returns to the boy's hand at almost the same speed and kinetic energy with which he threw it. (Some of its energy, due to wind resistance, was turned into heat energy.)

Is the motion of a pendulum bob an example of how energy can be changed from one type to another? Explain.

Other forms of energy. Besides mechanical energy discussed above, there are other forms of energy. While difficult to define with precision, *energy may be conveniently described as the ability to do work.* Hence all forms of energy may be converted to work units such as foot pounds. In the next chapter, we shall study about *heat energy.*

When we speak of *electric energy,* we mean the kind that produces the flow of an electric current. *Nuclear energy* is now used to generate heat energy which in turn is changed to mechanical energy and then into electric energy.

Light, sound, and *magnetism* are also forms of energy, about which we shall study later. All of these can produce motion or changes in matter; all have the capacity to do work.

The law of conservation of energy and matter. A moving automobile has kinetic energy. Where did it get this energy? We agree that it comes from the gasoline. Gasoline is a source of potential energy identified as chemical energy. When gasoline burns in the engine, chemical energy changes into heat energy, causing the burning gases to expand with great force against the automobile pistons. Heat energy is thus converted to mechanical energy, moving the parts of the car and giving it kinetic energy of motion.

The law of conservation of energy states that we can neither create nor destroy energy, but can only change it from one form to another. An exception to this principle became evident when scientists found that small amounts of *matter* were sometimes changed into huge quantities of *energy.* This discovery, *predicted* by Albert Einstein over half a century ago, is the source of *nuclear energy* about which we shall study later in the text.

We now combine the matter-to-energy principle and the law of conservation of matter into the following general statement. In any action, *the total amount of matter and energy in the universe does not change.* This far-reaching principle is one of the most productive generalizations in the vast field of scientific thought. Many experiments confirm this statement and no exceptions to this law are known.

Quick Quiz

1. How are work and energy related?
2. If a force acts on a body perpendicular to its motion, is work accomplished? Explain.
3. Explain the difference between work and power.
4. How may falling water do work?
5. How do water turbines develop power?
6. List six reasons for building dams.
7. Why are dams wider at the bottom than at the top?
8. Why are arch dams constructed?
9. Explain the difference between potential energy of elevation and kinetic energy. How may each be computed?
10. Illustrate how kinetic energy may be changed into potential energy.
11. List five forms of energy. How are they related?
12. Explain the meaning of the law of conservation of matter and energy.

E ENGINES

The era of power. The simple machines that you studied earlier in this chapter were invented centuries ago. Although man multiplied his strength with them, he still had to supply the input force.

At first he used muscle power, either his own or that of his beast of burden. However, with the invention of the *steam engine,* man had found a device that changed potential energy of fuel into useful work. Now he could let the engines run his machines. Since

4-57. Experimental ion engine, a type of rocket engine (left), is sealed into a huge vacuum tank (right) to simulate space environment. (NASA)

then he has built ever more powerful engines!

James Watt, an 18th century Scottish engineer, is usually credited with the invention of the steam engine, even though steam engines had been built before he was born. Watt improved the earlier wasteful models and made the steam engine more practical. This was the beginning of the "machine age."

The earliest steam engines were first used to pump water out of coal mines in England. Later they were used in the first locomotives and for running machines in factories. Eventually, the more efficient *steam turbine* was introduced. The development of the *gasoline engine*, early in this century, made possible the widespread utilization of automobiles and airplanes. Today, diesel-electric locomotives have largely replaced those powered by steam engines. *Jet engines* have been developed for high-speed airplanes. *Gas turbines* are now being developed for use in automobiles, trucks, buses, ships, locomotives, and electric power plants.

Engines run by *atomic energy* and *solar energy* are available for special purposes. By far the most powerful engines of all are the *rocket engines*. They hurl huge space probes and satellites from the earth and drive rocket planes faster than bullets. All of these engines are devices that convert chemical energy to useful work. (See Fig. 4-57.)

The reciprocating steam engine. You have undoubtedly seen steam push up the cover on a kettle. The steam engine operates on this very principle, as shown in Fig. 4-58. Steam under pressure exerts a force in all directions, enabling it to push a *sliding piston*.

Steam turbines are more efficient. All kinds of engines can be grouped either as *reciprocating* or *nonreciprocating* engines. The action of the back-and-forth motion of the piston in the

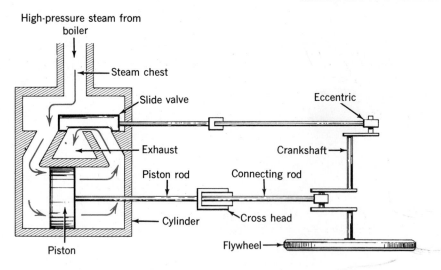

4-58. Cross-sectional view of the inside of Watt's simple slide-valve steam engine. The high-pressure steam on the piston causes rotary motion in the flywheel and shaft.

cylinder of a reciprocating engine results in a jerky motion and causes vibrations. Much energy is wasted because the piston has to stop and then start again at the end of each stroke, resulting in a lowering of efficiency. This low efficiency is undesirable for many purposes.

Nonreciprocating engines, or *steam turbines,* rotate with a steady, continuous motion. They work smoothly, cause almost no vibration, and waste less energy than the reciprocating-type engine. Turbines are more efficient and more compact; that is, they take less space for a given amount of horsepower. All large electric generating plants and large ships use turbines rather than the reciprocating engines.

How does the turbine work? The steam turbine works like a high-speed windmill, as shown in Fig. 4-59. Nozzles point the steam at a proper angle against *movable blades* mounted on a

shaft, making them spin at a high speed. In most turbines, after passing one set of movable blades, the steam is directed by a set of *fixed blades* against the next row of movable blades, as shown in Fig. 4-60. The set of fixed blades is mounted in the turbine case. Look closely at Fig. 4-61 and you will be able to see these blades in the lower casing.

Notice also in Fig. 4-61 that each set of movable blades is larger than the last set. Entering steam strikes the smallest set of blades first. The steam is then allowed to expand as it strikes progressively larger sets of blades in passing through the turbine. More power can be obtained from the steam as it rushes through the turbine from the high-pressure end to the low-pressure end.

Many electric generators are run by steam turbines that have an output of over 100,000 horsepower. This is enough power for a city of 50,000

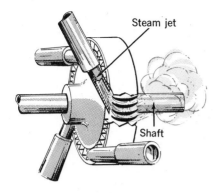

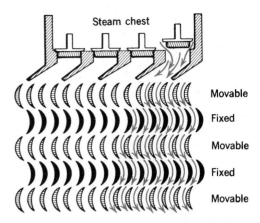

4-59. The force of the expanding high-speed steam from the steam jet is directed against the cupped blades of the turbine. The blades are attached to the end of the shaft so that the force of the steam causes the shaft to rotate. Devices on the spinning shaft can then be used to make the turbine do useful work.

4-60. Starting with the high-pressure steam from the steam chest, follow the path of the steam as it expands through the turbine. Movable blades are attached to the shaft.

people. Yet, one machine generates it in a space about the size of an average classroom. The steam for modern turbines may have a pressure as high as 2000 lb/in.^{2} at a temperature of 1000° F.

Steam turbines operate efficiently only at high speeds. For generating electric power, the turbine shaft is joined directly to the shaft of a high-speed electric generator. However, a ship's turbine is connected to the propeller shaft through gears that *reduce* the speed. This is because screw propellers are more efficient at lower speeds. On some ships and trains, the turbine runs an *electric generator*. The electric current then runs powerful motors that drive the ship or train.

4-61. The movable blades of a 100,000 kilowatt steam-turbine generator are being lowered into the casing, which holds the fixed blades. (General Electric Co.)

Internal combustion engines. Steam reciprocating engines and steam turbines form a class of engines called **external combustion** engines. That is, the fuel burns under a boiler located *outside* the engine itself. Gasoline and diesel engines are examples of another class called **internal combustion** engines because the fuel burns *inside* the engine cylinder.

The most common gasoline engine is the *"four-stroke"* engine. This does not refer to the number of cylinders, but to a *cycle* of operation. These engines are used extensively in automobiles and in many airplanes.

Refer to Fig. 4-62 for the steps in the operation of the four-stroke engine. The first stroke is the **intake.** The piston slides down during the intake stroke, causing the formation of a low-pressure area in the upper part of the cylinder. A mixture of air and gasoline vapor from the *carburetor* is pushed into the cylinder through the open *intake valve*. The *exhaust valve* is closed at this time.

Next comes the **compression stroke,** during which the piston travels upward. Both the intake and the exhaust valves are closed. As the piston moves up, it squeezes or *compresses* the air-gasoline vapor into a smaller space.

The *power stroke* takes place next. Just before the piston reaches the top of the stroke, an electric spark jumps across the gap of the spark plug as shown in Fig. 4-63. This fires the highly combustible air-gasoline mixture. The resulting high pressure of the hot burning gases forces the piston down in the cylinder. The power stroke is the only stroke that does work.

During the fourth stroke, the piston travels up again, pushing the burned gases out through the open exhaust valve. Hence, we call this the **exhaust stroke.**

Since there is power during only one of the four strokes, there must be

4-62. The four strokes of the 4-cycle gasoline engine.

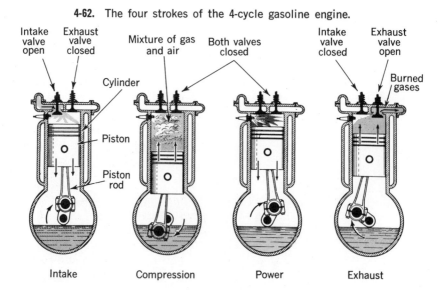

Intake   Compression   Power   Exhaust

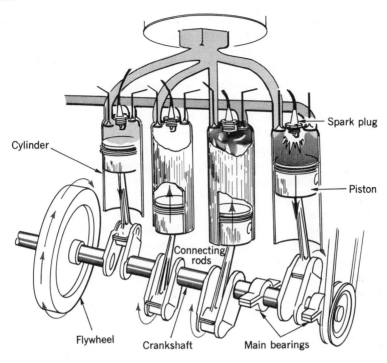

4-63. Diagram showing the application of a power stroke in a four-cylinder engine causing rotary motion of the shaft. Can you tell what is happening in the cylinder to the extreme left?

some way of keeping the piston moving during the other three strokes. This is done by connecting a flywheel to the crankshaft to the engine. The flywheel's inertia keeps the piston moving during the other strokes.

If automobile engines had only one cylinder, they would give a jerky ride. The first automobile engines had only one cylinder, and the whole car shook and vibrated each time that the cylinder fired. The more cylinders that an engine has, the smoother its operation becomes.

Transmission of power. Again examine Fig. 4-63. Notice that each piston is connected to the crankshaft. The cylinders do not all fire at the same time. They are *timed* so that first one, then another, then a third fires, and so on. In this way, there is a steady succession of power strokes being transmitted to the crankshaft.

The *connecting rods* of the pistons turn the engine crankshaft with a smooth, continuous rotation. The crankshaft is connected to the *driveshaft* through *transmission gears* and a *clutch*.

The "transmission" permits you to shift gears to get the best *gear ratio*, or mechanical advantage, for a given situation. Of course, the automatic transmission does all this for you. In *low gear*, the driveshaft turns much slower than the engine does. This supplies a large torque to the rear wheels for starting and for steep climbs.

The *clutch* is usually made of *friction plates* that connect the engine crankshaft to the driveshaft that is coupled to the rear wheels. Normally, these plates are held tightly pressed together by steel springs. When you depress the clutch pedal, the plates are separated, and the engine power is not transmitted to the rear wheels. We say the car is not in gear or is in *neutral*.

The driveshaft is connected to the rear axles through a *differential*. This is a set of gears that permits each rear wheel to turn independently of the other. This is necessary when turning a corner, as the outside wheel must turn faster than the inner one.

The *carburetor* is a device for vaporizing the gasoline and mixing it with the proper amount of air.

Most automobile engines today have six or eight cylinders, while airplane engines often have many more. One aircraft engine has 28 cylinders, arranged like the spokes of a wheel, in four rows of seven cylinders each. Such engines deliver between 2000 to 3000 horsepower. They are very compact and weigh less than one pound per horsepower. These engines require no flywheel. Why not?

Gasoline engines are more efficient than reciprocating steam engines. The best gasoline engines change about 25–30 percent of the available energy of the fuel into useful work. The cooling system, the exhaust gases, and friction waste the rest of the energy. The old-type steam locomotives, by contrast, had an efficiency as low as 5–8 percent. Stationary steam engines have efficiencies up to about 20 percent,

while high-speed steam turbines are about 30 percent efficient.

A gasoline engine can be started or stopped on a moment's notice. A steam engine, on the other hand, cannot be started until there is enough steam pressure to make it function. Gasoline engines also develop a lot of power in a comparatively small space while steam engines take up a considerable amount of space for the power they produce.

There are some disadvantages of gasoline engines. They can run only in one direction. You cannot make them run backwards. Reciprocating steam engines can be run either forward or backwards simply by shifting the slide valve. This disadvantage in gasoline engines is overcome by having a *reverse gear* to use when we want to back up.

The cost of fuel is also an important item in the operation of engines. In most cases, coal is cheaper than gasoline. Many large power installations commonly burn coal or coke, although fuel oil is popular also.

Diesel engines. The chief difference between diesel engines and the gasoline engines is in the way the fuel is ignited. In gasoline engines, an electric spark jumps between the points of a spark plug. In diesels, there are no spark plugs. Instead, the heat generated by the high compression of the air sets off the rapid combustion of the fuel.

In the diesel, *air* enters the cylinder during the *intake stroke*. Then the rising piston squeezes the air to about 1/18 of its original volume. This high *compression* makes the air so hot that it can ignite the fuel. At the proper time, an ***injector*** sprays fuel oil into the cylinder, and very rapid burning takes place. The expanding hot gases push the piston down in the *power stroke.* This is then followed by the *exhaust stroke.*

The **compression ratio** of an internal combustion engine of this kind may run as high as 18 to 1 as compared to a compression ratio of some of our modern automobile engines which may run as high as 10 to 1. *Compression ratio of an engine is the comparison of the space a fuel mixture takes up before compression with its volume after compression.* (See Fig. 4-64.)

Diesels use a fuel oil that is much like kerosene and is cheaper than gasoline. Also, diesels have higher efficiencies than do gasoline engines, largely

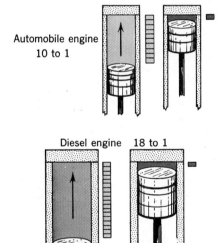

Automobile engine
10 to 1

Diesel engine   18 to 1

4-64. The diesel engine is highly efficient because of its high compression ratio by comparison with the modern automobile engine.

because of their higher compression ratios. Their efficiencies may be as high as 40 percent.

Many submarines, tugboats, fishing vessels, and even small ocean liners use diesel engines. Large trucks, buses, and power shovels make use of diesel power. Small plants for generating electricity operate on diesels also. On diesel-electric locomotives the diesel engine runs an electric generator. This produces the current to run the electric motors that drive the locomotive.

Jet engines. *Jet engines* make application of Newton's third law. There are several types of jet engines, but they all work on the action-reaction principle, previously discussed. The *turbojet* has a long shaft through its center with air-compressor blades on the front end and turbine blades in the rear as shown in Fig. 4-65. The *compressor* takes in large volumes of air and forces this air into the *combustion chamber.* Here it comes in contact with a fuel, usually kerosene, that is sprayed in and burns with a hot, roaring flame.

The hot exhaust gases force their way through the turbine blades. This makes the turbine turn at high speed, and the spinning rotor runs the air compressor at the front. The gases pass out of the jet at the rear of the engine.

The turbojet engine is used to power jet aircraft. The action on the high-speed gases at the rear produces a forward reaction against the plane. This is the **thrust,** or force that drives the plane forward. The turbojet engine uses much fuel, but it supplies a thrust that can push a plane to speeds greater than twice that of sound.

Another type of jet is the *bypass-jet* or *fanjet* (Fig. 4-65). This engine is similar in operation to the turbojet. However, it is more efficient, especially at low speeds, more powerful, and *quieter* in its operation. Jet noise comes mostly from the shear-like action between the high-speed column of exhaust gases and the relatively slow-moving air surrounding the engine. In the fanjet, the "bypass" air stream forms a *buffer* zone between these two gas layers, causing a reduction in noise.

The *ramjet,* often called the "flying stovepipe," has no turbine, rotor, or compressor. It can · operate only at speeds so high that air is rammed into the intake without the need of the air compressor of the ordinary turbojet. It

has no moving parts and is able to deliver considerable power at a higher efficiency.

Combustion turbines. Engineers and scientists worked a long time to develop an internal combustion engine of the turbine type. They wanted to get away from the jerky to-and-fro motion of the pistons, which resulted in a considerable waste of energy. The *combustion turbine,* like the turbojet, burns the fuel inside the engine. However, it uses all the energy from the burning gases to turn a turbine that is geared to the machine it runs.

Either powdered coal or oil can be used as fuel for such an engine. The

4-65. Three types of jet power plants.

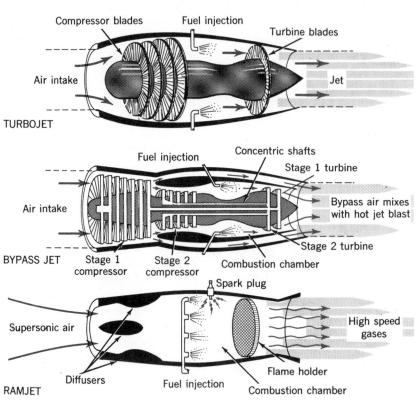

4-66. These modern jets are powered by turbojet engines like the one illustrated in Figure 4-65. (Top: US Dept. of Defense; Bottom: General Dynamics Corp.)

problem was to find suitable construction materials, especially for the turbine blades. The high speeds and high temperatures make it impossible to use ordinary steel. Special *alloy steels* are needed for the blades and for the combustion chamber.

Combustion turbines are finding some use in locomotives and electric generating plants. Experimental automobiles are being powered by gas turbines. A modification of the gas turbines, called the *free-piston engine*, may have a future in these fields. A piston, sliding back and forth in a double-headed cylinder of a gasoline engine, compresses the exhaust gases. It then forces these gases through a turbine. This is a less costly turbine that turns at slower speeds than the true gas turbine does.

Rocket engines. *Rocket engines*, like jets, operate on the action-reaction principle. They differ, however, in that the rocket engine carries its *own oxidizer*, while the jet does not. Hence, unlike the jet, the rocket engine can operate *outside the earth's atmosphere*, as it does not require oxygen from the air.

The source of power consists of a fuel and an *oxidizer. An oxidizer is a substance, not necessarily containing oxygen, that supports the combustion of a fuel.* Rocket engines burn either solid or liquid propellants.

Liquid oxygen, called *lox,* is widely used as an oxidizer. However, other oxidizers, such as hydrogen peroxide, fuming nitric acid, and fluorine can be used.

Some liquid fuels used in rocket engines are gasoline, alcohol, ammonia, hydrazine (N_2H_4), and liquid hydrogen.

Solid-fuel rocket engines operate much like old-fashioned Fourth-of-July rockets. The mixture of solid fuel and oxidizer is molded with a central opening that acts as the combustion chamber.

Engineers had difficulty, at first, trying to control the rate of burning in the solid-fuel system and in turning the reaction off and on. Among their many accomplishments is the use of ultrasonic sound waves for stopping the burning action.

The fuel burns with an intensely hot flame that would melt any metal. Hence, the combustion chamber and exhaust vents are lined with high-melting-point *ceramic* materials, and the walls of liquid-fueled engines are cooled by the cold incoming fuels.

What is meant by specific impulse? The sole purpose of a rocket engine is to produce thrust. The greater the speed of the exhaust gases, the greater the thrust. The gas speed, in turn, is governed largely by the temperature of combustion. Liquid hydrogen makes an ideal fuel for two reasons. First, it burns with *lox* to produce a very high temperature. Second, the light weight of the hydrogen atoms means that its combustion gases have a higher speed for any given temperature. Hence, although liquid hydrogen is very hard to handle, it is used in rocket engines.

4-67. The X-15 flying research laboratory is a rocket-powered vehicle having a thrust equivalent to 400,000 horsepower. It holds the world's aircraft record for altitude (66 miles) and speed (over 4,100 miles/hr). (NASA)

4-68. Ground test-firing of 1.5-million-pound-thrust engine for SATURN Rocket. (NASA)

The *specific impulse* of a rocket engine and its fuel is a rating of its efficiency. Specific impulse is found by multiplying thrust (lb) by burning time (sec) and dividing by the weight (lb) of the propellant. Thus the specific impulse is usually given in seconds. The higher the specific impulse, the greater the engine efficiency. The specific impulse of liquid hydrogen fuel with a liquid oxygen oxidizer in modern rocket engines is about 375 seconds.

Of all types of power plants, rocket engines furnish by far the most power per pound of engine weight. Rocket engines with two million pounds of thrust, when moving at 15,000 mph, develop 80 million horsepower! (See Fig. 4-68.)

Quick Quiz

1. What is an engine? Does it create energy? Explain.
2. How is the to-and-fro motion of a piston translated to rotary motion?
3. Explain the difference between reciprocating engines and turbines.
4. How does the efficiency of a steam turbine compare with that of a reciprocating steam engine?
5. What is the difference between an internal and external combustion engine?
6. Explain the operation of the four-stroke-cycle automobile engine.
7. Why is a six-cylinder engine better than a one-cylinder engine of equal power?
8. List three advantages of gasoline engines over steam engines.
9. Describe three differences between diesel engines and gasoline engines.
10. What is an oxidizer? Does it always contain oxygen?
11. Name four substances that can be used as rocket fuel.

SUMMARY

A vector is a quantity, such as force or velocity, that has magnitude and direction. Vectors may be added to find their resultant, which is a single vector that can replace the others. Friction and gravity are common forces.

A machine is any device used to change the amount, speed, or direction of a force. The simple machines include the lever, pulley, wheel-and-axle, inclined plane, wedge, and screw. In using any machine, whatever is gained in force, must be lost in distance or speed. Because of friction, the amount of energy or work that is put into the machine is always greater than the amount of work that the machine does. This is in keeping with the law of conservation of energy.

Gravitation is the mutual force of attraction between all bodies in the universe. The greater the masses, the greater the force of attraction between them; and the greater the distance between their centers, the less the force. Newton's first law states that an object does not change its motion unless an unbalanced force acts on it. This tendency of a body to resist any change in motion is called inertia, and is a property of all matter.

Newton's second law states that the acceleration of a body depends directly upon the amount of net force acting on it, and inversely on the amount of mass it contains. The third law states that there is an equal and opposite reaction for every action between two bodies. The momentum of a body is the product of its mass and velocity. When two bodies interact, the momentum gained by one always equals that lost by the other. There is no change in total momentum.

A buoyant force pushes up on objects immersed in a fluid. Archimedes' principle states that this force is equal to the weight of the displaced fluid. An object floats in a fluid only if its weight is less than this buoyancy; that is, less than the weight of an equal volume of the fluid.

Energy is the capacity for doing work. Potential energy is energy of position or condition. Kinetic energy is energy that a body has because of its motion. Kinetic energy depends upon the mass of an object and its speed. Energy can be changed from one form to another.

Heat, electricity, light, sound, and magnetism are all forms of energy. Nuclear and chemical reactions can set free much energy contained in the atom. In nuclear reactions a measurable amount of matter is converted to energy. The law of conservation of matter and energy states that the total amount of matter and energy in the universe does not change.

Engines are devices that convert energy from one form to another, usually from the chemical energy of the fuel to useful work.

CHAPTER REVIEW

Vocabulary

Match the words in Column A with the *best* response in Column B. Do not write in your book.

Column A	Column B
1. friction	a. a device that changes the amount, speed, or direction of a force
2. torque	
3. machine	b. force acting on a unit area of surface
4. IMA	c. $a = k(F/m)$
5. work	d. resistance to motion caused by one surface rubbing against another
6. efficiency	

7. inertia
8. velocity
9. acceleration
10. Newton's 2nd law
11. momentum
12. adhesion
13. pressure
14. buoyancy
15. specific gravity
16. Boyle's law
17. power
18. diesel
19. oxidizer

e. substance that supports the combustion of a rocket fuel
f. a measure of the amount of work that can be done in a given time
g. density of a substance compared to the density of water
h. tendency of a mass not to change its state of motion or rest
i. pressure times volume of a given gas as a constant
j. output work divided by input work
k. force of attraction between unlike molecules
l. product of force and the perpendicular distance from fulcrum
m. an internal combustion engine
n. product of mass and velocity
o. force that pushes up on objects placed in a fluid
p. a measure of energy transfer
q. change in velocity in unit time
r. ratio of distance effort moves to distance resistance moves
s. speed in a given direction

Questions: Group A

1. Explain the difference between high mechanical advantage and high efficiency.
2. Which of the simple machines are noted for their high mechanical advantage?
3. Is friction ever desirable? Explain.
4. What is uniform motion? Is accelerated motion uniform? Explain.
5. By using a stop watch and a stone, explain how you could determine the approximate depth of a deep vertical mine shaft.
6. Why does the cultivating of topsoil slow up evaporation of water from its surface?
7. Explain what is meant by saying that liquid pressure is independent of the shape of the container.
8. How, without tasting them, could you determine which of two sugar solutions was the more concentrated?
9. If a substance has a specific gravity of 0.9, will it sink or float in water? Why?
10. What does the kinetic energy of an object depend upon? Potential energy of elevation?
11. How is gasoline used to produce kinetic energy?
12. Explain the function of each of the following parts of the automobile: carburetor, differential, clutch, and transmission.
13. List two advantages of diesels over gasoline engines.

14. Explain how the to-and-fro motion of an engine piston is changed to rotary motion of a shaft.
15. Why are steam engines not used to power airplanes?

Questions: Group B

1. Is the center of gravity of an object always located within it? How would you determine the general location of the center of gravity of a kitchen chair?
2. How are the single pulley and wheel-and-axle related to the lever?
3. Diagram a pulley system with which you could lift a 600-lb piano by pulling down with a 100-lb force on a rope (assume no friction).
4. Why does a slowly-moving freight train have more momentum than a high-speed bullet?
5. Discuss the force that keeps the moon in its orbit.
6. If twice the net force gives twice the acceleration, why does a 10-lb stone not fall twice as fast as a 5-lb stone?
7. If you had a cubic foot of an unknown substance, how could you calculate whether it would float in water?
8. Explain how you would determine the specific gravity of lead.
9. Determine from the specific gravity table on page 220 if lead will float in mercury.
10. If the pressure of a confined gas is increased three times, what happens to the volume? Assume the temperature remains unchanged during the process.
11. Write these words in the order in which the parts are actually connected in a power plant: turbine, generator, basin, and penstock.
12. Explain how a diesel engine operates.
13. How is noise reduced in a fanjet engine in flight?

Problems

1. A force of 10 lb acts on a particle in an easterly direction. On the same particle, another force of 15 lb acts at an angle of 50° to the south. Compute the resultant force, and determine its direction from the 10-lb force.
2. A 500-lb cart is rolled up a 20-ft plank to a platform 5 ft high by an effort of 150 lb parallel to the plank. Find: (a) the ideal mechanical advantage, (b) the actual mechanical advantage, (c) the input work, (d) output work, and (e) the efficiency.
3. The movable pulley block of an oil rig is supported by 8 strands of wire rope. (a) What is the ideal mechanical advantage? (b) Neglecting friction, a pull of 500 lb on the haul rope would hold a weight of how many pounds?
4. An object is dropped from a high building. How far does the object fall in 5 seconds? What is its velocity at the end of this time? What is its *average* velocity during the fall? If it takes 7 seconds for the object to hit the ground, compute the height of the building.

5. If a 10-lb gun fires a 1-oz bullet at 1600 ft/sec, what is the recoil speed of the gun? Draw a vector diagram for this situation.

6. Your car is slowed down from 50 mph to 20 mph in 6 seconds. What is your deceleration in mph/sec?

7. A spiral spring hanging vertically stretches 3 inches when loaded with a 2-lb weight. (a) How much would a 1-lb weight stretch the spring? (b) A 3-lb weight? (c) How much weight would be required to lengthen the spring a total of 7½ inches? (d) What assumption did you make in obtaining your answers?

8. One piston of a hydraulic press has an area of 1 in.^{2} The other piston has an area of 25 in.^{2} If a force of 150 lb is applied on the smaller piston, what will be the total force on the larger piston?

9. A bottle weighs 54 grams when filled with kerosene and 60 grams when filled with the same volume of water. The empty bottle weighs 30 grams. Compute the specific gravity of the kerosene.

10. A piece of metal weighs 190 grams when completely submerged in water. If its volume is 80 cm^3, how much does the metal weigh in air?

11. If the pressure of 1 ft^3 of a gas is increased from 15 lb/in.^{2} to 105 lb/in.^{2}, what will be its new volume? Assume the temperature remains the same during the process.

12. A boy weighing 130 lb climbs an 8-foot vertical ladder in 4 seconds. Determine (a) the work done; (b) the power required; (c) the horsepower; and (d) the kilowatts.

13. A 10-lb object moves with a speed of 25 ft/sec. Find the kinetic energy of the body. How much work is needed to stop the object?

14. A horizontal force of 50 lb is required to drag a loaded box weighing 250 lb a distance of 75 ft along a level roadway. How much work is accomplished? If the box is lifted by a crane to a vertical height of 75 ft, how much work is done?

5 MOLECULAR MOTION

A TEMPERATURE AND ITS MEASUREMENT

The nature of heat. We have seen that matter is continuously changing. Solids are converted into liquids, liquids into gases, and one compound into another. All of these changes involve *energy, that which produces physical or chemical changes in matter*. We have also seen that *work* is a measure of energy transfer, and that energy may be changed from one form to another.

Experiments show that heat energy is *absorbed* when liquids vaporize to gases and *liberated* when gases condense into liquids.

When a substance is heated, the molecules in it begin to move about more violently. They hit one another, bouncing back actively from these collisions. The hotter the object becomes, the faster the molecules move about. At low temperatures, the molecules slow down. We say that *heat is a form of energy possessed by a substance because of the motion of its molecules*. That is, the movement of molecules is related to the capacity of the body to do *work*.

Temperature scales. The *Fahrenheit* (**F**) temperature scale is used by English-speaking peoples for ordinary work. The *Celsius* (**C**), or centigrade scale, is used almost exclusively in other countries, and by all scientists. A thermometer can be marked in either or both scales.

The Fahrenheit thermometer reads 32° in melting ice, and 212° in steam from boiling water. There are 180 degrees between the freezing and boiling temperatures of water. Zero degrees on the Fahrenheit scale does not mean the complete absence of heat. Daniel Fahrenheit, who developed this scale, assigned a value of zero for the temperature of a mixture of ice and salt, the lowest temperature he could obtain at the time.

On the Celsius scale, water freezes at 0° and boils at 100°. You can see that there are 100 degree marks between the freezing and boiling points. (See Fig. 5-1.) There is nothing magic about a temperature scale; you can devise one of your own very easily! Choose any liquid as a standard, and arbitrarily assign convenient values to its boiling and freezing temperatures in order to "fix" two points. Then you can mark off the equal divisions on the thermometer. Of course, you would need to teach other people to use your scale so that they would know what you were talking about when you gave them a reading on your own "home-made" temperature scale.

An *optical pyrometer* (py-rom-eh-ter) is an electric device used to measure high temperatures. The pyrometer makes it possible to compare the brightness of a very hot body to be measured with the brightness of the filament of an electric lamp. If the hot body and the pyrometer filament have the same brightness, they have the same temperature. (See Fig. 5-2.)

5-2. The temperature of molten steel is checked with an optical pyrometer as the steel pours from a ladle into a mold. (Bethlehem Steel Corp.)

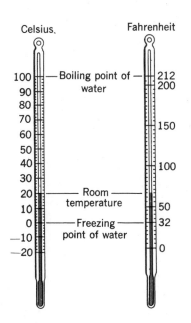

5-1. Compare the height of the mercury column in the Celsius and Fahrenheit thermometers.

What are standard conditions of temperature and pressure? In Chapter 4 we mentioned the fact that normally the atmosphere at sea level will support a column of mercury 30 inches (760 mm) in height. Scientists express this fact by saying that the barometric pressure of the atmosphere under normal conditions is 760 mm of mercury. This is arbitrarily called the *standard pressure,* or *one atmosphere.*

Furthermore, 0° C is arbitrarily taken by scientists to mean *standard temperature.* When you hear about gases at *standard* conditions of *temperature and pressure* (STP) it means that the gas is at a temperature of 0° C and a pressure of 760 mm of mercury.

What is the difference between heat and temperature? A change in reading on a glass thermometer indicates that heat was lost or gained by the thermometer bulb. Suppose a hot iron ball at 185° F is placed in cold water at 40° F. As you know, heat will go from the hot ball to the cold water. *Thus,* *temperature can be expressed as a* *measure of the tendency of objects to* *transfer heat to, or absorb heat from,* *other objects.*

The temperature, or degree of heat, can be read directly on the thermometer. Heat on the other hand cannot be measured directly, as we shall see in the next section. It is measured by its effect on matter, and this is done indirectly. Usually we are not interested in the total heat energy that objects contain, but only in the amount of heat energy that is transferred from one object to another.

You can readily see that one hundred grams of water has ten times as much heat energy as ten grams of water, if *both* are at the same temperature. A burning match has a much higher temperature than a steam radiator, but the heat produced by the match is not enough to warm even a very small room.

How can the accuracy of a thermometer be checked? You can check a Celsius thermometer to make sure it gives the correct reading at freezing by using the apparatus shown in Fig. 5-3. Put the bulb of the thermometer into small pieces of melting ice. Be sure to wait until the mercury in the thermometer has reached the lowest point before reading it. The thermometer should read 0° C, the temperature of the melting ice.

Figure 5-4 shows how you can check another reading on your thermometer. Read the thermometer after steam has been coming out of the outlet for at least several minutes. Pure water boils at 100° C at sea level at standard pressure. Can you suggest a reason why your reading may be dif-

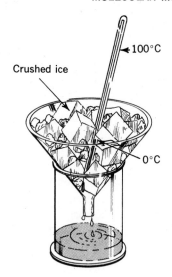

5-3. A Celsius thermometer should read 0° when placed in melting ice.

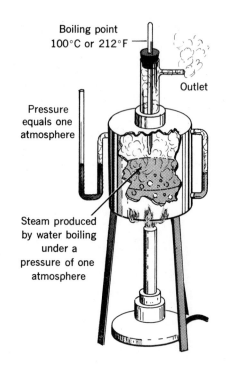

5-4. At a pressure of one atmosphere, or 760 mm of mercury, a Celsius thermometer should read 100° when placed in escaping steam.

ferent even if you have an accurate thermometer?

What is absolute zero? We have seen that as the temperature of a substance is raised, the speed of its molecules increases and more heat energy is contained in the matter. Similarly, if the temperature of a substance is lowered, the molecular motion decreases and less energy is contained in the matter.

There is, however, a temperature at which there is complete absence of heat. We call this point *absolute zero.* At this temperature, all of the heat of any substance has been lost and *molecular collisions cease.* This temperature is −273.16° C (−459.69° F) or **0° Absolute.** Scientists have cooled matter very very close to absolute zero, and have studied the behavior of matter under these conditions.

When helium gas is cooled to a liquid near absolute zero, it displays very unusual properties. At this temperature, liquid helium creeps up the sides of its containing vessel. It also becomes a good conductor of heat. Some metals that are relatively poor conductors of electricity at ordinary temperatures become *superconductors* when cooled to temperatures near absolute zero. (See Fig. 5-5.)

What is boiling? When water is warmed in a glass beaker, small bubbles of gas rise to the surface. This is air that was dissolved in the water. As heating is continued, small bubbles of steam form at the bottom. Finally, steam bubbles are produced so rapidly that they rise through the liquid, reach the surface, and escape into the air. The liquid is now *boiling. Boiling occurs in any liquid when the pressure produced by the vapor within the*

liquid is equal to the pressure of the atmosphere on its surface. Each *pure* liquid has a definite boiling point at a particular atmospheric pressure. The boiling point of ether is 35° C, and of glycerol is 290° C.

The temperature of a boiling liquid does not rise if more heat is applied; it just boils more vigorously. Its temperature remains constant until all of the liquid has been vaporized.

Solids dissolved in a liquid change its boiling temperature. For example, salt water boils at a higher temperature than pure water. Usually, solids dissolved in liquids *raise* the boiling temperature.

At high altitudes, the boiling temperature of liquids is decreased. This is because the atmospheric pressure is less. On the other hand, temperature of boiling water in a closed vessel rapidly goes much higher than 100° C, or

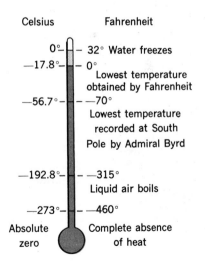

Celsius	Fahrenheit
0°	32° Water freezes
−17.8°	0° Lowest temperature obtained by Fahrenheit
−56.7°	−70° Lowest temperature recorded at South Pole by Admiral Byrd
−192.8°	−315° Liquid air boils
−273°	−460°
Absolute zero	Complete absence of heat

5-5. Absolute zero is far below the zero on either the Celsius or Fahrenheit scales. What happens to molecular activity at absolute zero?

212° F. For example, some steam turbines operate with a pressure of about 2000 lb/in.² or more. Under these conditions, the temperature of the boiling water may be 1000° F.

Boiling water at reduced pressure. You can make even cool water boil by reducing the pressure of the air above its surface in a closed container. Take a strong, round-bottomed flask half full of water and boil the water vigorously for a few minutes. Then stopper the flask tightly and put it upside down on a ring stand as shown in Fig. 5-6. The boiling stops as the flask and its contents cool.

Now pour some cold water over the flask. The cold water condenses some of the water vapor in the space above the water in the upper part of the flask. This in turn produces a *lower* pressure above the water. The water then starts to boil again under this reduced pressure. This demonstration shows that

5-7. The temperature in the pressure cooker is higher than the normal boiling temperature.

when the pressure is lower, water boils at a temperature below the normal boiling point of 100° C.

Pressure cookers. *Pressure cookers* are used to raise the boiling temperature of water so that the foods can become hotter and cook more rapidly. When water is heated in such a vessel, the pressure of the enclosed steam raises the boiling temperature above its normal value.

Pressure cookers are especially useful at high altitudes where the normal boiling temperature of water may be too low to cook the food properly. (See Fig. 5-7.) Pressure cookers not only save time but fuel as well. A modified form of a pressure cooker, called an *autoclave,* is used for sterilizing equipment in hospitals and laboratories.

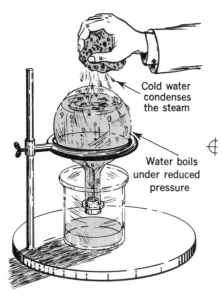

Cold water condenses the steam

Water boils under reduced pressure

5-6. Cold water on the outside of the flask lowers the pressure within the flask and boiling starts again.

Quick Quiz

1. How does an optical pyrometer measure temperature?
2. What are standard conditions of temperature and pressure?

3. Distinguish between temperature and heat.
4. Explain how you would check the accuracy of a Celsius thermometer.
5. How is heat energy related to the motion of molecules of a substance?
6. What is meant by absolute zero? What happens to matter at this temperature?
7. What effect does an increase of pressure have upon the boiling temperature of liquids? A decrease in pressure?
8. Does a liquid become hotter as it is boiled away more vigorously? Explain.
9. What happens to the boiling temperature of a liquid when dissolved solids are added to it?

B HEAT AS A FORM OF ENERGY

Sources of heat. We have seen that heat is a form of energy and that when molecules receive energy from a warmer object, they move about more energetically.

Heat is obtained through the conversion of other forms of energy. We shall examine some important examples:

1. *Mechanical energy.* Hammering a piece of metal causes it to heat up. Compression of the air in a diesel engine cylinder heats the air to a high temperature.

2. *Chemical energy.* In chemical reactions, energy stored within the molecules is released as heat energy when new substances are formed. The burning of coal, wood, oil, and gasoline are examples of sources of heat due to chemical action. However there are certain chemical reactions in which heat is absorbed.

3. *Electric energy.* When an electric current passes through substances, heat is produced. The conversion of electric energy into heat is accomplished in electric toasters, irons, ranges, and heaters.

4. *Radiant energy.* Light and heat rays from the sun and other sources heat the objects they strike. Practically all of the heat on the earth originates from *nuclear reactions* that take place on the sun. The interior of the earth is also a source of heat energy from nuclear reactions (radioactivity).

Heat causes substances to expand. Gases, liquids, and solids expand when heated, and shrink when cooled. Heat produces more active collisions of molecules and makes them move farther apart, increasing the space between molecules. At lower temperatures the molecular vibrations decrease, permitting the molecules to move closer together.

We can show expansion of gases by a simple experiment. Set up a flask and U-tube as shown in Fig. 5-8. Add a little colored water to the glass bend. Now put your hand on the flask for a minute or two. The air in the flask becomes slightly warmed and expands. Observe that the water in the U-tube rises in the open end. Now if you cool the flask, the liquid level drops. In the same way, you can show that any gas occupies a greater volume when it is heated.

You can do another experiment to show the expansion of liquids. Fill a flask with colored water and put in a rubber stopper and glass tube as shown in Fig. 5-9. Mark the height of the colored water in the tube. Heat the

Air is warmed and expands

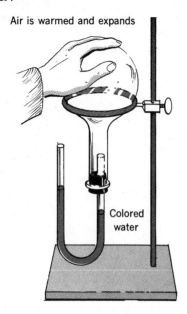

Colored water

5-8. Heat causes the gas in the flask to expand, pushing level of liquid down.

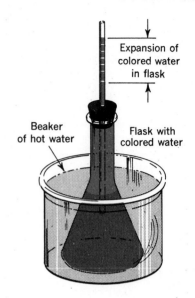

Expansion of colored water in flask

Beaker of hot water

Flask with colored water

5-9. As the water in the flask is heated, the expansion of the water in the flask is indicated by the rising levels in the glass tube.

flask by putting it into some hot water. Observe the colored water rise in the tube as the result of expansion. How is the size of the glass flask affected by the increase in temperature? Do you think that its expansion is greater or less than that of the water? This difference in rate of expansion accounts for the operation of ordinary glass thermometers.

We can show the effect of heat on the size of solids by the use of the apparatus in Fig. 5-10. At room temperature, the ball will just get through the ring. When the ball alone is heated, it expands and will not fit through the ring. Now if the ring is also heated, the ball fits through the ring once again. Obviously, heating the metal has caused it to expand.

Gases expand more than liquids or solids. Investigations show that gases expand more than liquids and liquids expand more than solids under the same conditions. Gases expand more than 10 times as much as water, and about 100 times as much as steel.

Different liquids expand at varying rates. Each solid has its own rate of expansion that is different from other solids. However, gases differ from liquids and solids in that *all gases expand and contract at the same rate.*

The coefficient of volume expansion. When the temperature of a liquid is raised one degree, the actual increase in volume is a small fraction of the original amount. This fraction is called the *coefficient* (koh-eh-*fish*-ent) *of volume expansion.*

Of course, 100 ml of a liquid expands 100 times as much as one ml of the liquid does. Also, a 10-degree rise in temperature, causes 10 times as much expansion as a rise of one degree. Thus, if we know the coefficient of volume expansion of a substance, the original volume, and the number of degrees change in temperature, we can calculate the change in volume by multiplying these factors.

SAMPLE PROBLEM

How much does the volume of 48 liters of water increase when heated from 10° C to 60° C? The coefficient of volume expansion for water is 0.00019/C°.

SOLUTION:

Step 1. The change in temperature is 60° C − 10° C = 50 C°.

Step 2.

Expansion = (coefficient) × (volume)
            × (temperature change)

Step 3.

Expansion = (0.00019/C°) × (48 l)
                       × (50 C°)

= 0.46 liter

Hence, 48 liters of water at 10° C occupies 48 + 0.46, or 48.46 liters at 60° C.

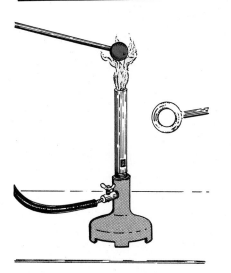

5-10. After being heated, the metal ball will no longer fit through the ring, as it did at room temperature.

The increase is especially noticeable when you have large amounts of liquids. For example, a delivery truck emptied 1500 gallons of gasoline at 90° F on a hot summer day into an underground tank at a service station. A few hours later the gasoline had cooled to 50° F and its volume had shrunk by more than 20 gallons.

The coefficient of linear expansion. We have seen that gases, liquids, and solids expand in all directions when they are heated. Engineers are often concerned with the changes in *length* of solids. An increase in length is called *linear expansion. The fractional increase in length when the temperature of a solid is increased one degree, is called the* **coefficient of linear expansion.** Examine the table of coefficients below.

COEFFICIENT OF LINEAR EXPANSION

(per Celsius degree)	
Pyrex	0.000003
Glass	0.000009
Iron	0.000011
Steel	0.000013
Copper	0.000017
Brass	0.000019
Aluminum	0.000023

SAMPLE PROBLEM

The steel center span of the Verrazano-Narrows Bridge—the world's longest suspension bridge—is 4260 ft long. If the temperature rises 22 C°, how much will this bridge expand?

SOLUTION:

Step 1. From the table above, the coefficient of linear expansion for steel is 0.000013/C°.

Step 2.

Expansion = (coefficient) × (length)
                         × (temperature change)
       = (0.000013/C°) × (4260 ft)
                         × (22 C°)
       = 1.2 ft

One way of allowing for such expansion is to use finger-like gratings at each end of the roadway. They fit loosely into each other and permit adjustment to changing length. Next time you go over a long bridge, see if you can find out what was done to take care of the expansion and contraction.

For the same reason, spaces may be left between the steel rails of a railroad track to allow for the expansion of the rails. (See Fig. 5-11.)

Other examples of expansion. Have you ever cracked a glass tumbler by pouring very hot water into it? The inside surface was heated and expanded faster than the outer surface because glass is not a very good conductor of heat. This difference in expansion rates between the inner and outer surface made the glass crack. If the glass is thin, there is less chance that it will crack. Why?

Pyrex glass has become very popular for laboratory glassware, and for baking dishes in the home. This glass differs in composition from ordinary glass and expands only about ⅓ as much, as shown in the linear expansion table. Because of the smaller rate of expansion, there is less effect when the temperature changes. Pyrex withstands sudden heating and cooling very well.

How does a thermostat work? Automatic temperature regulators, called *thermostats,* control the burning of fuel in many furnaces. Many of these de-

5-11. Special couplings are used to prevent railroad tracks from warping when heat expands the rails. (Association of American Railroads)

vices contain a small bar made of two layers of metal that expand at different rates when heated.

The two-metal bar shown in Fig. 5-12 is made of a strip of brass riveted to a strip of iron. When this bar is heated, the brass expands more than the iron, causing the bar to bend.

In a thermostat, when the strips bend in one direction, they touch a contact point. This allows electric current to flow, which starts the electric

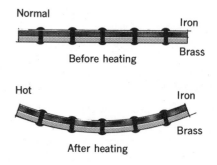

Normal
                                              Iron
                                              Brass
        Before heating

Hot
                                              Iron
                                              Brass
        After heating

5-12. Iron and brass expand at different rates when heated.

motor that controls the fuel supply to the furnace. When the bar bends in the other direction, the current stops when the contacts separate. By using a thermostat, you can keep the temperature of your home within a few degrees of any desired setting.

Calories measure the quantity of heat. We learned that while temperature is measured directly, heat is measured indirectly by its effect on matter. Heat cannot be measured with a yardstick, or weighed on a balance. Water is used as a standard because it is convenient, and because reasonably pure water can be easily obtained the world over. *The calorie is defined as the amount of heat required to raise the temperature of one gram of water one Celsius degree.* The calorie represents a very small unit of heat. A small stick of wood weighing one ounce gives off about 100,000 calories when it is burned completely. Many millions of calories are stored in a single ton of coal.

Suppose we burn some fuel and raise the temperature of 50 grams of water from 20° C to 90° C. If one calorie raises 1 gram of water 1 C°, then 50 calories are required to raise 50 grams of water one degree; and a rise in temperature of 70 degrees will require $50 \times 70 = 3500$ calories, or 3.5 kilocalories.

We also use a large unit of heat, called the large *Calorie* when discussing the energy rating of foods. One large Calorie equals one thousand regular calories, and so is also known as the *kilocalorie*.

The British thermal unit. Engineers generally measure heat in the *British thermal unit*, abbreviated *Btu*. The *Btu is the amount of heat required to raise the temperature of one pound of water one Fahrenheit degree.* One Btu equals 252 calories.

Users of coal are interested not only in the price per ton, but also in the number of Btu per pound of coal. Coal that contains 14,500 Btu per pound, will produce 7 percent more heat than coal with only 13,500 Btu/lb. You need fewer tons of the better grade coal to obtain the same amount of heat.

The mechanical equivalent of heat. We have seen how matter can be changed from one phase to another or from one position to another, and that energy is lost or gained in the process. We have seen how energy can be changed from one type to another. And we have examined the use of machines in the transfer of energy. The study of energy changes is of great interest to scientists.

You can easily experience the fact that mechanical energy can be changed into heat energy by vigorously rubbing the palms of your hands together. In this case you are converting the mechanical energy of motion of your hands into heat energy which you can feel.

Joule (jool), an English scientist, was the first to show that there is a quantitative relationship between mechanical energy and heat energy. He determined by experiment how much work it took to produce a definite amount of *heat* energy. He found that *one British thermal unit of heat results from 778 ft-lb of work.* This value is called *the mechanical equivalent of heat, or Joule's equivalent.* (See Fig. 5-13.)

What is specific heat of a substance? By definition, one gram of *water* gives up one calorie of heat

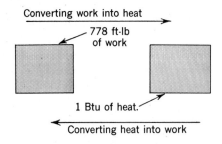

Converting work into heat

778 ft-lb
of work

1 Btu of heat.

Converting heat into work

5-13. Units of heat energy are interchangeable with units of mechanical energy, or work.

when its temperature is lowered one Celsius degree.

Other substances, however, liberate different amounts of heat when the temperature is lowered one degree because they have varying *heat capacities. The number of calories required to raise the temperature of* **one gram** *of any substance one Celsius degree, or the number of Btu necessary to raise the temperature of* **one pound** *of any substance one Fahrenheit degree, is called its* **specific heat.** The specific heat is different for different substances.

In the metric system, we say that water has a specific heat of 1.00 cal/g C°. This means that it takes one calorie of heat to raise the temperature of one gram of water one Celsius degree. In the English system, we say that water has a specific heat of 1.00 Btu/lb F°. Again, this means that it takes one Btu of heat to raise the temperature of one pound of water one Fahrenheit degree. In these two examples, we are merely restating our definition of each heat unit.

Because it takes only 0.09 calorie to raise the temperature of one gram of brass one Celsius degree, the specific heat of brass is 0.09 cal/g C°, or 0.09 Btu/lb F°. Specific heats of var-

ious substances are determined experimentally in the laboratory. The table below gives the specific heats of some common substances.

SPECIFIC HEATS OF SOME COMMON SUBSTANCES

($cal/g \; C°$ or $Btu/lb \; F°$)	
Aluminum	0.21
Brass	0.09
Ice	0.50
Iron	0.11
Lead	0.03
Steam	0.48
Water	1.00
Zinc	0.09

Observe that the specific heat of water is the highest of those substances listed in the table. In fact, the specific heat of water is one of the highest among *common* substances. The specific heat of liquid ammonia (NH_3) is 1.2. (See Fig. 5-14.)

SAMPLE PROBLEM

How much heat is required to raise the temperature of 750 grams of iron from 10° C to 130° C?

SOLUTION:

Step 1. From the table, the specific heat of iron is 0.11 cal/g C°. The temperature change is 130° C − 10° C = 120 C°.

Step 2.

Heat = (specific heat) × (mass)
$$\times \text{(temperature change)}$$
$$= (0.11 \text{ cal/g C°}) \times (750 \text{ g})$$
$$\times (120 \text{ C°})$$
$$= 9900 \text{ cal}$$

SAMPLE PROBLEM

How much heat is required to heat 100 lb of aluminum from 35° F to 245° F?

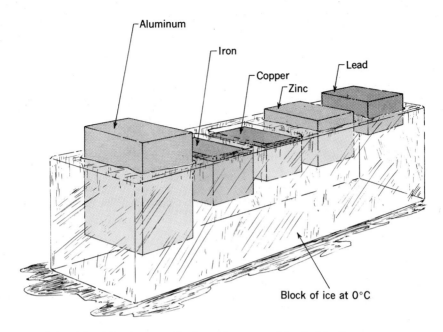

5-14. These blocks are all of equal mass and heated to the same temperatures. Because of different specific heats, they melt the ice to different depths.

SOLUTION:

Step 1. The specific heat of aluminum from the table is 0.21 Btu/lb F°. The temperature change is 245° F − 35° F = 210 F°.

Step 2.

Heat = (specific heat) × (mass)
        × (temperature change)
    = (0.21 Btu/lb F°) × (100 lb)
        × (210 F°)
    = 4410 Btu

Why is specific heat an important physical property? The specific heat of a substance often indicates if it is suitable for certain purposes. For example, aluminum utensils hold twice as much heat as iron items of equal

weight. You can verify this fact by studying the table on specific heats.

The high specific heat of water accounts for the relatively *uniform climates* of places· near large lakes or the ocean. Dry soil has a much lower specific heat than water and tends to warm up rapidly during the day and cool off rapidly during the night. However, a large body of water in the region will not warm up or cool off as fast as the land areas. This tends to keep the temperature more uniform.

Heat accounts for melting and boiling. Materials melt or change from solid to liquid when sufficient heat is applied. By increasing the heat, you can change the liquid into a gas or vapor. For example, water evaporates to form a vapor.

Heat is always involved in such a change of phase because the rearrangement of the molecules in a substance involves a change in energy. Melting ice absorbs heat energy in changing from ice to water even though no change in temperature takes place. Water gives off heat when it freezes to form ice. Condensing steam gives off energy as it changes into water. Heat energy must be absorbed by boiling water to convert it into steam.

Heat of fusion. Careful measurements in the laboratory have shown that it takes 80 calories of heat to change one gram of ice at 0° C to water at the same temperature. *The heat which is absorbed and used up in the melting process is called the heat of fusion.* Ice has a high heat of fusion when compared with other substances. This makes it useful in ice boxes and coolers because the melting of each gram of ice requires 80 calories of heat energy. This heat is obtained largely from the food inside the container. (See Fig. 5-15.)

What is meant by heat of vaporization? Water at 100° C does not change into steam until 540 calories of heat have been absorbed by each gram of the boiling water. The heat necessary for this change of phase to take place is called the *heat of vaporization.* It takes 100 calories to bring one gram of water from 0° C to 100° C. However, to change this water into steam, more than five times as much heat is required (540 cal/g). Thus, water has a very high heat of vaporization compared to other liquids. For example, the heat of vaporization of ammonia is 341 cal/g and for mercury it is only 68 cal/g. (See Fig. 5-16.)

When steam condenses into hot water, the stored-up heat of vaporization is set free. Can you see why steam is used for heating buildings?

SAMPLE PROBLEM

How much heat energy is required to change 10 grams of ice at 0° C into steam at 100° C?

SOLUTION:

Work the problem in the following steps: (1) find the heat needed to melt the ice; (2) find the heat required to heat the wa-

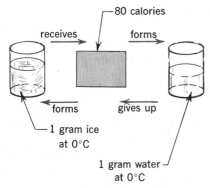

5-15. How much heat is needed to convert 100 grams of ice at 0° C to water at the same temperature?

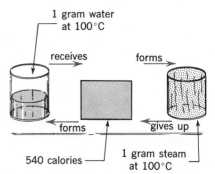

5-16. It takes 540 calories of heat to change 1 gram of water at 100° C to steam at 100° C. What happens when this process is reversed?

ter from 0° C to 100° C; and (3) find the heat needed to change the water into steam. Then add (1), (2), and (3) to determine the total amount of heat energy required.

Step 1.

Heat = (heat of fusion) × (mass)
= (80 cal/g) × (10 g)
= 800 cal

Step 2.

Heat = (specific heat) × (mass)
× (temperature change)
= (1.00 cal/g C°) × (10 g)
× (100 C°)
= 1000 cal

Step 3.

Heat = (heat of vaporization) × (mass)
= (540 cal/g) × (10 g)
= 5400 cal

Step 4. The total heat required
= 800 cal + 1000 cal + 5400 cal
= 7200 cal

Refrigeration. We can cool things by taking advantage of the heat of vaporization of a substance. A refrigerator, for example, employs such a principle. If your hand is wet and a breeze blows on it, your hand feels cool. The water evaporates and your hand supplies most of the heat of vaporization that is needed to change water into a vapor. This loss of heat cools your hand.

Now suppose that we have some liquid ammonia in a tube under high pressure. If we let it pass through a valve into a low pressure space, it will turn into a gas, or evaporate. In vaporizing, it absorbs heat, resulting in the cooling of the surrounding area. This process is used commercially by *cold storage plants* for ice-making and refrigeration.

How ice is made. Study Fig. 5-17 to see how ammonia gas is employed in a process of icemaking. In vaporizing, the ammonia gas takes heat from the *brine* (salt water) tank. The ammonia gas then goes to a pump, where a piston compresses it into a liquid again. As it condenses, it gives off heat. Water, running over the coils, absorbs this heat from the ammonia. The liquid ammonia is then ready to go through the valve and repeat the process.

In more modern applications, ammonia has been replaced in electric refrigerators, air-conditioning units, and freezers by another substance called *Freon,* a more effective *coolant.* Freon is a nontoxic and noncombustible substance.

Instead of water air is used to cool the coils. An electric motor drives the compressor pump, and a fan keeps the air circulating over the coils.

Would keeping the door of an electric refrigerator open on a hot summer day cool the kitchen? Can you explain your answer?

The unusual behavior of water. When hot water is cooled, it *contracts* as the temperature drops to about 39° F, or 4° C. Below this temperature, it does not contract as other liquids do when they are cooled, but *expands* until it reaches its freezing point of 0° C. *Hence, water has its greatest density at 4° C.*

This peculiar behavior of water between 39° F and 32° F is of great importance to all of us. For, if water kept contracting until it got down to 32° F, the coldest water would sink to the bottom of a lake, because it would be more *dense* than the water on the bottom. The entire lake would then cool down to 32° F and it would freeze

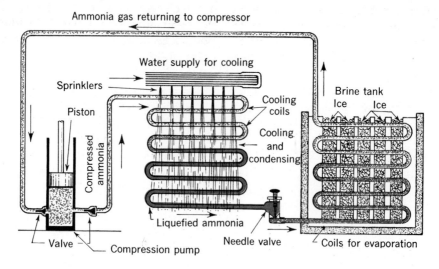

Ammonia gas returning to compressor

Water supply for cooling

Sprinklers

Piston

Cooling coils

Brine tank
Ice   Ice

Compressed ammonia

Cooling and condensing

Liquefied ammonia

Valve

Compression pump

Needle valve

Coils for evaporation

5-17. This diagram shows how the heat of vaporization of a gas is used in the refrigeration process.

from the bottom, killing fish and other animal life. In the summer, there would not be enough heat available to melt all the ice.

Fortunately, this does not happen. When the water is cooled below 39° F, it becomes *less* dense because it expands. *It stays on top, and only the top layer is cooled to the freezing point.* When the water freezes, it continues to expand and the ice floats on top. It acts like a blanket and protects the rest of the water from rapid freezing. (See Fig. 5-18.)

Water close to the surface of ice is at 32° F, while water at the bottom is at 39° F, because it has the greatest density at that temperature. If you ever fished through ice in winter, you know that the fish are usually found at the bottom. The water is about 7 Fahrenheit degrees warmer there than at the surface.

Water is the most important exception to the general rule that a substance *contracts* when it changes from

a liquid to a solid. The volume occupied by ice is about 1.1 times that occupied by the water from which it was formed. This is why ice floats on water. (See Fig. 5-19.)

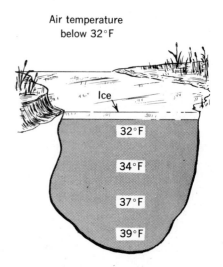

Air temperature below 32°F

Ice

32°F

34°F

37°F

39°F

5-18. When the air temperature is below freezing above the ice layer, the water at the bottom of a lake is warmer than the water near the surface.

Heat transfer. Heat moves from an area of higher temperature to one of lower temperature. When the two temperatures are the same, no more heat transfer will take place. Often this transfer of heat is desirable. For example, when we build a fire in our furnace, the rooms are warmed by the hot air, or hot water, or steam, or by direct radiation. *Heat is transferred from one place to another by conduction, convection, and radiation.* Let us examine these three methods of heat transfer.

Silver *conducts* heat very rapidly and efficiently. If a hot liquid is stirred with a silver spoon, the handle of the spoon becomes hot almost immediately. If you use a wooden spoon, the handle will not even get warm.

Heat from the liquid is transferred to the molecules of a metal that are in contact with the liquid. These molecules then transfer the heat to adjoin-

ing molecules, and so on throughout the entire mass of the metal. *Conduction is the transfer of heat from molecules to adjoining molecules by collision.* Figure 5-20 slows the relative conductivity of several common metals.

Solids are better conductors of heat than liquids; liquids are better than gases. Molecules of most solids are closer together than those of liquids, and the molecules of liquids are much closer together than those of gases. (See Fig. 5-21.)

Poor conductors are good insulators. Materials that are very poor conductors of heat are called *insulators*. Cork, sawdust, and snow have quite a lot of enclosed "dead air" between their particles and are good insulators. "Dead air," or air that does not circulate, is one of the best insulators of heat. Clothes keep us warm in winter principally because of the air in the spaces between the fibers.

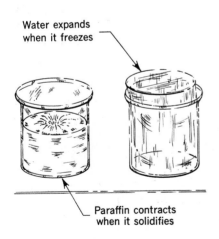

5-19. Most substances, such as paraffin (shown on the left), contract when they become solid. However, water (on the right) is one of the few exceptional substances which will expand upon solidification.

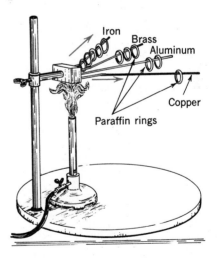

5-20. Conductivities of various metals are compared by the ease with which paraffin rings melt. From the diagram, how does the conductivity of aluminum compare with that of iron?

During the last few years, a great deal of attention has been paid to the problem of home insulation. Many fluffy materials, as well as boards of soft, fibrous texture, are now extensively used as heat insulators. These materials, installed in the outside walls of a building and above ceilings, keep heat from escaping in winter and from entering during the summer, and thus reduce fuel consumption.

Convection takes place in fluids. Warm liquids and gases are lighter than equal volumes that are cooler. Hence, cooler portions sink and push up the lighter, warmer material. *Unequal heating* is responsible for this rising and sinking movement. Currents of liquids and gases that are set up by this unequal heating are called *convection currents*. **Convection is the** *transfer of heat by the movement of liquids and gases.* Why is convection impossible in solids? Explain.

Convection in a liquid may be illustrated by the following experiment. Heat the lower edge of a large glass beaker of water with a very low flame as in Fig. 5-22. Drop a few crystals of dye on the water surface close to the side that is being heated. As the dye dissolves, watch the movement of the colored portions of the fluid in the beaker. This illustrates how convection currents are formed in a heated liquid.

The *hot-air furnace* is a common application of heat transfer by convection. Figure 5-23 shows how the air currents rise and fall in a hot-air furnace system.

Heated gases rise in chimneys by convection. This results in a "draft" of

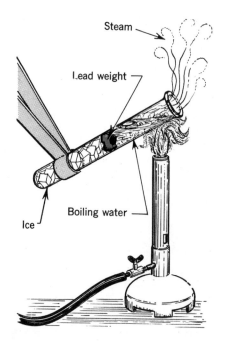

5-21. Because water is a poor conductor of heat, boiling water and ice can exist in the same vessel.

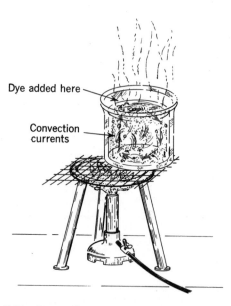

5-22. Convection currents result in fluids because of unequal heating. Arrows indicate circulation of liquid when heat is applied to lower left edge of beaker.

fresh air through the firebox. Many modern furnaces use blowers rather than depending on a natural draft to draw in air through the firebox.

In *hot-water* heating, water is circulated through the radiators in the room by convection. Heat is given up to the cold room, and the cooler denser water flows back to the furnace and is reheated. In some systems a pump is used to force the water through the radiators.

Heat from the sun is received by radiation. If you hold your hand below a lighted electric lamp, you can feel the heat. Since your hand is *below* the lamp, the heat is not transferred by convection. Why not? Conduction will not explain the warmth either because air is a poor conductor of heat. Your hand is warmed by *radia-*

tion, a third method of energy transfer. **Radiation is the transfer of energy in waves through space.** Although conduction and convection must have a material medium for heat transfer, *radiant energy* can be transferred in a vacuum. We continually get heat from the sun by radiation.

One method of heating homes is the use of *radiant heat.* In a radiant-heating system, steam or hot water is circulated through pipes in the floor, walls, or ceilings. These warmed surfaces radiate heat into the room, giving constant temperature even in cold weather. *Solar heating* takes advantage of the sun's energy directly.

Dark-colored objects absorb much radiant energy. For this reason, light-colored clothes are more comfortable in hot weather, since they *reflect* more

5-23. Can you explain from this diagram how a hot-air furnace transfers heat by convection?

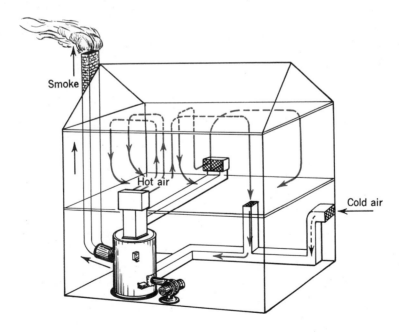

Smoke

Hot air

Cold air

radiant energy than they *absorb*. Polished mirrors also make excellent reflectors of radiant energy. "Thermos" bottles have a mirror-like coating that reflects the radiant energy from hot liquids back into the bottle. This helps to keep the liquid hot for a longer time. Further, there is always a vacuum between the double walls of the container that tends to eliminate heat transfer by conduction and convection. For the same reasons, cold liquids are kept cold for longer periods of time also.

Quick Quiz

1. List three sources of heat other than the burning of fuels.
2. Name two ways in which the expansion of gases differs from that of liquids and solids.
3. Why is it often necessary to leave a space between steel rails when building a railroad during cold weather?
4. Does a thermometer in a kettle of hot water measure the amount of heat contained in the water? Explain.
5. Which way will a bimetal bar made of copper and steel bend if placed in a freezing mixture of water and ice? Explain.
6. What is meant by the mechanical equivalent of heat? What is its numerical value?
7. Why is the specific heat of a substance an important property?
8. Explain why a block of ice in a warm room takes so long to melt.
9. A hot drink burns more when you drink it from a metal cup than from a china cup. Why?
10. As water is cooled from 50° F to 32° F, what happens to its density?
11. Explain how only the top layer of a lake is cooled to the freezing point, while the bottom part does not freeze.
12. Explain and give an example of the transfer of heat by conduction. By convection. By radiation.

C   FUELS AS A SOURCE OF HEAT

What is fuel? Petroleum and natural gas together provide about ¾ of the total U.S. supply of energy. Coal and its products supply most of the remainder. In this section, we shall study about solid and gaseous fuels.

When substances burn, they give off heat. However, this characteristic alone does not make them good fuels. *A fuel is a substance that can be burned to give off heat at a reasonable cost.* Good fuels are convenient to store, leave little unburned residue, and burn clean. Further, the burning fuel should produce no objectionable by-products. Coal, petroleum, and natural gas are examples of good fuels that meet these conditions. Gas and fuel oils leave no ash, produce little smoke when they burn, can be automatically regulated, and are abundant and relatively inexpensive.

All of our common fuels contain carbon. We have seen that this is the case in our study of hydrocarbons. Except for *charcoal* and *coke*, which contain carbon only as a free element, most fuels are mixtures of both free carbon and carbon compounds. Because of its importance in our industry, coal is sometimes called "black gold" or "black diamond." All solid fuels contain some matter that does not form a gas when burned, but remains as *ash*. The amount of ash in a solid fuel affects its value as a fuel.

What fuels shall we use? The kind of fuel used in a community depends chiefly upon its cost and availability. Wood is still being used as a chief fuel in some of our rural areas. Some northwestern communities use sawdust from nearby lumber mills to heat homes and public buildings.

People in communities near deposits of hard or soft coal are likely to utilize these resources. Many industries requiring the use of large amounts of coal are located near these sources of fuel.

Study Fig. 5-24 for comparing heat values of several common fuels.

Coal comes from the distant past. The origin of coal dates back some 300 million years to the *Carboniferous* period of the earth's history. Scientists believe that coal is basically the buried remains of tropical plants that grew a long time ago, when many swampy sections of the earth were covered with very dense vegetation. As huge tree-ferns and mosses died and fell, layer upon layer piled up and decomposed. Eventually these materials became covered with soil and rock. Pressure, heat, and chemical changes slowly continued to convert these remains into what we now call *coal*. It is likely that this process of coal formation continues even today. (See Fig. 5-25.)

Peat is the first stage in the formation of coal. *Peat* is a soft, brown, spongy material made of vegetation that has undergone partial decomposition through the action of heat and pressure. The fibrous structure of peat clearly indicates its plant origin. Peat bogs are found in Michigan, Wiscon-

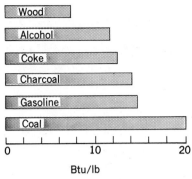

Btu/lb

Heat values of some common fuels (approximate)

5-24. Compare the Btu content per pound of wood with that of coal.

sin, and Pennsylvania. Although peat contains a high percentage of moisture, it has been used as a fuel in Europe for centuries.

Continued decomposition of peat over a long period of time caused it to lose most of its fibrous appearance and to become **lignite,** or "brown coal." It is a harder material than peat, contains less moisture, and a higher percentage of carbon.

5-25. A fossil imprint of an ancient fern plant is clearly recorded in this sample of coal. (National Coal Association)

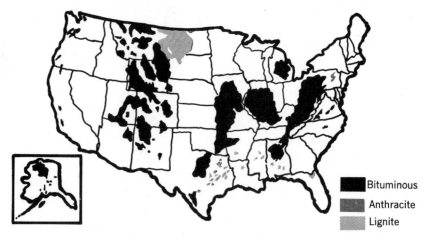

5-26. The United States has about one-third of the world's known supply of coal.

Through the ages, continued heat and pressure have converted some of the lignite deposits into *bituminous* (by-*too*-min-us) or *soft coal*. Bituminous coal contains even less moisture than lignite. However, it contains volatile matter (matter that vaporizes easily) that forms flammable gases when heated.

In some places, notably in eastern Pennsylvania, the folding of the earth's crust has produced still greater pressure. This increase in pressure changed some of the bituminous coal into *anthracite* (*an*-thruh-syte), or *hard coal*. Anthracite usually lies deeper in the ground than bituminous coal. It contains a higher percentage of carbon and a lower percentage of volatile matter.

It may be difficult to picture in our minds the great changes that converted plant materials into black, glossy, hard coal. However, we should remember that these changes took place over millions of years. (See Fig. 5-26.)

Solid fuels vary in composition. We have seen that the moisture and car-bon content of different kinds of solid fuels varies. Even different samples of the same kind of solid fuel show variations in composition. A high percentage of moisture content in a fuel lowers its heat value. Why? Peat and lignite contain much moisture and hence their heat values are low.

In this country we burn little lignite because we have larger supplies of better fuels. Some countries must use peat and lignite even though these are smoky fuels that leave a good deal of ash.

Anthracite sells for a higher price per ton than bituminous coal. It is a cleaner-burning fuel, producing less smoke and odorous gas. Its heat value is higher than that of some bituminous coal. However, *high-grade* bituminous coal furnishes more heat per pound than any other coal.

The most important coal is bituminous. Bituminous coal is the most important solid fuel as well as the most plentiful grade of coal. We are fortunate to have rather large deposits of bituminous coal in the United States. Mined in some thirty-seven states in our country, bituminous coal serves as the chief fuel in steam-electric generating plants.

Unless soft coal is properly burned, a loss of fuel and heat results. The formation of black smoke and soot is caused by incomplete burning of the volatile matter in the coal. If the coal is properly fed into the firebox, less smoke is produced and more heat is obtained. Today, in many factories soft coal is ground into powder and blown into the firebox with a blast of air. In this manner the coal burns like a gas, with greater efficiency.

Anthracite is a good household fuel. Hard coal has a very high percentage of carbon, and is a slow-burning, long-lasting fuel. There is little volatile matter in this fuel, and its burning produces almost no flame or smoke. This fuel is widely used in the eastern part of our country as a household fuel be-

5-28. Red hot coke is being discharged into a railroad car. (Bethlehem Steel Corp.)

cause most of it comes from nearby anthracite deposits in eastern Pennsylvania. (See Fig. 5-27.)

Coke is made from coal. If soft coal is heated between 700° C and 1000° C in the absence of air, it decomposes to form *coal gas, a mixture of liquids,* and a residue called *coke.* A process of this nature is called *destructive distillation. Coke* is a hard, porous, solid fuel. It varies in color from gray to black, and contains a higher percentage of carbon than coal does. Thousands of tons daily are prepared in huge ovens by driving off the combustible materials from bituminous coal. (See Fig. 5-28.)

Most of the coke made today is used by the iron and steel industry. In some cities, soft coal is heated to form coal gas to be used as a fuel. The coke residue is sold as a by-product.

5-27. The "continuous mining" machine can do all the work of cutting, breaking down, and loading coal inside a coal mine. This machine can "chew" about 8 tons per minute. (Joy Manufacturing Co.)

Modern coke ovens produce many valuable by-products. Included among them is *ammonia,* which is used in making fertilizers and explosives. The coke-oven tar is processed into materials used for making dyes, perfumes, flavors, and medicines. Synthetic rubber, antiseptics, anesthetics, and synthetic textile fibers such as nylon, as well as many thousands of other products, are made from substances distilled from bituminous coal.

Coke can be prepared in the laboratory. Coke can be conveniently made in the laboratory by connecting a Pyrex test tube with another ordinary test tube and jet, as shown in Fig. 5-29.

Nearly fill the Pyrex test tube with small pieces of soft coal. Heat the tube strongly with a burner. Light the coal gas that comes from the jet tube. A tar-like liquid condenses in the vertical tube. This liquid contains ammonia, oils, and coal tar. More than one hundred marketable products may be

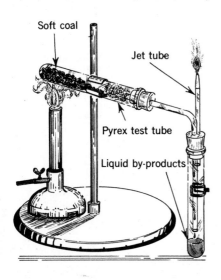

Soft coal

Jet tube

Pyrex test tube

Liquid by-products

5-29. Coke or charcoal can be made in the laboratory with this basic apparatus.

manufactured from the coal tar alone.

After heating the coal for about 10 minutes, break open the Pyrex tube and examine the coke you have made. Ignite it and observe how it burns.

Charcoal. You have probably seen *charcoal* left over from a wood fire or have used charcoal in your cook-outs. To make charcoal in large quantities, furnaces such as the one shown in Fig. 5-30 are used. Wood is loaded on steel cars that are pushed into a heating chamber. Gas is burned in flues that surround the chamber. The heat drives off the volatile matter from the wood. In this destructive distillation of wood, the solid residue is known as **charcoal.**

Besides charcoal, this process yields wood alcohol, acetic acid, wood tar, pitch, and creosote. These useful by-products are as valuable as the charcoal.

Charcoal, like coke, burns with almost no flame because it contains no volatile matter. Coke and charcoal are essentially carbon and they make excellent reducing agents in many chemical processes, as we have seen previously. Charcoal gives a hot, smokeless flame, but it is too expensive for heating homes. There are many industrial uses for charcoal, such as making special steels; and absorbing objectionable substances, as in water purification and air-conditioning.

To make charcoal in the laboratory, put some small pieces of wood in the Pyrex test tube that is connected as shown in Fig. 5-29. Heat the wood strongly for 10 to 15 minutes, burning the gas that comes out of the jet tube. After most of the volatile matter has been driven off, remove the charcoal.

Coal gas. In the manufacture of coke by destructive distillation of bi-

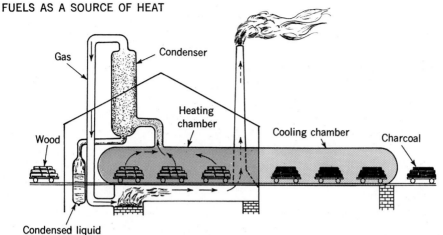

5-30. From the sketch above explain the commercial preparation of charcoal from wood.

tuminous coal, *coal gas* is a valuable by-product. The crude gas contains valuable impurities.

Coal tar, one of these impurities, is removed by cooling the coal gas. Then the gas is "washed" by a spray of cold water, which removes the highly soluble ammonia. In some plants, the ammonia is combined with sulfuric acid to form ammonium sulfate, which is then sold as a fertilizer.

Odorous sulfur compounds are next removed from the coal gas by having them react with iron oxide. The purified gas finally goes to huge storage tanks for ready usage. (See Fig. 5-31.)

Natural gas. Many communities in the United States use *natural gas* as a fuel for cooking and heating. Natural gas is almost pure methane, CH_4. It is formed by the decomposition of organic matter under water. It is sometimes referred to as *marsh gas* because it is found bubbling from the surface of the water of marshy areas.

Natural gas frequently is found underground in regions where coal and petroleum are found. Wells are drilled

through rock layers to the porous sandstone layers that yield the gas. Natural gas is a very desirable fuel, furnishing more heat per cubic foot than do other fuel gases. Gas wells range in depth from a few hundred to several thousand feet.

Today, natural gas is replacing coal gas and other household fuels. It is sup-

5-31. These spherical tanks are most efficient for storing butane, propane, and other gaseous fuels under pressure. (Standard Oil Co. (NJ))

5-32. Natural gas pipelines are laid under rivers and over hills and mountains. (El Paso Natural Gas Co.)

plied to most cities and towns in our country by means of a network of underground pipe lines totaling over 400,000 miles in length. (See Fig. 5-32.)

Water gas is an important fuel for industrial purposes. It may sound strange to talk about *water gas* since water will not burn. Yet water, in the form of steam, and hot coke combine to make an important industrial fuel.

Burning coke is first heated white hot by blowing air through it. The "air run" is necessary in order to heat up the coke. The supply of air is then cut off

and steam is allowed to pass through the hot coke. After a short time, the steam is shut off and the coke is reheated by a blast of air. This alternating process continues until all of the coke is used up. Water gas is produced only during the "steam run." In the reaction between the coke (carbon) and steam (water), carbon monoxide and hydrogen are produced and both of these gases are combustible,

$$C + H_2O \rightarrow CO \uparrow + H_2 \uparrow$$

The mixture of carbon monoxide and hydrogen is called *water gas.* It may be used either as a fuel or as an industrial source of carbon monoxide and of hydrogen.

Water gas is frequently enriched. Water gas is often enriched by mixing it with other fuel hydrocarbon gases that have higher heat values. This is accomplished in a chamber that is filled with loosely stacked bricks. The waste gas from the "air run" of the making of water gas heats the bricks red hot. Fuel oil is then sprayed into the chamber. When the large molecules of fuel oil strike these hot bricks they are "cracked" into smaller gaseous hydrocarbon molecules. These gases are then fed into another chamber for mixing with the water gas.

A newer method of enriching water gas is to add propane (C_3H_8) or butane (C_4H_{10}) to it. You will recall that propane and butane are gases obtained from the refining of petroleum, or from natural gas.

Enriching water gas increases its fuel value. It also gives the gas an odor, which is desirable if the gas is to be used at home. Obviously, since both hydrogen and carbon monoxide are odorless, a person could not smell them if a leak developed in the gas line.

Bottled gas. Propane, butane, or a mixture of the two gases, can be compressed into a *liquid* and stored in steel cylinders. "Bottled gas" provides gas of high fuel value at a reasonable cost at locations that are remote from regular gas-line service. The liquid reverts to its original gaseous state when the pressure is reduced. The "bottles" may be conveniently refilled from a special delivery truck.

What happens when a hydrocarbon burns? We have seen that many liquid and gaseous fuels are composed primarily of hydrocarbons. Even coal is essentially composed of hydrocarbons, although it generally contains some carbon in a free state. Coke and charcoal

5-33. Researcher studies a new fuel to meet demands of space-age industries. (Aerojet General Corp.)

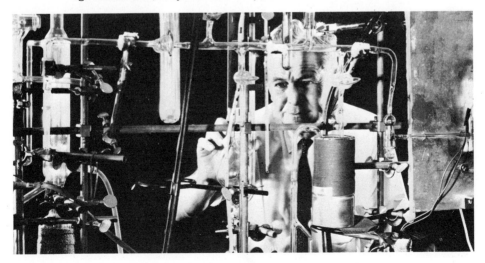

are forms of *amorphous,* or noncrystalline carbon.

Generally speaking, when a hydrocarbon burns, the products formed are carbon dioxide, carbon monoxide, and water, with the liberation of heat energy. We get **complete combustion** when a fuel burns with an *excess* of oxygen. For example, when methane burns under this condition, carbon dioxide, water, and heat are the products formed,

$$CH_4 + 2O_2 \rightarrow CO_2 \uparrow + 2H_2O + heat$$

On the other hand, when there is a *deficient* supply of oxygen available for combustion of the hydrocarbon, **incomplete combustion** occurs. Under this condition, there is not enough oxygen for complete combustion to take place, and the resulting products are carbon monoxide, water, and heat,

$$2CH_4 + 3O_2 \rightarrow 2CO \uparrow + 4H_2O + heat$$

Breathing carbon monoxide gas can cause death or permanent brain damage. The gas combines with the *hemoglobin* of the red blood cells more readily than oxygen does. This makes these cells useless for carrying the vital oxygen that our tissues need.

Crystallized carbon. Carbon also occurs in two crystalline forms, *diamond* and *graphite*. This is in addition to the *amorphous,* or noncrystalline forms contained in coke and charcoal.

Under conditions of great heat and pressure, carbon crystallizes to form a

5-34. Heat and pressure have produced these man-made diamonds. (General Electric)

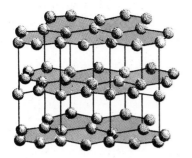 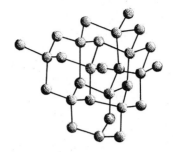

5-35. The arrangement of carbon atoms in "slippery" graphite crystals (left) compared with "hard" diamond (right).

very hard substance called diamond. It is the purest form of carbon. Diamond is the hardest natural substance known. Because of this, industrial diamonds are used for cutting and grinding metals, and for bits in drilling oil wells and tunnels.

The principal natural sources of diamond are the Belgian Congo, Brazil, and South Africa. When found in the mine, diamonds do not have the shape or luster of gems. Their brilliance and beauty depend on the skillful manner with which they are cut and polished.

After many years of research, scientists have learned to make small diamonds for industrial purposes. A pressure of about 400 tons per square inch and a temperature of about 5000° F are required to convert high-carbon compounds into diamonds. These synthetic diamonds possess the same properties that the natural diamonds do and are being widely used in industry. (See Fig. 5-34.)

Graphite. The word *graphite* comes from a Greek word meaning "to write." Graphite mixed with clay is used as the "lead" in your writing pencil. Particles of graphite are often suspended in oil and used as a *lubricant*. Graphite

is also used as a *moderator* in nuclear reactors, serving to slow down fast-moving neutrons.

Graphite is a soft, grayish-black, greasy substance. Its carbon atoms form a crystal pattern that is different from that of the carbon atoms of diamond. (See Fig. 5-35.) As a result of the unusual arrangement of the carbon atoms, graphite has quite different properties. It is as soft as diamond is hard. It is a fairly good conductor of electricity, while diamond does not conduct electricity at all.

Natural graphite is mined in Ceylon and Siberia. New York and Pennsylvania also produce some graphite. Artificial graphite is sometimes made from anthracite coal or coke in an electric furnace.

Quick Quiz

1. What are some characteristics of a good fuel? List three advantages of gas as a fuel.
2. Trace briefly the stages in the development of coal.
3. Compare the carbon content and the moisture content of anthracite with that of bituminous coal.

4. What are two advantages of anthracite over bituminous coal?
5. Describe how coke is made. What are some of the other products that are obtained from the destructive distillation of soft coal?
6. How is charcoal made? Name four uses of charcoal.
7. What are two widely used household fuels in your community? Why are these particular fuels used?
8. What is the composition of natural gas? Discuss some of its advantages as a fuel.
9. What products are formed by the complete combustion of a hydrocarbon fuel? Incomplete combustion of a hydrocarbon fuel?
10. What is amorphous carbon? List two examples.
11. How are diamonds produced in the earth's crust?

SUMMARY

Thermometers can be checked by using melting ice and boiling water. At absolute zero, the collision of molecules ceases.

Heat is a form of energy. The hotter the object, the more violent the motion of its molecules and the greater their energy. Temperature is a measure of the tendency of an object to transfer heat to, or absorb heat from, other objects. Gases expand more than liquids, and liquids more than solids.

Heat is transferred from one object to another by three methods: conduction, convection, and radiation. Conduction is the transfer of energy from molecule to molecule by collision. Convection is the transfer of heat by movement of fluids. Radiation is the transfer of energy by waves.

Fuels are substances that can be burned to give off heat at a reasonable cost. They contain carbon as an element or in compounds. Coal was formed from the buried remains of plant materials. Peat is the fibrous material that is the first stage in the formation of coal. Lignite, or brown coal, is the next stage. Through the ages, lignite has changed to bituminous coal, or soft coal. In some places bituminous coal has become anthracite, or hard coal.

Coke is made by the destructive distillation of soft coal. Coal gas and many other substances are obtained as by-products. Charcoal is made by heating wood in the absence of air or oxygen.

Diamond and graphite are forms of crystallized carbon. Diamond is one of the hardest and graphite one of the softest solids known.

CHAPTER REVIEW

Vocabulary

Match the words in Column A with the *best* response in Column B. Do not write in your book.

Column A	Column B
1. Celsius	a. amount of heat required to raise the temperature of 1 lb of water 1 F°
2. temperature	

3. heat
4. calorie
5. Btu
6. heat of fusion
7. heat of vaporization
8. conduction
9. convection
10. radiation
11. peat
12. bituminous
13. anthracite
14. destructive distillation
15. charcoal
16. natural gas
17. water gas
18. CO_2 and H_2O
19. amorphous
20. graphite

b. composed chiefly of methane
c. first stage in coal development
d. products of complete combustion of a hydrocarbon
e. energy possessed by a substance because of its molecular motion
f. transfer of thermal energy through space
g. crystalline form of carbon
h. hard coal
i. amount of heat absorbed by a solid in changing to a liquid
j. amount of heat absorbed by a liquid in changing to a gas
k. non-crystalline
l. thermometer scale
m. amount of heat required to raise the temperature of 1 g of water 1 C°
n. transfer of heat by movement of fluids
o. process of breaking up a substance by heating it in a closed vessel without air or oxygen
p. material produced by destructive distillation of wood
q. soft coal
r. mixture of CO and H_2
s. measure of the tendency of an object to transfer heat to, or absorb heat from, other objects
t. transfer of heat from molecules to adjoining molecules

Questions: Group A

1. Why are pressure cookers used in high altitudes? How do they operate?
2. What happens to liquid helium when cooled to a temperature near absolute zero?
3. Where does our radiant energy come from?
4. What provision is made in the construction of concrete highways to allow for expansion or contraction?
5. What is the Celsius temperature at absolute zero?
6. Do you get more gasoline for your money in the winter or in summer, providing the cost per gallon is the same?
7. Why do solids expand when their temperature is increased?
8. What unusual property do some materials exhibit near absolute zero?
9. Why does steam at 100° C produce more severe burns than hot water at 100° C?
10. Mention several advantages and disadvantages of soft coal as a fuel.

11. Where is anthracite mined in the United States? Bituminous coal?
12. Name five substances produced by the destructive distillation of wood.
13. Describe how coal gas is made and purified.
14. How is water gas prepared? How is it enriched?

Questions: Group B

1. Why does a piece of ice float in water?
2. Under what conditions does boiling of a liquid occur?
3. Does the coefficient of linear expansion depend on the unit of length used?
4. A platinum wire may be tightly sealed into the end of heat-softened glass tubing, but a copper wire forms a loose seal with the glass. Can you suggest a possible reason for this?
5. The air above the ice in a pond is 20° F. What is the probable temperature of (a) the upper surface of the ice; (b) the water just beneath the ice layer; and (c) the water at the bottom of the pond?
6. Why is shiny aluminum foil sometimes used in the walls and ceilings of a building? Explain its action.
7. Explain what is meant by heat of fusion. Vaporization.
8. Why does a cold, thick drinking glass often break when boiling water is poured into it?
9. The specific heat of aluminum is 0.21. What does this mean?
10. Why do oceanic islands have relatively uniform temperatures?
11. Why was the plant material of the Carboniferous period not decayed completely?
12. Explain why the "air-run" is necessary in the production of water gas.
13. What is the composition of bottled gas? Explain its usefulness.
14. Explain why the breathing of carbon monoxide gas is dangerous.
15. How are synthetic diamonds prepared? List several uses for diamonds.
16. If diamond is strongly heated in an excess of oxygen, what is formed?

Problems

1. How much heat is available in a carload of coal (60 tons) if a test sample of it shows 13,500 Btu/lb?
2. How much energy is needed to heat 1050 g of lead from 25° C to 285° C, if the specific heat of lead is 0.03 cal/g C°?
3. A steel rail is exactly 39 ft long at 0° C. What will be the increase in length on a day when the temperature is 25° C, if the coefficient of linear expansion for steel is 0.000013/C°?
4. An oil tank holds 275 gallons at 30° C. What will be the volume of the oil when it cools to 10° C, if the coefficient of volume expansion of the oil is 0.001/C°?
5. Determine the number of calories of heat required to change 40 grams of water at 20° C to steam at 100° C.

6. Compute the Btu required to heat 10 lb of water from 40° F to its boiling temperature.

7. A sample of coal contains 13,500 Btu/pound. If all of this energy could be converted without loss, how many foot-pounds of work could a pound of this coal perform?

8. Determine the number of calories of heat necessary to change 10 grams of ice at 0° C to water at 100° C.

9. A cake of ice weighs 90,800 grams. How many calories will it absorb in melting? If the water freezes again, how many calories of heat will be liberated if the temperature did not change?

10. How much heat in calories will be required to vaporize 4200 grams of water at 100° C? How many Btu?

WAVE MOTION

6

WAVE MOTION

A WAVE MOTION AND SOUND

Energy and sound. We have seen that kinetic energy of motion and potential energy of position or condition are interchangeable. We also learned that heat energy was transferred from one point to another by the vibration of molecules of a substance, by the motion of fluids, and by means of waves through space. In this section we shall examine more closely the transfer of *energy* by means of wave motion. While there are several types of waves, each having certain properties and characteristics, all waves have some fundamental properties in common.

If you put tiny paper riders on a string of a piano, and strike the proper key, the paper riders will dance about as the string *vibrates.* Watch some sand or paper clips dance on a drumhead as you beat the drum, or listen to the ringing of a buzzer! The sound lasts only as long as the vibrations continue.

Sound may also be produced when objects collide. You notice this when you drop a book on the floor or let a drop of water fall into a pan. The collision causes vibrations. *Sound is a form of energy produced by the vibration of matter.*

Matter is necessary for sound to be propagated. A simple demonstration in the laboratory will show you that sound energy will not travel through a vacuum. (See Fig. 6-1.) As air is pumped from the bell jar, the sound gets weaker and weaker and finally disappears. To converse as you walked about on the airless moon, you would need pressurized helmets equipped with a radio. Some material medium such as a solid, liquid, or gas is needed to move sound energy from one place to another, so radio would have to be used.

Experiments show that sound travels best through solids. The dental drill sounds very loud to the patient because sound carries so well through the solid bone material of the skull. Observe how much louder the snap of a stretched rubber band sounds when you hold one end in your teeth!

If you hold a vibrating tuning fork firmly against one end of a stick and press the other end against the table top, the sound is louder than if the fork were allowed to vibrate only in the air.

If you have ever struck two stones together while you were swimming under water, you probably realized how much louder the sound was. Liquids are also good conductors of sound. It is known that certain animals, such as porpoises, communicate by underwater sounds. You will learn more about underwater sound when you read about *Sonar* later in this section.

The table below shows a comparison of the velocity of sound in air, water, and steel.

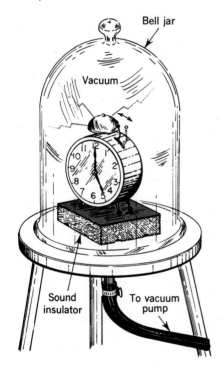

6-1. Demonstration to show that sound waves do not pass through a vacuum.

VELOCITY OF SOUND WAVES IN DIFFERENT SUBSTANCES AT 20° C

Air	1130 ft/sec
Water	4760 ft/sec
Steel	16,400 ft/sec

The speed of sound varies with temperature. Here is a way of measuring the approximate speed of sound. Stand in front of a good sound reflector, such as the side of a large building, several hundred feet away. Make a short, sharp sound, such as a yelp, or a handclap, or fire a blank cartridge from a pistol. With a stopwatch, find out how long it takes for the sound to travel to the wall and be *reflected* back as an echo.

On a cold day, if the wall is 1100 feet away, you should hear the echo in about two seconds after making the sound. Since it takes one second for sound to go from you to the wall, and one second to return, the sound travels at a speed of 1100 feet in one second.

Accurate measurements show that the speed of sound is greater on warm days than on cold days. Sound travels through air at about 1090 ft/sec when the temperature is 0° C. As the air gets warmer, sound travels about 2 ft/sec faster for each rise of one Celsius degree. This means that if the air temperature is 20° C, sound will go 40 ft/sec (2 × 20) faster, or 1130 ft/sec (1090 + 40).

It is easy to estimate how far away a lightning flash is by noting the lapse of time before you hear the thunder. Assuming that sound travels about 1100 feet per second, a count of 5 seconds means that the lightning is about a mile away.

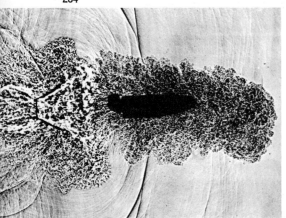

6-2. This amazing photo, taken in less than one-millionth of a second, "shows" the sound wave produced by a gun shell explosion before it can be heard. (Wide World Photos)

SAMPLE PROBLEM

A hunter fires a rifle and hears an echo from a vertical cliff 2.5 seconds later. How far away is the cliff if the air temperature is 28° C?

SOLUTION:

Step 1. The speed of sound in air is 1090 ft/sec at 0° C. At 28° C, sound travels 2 ft/sec/C° × 28 C°, or 56 ft/sec faster than at 0° C. Therefore the speed is 1090 ft/sec + 56 ft/sec, or 1146 ft/sec.

Step 2. In 2.5 seconds, the sound travels 1146 ft/sec × 2.5 sec, or 2865 ft.

Step 3. Therefore, the cliff is 2865 ÷ 2, or approximately 1430 ft away.

Wave characteristics. The study of wave motion is of such basic importance in science that we shall discuss it in some detail. Most waves are invisible. You cannot see sound waves or those of heat, light, and radio. However, since all waves have many common characteristics, we shall first study wave motion that we can see.

Float a cork in a quiet pool of water. Then drop a stone in the water nearby. The familiar circular waves travel outwardly, and the cork bobs up and down as the waves pass it. The cork shows what happens to the water surface when a disturbance passes through it. The important thing to observe is that the cork—and therefore the water surface—*did not* move along with the wave. As the wave or disturbance passed, the water itself just rose and sank a little, and finally returned to its original level. *Only the wave pattern of* **crests** *and* **troughs** *moved outward, not the water.*

Instead of dropping a stone into water, repeatedly tap the water with your finger, sending out a regular series of waves as shown in Fig. 6-3. Let us imagine that we can stop the motion for a moment. The distance measured from the crest of one wave to the crest of the adjoining wave, or from the trough to trough, is called the **wavelength.** The material that carries the wave or transfers the energy is called the **medium.** In this case, it is water. The *vertical* distance that a particle of the medium moves from its undisturbed position to the top of a crest or to the bottom of a trough is called the **amplitude.** The **frequency** refers to the number of waves that pass any given point in a certain period of time, usually one second.

The amplitude of a wave depends upon its energy. Clearly, if you tap the water gently, the amplitude will be very small. However, if you drop a large boulder into the water, you will produce a mighty wave of large amplitude.

As the wave travels along, it loses some of its energy through friction, and

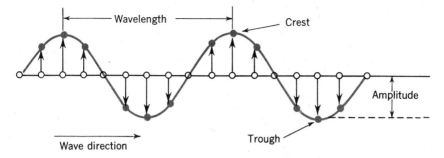

6-3. The movement of water particles, as a wave passes, on the surface of the water. The diagram shows a vertical cross-section of the disturbance at a given time.

the energy is also spread out over a longer wave front. Hence, the amplitude becomes smaller and smaller, until finally the wave dies out. This means that its energy has been dissipated into heat.

6-4. A ripple tank is used in the laboratory to study wave motion. (Educational Services, Inc.)

The ripple tank. Many important and fascinating experiments with water waves can be accomplished with a *ripple tank*. You can make one from an old window sash. As shown in Fig. 6-4, you can send waves on the surface of a thin layer of water in a glass-bottom tray such as the pane of a window. A light above the surface of the water is used so that shadows of the waves are projected onto a sheet of paper placed on the floor below.

Instead of tapping the water with your finger to produce waves, you can use a *rippler* run by a toy motor.

A hand-operated *stroboscope* can be used to "freeze" the motion in order to study various wave patterns. The stroboscope is a device which enables you to "stop" repetitive motion. That is, it makes moving objects appear to stand still. You can make one by cutting equally-spaced slots along the edge of a phonograph record as shown in Fig. 6-5. Look at the wave shadows through the slots, rotating the disk at various speeds, until the pattern seems to stand still.

What are transverse waves? You can easily represent the motion of surface waves in water by tying one end

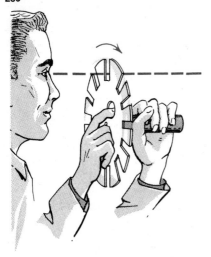

6-5. If the 12-slit stroboscope makes 2 revolutions in one second, you can "stop" repetitive motion of 1/24th-second-period.

of a long rope (or coiled spring) to your classroom wall and sharply shaking the other end up and then down as shown in Fig. 6-6. You will be able to observe the pulse move down the rope and reflect from the wall, similar to that of a water wave. Waves of this type are called *transverse waves*. This means that the parts of the rope or the particles of water move essentially *up and down* while the wave

itself moves along *horizontally*. We define a *transverse wave as one in which the particles of the medium move at right angles to the direction of motion of the wave.*

Longitudinal waves. There is another type of wave which should be considered in our study of wave motion. To demonstrate this, stretch a long, flexible, coiled spring vertically from a ceiling or high stand, as shown in Fig. 6-7. The toy called "Slinky" is excellent for this purpose. At the top of the spring, pinch a few coils of the wire together and release them suddenly, and watch the waves travel downward along the spring. These pulses are *not* made of the crests and troughs like those of a transverse wave. Instead, they contain *compressions*, where a few turns of the spring are bunched together, followed by *rarefactions* (rare-eh-*fak*-shuns), where the turns of wire are stretched apart. This type of wave is called a *longitudinal wave*. You can think of the compressions and rarefactions as corresponding to the crests and troughs of a transverse wave. (See Fig. 6-7.)

Observe that, while the wave moves lengthwise along the vertically-hung

6-6. A transverse wave moving to the right is demonstrated with a rope.

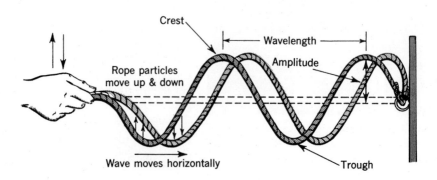

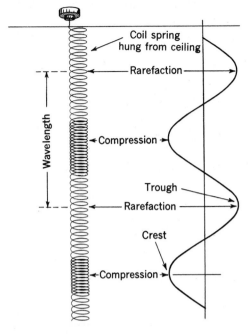

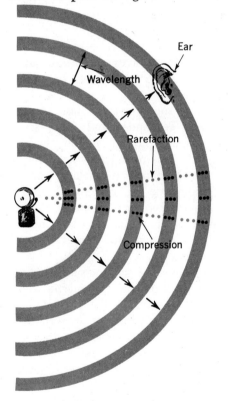

6-7. Compressions in a longitudinal wave (left) may be compared to crests in a transverse wave (right).

through all phases of matter: solids, liquids, and gases. Sound waves are longitudinal waves because the particles of the medium vibrate back and forth along the direction of motion. When even a loud sound wave travels through air, the *amplitude* of vibration of the air molecules is only about a millionth of a millimeter! (See Fig. 6-8.)

A transverse disturbance in a material medium, however, travels only *through* solids. This fact supports the theory that the core of the earth must be liquid, since transverse waves are unable to pass through it. The trans-

spring, no one turn of wire runs along with it down the spring. Any given turn of wire slides back and forth only a short distance and passes the energy along the entire length of the spring. Hence, a **longitudinal wave** is one in which *the particles of the medium move back and forth in the same direction that the wave itself moves.*

You may think of the wavelength of a longitudinal wave as the distance from one compression to the next, or from one rarefaction to the next. The *amplitude* is the maximum distance forward or backward from its undisturbed position that any particle (in this case a single turn of wire) of the medium moves. How could you use "Slinky" to demonstrate transverse waves?

Sound waves are longitudinal waves. Longitudinal waves can pass

6-8. The vibrating bell (left) causes a sphere of compressions and rarefactions of the air molecules.

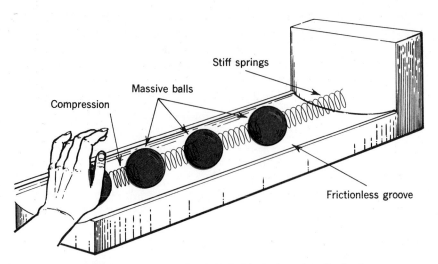

6-9. A sudden shove on the ball (left) starts a longitudinal wave that moves back and forth.

verse water waves discussed earlier do not pass *through* water, only along its surface.

How sound waves pass through matter. To understand how sound waves pass through matter, look at Fig. 6-9. This model shows a series of steel balls connected by elastic springs, all sliding on a "frictionless" groove. The balls represent the atoms of some elastic medium such as steel, and the spring represents the forces between the atoms.

Suppose you gave a sudden shove to the left-hand ball. Its inertia would carry it forward to the right so that the spring in front of it would be compressed. This would shove the next ball forward and the compression would travel from ball to ball setting up a longitudinal disturbance. This disturbance would then be reflected back and forth from end to end until all its energy is used up.

Now relate in imagination the above experiment with that shown in Fig. 6-10. When you stroke the rod with a damp cloth until it squeals, high-frequency sound waves are generated that reflect back and forth from one end of the rod to the other. These *longitudinal* disturbances along the rod cause the pith ball to bounce away.

The disturbances that run through the rod do more than kick out the pith ball at the end—they also disturb the neighboring air molecules in the same way. This creates the sound waves that you hear as a squeal.

Why does the speed of sound through different media vary? Refer again to Fig. 6-9. Suppose we replace the balls with some that have greater mass, and hence more inertia. Clearly, they will be more sluggish, and the *elastic* forces will not be able to whip them back and forth as rapidly. Therefore, we say that the waves will travel at slower speeds.

Next try changing the springs instead of the balls. Give the springs more elastic strength by making them stiffer. Now they can exert more force on the balls and speed up the wave motion.

We can draw several tentative conclusions from this discussion: (1) the greater the *elasticity* of the medium, the *greater* the wave velocity, and (2) the greater the *density* of the medium, the *less* is the wave velocity. Of course, our conclusions would have to be verified by a series of laboratory investigations. Indeed, experiments show that sound travels more rapidly through solids and liquids than through gases because the ratio of *elasticity to density* is greater.

We have seen that the speed of sound increases as the air gets warmer. Although the elasticity of the air remains the same with increasing temperature, the density decreases, hence the ratio of elasticity to density increases.

The sensation of sound is produced in the brain. Let us trace the action from the sound wave to the sensation of hearing.

Sound waves from a telephone receiver enter the ear as shown in Fig. 6-11. The *outer ear* is shaped to collect the waves and lead them down the *ear canal* to the *eardrum*. The sound waves cause this thin membrane to vibrate. As the eardrum vibrates, three little hinged bones in the *middle ear* pass the vibration along to the *inner ear*.

The inner ear is filled with liquid in which are found the many *end-fibers* of the *auditory nerve*. As the sound waves spread through the liquid, they vibrate these nerve endings. This causes the auditory nerve to send electric disturbances to the auditory center of the brain, which produces the sensation we recognize as sound.

What determines the pitch of sound? The frequency of a vibrating object or of a wave is the number of complete vibrations in a certain period of time. This is usually measured by the number of waves that pass a given point in one second. Pitch refers to the effect of frequency on our

6-10. Energy contained in the longitudinal disturbance set up in metal bar causes the pith ball to vibrate.

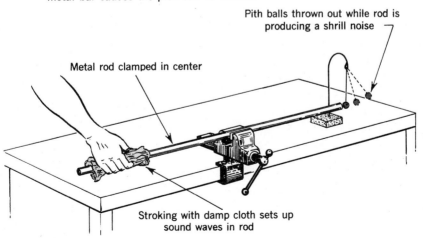

Pith balls thrown out while rod is producing a shrill noise ⌐

Metal rod clamped in center

Stroking with damp cloth sets up sound waves in rod

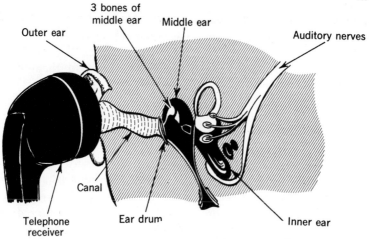

3 bones of
middle ear   Middle ear

Outer ear   Auditory nerves

Canal

Telephone   Ear drum   Inner ear
receiver

6-11. Sound energy from a telephone receiver excites the auditory nerve fibers of the inner ear to cause the sensation of hearing.

ears. The greater the number of waves per second that strike our eardrums, the higher is the pitch of the sound. The common unit for expressing frequency is *vps*, meaning "vibrations per second," or *cps*, meaning "cycles per second." Humans are capable of hearing sound if the frequency is between about 20 vps and 20,000 vps.

6-12. Wave pattern on the top is twice the frequency of wave on the bottom. The two waves have the same amplitude. (RCA Laboratories, Princeton, NJ)

These limits vary considerably with different people. And they also vary with the same people at different times during their lifetime. The upper limit falls off considerably as we get older. Many animals, such as dogs and bats, can hear sounds of much higher frequency than humans.

Low-frequency waves, say from 20 to 200 vps, produce deep bass (base) tones. *High-frequency* waves, from 8000 vps and up, produce high-pitched or shrill tones. (See Fig. 6-12.)

Ultrasonics. Sounds whose frequencies are above 20,000 vps are called **ultrasonic.** These sounds cannot be heard by humans. Today, industry makes wide use of ultrasonics. Objects can be cleaned by dipping them into a liquid in which ultrasonic waves are generated. Objects are tested for cracks or flaws by passing ultrasonic waves through them. Ultrasonic waves are used by dentists in the cleaning of teeth, and they also have various medical applications. (See Fig. 6-13.)

Sonar is used for underwater surveying, detection, navigation, and communication. It makes use of a narrow beam of ultrasonic waves, just as *radar* uses a beam of high-frequency radio waves. In sonar a pulsed beam is sent through the water and reflected back to the receiver.

The *fathometer*, which is used to measure ocean depths, makes use of sonar. Sonar is used by submarine crews to detect the presence of other ships and for help in navigating. Commercial fishermen may even use sonar to help locate schools of fish. Certain animals, particularly bats and porpoises, make use of well-developed, *natural* sonar systems.

Frequency and wavelength are related. Consider what happens when a *tuning fork* vibrates and sends out an expanding "bubble" of waves like that diagrammed in Fig. 6-14. Suppose that the fork has a frequency of 500 vps. That is, it sends out 500 complete waves in one second. If the waves are each 2 ft long, and are placed end-to-end as shown in the diagram, at the end of one second the first wave must be 1000 ft away (500 waves, each 2 ft long, have left the fork). In other words, it must have traveled at a speed of 1000 ft/sec. Notice that this speed is obtained by multiplying the frequency (500) by the wavelength (2). This fact can be expressed as the equation,

$$V = F \times L$$

where V is the velocity, F the frequency of vibration, and L the wavelength. This equation is of considerable importance in the study of science because it can be used for *all* kinds of waves as well as for sound waves.

For any one kind of wave in any one medium for a particular temperature. the velocity V, does not change. If the frequency is doubled to 1000 vps, the wavelength becomes half as much, or 1 ft. Likewise, if the frequency is cut to 250 vps, the wavelength becomes 4 ft. The high-pitched, high-frequency sounds have short wavelengths. The wavelengths of *audible sounds* range from less than an inch to about 55 feet.

6-13. Sound waves in this ultrasonic washing machine clean by forming and collapsing small bubbles on the surface of this electrical circuit panel. (Acoustica Associates, Inc.)

SAMPLE PROBLEM

The musical tone called "middle A" is produced by a sound wave whose frequency is 440 vps. What is the wavelength of sound of this frequency, if the temperature of the air is 68° F (20° C)?

SOLUTION:

Step 1. The velocity of sound at 20° C is 1090 ft/sec + 2 ft/sec C° × 20 C°, or 1130 ft/sec.

Step 2. $V = F \times L$, or $L = V/F$

Step 3. Substituting,

$$L = \frac{1130 \text{ ft/sec}}{440 \text{ waves/sec}}$$

$$= 2.57 \text{ ft/wave}$$

What determines the loudness of a sound? The more energy a wave contains, the greater its amplitude. The effect of this energy on our ears is called *loudness.*

A sound becomes fainter as you go farther away because the amplitude of the wave rapidly decreases. When you are twice as far away, it sounds only one-fourth as loud. When you are three times the distance away from the sound source, it sounds one-ninth as loud. We say that the *intensity* or loudness *of sound varies inversely with the square of the distance.* This is the same "inverse-square law" that applies to gravity, heat, light, and radio waves.

The inverse-square relationship holds *only* in "free space," when the waves are not reflected or focused. For example, it does not hold true in your classroom. Here the sound reflected from the walls and ceiling *reinforces* the original sounds. Also, if you *focus* the sound by using a *megaphone,* the sound doesn't fade away as rapidly.

Measuring the loudness of sound can be accomplished by using a *decibel meter.* The sound waves strike a microphone producing an electric current the size of which depends on the loudness. The current is then amplified and registered on a meter calibrated in *decibels,* which are *the units of sound intensity.*

6-14. Five hundred waves per second, each two feet long, placed end-to-end extend 1000 feet, or the frequency times the wavelength equals the velocity.

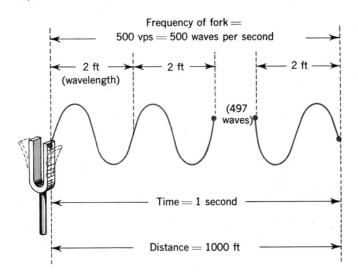

A sound that is *barely audible* to a person with good hearing is assigned a value of *0 decibels* (*db*). This is called the *threshold of hearing*. A sound is rated as 1 db louder than another if it is just enough louder so that you can detect the slight difference. Decibel ratings of some common sounds are given in the table below.

Sound	Decibels
Threshold of hearing	0
Whisper	10–20
Quiet office	20–40
Automobile	40–50
Conversation	60
Heavy traffic	70–80
Air drills, riveters	90–100
Thunder	110
Threshold of pain	120

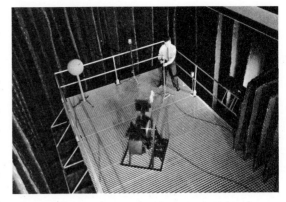

6-15. This ultra-soundproof room is used by physicists for conducting experiments in a quiet environment. (RCA Laboratories, Princeton, NJ)

Acoustics. We speak of the acoustics (uh-*koo*-stix) of a building meaning the "hearing qualities" it has. That is, if a building is so designed that the audience can hear well, we say it has good acoustics. The word *acoustics* also refers to the branch of science that deals with the study of sound. (See Fig. 6-15.)

We have already referred to an *echo* as a reflected sound. But you cannot hear the echo if the reflected sound gets back to you sooner than about one-tenth of a second after you heard the original sound. Since sound can travel a little over 100 ft in this time, it is clear that the reflecting surface must be more than 50 ft away if you are to hear the echo.

In some places, as in a steep-walled canyon or in an auditorium, the sound waves may be reflected back and forth several times. This gives rise to *reverberation* (ree-vur-ber-*ay*-shun), or multiple echoes. If the walls of a canyon strongly reflect the waves, the reverberation period remains audible too long and produces poor acoustics. In that case, the walls and ceilings may be covered with *acoustical tile* or some other material to absorb some of the sound energy.

Quick Quiz

1. What is sound? What causes it?
2. How would you demonstrate that sound does not pass through a vacuum?
3. Through what phase of matter does sound travel fastest? Slowest?
4. How would you show that sound travels through liquids? Solids?
5. Explain the meaning of ultrasonics.
6. How many times greater than the speed of sound in air is the speed of sound in steel?
7. How much faster does sound travel through air at 30° C than at 0° C?
8. Calculate the speed of sound in air at −20° C.

9. What is meant by amplitude of a sound wave? What is the effect of amplitude of a sound wave on its loudness?

10. Explain the difference between transverse and longitudinal waves.

11. A student "freezes" the motion of a pendulum bob at one end of its swing with a 2-slit stroboscope that rotates at two revolutions per second. How many times does the student see the pendulum in one second? What is the *time* for one complete sweep of the pendulum bob?

12. What is the difference between frequency of sound and its pitch?

B SOUND AND MUSIC

Noise differs from a musical tone. When you strike your desk with a ruler, or drop a drinking glass on the floor, *irregular* vibrations are produced. The resulting sound is displeasing to the ear and is termed *noise*. A *noise has a very irregular pattern of vibration.*

All musical tones have a very *regular* frequency rate. Their wave patterns may be very simple like the two wave forms shown in Fig. 6-16, or they may be complex as shown in Fig. 6-17. However, the basic frequency pattern of a musical tone remains unchanged.

Generally musical tones have a pleasing effect on the ear. You may find noises pleasant or unpleasant. The distinction, however, is not whether you like or dislike them, but in the regularity or irregularity of their wave patterns.

Characteristics of a musical tone. A musical tone can be recognized by its *pitch, loudness,* and *quality.* In the last section we discussed the first two of these, pitch and loudness. We saw that pitch depends upon the frequency and that loudness depends upon the energy, or the amplitude, of the sound wave. But what is meant by *quality?*

Suppose that a pianist and a clarinetist in the next room take turns playing a note of the *same* pitch and loudness. You could still tell them apart, even if you could not see the instruments. It is this third characteristic, called *tone quality,* that helps you to identify the source of the sound. *The quality of a musical tone depends on the complexity of its wave pattern.*

Sound waves can be changed to electrical impulses and displayed on a screen by a laboratory instrument called an *oscilloscope.* This device can make the pattern of waves visible so that measurements and comparisons can be made. Now examine Figures 6-16 and 6-17 again. Notice how the waves differ in detail. It is differences such as these that determine the quality of a musical tone.

The Doppler effect. You may have heard the pitch of the horn on an approaching car drop abruptly as it passed by quickly. The *pitch* of the horn changes, even though the *frequency* of the sound which the horn emits is constant. The pitch of a sound produced by a vibrating object depends upon the frequency of vibration. However, the pitch of the sound you actually hear, depends upon the number of vibrations per second that

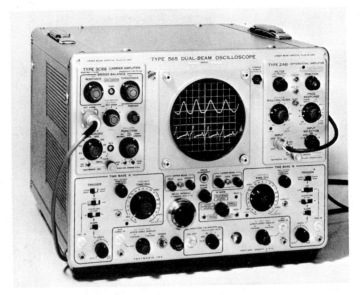

6-16. A cathode-ray oscilloscope is used to show waveform patterns on the screen. (Textronics, Inc.)

strike your eardrum. Hence, if the sounding object is *moving towards* you, or you are *moving towards* it, the pitch is higher. More waves reach your ear each second than would be the case if you and the object were stationary.

On the other hand, the pitch of a vibrating object that is *moving away* from you, or that you are moving away from, is lowered. *The rise or fall of pitch that is due to relative motion between the observer and the source of sound is called the **Doppler effect.*** The Doppler effect applies to all types of waves, not to sound waves alone. (Study Fig. 6-18.)

How is the frequency of vibrating strings changed? Stretched strings may vary in diameter, tension, length, and material. It is easy to demonstrate in

6-17. A complex wave pattern of a cornet as shown on the oscilloscope. (Bell Telephone Laboratories)

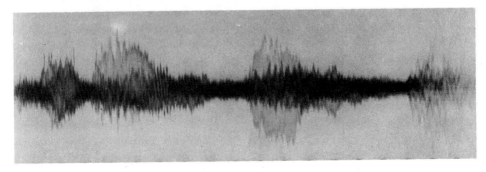

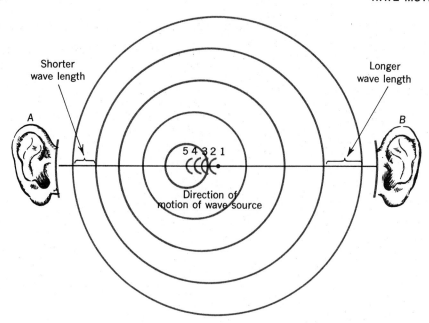

6-18. As the source of sound moves from 1 to 5, A hears the higher pitch and B hears the lower pitch.

the laboratory that there are three factors that affect the frequency of a vibrating string: its *length, tension,* and *mass.*

The longer a string, the slower it vibrates, and the lower will be its frequency. You know that the deep bass notes of the piano or harp are produced by the longer strings. While he is playing, the violinist raises the frequency of a string by touching it, thus effectively shortening it. Experiments show that the frequency of a vibrating string is *inversely proportional to its length.* For example, if you make a string half as long, its frequency is doubled.

Increasing the tension also makes a string vibrate more rapidly, giving a higher frequency. If a string sounds "flat," or too low in pitch, the violinist will tune it by turning a peg to tighten it, thus increasing its tension and frequency. The *frequency* of a string is *directly proportional to the square root of its tension.* Hence, to *double* the frequency of a string, you must increase its tension *four* times.

You have probably noticed that the bass strings of a piano are not only longer and under less tension, but they are *heavier.* Manufacturers often wrap a steel wire with a tight coil of silver or bronze wire to increase its *mass.* The heavy wire has more inertia, and therefore vibrates more slowly, at a lower frequency. The *frequency of a vibrating spring is inversely proportional to the square root of its mass per unit length.*

Interference of waves. You may think of interference as being the *reinforcement* or *destruction* of two waves as they get "in step" or "out of step." Figure 6-19 illustrates the joint effect produced by the two waves of slightly different frequency. When the waves are "in step" or *in phase*, they *strengthen* each other. And when they are "out of step" or *out of phase*, they *weaken* each other.

As you can see in the diagram, the two waves are in phase, *crest matching crest* and *trough matching trough*, at the points marked *R*. Here the two waves reinforce each other. At other places, marked *D*, they are out of phase, with a *crest meeting a trough*. At such places, the waves weaken or destroy each other. *This interaction between waves is called interference.*

Interference occurs under certain conditions in all kinds of waves: water waves, sound waves, and light waves. For example, Fig. 6-20 shows a pattern of water waves, while Fig. 6-21 is a sound wave pattern made visible by a scanning process. Soap-bubble films and oil films on water produce rainbow colors by the interference of light waves. (See cover photograph.)

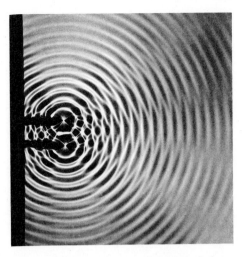

6-20. Interference pattern produced in a ripple tank from two point disturbances of the same frequency. (Educational Services, Inc.)

How are beats produced? Let us see what may happen when we obtain interference between two *sound* waves. If Fig. 6-19 represents two sound waves, we notice that their combined wave form has a large amplitude at points marked *R* and small amplitude at *D*. This means that you will hear a difference in loudness. This is so because the loudness of a sound depends on the amplitude of its wave form.

These *pulsations* in loudness produce a throbbing sound, called **beats.** To determine the number of beats per second produced by two tones, find the *difference* between their frequencies. Thus, if one tuning fork is vibrating at 256 vps and another at 254 vps, you will hear *two* beats per second.

Fundamentals and overtones. If you pluck a stretched string lightly in the middle, it will vibrate as a whole, in one segment, as shown in Fig. 6-22 (top). The tone you hear is called the

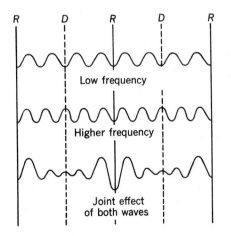

6-19. Two waves of different frequencies combine to produce interference.

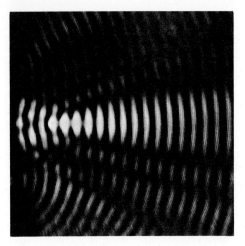

6-21. A photograph of an interference pattern formed by sound waves. (Bell Telephone Laboratories)

fundamental. It is the *lowest note* that a vibrating string can produce.

However, if you pluck the string a quarter way from one end, it will not only vibrate as a whole but also in segments, as shown in Fig. 6-22 (bottom). The tone you now hear has a different *quality.* Besides the fundamental, there is now present the *first overtone.* **Overtones** are higher-pitched tones produced by an object as it vibrates in segments. Overtones form tones whose frequencies are whole-number multiples of the fundamental frequency. For example, if the frequency of the fundamental is 100 vps, the frequency of the *first overtone* is 200 vps, and that of the *second overtone* is 300 vps.

The *number and the strength of the overtones determine the quality of a musical tone.* Actually, the vibrational patterns of the strings of musical instruments are very complex. A string vibrates not only as a whole but also in many segments, and many overtones are produced. Most of these over-

tones blend well with each other and with the fundamental, producing a harmonious effect. For this reason, overtones are often referred to as *harmonics.*

Resonance. When you say that two things are *in tune* with each other, you mean that they are in *resonance.* **Resonance** occurs when vibrating objects have the *same natural frequency.* It is a very broad term that applies to all waves and to vibrating objects in general.

A basic fact of resonance is that a vibrational system (tuning fork, piano string, radio) can absorb energy only of its own natural frequency.

Resonance can be demonstrated in the laboratory by using two mounted tuning forks of the *same* natural frequency placed close together as shown in Fig. 6-23. When you strike one of

String vibrating as whole gives off tone
called the fundamental

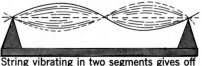

String vibrating in two segments gives off
tone called the first overtone

6-22. This diagram shows how the same string can produce both its fundamental (top) and its first overtone (bottom).

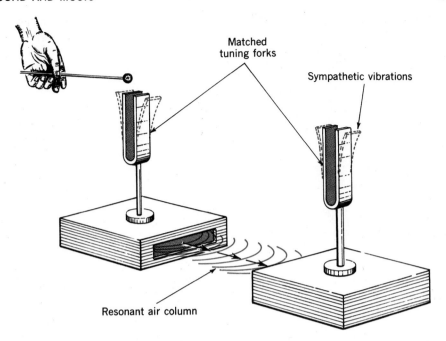

Matched
tuning forks

Sympathetic vibrations

Resonant air column

6-23. When two tuning forks have the same natural frequency, sound waves from one tuning fork (left) cause the other fork to vibrate sympathetically (right).

them, the other one begins to vibrate by resonance. However, if you change the frequency of one fork by wrapping a heavy rubber band around the end of one prong, it does not respond when the other fork is struck. You no longer have the condition for resonance. Can you see why?

Try the following experiment. Press down the loud pedal of a piano to free the strings. Then sing a note, such as "a-a-h-h," very loudly. The piano will respond by sounding the *same tone*. The sound waves of your voice strike all of the strings, but only those strings that have the right frequency are able to pick up the energy and start vibrating.

Resonance is of great importance in every branch of science. For exam-

ple, when we *tune* a radio set, we are adjusting its frequency to match that of the radio waves we want to receive. When we get resonance in sound waves, however, as in the experiments mentioned above, we often call the result *sympathetic vibrations*.

Air columns can also be resonant. You can demonstrate the fact that, under certain conditions, columns of air produce resonance. Let us hold a vibrating tuning fork over a cylinder as shown in Fig. 6-24. As the prongs of the fork vibrate back and forth over the air column, they send down waves that reflect back up from the surface of the water.

As we gradually add water to the cylinder, we find that there is a certain water level at which the tone from the fork sounds loudest. The sound wave reflected by the water surface meets the direct wave produced by the tuning fork exactly *in phase*. This causes the column of air in the cylinder to vibrate sympathetically, or to resonate with the vibrating fork, producing a more intense sound.

Laboratory experiments show that there is a relationship between the wavelength of the sound produced by the vibrating fork and the height of the air column under conditions of resonance. In this case, *the length of the resonant air column turns out to be one-fourth the fundamental wavelength of the sound it reinforces.*

SAMPLE PROBLEM

If the length of the resonant air column in Fig. 6-24 is 2.5 ft long, what is the frequency of the tuning fork? Assume the temperature of the air to be 0° C.

SOLUTION:

Step 1. At resonance the wavelength is four times the length of the resonant air column, or $L = 4 \times 2.5$ ft $= 10$ ft. Speed of sound at 0° C = 1090 ft/sec.

Step 2. $V = F \times L$, or $F = V/L$

Step 3. Substituting given and known values,

$$F = (1090 \text{ ft/sec})/10 \text{ ft}$$
$$= 109 \text{ vps}$$

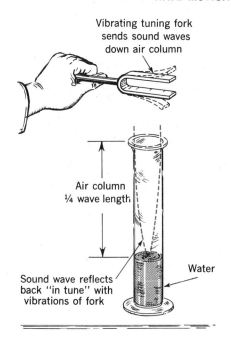

Vibrating tuning fork sends sound waves down air column

Air column ¼ wave length

Water

Sound wave reflects back "in tune" with vibrations of fork

6-24. An air column of the proper length reinforces the sound from the tuning fork.

How can we control the frequency of wind instruments? Musical tones of wind instruments can be controlled by varying the length of resonant air columns. When a trombonist works the *slide* of his instrument in and out as he plays, he is lengthening and shortening the air column. A short column is in resonance with the more rapid vibrations of the musician's lips and, as a result, a tone of higher frequency is produced.

In some instruments, such as the trumpet, clarinet, and saxophone, the player changes the effective length of the air column by using *keys* or *valves*. The player uses his finger tips to open and close *holes* along the side of the flute. When the player closes an opening of such an instrument, does the frequency rise or fall?

In other wind instruments, such as the bugle, there is no way of changing the length of the air column. To produce different tones with the bugle, you change the tension of your lips and the force with which you blow. By doing this, you can produce different higher-pitched overtones. Similarly, the trombonist can produce different tones from one setting of the slide.

The experiment in Fig. 6-24 made use of an air column that was *closed* at the lower end. This is known as a **closed pipe.** However, most wind instruments have air columns that are *open* at each end. Such air columns are known as **open pipes.** *The length of an open pipe is one-half the wavelength of the fundamental sound that it reinforces.*

The pipe organ has many different kinds of pipes, some open and some closed. The xylophone is often provided with closed pipes hanging under the wooden bars. The effective length of each pipe is made just right so as to be in resonance with the bar directly above it.

What are forced vibrations? Musical instruments of an orchestra are generally classed as *wind, string,* and *percussion* instruments. As you have just learned, the loudness of the tones produced by wind instruments is increased by the condition of resonance. The string instruments, however, often make use of *forced vibrations* to increase the loudness.

Suppose we set a tuning fork in vibration and then press its stem against the top of a table. The tone we hear becomes louder when the fork is in contact with the table because the fork *forces* the table top to vibrate with the same frequency. It does this even though the natural vibration rate of the table top is different from that of the fork. If you use a fork of different frequency, the table top is again forced to vibrate at this new frequency, and again the sound is amplified. Since the table top has a much larger vibrat-

ing area than the tuning fork, these **forced vibrations** produce a more intense sound wave.

The strings of the piano give louder tones than those of the zither or harp for the same reason. The piano strings are mounted on a *sounding board,* in which they produce forced vibrations. Similarly, forced vibrations in the wooden body of the violin reinforce the sounds produced by the strings.

Rhythm, melody, and harmony. To the composer, the performer, and the listener, music is an *art.* But music is basically related to *science* and is somewhat *mathematical* in nature!

The principal factors of a musical composition are *rhythm, melody,* and *harmony.* **Rhythm** is the timing pattern, or *tempo.* **Melody** is the effect of single tones as they follow each other in succession and is often called the *tune.* **Harmony** is the combined effect of two or more tones sounded together. Musical tones sounded together in harmony form a *chord.*

From experience, you know that certain tones harmonize well. Other tones produce an unpleasant effect, or *discord,* when you hear them sounded together. Whether you get harmony or discord depends almost entirely upon the *mathematical ratios* of the frequencies of the tones.

When two tones sounded together produce only a few beats per second, you are apt to like the throbbing, pulsating effect produced on the ear. However, beginning at about 8 beats per second and increasing up to about 32, the effect becomes more and more disagreeable.

You can demonstrate this fact by striking the keys on middle *C* and *D* on the piano simultaneously. Their vibration rates are about 262 and 294 vps, respectively. When you subtract these frequencies, you find they are 32 beats per second. This number of beats produces a discord. Beyond 32 beats per second, the effect gradually becomes more pleasing. This is because the beats now form a new tone of their own, called a *beat tone*.

Tones sounded together harmonize well and form a pleasing chord if there is no unpleasant beating between the fundamental tones or their overtones.

Pleasing chords have specific mathematical ratios. If the frequency ratios of two tones are small whole numbers, they form a pleasing chord. These ratios may be expressed as 1:2, 1:3, 2:3, 3:4, etc. If the frequency ratio is 1:2, the chord is called an *octave*. For example, if middle *C* on the piano has a frequency of 262 vps, then the frequency of the *first* octave, the eighth note above, is twice 262, or 524 vps. How would you find the frequency of the *second* octave above middle *C?*

The development of our musical scale. You are probably familiar with the *major chord* made up of the three musical tones called *do, mi, sol.* For at least 2500 years, this has been recognized as the "sweetest" of the three-toned chords. The frequency ratio of these tones is 4:5:6. That is, if the *do* has 400 vps, the *mi* will have 500 vps, and the *sol* will have 600 vps.

The major scale was first constructed from three of these 4:5:6 chords, properly placed. An octave on this scale includes the notes *do, re, mi, fa, sol, la, ti, do,* played with the *white keys* of the piano.

This musical scale had an important deficiency. It gave a scale whose successive notes did not have a regular increase in frequency, thus causing serious variations in frequency if music were played in another *key.* In fact, some of the jumps were about twice as much as others, and were called *whole tones.* Additional strings were then inserted in the piano between the whole-tone strings so that all of the jumps were by *half-tones.* These added strings are struck by the *black keys* of the piano, five added keys for each octave. This made a total of 12 "half-tone" intervals in the total octave.

The next stage in the development of the musical scale consisted in averaging out these 12 irregular frequency jumps. This scale is called a "tempered scale." The frequency of any note in the tempered scale can be obtained by multiplying the frequency of the preceding note by the factor 1.06. If you take the frequency of any string and multiply it by 1.06 twelve times, your final result will be about *twice* the frequency you started with. In other words, you have gone up *one octave.*

You can now see that as a result of this averaging, the modern major scale does not have the true 4:5:6 ratio for *do-mi-sol* chords. For example, if you start with *do* of 262 vps, middle *C,* the *mi* above has 330 vps, and the *sol* 392. If you reduce these numbers by dividing each by 66, you find that they have almost, but not quite, the 4:5:6 frequency ratios. (See Fig. 6-25.)

Sound recording and reproducing. The early phonographs worked on a very simple principle. A needle was caused to vibrate by the irregularities in the spiral groove of the record. The vibrating needle in turn caused

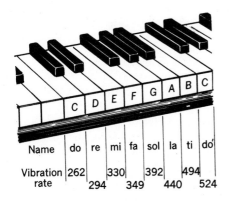

Name	do	re	mi	fa	sol	la	ti	do
Vibration rate	262	294	330	349	392	440	494	524

6-25. This diagram shows the tempered musical scale (white keys) in a piano starting with middle C as 262 vps.

a *diaphragm* to vibrate and give off sound.

In modern electronic record players, the vibrations of the needle produce a *fluctuating electric current*. This is amplified and, in turn, operates a *loudspeaker.*

Hi-Fi equipment records and reproduces all *audible frequencies* with *high-fidelity* or "true" quality. The human voice, for example, sounds perfectly natural when reproduced by Hi-Fi. The most recent development in sound reproduction is the *stereo-phonograph.* The term "stereo" refers to depth or dimension, sometimes referred to as *3-D.*

To understand the *depth* reproduction, you realize that in normal hearing, you pick up the sound with *both* ears, each of which hears the sound from a slightly *different* direction. In making stereo records, two "pick-up" microphones are used, and they make two sound tracks on the same record. These are played back through two loudspeakers that give a life-like depth or directional effect to the sound.

The tape recorder has some advantages over the plastic disk-type phonograph record. The recording "head" magnetizes a track of iron or iron oxide powder on a reel of tape. The magnetic pattern corresponds to the sound pattern being recorded.

When the tape is played back, the magnetism produces feeble currents in the *pick-up coils.* These currents are amplified and operate the loudspeaker. The program on the tape can be wiped off by a magnet, and thus the tape can be used over again. Tape recorders can be of the Hi-Fi, stereo type.

The recording of TV programs on magnetic tape represents a technological triumph. Six recording heads produce magnetic patterns on a tape 2 inches wide. The program can then be re-broadcast by using this *videotape* at any convenient time.

Quick Quiz

1. How does noise differ from a musical tone?
2. List three sounds that you would classify as noise. As musical tones.
3. Explain three characteristics of a musical tone.
4. What is the Doppler effect?
5. What factors determine the frequency of vibration of a stretched string? Tell the effect of each.
6. In wave study, what do we mean by interference?
7. Explain how beats are formed.
8. What is meant by the fundamental frequency of a string? When is it produced?
9. What is meant by resonance?
10. What must be the length of a closed pipe to reinforce a particular tone?
11. What is meant by the tempered musical scale?

SUMMARY

Sound is produced by vibrations of solids, liquids, or gases. Sound waves travel most rapidly through solids and most slowly through gases. They cannot pass through a vacuum. Sound waves travel at a speed of 1090 ft/sec through air at 0° C. Speeds higher than this are called supersonic.

Waves in which the particle motion is at right angles to the wave motion are called transverse. Sound waves are called longitudinal waves, because the particles of the medium that carries the wave move back and forth in the same direction that the wave itself moves.

When an object such as a string is vibrating as a whole, it produces its lowest note, called the fundamental. Usually it is also vibrating in smaller segments, producing higher-pitched notes called overtones, or harmonics. These overtones determine the quality of the musical tone.

We can change the frequency of a stretched sting by changing the length, tension, or mass. Resonant closed pipes are one-fourth the wavelength of the sound waves that they amplify; while open pipes are one-half the wavelength.

Interference between waves results from their getting in and out of phase. They strengthen each other when in phase and weaken each other when out of phase. Interference between two sound waves of different frequency forms audible beats.

Resonance is the condition whereby a vibrating object can absorb energy of its own natural frequency. The sound produced by wind instruments comes from resonating air columns. Resonance accounts for sympathetic vibrations. Forced vibrations are those of any frequency produced in an object that is in contact with some other vibrating body.

CHAPTER REVIEW

Vocabulary

Match the words in Column A with the *best* response in Column B. Do not write in your book.

Column A	Column B
1. sound	a. effect of frequency of sound waves on the ears
2. wavelength	b. condition whereby an object is set into vibration by absorbing energy of its own natural frequency
3. transverse wave	
4. longitudinal wave	
5. ultrasonics	c. the reinforcing or weakening of two waves as they get in or out of phase with each other
6. medium	
7. frequency	d. sound pulsations
8. loudness	e. lowest tone produced by vibrating body

9. decibel
10. reverberation
11. noise
12. musical tone
13. pitch
14. interference
15. beats
16. fundamental
17. overtones
18. quality
19. resonance
20. major chord

f. material that carries sound waves
g. tones produced by a body as it vibrates in two or more segments
h. caused by number and strength of overtones
i. sound waves having regular frequency pattern
j. ratio of velocity of wave to its wavelength
k. depends on energy of a wave
l. multiple echoes
m. sound frequencies above 20,000 vps
n. one in which particles of the medium move at right angles to direction of wave motion
o. has a frequency ratio of 4:5:6
p. unit of sound intensity
q. form of energy produced by vibration of matter
r. distance from one part on a wave to corresponding part of the next wave
s. sound having irregular wave pattern
t. one in which the particles of the medium move in the same direction as the wave moves

Questions: Group A

1. What are compressions and rarefactions? Do these refer to transverse or longitudinal waves?
2. What happens to the speed of a longitudinal wave if the medium is made more elastic? Denser?
3. Why does sound travel more rapidly through steel than through air?
4. List several uses of ultrasonics.
5. What is meant when one talks about the acoustics of an auditorium?
6. How are overtones produced in vibrating strings? How are they related to the fundamental?
7. Describe a demonstration that illustrates a condition of resonance.
8. Give two examples of forced vibrations.
9. The trumpet player starts the sound with his vibrating lips, but what produces the musical tones that you hear?
10. What are the three principal factors of a musical composition?
11. If two tones form a pleasing chord, what is true of their frequencies?
12. What is the frequency ratio of the do-mi-sol chord?

Questions: Group B

1. If you shout at a wall 40 ft away, can you hear an echo? Explain.
2. Does a transverse wave move through a solid? A liquid? Explain.
3. Describe the demonstration with steel balls that helps explain how sound waves pass through a medium.
4. If all gases are equally elastic, do you think sound travels more rapidly through air or through hydrogen? Why?
5. Why does sound travel more rapidly through warm air than through cold air?

6. If one noise is rated at 10 db and another at 11 db, in what way would they sound different?
7. How are sympathetic vibrations produced? Why are they important?
8. In what two ways may the trombonist raise the pitch as he plays?
9. What is the chief cause of musical discord?
10. As you run up the scale on a piano, playing both the white and black keys, the frequency of each tone is how many times greater than the previous one?

Problems

1. You hear the echo two seconds after firing a shot. How far away is the reflecting surface if the temperature is 20° C?
2. What is the wavelength of the lowest pitched sound you are able to hear? Assume a frequency of 20 vps and a temperature of 20° C.
3. An ultrasonic generator sends 500,000 waves per second through the ocean. If each wave is 0.01 ft in length, what is the speed of sound in ocean water?
4. You first heard a police siren 800 ft away. By the time it was only 200 ft away how much louder did it sound?
5. A siren disk has 100 equally-spaced holes and is spinning at 3000 rpm. The speed of sound in the air is 1000 ft/sec. (a) What is the speed of the disk in revolutions per second? (b) What is the frequency of the sound produced? (c) What is the wavelength of the sound? (d) What is the air temperature?
6. (a) What is the wavelength of a tone that resonates with a closed pipe two feet long (temperature, 0° C)? (b) What is the wavelength of a sound that resonates with an open pipe two feet long? (c) Which of the two pipes sounds a note of the higher frequency?
7. A piano wire is vibrating as a whole, in one segment, at 440 vps. (a) What is the frequency of its fundamental tone? (b) What is the frequency of its first overtone? (c) What is the frequency of its second overtone? (d) What is the frequency of the tone three octaves above the fundamental? (e) What is the frequency of the tone one octave below the fundamental?
8. If the *do* of a chord has a frequency of 880 vps, what is the frequency of the *mi* above? The *sol*?
9. Two tones of 400 vps and 430 vps form how many beats per second when sounded together? Do they make a pleasing chord?
10. A violin string whose frequency is 262 vps is shortened to two-thirds of its former length. (a) What is the new frequency? (b) If its first tone is called *do*, what is the new tone called?

7   *LIGHT*

A THE NATURE OF LIGHT

What is light? The early caveman, watching the flickering flame, thought the yellow light of his campfire was a magical, mysterious spirit. Today, however, we know that light is a form of energy that bathes the whole universe. Without light and similar radiations, this would be a lifeless world—cold, dark, and dead.

The first significant studies on light were carried out during the 17th century by Isaac Newton and Christian Huygens. Newton believed that a beam of light must be composed of a *stream of particles*. This theory explained why the images in mirrors were sharp. The *particle theory* could also be used to explain the action of light as it passed through lenses, and the formation of shadows.

Huygens, however, soon developed a different theory. He believed that light traveled in *waves*. Waves do not travel in straight lines, but bend around objects, thus, are supposedly not capable of presenting sharp, clear images in mirrors and lenses. Huygens contended, however, that the waves of light were so tiny that there was no visible distortion in typical mirrors and lenses, and in the formation of shadows.

Later, in the early 19th century, Thomas Young supported the wave theory by showing *interference bands* in light. Bright bands were formed when one set of waves joined another set in such a way that crests and troughs were reinforced. Dark bands were formed when crests and troughs canceled each other. Only waves can exhibit the property of interference.

In the early 20th century, the ideas changed again when Max Planck and Albert Einstein brought back Newton's particle theory. They discovered that light was always emitted and absorbed in individual bundles of energy called *photons*. This is basically the theory we believe today.

What are photons? Scientists discovered that light acts both like waves and like particles. We know that *light* *is a form of energy* that travels from one place to another in the form of waves. However, light is *emitted from matter* and it is *absorbed by matter* in separate bundles or particles. We call a *particle* of light a **photon.** (See Fig. 7-1.) Each photon consists of light of a certain frequency. *The energy of a photon depends upon the frequency of the light wave.* For example, a photon of violet light, which has twice the frequency of red, has twice the energy. The photons of ultraviolet light and X rays are even more energetic.

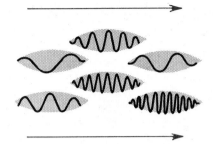

7-1. This highly imaginative drawing of photons of light shows all the packets going at the same speed but vibrating with different wavelengths and frequencies.

We learned from the atomic theory that matter exists in *separate, distinct particles.* This new theory tells us that energy also comes in little packets. The *quantity of energy* carried by *each* photon is called a *quantum,* and this is the basis of the **Quantum Theory.**

How is light produced? *Light is emitted by excited atoms.* It can be produced by any of the following methods:

1. By heating something until it becomes so hot that it gives off light. We say a thing is **incandescent** when it is glowing hot.

2. By a *chemical action* such as combustion. The burning of a match or a candle is a good example.

3. By passing an *electric current* through a gas, as in neon lighting.

4. By the process called **fluorescence.** Certain substances glow when hit by strong radiations, as in *fluorescent lighting.*

Whatever method used, basically light is produced whenever electrons fall from one energy level in an atom to a lower level. We can compare the electrons of atoms with earth satellites. It takes more energy to lift a satellite

into an orbit 400 miles above the earth than into one only 200 miles up. We say the first satellite is at a *higher energy level.* Later, as it falls back to earth, it releases this extra energy in the form of heat.

Similarly, the nucleus of the atom has satellites called electrons in orbit at various energy levels. *An electron may absorb energy and be lifted to a higher energy level.* When this electron falls back, it gives *off* this extra

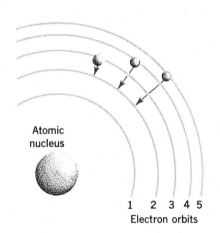

Atomic nucleus

1 2 3 4 5
Electron orbits

7-2. When electrons drop from one energy level to a lower energy level, they may radiate light in the visible range.

energy in the form of radiation. When this radiation is in the visible part of the electromagnetic spectrum, it is called *light energy*. (See Fig. 7-2.)

The four methods of producing light are actually ways of exciting atoms by raising their electrons to higher energy levels. In each instance, some other form of energy, such as heat or electricity, produces the excitation of the atoms.

Where does most of our light come from? The light that fills the universe comes from bright bodies called stars. For example, we get our daylight from the sun, our nearest star. The intense light of the sun and other stars is due to high temperatures produced by nuclear energy. The blinding flash of the hydrogen bomb explosion has a similar source.

The fact that light comes from the distant stars through practically empty space indicates that light can travel through a vacuum. *Light requires no solid, liquid, or gas medium to carry its waves.* In fact, we find that matter only *hinders* the passage of light. Matter *slows down, absorbs,* and *scatters* light. Hence, we see that light

waves must be quite different from sound waves, which cannot pass through a vacuum at all.

How is light polarized? Certain crystalline substances block all light waves except those that are vibrating in line with their crystals. (See Fig. 7-3.) When the atomic planes of the crystals are lined up horizontally, for example, they permit the passage of light waves vibrating only in a horizontal plane. In other words, only those waves that vibrate in line with the "crystal lattice" can pass through. This screening process is called *polarization* and the light that has been screened is said to be *polarized*. The fact that light can be polarized demonstrates that *light travels in transverse waves*. If light traveled in longitudinal waves, for example, such barriers would have no effect on the light.

There are ways of polarizing light waves other than by "combing" them through atomic-sized parallel slots. They are also polarized to a certain extent by *reflection*. For example, the glare of light reflected from a water surface, or any glossy surface, is partly polarized.

7-3. When the axes of the Polaroid sheets are parallel, light is transmitted (left). Light is not transmitted when the axes of the Polaroid sheets are perpendicular (right).

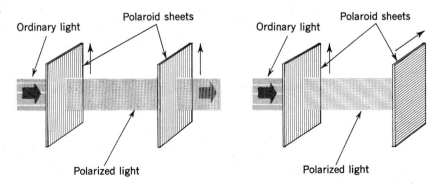

Ordinary light:random wavelengths   Monochromatic light:waves of equal length

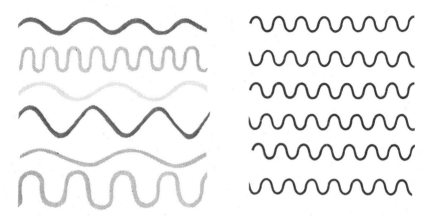

7-4. In monochromatic light, all waves are the same length.

Polarized light has many uses. If *polarizing glass* were used in automobile windshields and headlamps, it would reduce the glare of night driving. You may have used Polaroid sunglasses to reduce glare when driving in the sunlight. Some television pictures in 3-D have been developed by the use of Polaroid.

Polarized light is used to make *chemical analyses* of liquids, such as sugar solutions. Biologists use polarized light to bring out fine detail when examining specimens under a microscope. Engineers *improve the design of objects* by the use of polarized light. They make transparent plastic models of the objects and subject them to various stresses. When viewed under polarized light, the colored patterns indicate where the stresses are greatest.

Polarization is not limited to light alone. All of the waves of the electromagnetic spectrum can be polarized, a fact that is of great importance in radio, for example.

What is LASER? In 1960 scientists developed the first *LASER* device. It marked the beginning of harnessing the natural atomic powers of light. (Laser is a word made from the first letters of *Light Amplification by Stimulated Emission of Radiation*.) The radiation from a laser has the following properties:

1. It is **monochromatic.** White light consists of a wide range of frequencies. Even a highly selective colored light contains a wide range of frequencies. The light from a laser, however, is *all of the same frequency.* (See Fig. 7-4.)

2. It is **coherent.** Normally, light waves travel in random phase; that is, the crests and troughs of one wave are not lined up with the crests and troughs of another. In a laser, however, the *crests and troughs* of waves are all *in step* as shown in Fig. 7-5.

3. It travels in a *plane wave front.* Light normally tends to spread out in all directions in a spherical wave front. Even highly directional searchlight beams spread out significantly after a mile or more. Radiations from a laser, however, travel in *almost parallel lines with very little spreading* even

Coherent light: waves in step

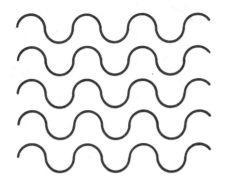

7-5. In coherent light, the wavelengths are lined up crest to crest and trough to trough.

at great distances. A laser beam, for example, was flashed to the surface of the moon 240,000 miles away and it spread to a diameter of only two miles. (See Fig. 7-6.)

How does the laser achieve these properties? Refer back to Fig. 7-2. The frequency of the light produced as electrons drop from one energy level to another depends upon the difference in levels. In a laser, only one particular drop is produced. Thus light of only one frequency (monochromatic light) is emitted.

Before an atom can emit a photon of light, it must have the energy to do so. In the laser, this energy is *"pumped in,"* usually from an external light source, and lifts the atoms to a higher energy level. At this point, the atoms are said to be *"excited."*

Excited atoms are unstable and can easily be triggered to give up their energy. Normally, the energy is released in a *random* succession of emissions. In a laser, however, the emissions are *stimulated.* The first random emission of a photon in a highly excited material is reflected back and forth from highly polished or mirror-like ends of the laser. With its great speed of almost 186,000 miles per second, it is easy to see that the single photon can strike billions of atoms in a fraction of a second, triggering the emissions of more photons. A *chain reaction* is built up and the entire energy stored in the atoms is released at once. *This is referred to as amplification.* Finally, the light bursts through a partially mirrored end of the laser.

7-6. The plane wave front of a laser (right) sends out a beam of light that spreads very little.

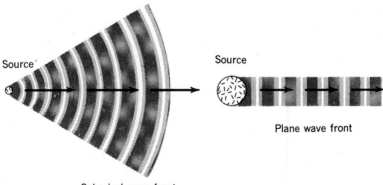

Source

Source

Spherical wave front

Plane wave front

The first laser devices were able to produce only bursts of light as described above. Now, however, there are many *continuous wave* (*cw*) lasers that emit a constant beam. Many materials have been successfully used in lasers, including gases, liquids, and solids.

What are some of the uses of lasers? There is a wide range of uses for this new discovery of science. A single continuous beam from a laser could theoretically be modulated to carry all the television programs of the world simultaneously. Thus, it has almost unlimited potential as a *communications medium.*

The laser can be operated as a *range finder.* By sending out a pulse and receiving the reflection, the time interval can be computed to determine the distance.

The laser can *amplify* radiations of *heat* as well as light. In addition, the laser beam can be *focused* to a microscopic point to multiply its power. In this way, temperatures of several millions of degrees have been produced.

The laser is also used in medicine. The highly controllable laser beam makes it suitable for *ultra-delicate surgery.* For example, the laser has been used to "weld" a detached retina to the back of the eye. Lasers have also been used for brain surgery and skin cancers.

What makes objects visible? We can see only by light that comes from other objects to our eyes. If the object itself produces the light, as does a piece of white-hot metal or a lighted lamp, it is said to be **luminous.**

Light from some other source may strike an object and bounce from it to our eyes. We then say the object is

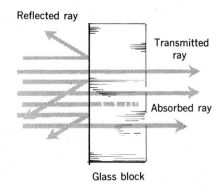

7-7. Light waves may be reflected, absorbed, or transmitted by the substance they strike.

illuminated. We see most things because they are *illuminated by light from some other source.*

In either case, light must come *from the objects* and then *enter our eyes,* if we are to *see* them.

When light waves strike a substance, they may be *reflected, absorbed,* or *transmitted,* as shown in Fig. 7-7. If the substance transmits none of the waves, we say it is **opaque** to light, and you cannot see through it.

If the waves pass readily through a substance, that substance is **transparent** to those waves. Glass, water, and air are transparent to light and you can see things clearly through them.

Many substances are neither opaque nor transparent, but are somewhere in between. These substances, such as frosted glass and waxed paper, are said to be **translucent.** Some light passes through translucent substances, but you cannot see things clearly through them.

Any light that is absorbed is converted into heat and warms up the material that absorbed it.

What is the speed of light? Light travels so fast that many early scientists believed that it traveled from one place to another instantaneously. In the 17th century, however, a Danish astronomer, Claus Roemer, estimated its speed by timing the eclipses of one of Jupiter's moons. He found that the moon disappeared routinely behind Jupiter every 42 hours, 28 minutes, except for one puzzling discrepancy. It was always a little late when the Earth was on the opposite side of the Sun from Jupiter. Roemer decided that this difference was caused by the travel time of light across the diameter of the earth's orbit. His calculations placed the speed of light near the present day figure of 186,000 miles per second. (See Fig. 7-8.)

Measuring the brightness of a lamp. We can measure the brightness of a lamp by comparing it with some *standard* source of light intensity. One such source is the *standard candle,* a light made according to exact specifications. The *intensity* or brightness of

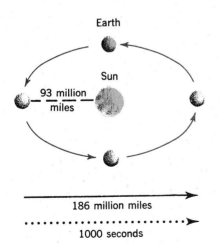

Earth

Sun

93 million miles

186 million miles

1000 seconds

7-8. Roemer calculated that light took 1000 seconds to cross the orbit of the earth.

this light at its source is referred to as one **candlepower** (1 *cp*). If a light bulb, for example, gives twenty times as much light as the standard candle, we rate it at 20 cp. Actually, we find the candlepower of a light bulb by comparing it with another that has already been standardized.

The *rate* at which light is *radiated* from a source is measured in **lumens.** *One standard candle radiates about 12½ lumens.* Thus, a 100 cp light gives about 1250 lumens. A modern 100-watt light bulb (*incandescent type*) produces about 130 cp of light.

How do we measure illumination? Often we are more interested in the *intensity* of light falling on a surface than we are in the brightness of a light source. When you are reading, you are more concerned with the brightness of the page than in the candlepower of the light bulb. The *illumination* that you obtain depends not only upon how bright the bulb is but also upon how *far away* it is.

We find that light intensity follows the *inverse square law.* That is, if you put the lamp twice as far away, you get only one-fourth the illumination. At three times the distance, the illumination becomes one-ninth as much.

The illumination produced by a 1-cp source 1 foot away has been commonly called the **foot-candle.** A 20-cp source 1 ft away would give 20 ft-candles. But if you moved it 2 ft away, you would get only *one-fourth* as much light, or 5 ft-candles. Hence, the formula:

Illumination in ft-candles $= \dfrac{cp}{ft^2}$

SAMPLE PROBLEM

What illumination falls on a book that is held 3 ft away from a 90-cp lamp?

SOLUTION:

Step 1.

$$\text{Illumination} = \frac{\text{candlepower}}{\text{ft}^2}$$

Step 2.
$$= 90 \div 3^2$$
$$= 10 \text{ ft-candles}$$

Illumination is often measured in another unit called the *lumen per square foot.* **One ft-candle = 1 lumen/ft².**

How does a photometer work? Put a drop of oil on a sheet of white paper and hold the sheet in front of a light source as shown in Fig. 7-9. The oil

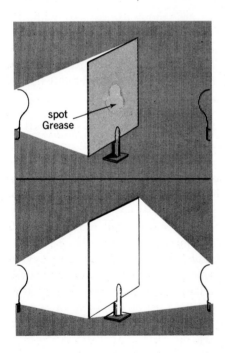

7-9. The grease spot seems to disappear when the front and back of the paper are equally illuminated.

spot looks bright, but when you hold it in front of a wall the spot looks dark. With care you can find a place between two light sources where the spot practically disappears. When this happens the light reaching each side of the paper is equally bright.

The *photometer* (foh-*tom*-eh-ter) works on the same principle. One type has a movable card with a grease spot in the center. You move this card back and forth between two lamps as shown in Fig. 7-10. One of the light bulbs is a standardized lamp, whose candlepower is known. The other is the lamp that you want to measure. You slide the card back and forth on the meter stick until you find the point where the grease spot is no longer visible. The illumination from each lamp is now the same, or *cp/ft² (left) = cp/ft² (right).*

SAMPLE PROBLEM

The grease spot in a balanced photometer is 2 ft from a 20-cp light bulb, and 4 ft from another bulb. What is the candlepower of the other bulb?

SOLUTION:

Step 1.

cp/ft² (unknown bulb) =
$$\text{cp/ft}^2 \text{ (known bulb)}$$

Step 2.
$$\frac{x \text{ cp}}{(4 \text{ ft})^2} = \frac{20 \text{ cp}}{(2 \text{ ft})^2}$$

Step 3.
$$\frac{x}{16} = \frac{20}{4} \text{ or } x = 80 \text{ cp}$$

What is a light meter? *Light meters,* often called *foot-candle meters,* are used to measure the illumination directly. The light meter usually contains a *photoelectric cell,* or *phototube.* This has a light-sensitive sub-

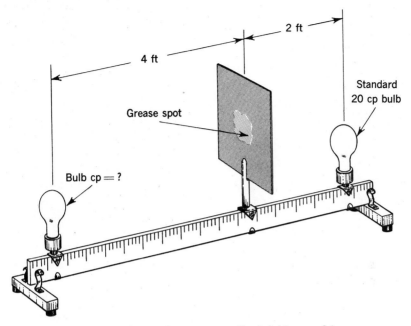

7-10. The photometer measures the brightness of lamps.

stance that produces a small *electric current* when light hits it. This current operates an electric meter. Because the current increases when the illumination increases, the light meter can be made to read directly in foot-candles, or lumens/ft².

A camera also "sees" by light given off by an object, or reflected from it. Hence, the photographer often uses a special light meter, called an *exposure meter,* to determine the brightness. The exposure meter does more than measure the brightness of the scene. It has movable dials that the photographer can adjust to coordinate the type of film used, the *exposure time,* and the right setting of the camera lens. (See Fig. 7-11.)

Is your home adequately lighted? Modern living puts a great strain on your eyes. Looking at television pro-

grams, or reading at night, may produce eye-strain. It is important to know the requirements for proper lighting.

The illumination in many homes is too low. Your electric light company will make a survey of the lighting in your home with a light meter and recommend improvements. It is common to find an illumination of 5 lumens/ft² where 20 to 30 are needed. Experts recommend *30 lumens/ft² for ordinary reading* and as much as *200 lumens/ft² for sewing.*

The illumination that you get in your home depends also upon the amount of reflected light. Lamps that might be satisfactory in a room with light-colored walls might be too dim in a room with dark surroundings.

The *distribution* of light, the formation of shadows and contrast, is also important. If you use an unshaded light

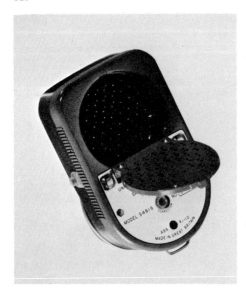

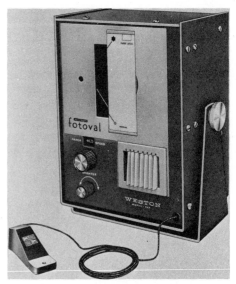

7-11. Illumination can be measured with an electric photometer (left) or exposure meter. The more intense the light the larger the currents generated inside these devices. (Weston Instruments, Inc.)

bulb that is poorly located, this produces a bad *glare* and sharp shadows. The softer and more *diffuse* the light, the better. (See Fig. 7-12.)

Images are due to reflected light. Light waves *reflect* well from smooth white surfaces or from glossy surfaces such as polished metal.

A flat, polished surface that reflects light well is called a *plane mirror.* As shown in Fig. 7-13, *the angle at which light is reflected from a mirror is the same as the angle at which it strikes the mirror.* We say that the *angle of reflection* equals the *angle of incidence.* A ball bouncing on the sidewalk obeys the same law of reflection.

When light is reflected from a plane mirror, the pattern of the light rays is undisturbed. In a sense, they are simply "folded over." Because of this, you can see *images* by looking into mirrors.

Figure 7-14 shows how an image is formed by a plane mirror. Note the path of the rays from the object **P** to the mirror and then to the eyes. Your eye has no way of telling that the light rays have been reflected. Instead, the light rays *seem* to be coming from a point behind the mirror, and you seem to see the object at this point. In Fig. 7-14, that point is marked **P'**, and is called the image of **P.** You have observed that images formed by plane mirrors are "life-sized"; that is, equal in size to the object. *The images are located as far behind the mirror as the object is in front of it.* Images in plane mirrors are said to be "left-handed" images. To see why, stand in front of a mirror and reach out your right hand to shake hands with your image. What do you observe?

Images formed by plane mirrors are called *virtual images.* They *can-*

not be projected on screens but can be seen only by looking into the mirror itself.

A rough surface does not produce images. Figure 7-15 shows the difference between *regular reflection* from a smooth surface and *irregular reflection* or diffusion from a rough surface. Note that when the light beam is diffused by reflection from a rough surface, the original pattern of the light is broken up. Therefore, no image can be formed. Instead, *diffusion makes the surface itself visible.*

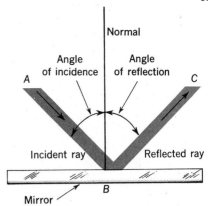

7-13. The angles of incidence and reflection are equal.

A perfect plate-glass wall mirror would be invisible. When you looked at it, you would see only images of other things, not the glass itself. On the other hand, when you look at a plastered wall, you see no images, only the wall itself.

What are curved mirrors? Curved mirrors may be either concave or convex. The inside of an orange peel has a *concave shape*, while the outside is *convex*. Curved mirrors are usually *spherical*. That is, they are shaped like a round section cut from a sphere.

You are familiar with the curiously distorted images seen in the curved mirrors often found in amusement parks. You find them also in the bowl of a silver spoon, in soap bubbles, or in the curved chrome on automobiles.

However, curved mirrors have more important uses. They are found in the world's largest *telescopes*. They *focus* the light from searchlights, auto headlights, and flashlights.

Concave mirrors can form small inverted images. In Fig. 7-16, a spherical concave mirror is represented. C is the center of the sphere of which the mirror is a segment and is called

7-12. A poor lighting arrangement (top). Notice the improvement when a reflecting surface and an additional light source are added. (General Electric Co.)

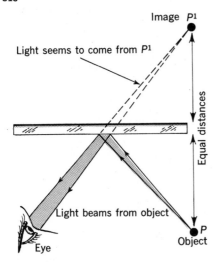

7-14. The light rays seem to reach your eye from a point behind the mirror.

PA = Principal axis   C = Center of
O = Object   curvature
O¹ = Image   F = Principal
                                         focus

7-16. The image formed by this curved mirror is a real image. It is found where the rays from the object O reconverge at O′.

the *center of curvature.* Line **PA** is called the *principal axis.* The point **F** is the *principal focus,* and all rays that reach the mirror parallel to the principal axis will be reflected through this *focal point.*

An object, such as the arrowhead **O,** is placed in front of the mirror at a point beyond **C.** A light ray from the tip of **O** parallel to the principal axis hits the mirror and then reflects

back through **F.** Another ray from **O** through **C** hits the mirror "head on" and reflects right back upon itself along the same path. The image of the object **O** is located where these two reflected rays cross at **O′.**

You can demonstrate that the concave mirror actually does form an image like this by doing the following experiment. Put a lighted candle several feet in front of a concave mirror, such

7-15. You get irregular reflection, or diffusion of light, from a rough surface.

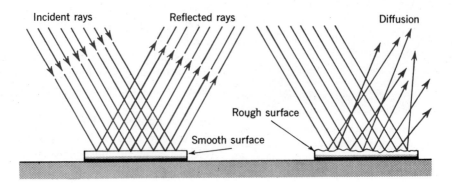

as a shaving mirror, in a darkened room. Move a small, thin card back and forth between the candle and the mirror until you see an image of the flame. The image will be *small* and *inverted*. It is called a **real image** because it *can be projected* upon a screen; in this case, the card.

Concave mirrors are used in telescopes. To see how a concave mirror is used in a reflecting telescope, suppose that in Fig. 7-16 **O** represents an area on the moon. Then **O'** will be its image, many times smaller than the object. However, it is so much brighter that you can look at it through a magnifying glass and get a clear, enlarged image of the moon.

The world's largest telescope at *Palomar Mountain,* California, contains a concave mirror 200 inches in diameter. Its construction was one of the great technical feats of all time. Telescope mirrors are not truly spherical in shape but are made *parabolic* to give more perfect images. The reflecting surface is usually coated with aluminum. (See Figs. 7-17 and 7-18.)

Curved mirrors have other uses. *Concave mirrors* make good *magnifiers.* If you put an object close to a concave mirror, the image formed in the mirror is *larger than the object.* This is how you see the magnified, erect image of your face in a shaving mirror.

The reflecting surface of a *convex mirror* bulges outward. The silvered balls used to decorate Christmas trees are good examples. Convex mirrors are sometimes used as rear-view mirrors for cars and trucks. Although the image is *smaller than the object,* it gives you a wide field of view. The image formed is a virtual image and cannot be projected.

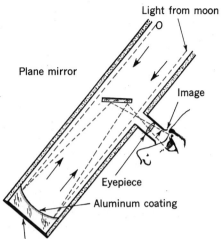

7-17. Reflecting telescopes combine concave and plane mirrors to bring the image to the eyepiece.

7-18. The 200-inch Hale telescope at the Palomar Observatory is the world's largest reflecting telescope. (Mt. Wilson and Palomar Observatories)

Quick Quiz

1. List four different ways of producing light.
2. When does an atom radiate light energy?
3. What is the chief source of light in the universe?
4. Why can you see a candle flame? A tree?
5. What evidence is there that light passes through a vacuum?
6. What three things may happen to a wave when it strikes a substance?
7. Distinguish between opaque, transparent, and translucent.
8. How is the grease-spot photometer used?
9. What is the relationship between the distance of an object to a plane mirror and the distance of its virtual image to the mirror?
10. What type of surface diffuses a beam of light? What type of surface produces regular reflection?
11. What is the difference between ordinary and monochromatic light?
12. What is a characteristic of a light beam of plane waves?
13. Does polarization of light give us evidence of the particle nature of light or the wave nature? Explain.
14. What are some uses of lasers?
15. Why are images formed in plane mirrors sometimes referred to as "left-handed" images?

B LIGHT AND LENSES

Seeing is not always believing. Have you ever noticed on a hot, dry afternoon that the highway ahead may look wet? You can see reflections in it, as you would in pools of water. But when you get there, you find it quite dry! This is a *mirage* much like those in well-known desert stories. A *mirage* is an *optical illusion* caused by the *bending* of light rays as they pass through air layers of different density.

Stand so that you can almost, but not quite, see a penny in the bottom of an empty cup. (See Fig. 7-19.) Without moving your eyes, pour water into the cup, being careful not to disturb the penny. The penny seems to rise in the cup until you can see it clearly. For the same reason, a straight stick appears to be broken when it is placed into water at an angle.

These effects are due to the fact that light does not always travel in straight lines. The beam of a searchlight, as shown in Fig. 7-20, is an example of light traveling in a straight line. Similarly, you cast a shadow mainly because light does not bend around you as it passes by.

However, careful investigation shows that light travels in a straight

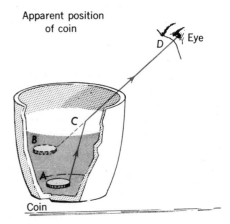

7-19. Objects under water seem to be closer to the surface than they actually are.

7-20. Searchlight beams from atop the Empire State Building show that light travels in straight lines.

line only so long as it stays in one medium such as air, water, or glass. When light passes from one medium into another of different density, it curves, or bends. The relative densities of the two media determines the amount of bending.

Refraction changes the appearance of things. To explain the apparent rise of the penny, look again at Fig. 7-19. You see the penny by light rays that reach your eyes from the penny. Line **ACD** represents one of these rays. As it passes from the water into the air, it bends sharply. *The bending of light as it passes from one transparent substance into another is called* **refraction.**

Your eye cannot detect this bending of the rays. Therefore, you see the penny along the direction **DC**, at point **B**.

What causes refraction? Light *refracts* because its speed is changed as it passes from one medium into another. Light waves passing from air into glass slow down from a speed of 186,000 miles per second to about 124,000 miles per second. This causes the *wave front* to swing around to a new angle.

We can compare this to a column of soldiers marching from smooth ground into swampy area. They cannot march as quickly in the swamp as they can on the smooth ground. Thus, if the column enters the swamp at an angle, it is swung around into a new line of march.

Note that when light passes from air *into a denser substance*, like water or glass, it travels at a *lower* speed. It bends *toward the perpendicular*, a line at right angles to the surface. This means that the *angle of refraction* (r) is less than the *angle of incidence* (i), as is shown in the prism of Fig. 7-21.

What is the index of refraction? The speed of light in different substances varies. Therefore, various substances have different abilities to bend light. We call this *refracting or bending ability*, the **index of refraction** of a substance.

You can compute the index of refraction of a substance by *dividing the speed of light in a vacuum by the*

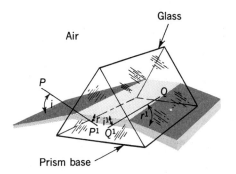

7-21. Refraction bends the light beam toward the base of the prism.

speed of light in that substance. For most purposes, we use the speed of light in air rather than in a vacuum, since there is so little difference between them.

The index of refraction is a *specific* property of a substance and can be used to identify that substance. For example, diamond has an *index* of 2.42, while ice has an index of 1.31.

SAMPLE PROBLEM

Calculate the index of refraction of glass in which light travels at 124,000 miles/sec.

SOLUTION:

Step 1. The formula is:

Index of refraction = speed of light in air ÷ speed of light in glass, or

$$IR = \frac{V_{air}}{V_{glass}}$$

Step 2. $IR = \dfrac{186,000 \text{ mi/sec}}{124,000 \text{ mi/sec}} = \dfrac{3}{2} = 1.5$

The index of refraction is a little greater for certain types of *optical glass.* This fact is important to the *lensmaker* who can make better *lenses* by using glass that has the proper index for his purpose. The indexes of refraction for several substances are shown in the table below.

INDEX OF REFRACTION

Vacuum	1.0000
Air	1.0003
Ice	1.31
Water	1.33
Glass (crown)	1.52
Glass (flint)	1.61
Diamond	2.42

The index of refraction of water is 1.33. Can you calculate the speed of light in water from this fact?

The atmosphere causes refraction. For most purposes we can disregard the difference between the speed of light in air and in a vacuum. However, this difference does result in a *slight* bending of light as it enters our atmosphere. Do you know that you can see the sun before it rises and after it sets? Looking at Fig. 7-22, suppose that you are at **C**, looking toward the setting sun. As the ray **ABC** enters the atmosphere, it bends as shown. Of course, this refraction is due to the fact that the ray is getting into *denser* air and, hence, is going more slowly. As you can see, the effect is to "lift" the sun above the horizon. This also occurs at sunrise and has the effect of lengthening the hours of daylight.

The twinkling of stars and the dancing of "heat rays" on a hot tin roof are caused by the changing refraction of the light as it passes through layers of air of different densities. When they are calculating star positions, astronomers must *correct* their readings to allow for atmospheric refraction.

The lens refracts light. A *lens* is a piece of *transparent* material having at least one curved surface. Lenses differ in shape, size, and material, but the chief purpose of all of them is to refract light. The amount of *refraction* produced by a lens depends both upon its *shape* and on the *index of refraction* of the material of which it is made.

You find lenses in telescopes, cameras, eyeglasses, microscopes, spectroscopes, movie projectors, and many other optical devices.

Observe the path of the light ray through the *prism* of glass shown in

Apparent position of sun

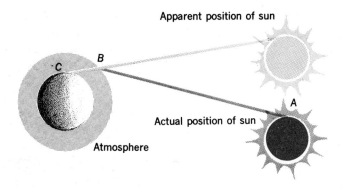

Actual position of sun

Atmosphere

7-22. The rays of the setting sun are refracted by the earth's atmosphere. Rays entering obliquely, AB, are shifted to a new path direction BC, causing the apparent sun position shown.

Fig. 7-21. The ray bends toward the perpendicular **PP'** as it enters the glass, and away from the perpendicular as it leaves. The effect is to bend the beam toward the base **AB**, the *thicker* part of the prism.

Two prisms may act like lenses. If you use a double prism, as in Fig. 7-23, the rays come together or *converge* after passing through the glass.

This results from the refraction of the light toward the thicker part of the prism. The *double convex lens* of Fig. 7-23 is simply a double prism smoothed down. Note that a *convex lens* is *thicker at the center* than at the edges. It always *brings* light rays together and so is called a *converging lens.*

If you put the two prisms together point-to-point, refraction causes the

7-23. The behavior of light rays when they are transmitted by lenses of different curvatures.

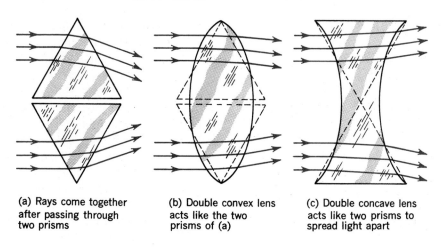

(a) Rays come together after passing through two prisms

(b) Double convex lens acts like the two prisms of (a)

(c) Double concave lens acts like two prisms to spread light apart

rays to spread apart. As shown in Fig. 7-23, you can make a double concave lens by smoothing down this double prism. A *concave lens, thinner at the center* than at the edges, tends to *spread* light rays apart. It is called a *diverging lens.*

What is the focal length of a lens? An ordinary magnifying glass is a good example of a convex lens. You can use it to do several interesting experiments. First, focus the light from the sun on a sheet of paper. The dazzling spot of light is a *real image* of the sun. It is so hot that it may char or burn the paper.

The image of the sun was formed at the *principal focus* of the lens. This is the point at which *parallel rays converge* after passing through the lens. Rays from any distant object are almost parallel to each other. In practice, we may consider any small object as much as 90 to 100 feet away from an ordinary lens to be a distant object.

The distance from the lens to the principal focus is called the *focal length* of the lens. (See Fig. 7-24.)

An experiment with a convex lens. Using a convex lens in a darkened room, catch the image of a bright, *distant* object on a sheet of paper. Observe that this is a *real image,* in full color, and is *smaller and inverted.* It is *located at the principal focus* of the lens.

The image is smaller than the object because it is nearer to the lens than the object was. The following formula shows how the distances and sizes of images are related to each other.

$$\frac{size\ of\ image}{size\ of\ object} = \frac{distance\ of\ image}{distance\ of\ object}$$

Notice that the left-hand ratio gives the *magnification* produced by the lens. For example, if the image is ten times as far away from the lens as the object, the magnification is ten times or *10X.* (See Fig. 7-25.)

The above formula applies to mirrors, as well as to all lenses, and is used in such optical instruments as microscopes, telescopes, and simple cameras.

This relationship between size and distance is shown in Fig. 7-26, which shows the *pinhole camera.* A small hole can be used instead of a convex lens to produce real images.

How do lenses form images? For this experiment, use a luminous object, such as a lighted candle, in a darkened room. Set up the equipment as shown in Fig. 7-25. Move the lens slowly along the stick until you get a clear, inverted, real image of the lighted candle on the screen.

To understand the principle behind the formation of the image, let us refer to Fig. 7-27. Suppose that your lens has a focal length of 2 ft, and the candle is 3 ft from the lens. Where will the image be? To find the image

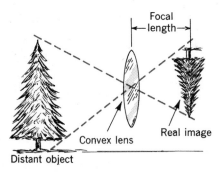

7-24. A real image of a distant object is formed at the principal focus.

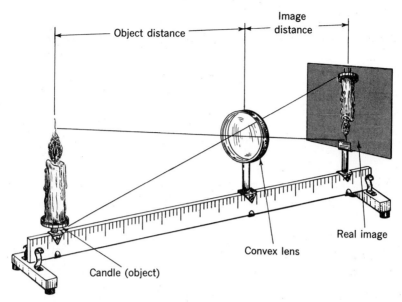

Real image

Convex lens

Candle (object)

7-25. The convex lens projects the real image on the screen.

of point **O**, you must find where rays of light from that point come together again after passing through the lens. You know that the *parallel ray* **OL** will *refract* through **F**, the *principal focus*. Another ray **OC** drawn through the center of the lens will pass straight through without bending. At the point **I**, where both intersect, you find the *image* of the point **O**.

If you repeat this construction for other points on the object arrow, you will find that the whole image will be located as shown in the diagram. It turns out to be 6 ft from the lens and, being twice as far away as the object, is also twice as large. Like all real images, it is *inverted*.

You can locate images by calculations. As you move the candle nearer and farther away, you will find that the image also changes its distance from the lens. However, object and

image locations are always related by the following formula

$$D_i = \frac{D_o \times F}{D_o - F}$$

where, as shown in Fig. 7-27, D_o is the object distance, D_i is the image dis-

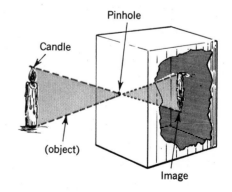

Pinhole

Candle

(object)

Image

7-26. Although a pinhole camera has no lens, the pinhole projects a real image just as a lens does.

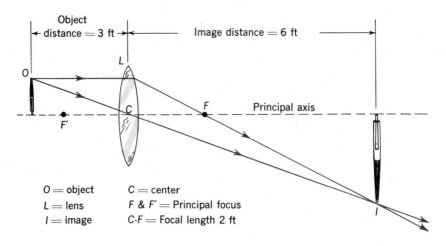

Object
distance = 3 ft →|← ————— Image distance = 6 ft ————→

L

O

C

F   Principal axis

F′

O = object   C = center
L = lens   F & F′ = Principal focus
I = image   C-F = Focal length 2 ft

I

7-27. Compare the size and distance of the image with the size and distance of the object. What kind of relationship exists between the sizes and distances?

tance, and **F** is the focal length. Instead of locating the image by constructing a diagram, we could have found it by *substituting* in this formula. If we let D_o equal 3 ft, and **F** equal 2 ft, then D_i turns out to be 6 ft $\left(\dfrac{3 \times 2}{3 - 2} = 6\right)$.

SAMPLE PROBLEM

A foot rule stands 12 inches away from a convex lens having a focal length of 3 inches. (a) Where is the image located? (b) How large is the image?

SOLUTION:

(a) *Step 1.* $D_o = 12$ in., and $F = 3$ in.

Step 2. The image distance,

$$D_i = \frac{D_o \times F}{D_o - F} = \frac{12 \times 3}{12 - 3} = \frac{36}{9} = 4$$

Therefore, the image is located 4 inches *beyond* the lens.

(b) *Step 1.* $D_o = 12$ in., and $D_i = 4$ in., S_o (the size of the object) = 12 in.

Step 2. Substituting in the formula, $\dfrac{S_i}{S_o} = \dfrac{D_i}{D_o}$, we get $\dfrac{S_i}{12} = \dfrac{4}{12}$, or $S_i = 4$

Therefore, the *length* of the image is 4 inches.

How can we project large images? In Fig. 7-27, as you move the object in toward **F′**, its image moves farther away and becomes larger. If you put the object just outside **F′**, the image becomes very large and far away. This is how you project slides (and movie films) on a screen. The object is the illuminated slide. A large, inverted image is then formed on the distant screen. Of course, you put the slide into the projector upside down. Why?

If you move the object closer to the lens, until it is right at **F′**, you get no clear image on the screen. Instead, the rays from the object are parallel after passing through the lens. If you put a lighted bulb at **F′**, you can project a parallel beam of light.

A convex lens acts as a magnifying glass. If you move the object still closer to the lens, inside **F′** (as in Fig. 7-28), the rays will spread apart after they go through the lens. Remember, you get *real images* only when rays coming from the object *converge* after passing through the lens. When the object is located *inside* **F′**, *no real image* can be formed.

However, you can see a *virtual image* by looking at it through the lens. As shown in the diagram, the image is *enlarged*, and *right-side-up*. To read with a magnifier, you hold it closer to the page than the focal length of the lens.

Cameras use convex lenses. Have you ever studied the action of a simple camera? The convex lens causes an image to focus on the film. When you take pictures of distant objects, the distance between the lens and the film at the back of the camera is the focal length of the lens. Can you see why?

To get sharp pictures of nearby objects, you have to increase the distance between the film and lens. That is why some cameras have focusing bellows to change the position of the lens.

A lens is really not necessary in a camera. As mentioned earlier, the *pinhole camera* uses a small opening instead. (See Fig. 7-26.) With a tiny hole, you can get sharp pictures, but you must make a long exposure. With a lens, you can get sharp pictures with a short exposure time.

Your eye is nature's own camera. Optically, your eye acts in a manner that is very similar to that of an ordinary camera. Moreover, it is linked to your brain somewhat as a television camera is connected to its transmitter. (See Fig. 7-29.)

Light enters your eye through the tough transparent skin called the *cornea*, where it is partly refracted. It then goes through a flexible *convex lens*, which causes the light to *focus on the retina* (*ret*-ih-nuh). Like the film of the camera, the retina is sensitive to light. The light striking the retina produces electric impulses that follow

7-28. A magnifying glass produces an enlarged virtual image.

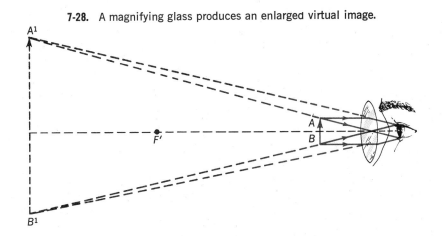

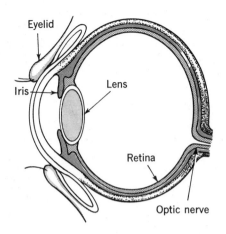

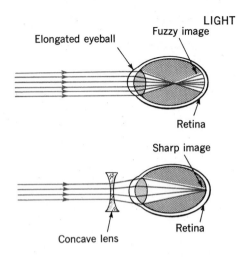

7-29. The iris acts like the diaphragm of the camera in regulating the amount of light that enters.

7-30. Concave lenses in eyeglasses correct for nearsightedness. Notice the position of the image before correction.

the *optic nerve* to the *visual center* of the brain.

The amount of light that can enter your eye is controlled by a colored, contracting ring called the *iris*. The iris is just outside the lens and acts like the *diaphragm* of the camera. Your *eyelids* correspond to the *shutter* of the camera which opens and closes to expose the film.

The lens of your eye is flexible. The lens of your eye can bulge out or flatten to focus on objects that are near or far away. To focus on nearby objects, muscles in your eye cause the lens to bulge out. The lens muscles are generally relaxed when focusing on objects twenty or more feet away.

Sometimes, however, people are *nearsighted* or *farsighted*. A *nearsighted* person has eyeballs that are elongated, or has lenses that are too thick. In either case, the image is brought to focus in *front* of the retina instead of on it. (See Fig. 7-30.) You can correct this by using *concave lenses*

in front of the eye. These are lenses that *diverge* or *spread out* the ray of light and counteract the converging effect of the eye lens.

The *farsighted* eyeball is too short or has a lens that is too flat. As shown in Fig. 7-31, a *convex lens* can correct this fault.

There are many other defects of the eyes caused by optical imperfections, or diseased conditions.

Movies are an optical illusion. You have seen how we project an enlarged image of a slide on a screen. *Movies* are a rapid succession of such projected images. Why do they seem to move?

When you look at a lighted lamp, a real image of the lamp glows on your retina, producing the sensation of vision in your brain. When the lamp is turned off, the image disappears, but you still "see" it for about $\frac{1}{10}$th of a second. This "lingering" effect is called *persistence of vision*.

It is this persistence of vision that makes movies possible. The projector

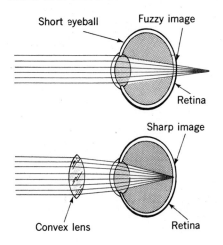

7-31. Convex lenses in eyeglasses correct for farsightedness, by focussing the image sharply on the retina.

throws a still picture on the screen. Then the screen is darkened for a very brief interval of time while the picture is replaced by a slightly *different* one. Again, the screen is illuminated. This process is repeated many times a second.

Due to persistence of vision, you continue to see the previous picture during the interval of darkness. The *illusion of motion* is due to the fact that each picture differs only slightly from the previous one and merges smoothly with it.

How does the refracting telescope work? As you learned in the previous section, the reflecting telescope uses a curved mirror to focus the light. The *refracting telescope* uses a *lens system*. (See Fig. 7-32.) A large *convex lens* called the *objective* is placed at the outer end of the long telescope tube. The objective lens of a telescope has a *long focal length*. This lens forms a real inverted image of a distant object near the lower end of the tube, at the principal focus of the lens. You look at this image through an *eyepiece,* a small *convex lens* that magnifies the image.

The *magnifying power* of this kind of telescope is found by *dividing the focal length of the objective* (**F**) *by*

7-32. How does the formation of an image in the refracting telescope differ from that in a reflecting telescope?

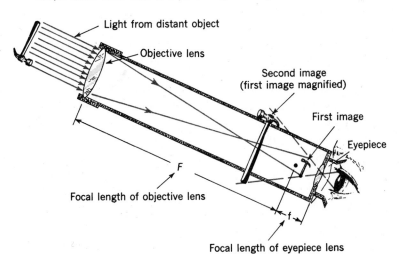

the focal length of the eyepiece (f):

$$\text{Magnification} = \frac{F}{f}$$

The image is upside down, but this is not a disadvantage in astronomy. To get upright images for other uses, another lens is put between the other two.

How does the compound microscope work? While the telescope enables you to see far into the universe, the *microscope* lets you view the tiniest objects of nature. Scientific knowledge expanded tremendously and new areas of research were opened with the invention and perfection of the microscope.

Like the telescope, the microscope also has two convex lenses. However, it is modified to form images of near and tiny objects. At the lower end of the tube you find the *objective*. (See Fig. 7-33.) This is a small *convex lens* of very *short focal length*. The object to be viewed is placed just *outside* the principal focus of this lens. A real, inverted and enlarged image of the object is formed near the upper end of the tube. You magnify this image by looking at it through the *eyepiece*. The overall *magnification* of a microscope is found by *multiplying the separate magnifications formed by each lens*. For example, if a microscope has an objective lens with a magnification of 44 diameters (44X) and the eyepiece has a magnification of 10 diameters (10X), the final magnification is 440 diameters (440X). The highest practical magnification you can get with the *optical microscope* is about 2000 diameters (2000X). The electron and field-ion microscopes give magnifications that are much higher than this.

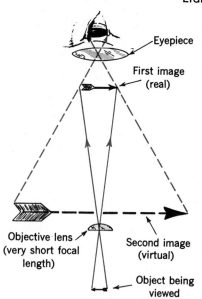

7-33. Compare this diagram of the compound microscope with the refracting telescope of Figure 7-32.

Quick Quiz

1. Why does a stick look broken when it is dipped into water at an angle?
2. Why does refraction occur?
3. When refraction occurs, in which way is the light ray bent?
4. How does a convex lens affect parallel light rays?
5. Why is a concave lens said to be divergent?
6. What is the relationship between the distances and sizes of objects and their images?
7. Where would you put a convex lens to throw an enlarged image of a lighted bulb on a screen?
8. Where do you put an object to look at it through a magnifier?
9. What kind of a lens must be used in a camera? Why?
10. What is persistence of vision?

11. In what part of a telescope do you find the objective lens? Describe the lens.

12. How does a concave lens differ in appearance from a convex lens?

C COLOR

What is color? In the first section of this chapter we saw that light is a form of energy that behaves both like particles and waves. It is the *wave characteristic* that is important in understanding color. Color is a property of light that depends entirely on the length of the light waves. The shortest wavelength visible to the human eye is violet, with about 60,000 waves per inch, and the longest visible wavelength is red, with about 30,000 waves per inch.

Most radiations are invisible. You can see things only by light whose frequency ranges from that of red light up to that of violet. There are wide ranges of radiations whose frequencies are much more and much less than ordinary light, but these are not visible.

All of these radiations, including light, are called electromagnetic waves. They are all the result of *electronic vibrations,* and travel at the speed of light, 186,000 mi/sec. They all can be refracted and reflected, and differ only in *frequency* and in *wavelength.* Together they make up the *electromagnetic spectrum.*

The radiations with frequencies below the red are called *infrared rays.* (See Fig. 7-34.) These radiations are given off by *hot* objects, and are commonly referred to as *radiant heat.* They give the sensation of warmth when they strike our skin.

The radiation just beyond the violet, with a higher frequency, is called *ultraviolet* light. You are probably already acquainted with some of the effects of ultraviolet light. Your camera film is very sensitive to ultraviolet (*black light*), but your eyes are not.

Ultraviolet rays of certain frequencies *tan* your skin, others *kill bacteria,*

7-34. Visible light comprises only a small portion of the electromagnetic spectrum. Slanted lines are used to indicate that the different divisions overlap.

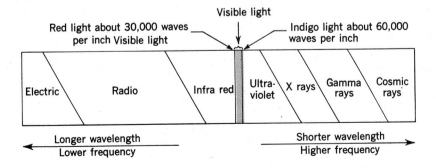

Visible light

Red light about 30,000 waves per inch Visible light — Indigo light about 60,000 waves per inch

| Electric | Radio | Infra red | Ultra-violet | X rays | Gamma rays | Cosmic rays |

Longer wavelength / Lower frequency ← → Shorter wavelength / Higher frequency

and still others cause substances to *fluoresce,* or glow.

Beyond ultraviolet are the *X rays,* with still higher frequencies. You are familiar with some of their uses and will study more about them later on.

Still higher in frequency are the *gamma rays.* These are produced by disturbances in the nucleus of the atoms. Some *radioactive* elements, such as radium, emit gamma rays.

Actually, there is no sharp dividing line between the different sections of the electromagnetic spectrum. They overlap, as shown in Fig. 7-34. For example, the low infrared may be used as high-frequency radio waves. Furthermore, there are powerful electronic tubes that generate X rays that are identical to gamma rays.

How are frequency and wavelength related? How is it that all of these radiations can have different frequencies and yet travel at the same speed? We have seen that we find the speed or velocity by multiplying the frequency by the wavelength. The formula is $V = F \times L$. If one wave has a higher frequency than another, it must have a shorter wavelength.

For example, while the waves of violet light have about twice the frequency of the red waves, their wavelengths are only half as long.

For all waves, high frequency means short wavelength, and vice versa. In other words, *whether we speak of **high-frequency** radiation or of **short-wave** radiation, we mean the same thing.*

How are colors formed from white light? Have you ever been puzzled by the sudden appearance of color in colorless objects? Rainbow colors may

7-35. White light can be refracted to produce a spectrum. The range of colors from red to violet are dispersed on the screen in the order of longest red wavelength to the shortest violet wavelength.

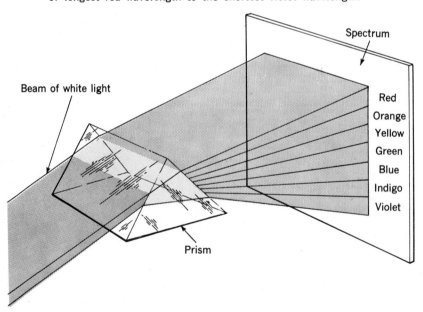

shimmer over the surface of a sunlit soap bubble. A colorful *iridescence* may appear when a thin film of oil spreads over a wet pavement. Drops of dew on a spider's web may suddenly sparkle like colorful jewels.

Sir Isaac Newton was the first to make a scientific study of these effects. When he allowed a beam of sunlight to pass through a glass prism, he found that the light spread out into various colors, called a *spectrum*. (See Fig. 7-35.) When he blended these colors together again by using a second prism, he regained the beam of white light. He showed that all of the colors mingled together produce the sensation of white. The prism merely *sorts out the colors*, and lets each one *produce its own effect on your retina.*

The prism causes light of each color to refract differently. As you can see in Fig. 7-35, the *violet is bent most* and the *red the least*. So we find red at one end of the spectrum, followed by *orange, yellow, green, blue, indigo,* and *violet*, and all the variations in between.

You remember that the speed of light changes as it goes from one medium to another. This change in speed causes light to bend or *refract*. *Violet* light is slowed down the *most* when it passes into glass, while *red* is slowed down the *least*. This is because violet light has a shorter wavelength than red. Since the wave of violet light is slowed down more than the waves of the other colors in the denser glass prism, it is bent the most.

What is a spectroscope? The prism of glass can be used in an instrument called a *spectroscope* to make careful analyses of light. A simple spectroscope is shown in Fig. 7-36. Essentially, it consists of a prism to *refract* the light and a *system of lenses* to view the spectrum produced. It has a *scale* on which you can read directly the wavelength of light, or else the angle at which you see the light of a particular wavelength.

Some spectroscopes use a *diffraction grating instead of a prism*. This is a plate containing *equally-spaced* parallel lines, thousands to the inch. The light *passes* through it or, in some types, *reflects* from it. The wavelengths of particular colors are then studied.

You can use an **LP** phonograph record as a diffraction grating. Hold one horizontally in front of you, at near eye level, and look at the light from a ceiling lamp reflected from it. Sometimes you get the same rainbow effect by looking at a light through a textile of very fine weave. The principle of the diffraction grating is more fully discussed in a physics textbook.

The spectroscope may be used to identify elements. You can use a spectroscope for *chemical analysis*. When the atoms of chemical elements are disturbed, each element radiates light of certain specific wavelengths. That is, the wavelengths of light produced by one element are different from those produced by any other element.

For instance, when you look through a spectroscope at the light from a neon sign, you see a pattern of bright lines that can be produced only by the element neon. If some mercury vapor is also present, you will see another different pattern of lines that is due to the mercury. That is how we know that neon and mercury, as well as over fifty other chemical elements, exist on the sun. They are "finger-printed" by their light-wave pat-

7-36. The principal parts of a Bunsen spectroscope. (Courtesy of Bausch & Lomb, Inc., Rochester, NY)

terns in the spectroscope. With the aid of the spectroscope, a chemist can detect an element in a substance even if there is only a trace present.

What causes a rainbow? Under certain conditions, *raindrops* act like tiny *prisms*. They refract the sunlight and spread it out into a spectrum of color called the *rainbow*. Figure 7-37 shows the path of two rays through a raindrop. Note that the ray of red light (R) is *reflected* and then *refracted* so that it appears in the lower part of the rainbow.

The combined effect of thousands of drops, all located at the same angle from the observer, makes the complete rainbow. As you face a rainbow, the sun is usually at your back and low in the sky.

What gives an object color? How can some things look white, others blue, and still others yellow when they are all illuminated by the same *white light*? It all depends on how they *absorb, reflect,* or *transmit* the light that falls on them.

An object is *white* if it *reflects* light of all wavelengths equally well. If an object *does not reflect* light at all, it is *black*. Black is the absence of light. Hence, a piece of velvet is black if it *absorbs light of all wavelengths,* and reflects none.

Hold a sheet of white paper in a beam of sunlight in a darkened room. Explain why you see a spot of white on the paper.

Now hold a pane of *red* glass in the beam in front of the paper. The paper now looks red. Apparently the glass is red because it *absorbs light* of all wavelengths *except* the red. It lets only the red pass through, and so only red reaches the paper. Why does the paper now look red? Remember that the white paper can reflect all light equally well. But if only red light falls on it, then red light is the only possible color of light the paper can reflect to your eye.

Now use green glass instead of red. What color is the paper now? Can you explain why?

What happens if the paper is colored? Let's use some paper that is dyed with a red pigment. Pigments are chemicals that have color because they

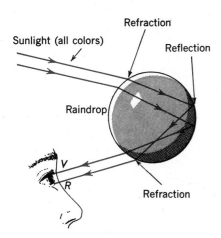

Sunlight (all colors)

Refraction

Reflection

Raindrop

Refraction

7-37. A rainbow is produced both by refraction and reflection of light by the raindrops.

AN OBJECT'S COLOR DEPENDS ON:

(1) The *kind* of light shining on it.
(2) Which *wavelength* of this light it is able to *transmit* if transparent, or
(3) Which *wavelengths* it is able to *reflect,* if opaque.

absorb light of only certain wavelengths. They are the color of the light that they reflect to our eyes. When sunlight falls on a sheet of red paper, naturally the paper looks red. The other colors of the sunlight are completely absorbed by the paper, and only the red light is reflected to your eye.

Hold the pane of *red* glass in front of the red paper in a beam of sunlight in a darkened room. There is only red light shining on the paper. This red is *reflected* and the paper still looks red. Now hold a *green* glass in front of the paper so that only green light falls upon it. The red paper *absorbs* green light. It can reflect only red; and, if no red reaches the paper, it reflects *no* light at all. Hence, the *red paper* looks black when illuminated by green light.

What are the primary colors? One way of studying the effect of mixing colors is to look at a *whirling disk* painted in various colors. Because of persistence of vision, you get the same effect as if all the colors were entering your eye at once. A better way is to *project beams of colored light* on the same spot of a white screen. When you project all the colors of the spectrum in this way, you get white. This is the opposite effect of sorting out different colors by a prism.

You can also get white light by projecting, in proper proportions, only *three* colors, namely *red, green,* and *blue-violet.* These are called the **primary colors.** By varying the amounts of any two or three of the primary colors, you can get a great many different colors.

What are complementary colors? Any *two* colored lights that *produce white* when mixed together are called **complementary colors.** Blue-violet and yellow are such a pair. Why do they combine to give white light? If you remove blue-violet from all the spectral colors, those left when mixed produce the effect of yellow in your mind. Therefore, mixing blue-violet and yellow is like mixing all the spectral colors. Red and blue-green are also complementary. Can you explain why laundry bluing helps whiten clothes that have become tinged with yellow by age?

You can use *retinal fatigue* to see the complement of a color. Stare fixedly at a bright yellow card for about a minute and then quickly look at a sheet of white paper. You seem to see a card with a bluish tint. When you stared at the yellow card, retinal fatigue made your retina insensitive to yellow light. When you then looked at the white paper, light of all colors entered your eye. But since the yellow didn't "register," you saw blue, the complement of yellow.

What happens when we mix paint pigments? Perhaps you thought that mixing yellow and blue-violet should give you green, not white. *And so it does, when you mix pigments!* So far we have been *mixing light.* Grind some yellow chalk and blue chalk together with a little water. The mixture should be *green.*

Yellow chalk appears yellow because it absorbs the blue, indigo, and violet light. The blue chalk absorbs the red, orange, and yellow. Neither absorbs the green, which is the only color that can be reflected from the mixture and enter your eyes.

The *four-color printing process* is a good example of mixing pigments. The colored picture is built up by printing the same piece of paper from four plates, one after the other. Each plate is inked with a different pigment, one red, one blue, one yellow, and one black. *Red, blue,* and *yellow* are called the three *primary pigments.*

How is the Doppler effect applied to light waves? As explained in the chapter on sound, the *Doppler effect* is the *shift in frequency* that occurs whenever a wave source moves toward or away from you. In Fig. 7-38, let us suppose that a light-source, such as a star, is stationary at point 1. It is giving out circular waves, each having point 1 as its center. Each wave front would be separated from the next by a distance, or *wavelength,* labeled **a** and **b.** Suppose the star moves rapidly toward the right. Now each new circular wave front starts from *new centers,* marked **2-3-4-5-6.** Notice what effect this motion has on the wavelength of the light. The light coming to **A** would have a *shorter wavelength* or a *higher frequency* than that at **B.**

If the star were *actually* green, its light would *appear* bluish to an observer at **A.** The reason, of course, is that blue light has a higher frequency or shorter wavelength than

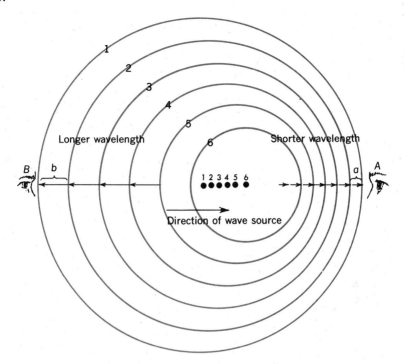

7-38. The Doppler effect. The row of numbered 1–6 dots shows where each wave started, as the source moved to the right. Note that A receives more waves per second than B.

green. What about the person at **B**? To him the light would have a yellowish tinge, at a lower frequency than the green.

If the shift in frequency of light from a star is known, its speed can be computed. We examine the light from a star in a spectroscope. If we find that all the *spectral lines* of an element are shifted down toward the red end of the spectrum, we know that the star is going away from us. For example, recent observations showed that the most distant stars within the range of the Mt. Palomar telescope are racing *away* from us at a speed of about 90,000 miles a second, almost half the speed of light!

The Doppler effect has several important uses in radio. For example, the *radar* speed-trap is an application of it. A radar beam reflects at a different frequency from a moving car than from a stationary one. The shift in frequency depends upon the speed of the vehicle. Recently, a more precise system of navigation by satellites has been developed by applying this same principle.

Quick Quiz

1. Why does a prism spread a beam of white light?
2. What determines the color of light?

3. Explain why one object looks black and another white.

4. Name a pair of complementary colors.

5. What causes a rainbow?

6. Why does high frequency mean short wavelengths?

7. Discuss the four-color printing process.

8. Discuss the Doppler effect. Include (a) cause and (b) applications.

9. Describe the structure and use of the spectroscope.

10. How does the structure of a red ray of light differ from that of blue?

11. Name six kinds of radiations included in the electromagnetic spectrum.

SUMMARY

Light is a form of energy that radiates from atoms when their electrons are disturbed, usually by heat or electricity. Light is emitted or absorbed in small units called photons, which travel by a wave-like motion. In a laser, the radiations of light are all of the same frequency and in step with one another.

Substances are classed as transparent, translucent, or opaque, depending on how well they transmit light. The speed of light in a vacuum, the greatest speed attainable, is about 186,000 miles per second.

The law of reflection states that the angle of incidence equals the angle of reflection. Regular reflection from smooth surfaces may form images. Irregular reflection from rough surfaces produces diffused light and no images. Concave mirrors are used in reflecting telescopes to produce images, and in lamps to produce parallel beams of light.

When light passes at an angle from one transparent substance into another of different density, it bends, or refracts. Refraction explains the action of optical instruments that use lenses or prisms. Concave (diverging) lenses cause light rays to spread apart. Convex (converging) lenses cause light rays to come together.

The eye is much like a camera in structure and action. Nearsightedness can be corrected by concave lenses; farsightedness by convex lenses.

When a beam of sunlight passes through a prism, it spreads out into a rainbow of colors called a spectrum. The color of light depends upon its wavelength. The spectroscope is used to analyze light and measure its various wavelengths.

The color of an object depends upon the kind of light that hits it, and upon the kind of light it can transmit or reflect. A complementary color is one that mixes with another to make white light.

The Doppler effect is the shift in frequency of waves due to the motion of their source. This has the effect of changing the color of light coming from a moving source.

CHAPTER REVIEW .

Vocabulary

Match the words in Column A with the *best* response in Column B. Do not write in your book.

Column A

1. photon
2. incandescent
3. polarization
4. laser
5. luminous
6. illuminated
7. opaque
8. transparent
9. reflection
10. diffusion
11. angle of incidence
12. concave
13. convex
14. refraction
15. nearsightedness
16. farsightedness
17. spectrum
18. spectroscope
19. primary colors
20. complementary colors

Column B

a. able to transmit light so that you can see objects clearly through it
b. angle at which light strikes a mirror
c. band of rainbow-like colors formed when white light passes through a prism
d. bending of light rays as they pass from one substance into another
e. device that separates light into different wavelengths
f. glowing hot
g. light amplification by stimulated emission of radiation
h. not able to transmit light
i. process of screening out all waves except those that vibrate in one particular plane
j. producing and emitting its own light
k. red, green, and blue-violet
l. scattering of light rays
m. shaped like the inside of an orange peel
n. shaped like the outside of an orange peel
o. single "packet" of light radiation
p. the turning back of light waves from a substance
q. two colors that produce white light when mixed
r. visible by light that it receives and reflects
s. weakness in distant vision
t. weakness in near vision

Questions: Group A

1. What is the speed of light in air?
2. Name a unit of lamp brightness.
3. Do you think a cat or owl could see things in a totally dark room? Explain your answer.
4. Define foot-candle. What does it measure?
5. What causes a mirage?
6. How is the index of refraction calculated?

7. Where do rays from a distant object converge after passing through a convex lens?
8. Given the object and image distances, how could you calculate the focal length of a convex lens?
9. Name the spectral colors in order of decreasing frequency.
10. What two facts determine the color of an opaque object?
11. Describe the use of a spectroscope.
12. How are X rays and infrared rays alike?
13. What color results when the three primary colors are equally mixed?
14. What happens when pigments of the three primary colors are properly mixed?

Questions: Group B

1. Can you see real images in your bathroom mirror? Explain.
2. What is the significance of monochromatic light waves in a laser?
3. What is the significance of coherent (or in step) light waves in a laser?
4. If a lighted bulb is placed at the principal focus of a convex lens, what happens to the light rays that pass through the lens?
5. What is the cause of nearsightedness? How can it be corrected?
6. What is the cause of farsightedness? How can it be corrected?
7. How do you calculate the magnifying power of a telescope?
8. What is the relationship between frequency and photon energy?
9. Why does a white object look red when you look at it through a red glass?
10. Why does a red object appear to be black when viewed through a green glass?
11. Explain what retinal fatigue is and its connection with complementary colors.
12. What color do you get when you mix blue and yellow light? Blue and yellow pigments? Explain.
13. What happens to a beam of pure red light when you pass it through a prism?
14. How does light affect the temperature of the material that absorbs it?

Problems

1. If light from the sun takes 500 seconds to reach the earth, how far is it from the sun to the earth?
2. When you stand 10 ft in front of a plane mirror, exactly where is your image?
3. What is the illumination 10 feet away from a 100-cp lamp?
4. What happens to its apparent brightness as a torch moves from a point 30 ft away from you to a point 120 ft away?
5. Calculate the speed of light in water if the index of refraction for water is 1.33.

6. How long is the image of a foot-rule if it is located three times as far from the lens as the foot-rule itself?

7. If an object is 24 inches away from a convex lens whose focal length is 12 inches, where is the image located? How large is the image in relation to the size of the object?

8. Find the magnifying power of a refracting telescope if the focal length of the object lens is 20 ft, and the eyepiece, 3 in.

9. If certain radiations have a frequency of 60,000 waves per inch, how many waves per inch are there in radiations whose waves are three times as long?

10. What is the total magnification of a microscope if the objective lens magnifies the image 36 times and the eyepiece magnifies it 10 times?

ELECTRICAL

AND NUCLEAR ENERGY

8 CURRENT ELECTRICITY

ELECTRIC CURRENTS AND CIRCUITS

What is electricity? Electricity is a complete mystery to most people who use it daily. When you learn that an electric current is a *stream of electrons,* you may begin to understand its true nature. In the next chapter, Electronics, you will study the electron in greater detail. For the present, remember that *the electron is an atomic particle carrying a negative electric charge.*

Electrons exist in all atoms and can be detached from the atoms of certain elements quite easily. These freed electrons can then be pushed along through substances called conductors. Such a *stream of electrons moving along a conductor produces an electric current.*

In order to have some idea of what an electric current is, we should first try to understand how an electric current is produced. The simplest device used for this purpose is a voltaic cell. A voltaic cell is easily assembled by placing a strip of copper and a strip of zinc in a glass beaker containing dilute sulfuric acid. The chemical action of the acid with the zinc metal causes this plate surface to accumulate an enormous number of electrons on its surface. Compared to this large number of electrons, the copper plate has a much smaller number of electrons. This large difference in the number of electrons produces a *potential difference.* It is the potential difference that determines the ability or potential of the voltaic cell to push the excess electrons along some outside path from zinc to copper plate. This outside electron path along conducting wires is called a *circuit.* And the movement of electrons along this path or circuit is what we refer to as a *current.* The size of the current is determined by the number of electrons moving past a given point in a given time. The potential difference, or ability to push electrons at a faster or slower rate, is also known as voltage, or emf, and is measured in volts.

How is electricity produced? To produce an electric current, we must cause electrons to move along a con-

8-1. This electric generator was developed in 1878 by Elihu Thomson. (General Electric Co.)

ductor, such as copper wire. Seven different ways in which this is done are listed below. Except for some *superconductors,* we must supply *energy* to maintain the electric current.

1. *Electric generators* produce the voltage necessary for a current in our big power lines. Either water power or steam power usually is used to run such generators. In a typical power generator, *mechanical energy* is changed to *electrical energy.* In many conversion processes, *heat energy* is used to provide the mechanical energy. The heat energy, in turn, comes from the burning of fuels or from nuclear energy.

2. A source of energy widely used to provide electric current is *chemical action.* This is what produces the potential difference in your flashlight or car battery which causes the current to flow. The electricity produced by a *fuel cell* also comes from chemical action.

3. Heat may be changed directly into electricity by a process called

the *thermoelectric effect.* When two dissimilar metals are joined to form a circuit, a current flows when heat is applied at a junction of the metals. This effect is increased if the other junction is cooled as is shown in Fig. 8-2. Such a device is called a *thermocouple.* Several such devices connected in series form a *thermopile.*

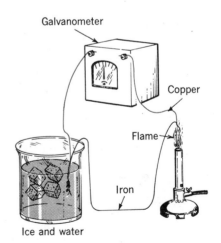

8-2. A thermocouple produces a current when heat is applied at one of the junctions.

In addition to generating electricity, this arrangement can also be calibrated to give temperature readings. Its effective measuring range depends on the types of metals used in the thermocouple. An iron-copper thermocouple, for example, is suitable for measuring temperatures up to 275° C, while a combination of platinum and rhodium is useful up to 1600° C.

4. Another means of generating electricity is by using *light energy.* When a beam of light strikes certain metals, electrons are set free. This action is known as the **photoelectric** effect.

5. Squeezing certain crystals generates tiny currents. We call this the **piezoelectric** (pee-ay-zo) effect.

6. Also, *static electric charges,* such as those that cause lightning, produce currents.

7. Today, we are perfecting ways to obtain electricity directly from *nuclear reactions.*

Potential difference produces electric current. To keep an electric current flowing, some sort of "pressure" must be applied. You can better understand this force by comparing it to a water system. In order to maintain a flow of water in the pipes, you must have *pressure.* You might obtain this pressure from the *difference of level* between a high reservoir and a water faucet. (See Fig. 8-3.) A similar type of "pressure" in an electric circuit is known as *potential difference.* Just as pumps produce *water pressure,* so batteries and generators are used to produce *electric pressure. This electric pressure is also called electromotive force (emf).* It is measured in *volts* by an instrument called a *voltmeter.*

8-3. A difference in water level causes a difference in pressure. The fountain on the left rises higher than the one on the right because the pressure head is higher on the left.

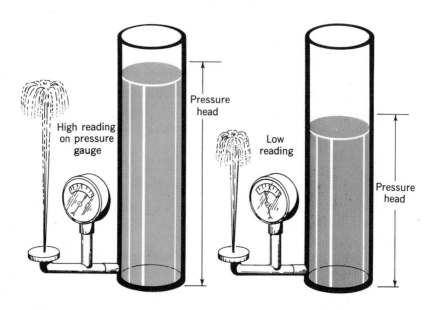

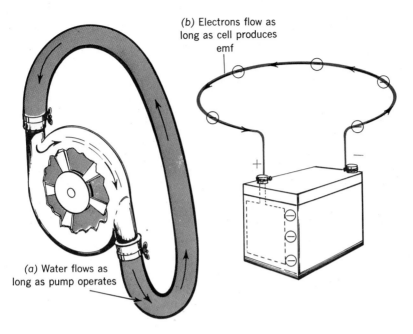

(b) Electrons flow as long as cell produces emf

(a) Water flows as long as pump operates

8-4. The voltage or emf of the cell is like the water pressure of the pump.

Electricity also acts like water in that an increase in pressure produces a larger current. An ordinary flashlight cell gives a pressure, or emf, of 1.5 volts. The use of two cells in series with a pressure of 3 volts produces a current that is twice as large. (See Fig. 8-4.)

Resistance affects current flow. You know that water flows better through a clean water pipe than through one that is clogged with scale. Similarly, a larger electric current is obtained if you cut down the *resistance* of the circuit. The electrical resistance of an object depends upon its *composition, length, thickness,* and *temperature.*

A *large pipe* can carry a greater current of water than a small pipe, and in like manner a *thick wire* can carry a *greater electric current* than a thin one. (See Fig. 8-5.)

The unit of electrical resistance is the *ohm,* which will be defined later. To give you an idea of what the ohm is, note that 1000 feet of No. 10 copper wire (*⅒th inch thick*) has a resistance of 1 ohm. If it were twice as thick, its resistance would be only ¼th ohm, and it could carry 4 times as much current under the same conditions. How much current would this wire carry if it were half as thick as No. 10 wire? What would the resistance be in ohms?

The resistance of a material also depends on its composition. Silver, copper, and aluminum, in this order, make the best conductors. A poor conductor, made from an alloy of nickel and chromium, called *nichrome,* offers about 50 times as much resistance as copper does. It is used extensively to make heating elements in toasters,

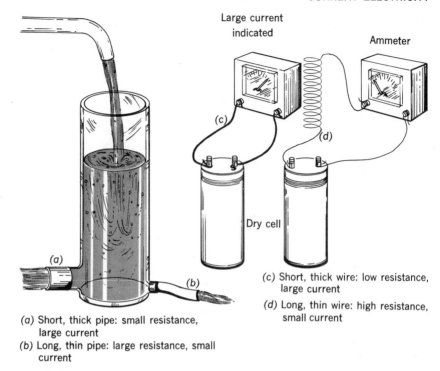

Large current
indicated

Ammeter

(c) Short, thick wire: low resistance,
    large current

(d) Long, thin wire: high resistance,
    small current

Dry cell

(a) Short, thick pipe: small resistance,
    large current
(b) Long, thin pipe: large resistance, small
    current

8-5. A thick wire, like a large pipe, can carry a greater current.

irons, and other electrical appliances. However, even nichrome is a better conductor than most nonmetals are. Such materials as glass and paraffin are very poor conductors, and are called **insulators.** They have billions of times the resistance of copper. Certain elements, such as germanium and silicon, whose resistances are between metals and nonmetals, are *semi-conductors.*

The longer a wire, the greater its resistance. If the resistance of 100 feet of wire is 1 ohm, 200 feet of the same wire will have a resistance of 2 ohms.

Temperature is another factor that affects resistance. The resistance generally *increases* as the conductor becomes *hotter,* and *decreases* when it becomes *cooler.* When you first plug

in a cold electric iron, it has a low resistance and there is a larger current in the circuit. You may notice that lights in the room dim for an instant as less current passes through the filaments. But the resistance of the heating element of the iron quickly increases as it heats up, and then the circuit has less current flow.

What are superconductors? In recent years there has been considerable interest by scientists and researchers in lowering the temperature of conductors to the vicinity of absolute zero, −460° F. Near that temperature some materials become *superconductive.* Their ability to conduct electric current increases hundreds of times. In some instances conductivity has been increased to the point where a current once started in a loop of superconductive material continues to travel in that loop *without any further addition of energy.* This flow of current that remains after the energy source is shut off is called **persistent current.** Thus, under these circumstances, there is apparently no resistance to the flow of electrons. Under normal conditions, you will recall, current stops immediately after the energy source is turned off.

Why should cold metals offer less resistance to current than hot metals? One theory holds that electrons in their passage through a wire are retarded by the constant movement of atoms in the wire. The atomic activity *increases* when the temperature is *raised,* and *decreases* when it is *lowered.* In other words, when a conductor is cooled, its atoms are less likely to get in the way of moving electrons. In some superconductors, the atoms are apparently slowed to a point where they do not hinder electron flow at all.

A rheostat controls the current in a circuit. You can control the amount of resistance in the electrical circuit by a device known as a *rheostat.* When connected to a light circuit it is used as a "dimmer." As the resistance is *raised,* the amount of current is *reduced,* and when the resistance is *lowered* the current flow is *increased.* You can build your own rheostat to control the current from a dry cell or battery, by using a glass of salt water and two ends of wire. Connect a lamp to your dry cell and place two ends of the wire into the glass of salt water as shown in Fig. 8-6. As long as the two wires are close together in the glass, enough current will flow to

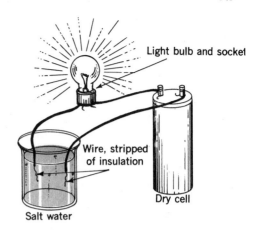

8-6. A simple rheostat can be used to vary the current flow in a circuit.

keep the lamp brightly lit. As you pull the two ends of the wire apart, however, the lamp dims because the resistance of the salt water is too great to permit the necessary flow of electrons. You may need to experiment with the amount of salt needed in the water and the distance between the two wires to get the desired results.

What is meant by an ampere? Just as a current of water is measured in *gallons per second,* so we could measure an electric current in electrons per second. But the electron has such a tiny charge that enormous numbers of them are needed to make even a small current. For example, *a pressure of 1 volt pumps 6.25 billion billion electrons per second through a resistance of 1 ohm.* A current of this size is known as an *ampere.* (A current of a little less than 1 ampere flows through a common 100-watt light bulb.)

The total electric charge of 6.25 billion billion electrons is called one **coulomb** (koo-lowm). An *ampere* is also defined as *a current that carries a charge of one coulomb per second.*

Thus, if we pump 6.25 billion billion electrons (or 1 coulomb of charge) through a wire *each second,* we have a current of *1 ampere.* A pressure of 1 volt pushes a current of 1 ampere through a resistance of 1 ohm. (The ampere is commonly abbreviated *amp,* and is measured with *an ammeter.*) (See Fig. 8-7.)

Ohm's Law. If 1 volt pushes 1 amp through 1 ohm, then 5 volts would be needed for 5 times as much current, or for 5 amps. If the resistance were now doubled to 2 ohms, twice as much pressure or voltage would be needed. That is, it would take a 10-volt pressure to push a 5-amp current through a 2-ohm resistance. You could calculate total pressure needed by using *Ohm's Law,* which states that:

$$\text{Volts} = \text{amperes} \times \text{ohms}$$

In this case, 5 amps $\times$ 2 ohms equals 10 volts.

You use Ohm's Law to solve for volts, amps, or ohms, whichever is

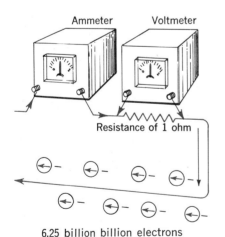

Ammeter   Voltmeter

Resistance of 1 ohm

6.25 billion billion electrons or 1 coulomb per second

8-7. One volt pushes 1 amp through 1 ohm of resistance.

missing, when you are given the other two.

SAMPLE PROBLEM

(a) How large a current will 120 volts send through a resistance of 2 ohms? (b) What is the resistance of an electric toaster if 120 volts sends a current of 5 amps through it?

SOLUTION:

(a) *Step 1.* We re-arrange the Ohm's Law formula to read:

Amps = volts/ohms.

Step 2. Amps = 120/2
= 60

(b) *Step 1.* Re-arranging the formula, we have:

Ohms = volts/amps.

Step 2. Ohms = 120/5
= 24

How do we measure electric power? As the current goes through electric appliances of your home, it produces such effects as *light* and *heat* in lamps, *motion* in the vacuum cleaner, and *sound* in the radio. The amount of current that leaves your home is exactly the same amount that enters. You pay for *the work that it does,* or the *energy* it liberates, on its way through. This energy is measured and calculated on your *electric bill.*

The unit of power is the *watt,* named in honor of James Watt, inventor of the steam engine. It takes one watt of power for a pressure of one volt to push a current of one ampere through a conductor. Hence, the formula used in calculating power is

Watts = volts $\times$ amperes

A larger unit of power, the *kilowatt*, is equal to *1000 watts*. To find the total power rating of a system, you add the *wattages* of all the appliances that are turned on.

SAMPLE PROBLEM

Find the total power of the following appliances: a toaster that draws a current of 5 amps on a 115-volt line; an electric range that uses a 5-amp current on a 230-volt line; and ten 100-watt light bulbs.

SOLUTION:

Step 1. The toaster uses 5 amps at 115 volts. Power = volts × amps = 115 × 5 = 575 watts

Step 2. The range uses 5 amps at 230 volts. Power = volts × amps = 230 × 5 = 1150 watts

Step 3. Ten lamps at 100 watts each. Power = 10 × 100 = 1000 watts

Step 4. The total power is 575 + 1150 + 1000 = 2725 watts, or 2.725 kilowatts.

Your electric "power" bill is *not* really a power bill at all. Electric bills are figured on the basis of *total energy used, not on power*. While one factory might have a huge power rating, but operate for only short intervals, another might have a much lower power rating, but operate for a full 24 hours every day. Obviously, bills cannot be calculated from power requirements alone.

The *unit of energy* is the *kilowatt-hour (kwh)*. This represents the work done when an appliance rated at one kilowatt of power is operated for one hour. The electric *meter* records the *number of kilowatt-hours used*. This is then multiplied by the *rate per kwh* to figure the cost. If the rate is 5¢ per

8-8. Your electric meter at home is called a watt-hour meter and measures energy in kilowatt-hours. (Con Edison)

kilowatt-hour, and you use 100 kwh, your bill will be 500¢, or $5.00. (See Fig. 8-8.)

How is an electric cell made? By 1800 two Italian scientists, Galvani and Volta, had learned how to produce electric currents from chemical action. Volta produced the first simple electric cell by dipping two different metals into various conducting solutions called *electrolytes*.

For example, let us see what happens when zinc and copper are dipped into dilute sulfuric acid. (See Fig. 8-9.) Atoms of zinc dissolve from the zinc plate and go into the acid solution as *positively charged zinc ions:*

$$Zn \rightarrow Zn^{++} + 2 \text{ free electrons}$$

The *free electrons* collect on the zinc plate and charge it *negatively*. Hence the zinc becomes the *negative pole*, or *negative electrode*, of the cell.

Meanwhile, hydrogen ions from the acid are removing electrons from the

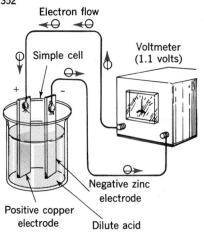

8-9. The emf of the cell depends upon the materials that make up the elements of the cell.

copper electrode to become molecular hydrogen.

$$2H^+ + 2 \text{ free electrons} \rightarrow H_2 \uparrow$$

This *loss* of electrons from the copper leaves it with an *excess of positive* charges. Hence, the copper becomes the *positive electrode* of the cell.

If you connect these electrodes with a conductor, electrons will flow from the zinc (where they are plentiful), to the copper (where they are scarce). Meanwhile, the chemical action maintains the electron supply, and keeps the current flowing.

An *electric cell* always consists of two electrodes in an electrolyte that acts chemically on at least one of them. The *electric energy* comes from the chemical energy of the materials of the cell.

Different electrodes dipped into various electrolytes produce different *electromotive* forces. For example, *zinc* and *carbon*, the electrodes used in the

ordinary *dry cell*, give 1.5 volts. (The dry cell is *not* really dry. It contains an electrolyte in paste form.) *The emf of a cell depends only on the materials it is made of, not its size.*

You can make a simple cell by placing two different metals such as a penny and a dime into a lemon. Its tiny current can usually be detected by connecting the wires to a *galvanometer,* as shown in Fig. 8-10. A *galvanometer is an instrument capable of detecting very weak currents.*

By joining cells together, you can make a *battery.* The cells can be arranged in *series* to increase the voltage or in *parallel* to provide increased current in a circuit. In a series arrangement, you wire the positive pole of one cell to the negative pole of the next. For example, 3 dry cells, each of 1.5 volts, connected in series, form a 4.5-volt battery. If these three dry cells are connected in parallel, however, they form a battery with still only 1.5 volts of pressure. In the parallel arrangement you connect the positive pole of one cell to the positive pole of

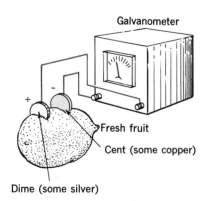

8-10. Small currents can be detected from this very simple cell consisting of two coins and a citrus fruit. The galvanometer measures the current.

the next, and the negative pole to negative pole, as shown in Fig. 8-11.

It is easy to make a lead storage battery. Dip two clean lead strips into a jar of dilute sulfuric acid. A thin invisible film of lead sulfate first forms on each strip. Pass a current from 2 or 3 dry cells through the solution for a few minutes. Bubbles of gas form around each plate and a brown coating forms on the positive plate. *Electrolysis* is taking place. *Oxygen* forms at the positive pole and reacts with the lead to form *brown lead dioxide. Hydrogen* is set free at the negative plate. The cell is being *charged.*

You can *discharge* the cell by connecting it to a small flashlight bulb, or a doorbell, as shown in Fig. 8-12. You can recharge it by using the dry cells again, being sure that the positive pole of the dry cells is connected to the positive plate of your storage

cell. By using a *voltmeter,* you will find that the electromotive force of this charged cell is about 2 volts.

This action takes place over and over again in your automobile *storage battery.* The charging current comes from the *generator.* The *ammeter* or red light on the instrument panel, indicates whether the battery is charging or discharging at any one time.

What is stored in the storage battery? Each cell of your car battery has a set of *plates of spongy lead* and another set of *lead dioxide plates.* The sulfuric acid acts on these plates while the cell is *discharging,* forming *lead sulfate* and *water.* A chemical equation for the reaction is

$$\underset{\text{lead}}{\text{Pb}} + \underset{\text{lead dioxide}}{\text{PbO}_2} + \underset{\text{sulfuric acid}}{2\text{H}_2\text{SO}_4} \rightarrow$$

$$\underset{\text{lead sulfate}}{2\text{PbSO}_4} + \underset{\text{water}}{2\text{H}_2\text{O}} + \text{energy}$$

8-11. A battery consists of cells connected in series (b). In this arrangement, the voltages are added. When the cells are connected in parallel (a), no increase in voltage is obtained.

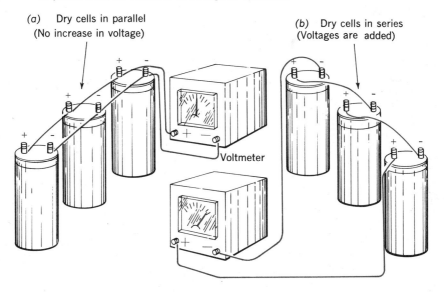

(a) Dry cells in parallel
(No increase in voltage)

(b) Dry cells in series
(Voltages are added)

Voltmeter

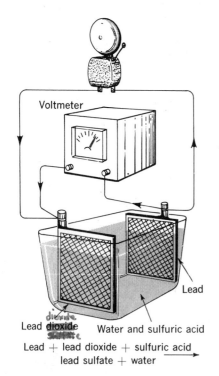

Voltmeter

Lead

Lead dioxide   Water and sulfuric acid

Lead + lead dioxide + sulfuric acid
lead sulfate + water ⟶

8-12. Discharging a lead storage cell. The charging and discharging is an example of a reversible chemical reaction.

To *charge* the battery, you send the current through it in the *opposite direction*. This reverses the chemical reactions,

$$2PbSO_4 + 2H_2O + energy \rightarrow$$
lead dioxide   water
Sulfate

$$Pb + PbO_2 + 2H_2SO_4$$
lead   lead dioxide   sulfuric acid

Notice that you *must put energy into the cell* to charge it. *It is this energy that is stored up in the form of chemical energy.* The storage battery *does not store up electricity!*

How do we tell if the storage battery is charged? Notice that water is formed during the *discharge* of the cell. Water is not as dense as the sul-

furic acid, and therefore the *specific gravity* of the solution drops as the cell discharges. If a *hydrometer* shows a specific gravity of about 1.25 to 1.30, the cell is fully charged. If it reads less than 1.15, it is discharged. We must add distilled water from time to time to replace the water that is lost by evaporation and by electrolysis.

The hydrometer reading only indicates whether a cell is charged or discharged. It does not tell you anything else about the *condition* of the cell.

What is a fuel cell? A *fuel* cell is somewhat like a conventional dry cell or storage battery because in each case, the electrical current results from a chemical reaction. In the fuel cell, however, liquid fuels are *consumed* somewhat as gasoline is used in a car engine. The fuel can be fed to the cell while it is operating instead of being stored within the unit as is the case with most conventional batteries. Another major difference is that a fuel cell is far more *efficient* than a dry cell or storage battery. It is capable of converting up to 80 percent of the fuel's potential energy into power. This compares with an efficiency of about 10 percent for thermoelectric and solar power systems, 15 to 20 percent for an automobile engine, 30 percent for a gas turbine, and 40 percent for a modern power station. It is quite possible, therefore, that some day you may see a car powered by a fuel cell instead of a gasoline engine. This cell will be so efficient that the car will travel up to 100 miles on a single gallon of fuel. In addition, the power source will be noiseless, without fumes, and have no moving parts to wear out. It is also likely that fuel cells will be used to generate electricity for home consumption, to operate self-propelled railroad cars, and run factory equipment. Now, however, it is being used, in a far more modest role, to supply the power for the electrical equipment in the Gemini and Apollo space capsules.

What is an electric circuit? The *electric circuit* is a *complete* conducting path for electrons. It is usually made of copper, which is a very good conductor of electrons. Silver is a better conductor than copper, but is too expensive for common use. Conductors may be protected by *insulating* them with a *nonconducting* material such as rubber and certain plastics.

What is meant by a short circuit? Sometimes a person using an electric iron is startled by a shower of sparks, and the room is plunged into darkness as the lights go out. Of course, a *fuse* has probably "blown," but just what did happen?

Let us suppose a person is using an electric iron in which the resistance of the nichrome wire in the iron is 23 ohms, and that the voltage is 115 volts. Then according to *Ohm's Law* (amps = volts/ohms), the normal current flowing is 115/23, or 5 amperes.

Now suppose that the insulation on the cord had become so worn that the copper wires *touched* together. We say that the wires "shorted" or that a **short circuit** was formed. The current could now flow across from one copper wire to the other, where they touched, without going through the high-resistance nichrome. This created a sudden and large *drop in resistance*, or a "short."

Suppose the resistance of the shorted circuit is only 1 ohm, instead of 23 ohms. It is easy to figure out that the current would become 23 times as great as it was, or 115 amperes. This large current produces intense heat and burns the insulation of the cord. If it flowed for more than an instant, it would permanently damage the wiring and might easily set the house afire.

Fuses and circuit breakers are safety devices. Of course, we must have protection against accidental short circuits. In the circuit leading from the outdoor power lines, there are *fuses* or *circuit breakers*. The current must go through them on its way to the outlets in the wall. The fuse contains a short length of wire which is made of an *alloy of lead* that melts easily. The *fuse* protects a circuit by melting when the circuit becomes *overloaded* with current.

A fuse stamped "20" will carry 20 amperes safely all day without overheating. If the current becomes much greater than 20 amps, the fuse wire melts and thus *breaks* the circuit. The 115-amp current would "blow" the fuse almost instantly.

Many homes and industries use magnetic **circuit breakers** instead of fuses. These are *electromagnetic switches* that *open* an overloaded circuit. They are more convenient than fuses, and *cheaper* in the long run.

Automatic circuit breakers are also used in the light circuits of many modern automobiles. If a "short" occurs while driving at night, the lights blink on and off. In older cars, when a fuse burns out, the lights go out at once, leaving the driver in a dangerous situation.

A wiring defect must be repaired before a fuse is replaced or circuit breaker re-set. An electrician can tell you the correct size of fuses or circuit breakers to use in most home circuits.

What is a series circuit? Although electric wiring is often complicated, there are really only two kinds of circuits, *series* and *parallel*. Sometimes a combination of these two is used. You recall that earlier we talked about dry cells being connected in series or in parallel to make batteries. This same type of arrangement is used in series and parallel wiring.

Figure 8-13 shows a string of 8 Christmas tree lamps. Here we have a single, undivided circuit. The current must go through all 8 lamps in turn, since there is no possible by-path. This is a *series circuit.*

In a series circuit, you can find the *total resistance* by *adding* the resistances of all the separate parts. In this case, if the resistance of each bulb is 70 *ohms*, the total resistance of the string of lights will be $8 \times 70 = 560$ ohms.

If the current that goes through one lamp is 0.2 *ampere,* then 0.2 *amp* is the current that goes through each of them. If one bulb in a series circuit burns out, then no current can flow through any of the bulbs because the circuit has been broken.

SAMPLE PROBLEM

(a) How many volts are needed to push a current of 0.2 amp through 8 lamps in series, if each bulb has a resistance of 70 ohms? (b) In the same circuit, how many volts are needed to push the current through each lamp bulb?

8-13. The same current flows through all parts of a series circuit.

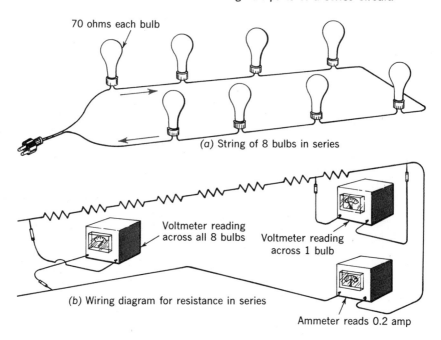

70 ohms each bulb

(a) String of 8 bulbs in series

Voltmeter reading across all 8 bulbs

Voltmeter reading across 1 bulb

(b) Wiring diagram for resistance in series

Ammeter reads 0.2 amp

SOLUTION:

(a) *Step 1.* Total resistance will be 8 × 70 = 560 ohms.

Step 2. Using Ohm's law formula and substituting:

Volts = amps × ohms
= 0.2 × 560 = 112

(b) *Step 1.* Here we apply Ohm's law to a single lamp only.

Volts = amps × ohms
= 0.2 × 70 = 14

Parallel circuits. A *parallel circuit,* shown in Fig. 8-14, is the type used most commonly in our homes. The current divides at **C** and forms two branches, **A** and **B.** (There could be any number of branches.) These branches join together again at **D.** The following facts apply to *parallel circuits:*

1. The *total current* flowing through the circuit equals the *sum* of the currents flowing through each of the separate branches.

2. If you *stop the current* in any branch, for example by unscrewing a lamp, current can still *pass through the other* branches.

3. As *more branches* are added to a parallel circuit, the total *resistance becomes less.* The more pathways you open for the current to flow through, the less resistance it meets.

4. In a parallel circuit, the *voltage* across all of the branches is the *same.* We can understand how this is so if we compare Fig. 8-14 to a river flowing downhill from **C** to **D.** The difference in level between **C** and **D** is the same regardless of which path is taken. In electric circuits, this difference in level is the voltage.

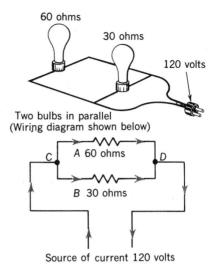

Two bulbs in parallel
(Wiring diagram shown below)

Source of current 120 volts

8-14. In a parallel circuit, different currents flow through the various parts of the circuit.

SAMPLE PROBLEM

(a) In the circuit of Fig. 8-14, find the current in each branch and also the total current. (b) In the same circuit, what is the total resistance?

SOLUTION:

(a) *Step 1.* In branch **A,** the resistance is 60 ohms, and the voltage is 120 volts. (In a parallel circuit, the voltage across all branches is the same.)

Step 2. Applying Ohm's law to branch **A:**
amps = volts/ohms = 120/60 = 2

Step 3. Applying Ohm's law to branch **B,** where the voltage is also 120 volts, and the resistance 30 ohms,
amps = volts/ohms, or 120/30 = 4

Step 4. In a parallel circuit, the total current is the sum of those in the branches, or 4 amp + 2 amp = 6 amp.

(b) *Step 1.* We now apply Ohm's Law to the complete circuit, where the *total voltage* is 120 volts, and the *total current* is 6 amp. Ohms = volts/amps, or 120/6 = 20, the total resistance.

B ELECTROMAGNETISM

Quick Quiz

1. List five sources of electric current.
2. Why do certain metals produce a photoelectric effect when a beam of light shines upon them?
3. What are four factors that affect resistance in a metal? Explain how the resistance is affected by each.
4. What is a superconductor? What is a persistent current?
5. Name two conductors and two non-conductors.
6. In what way are electromotive force and water pressure alike?
7. How is the fuel cell like a storage battery? How is it different?
8. What is the advantage in connecting several dry cells in series? What is the advantage of connecting them in parallel?
9. If all the bulbs on a string of Christmas tree lights go out when one bulb burns out, are they connected in series or parallel? How do you know?
10. Free electrons collect on the zinc plate of an electric cell while electrons are removed from the copper plate. Which are the negative and positive plates? Explain.
11. Why does the fluid in a storage battery have a higher specific gravity when it is charged than when it is discharged?
12. Why does the total resistance of a parallel circuit go down when you add more branches to the circuit?
13. Why is it safe to touch the poles of a dry cell?
14. What is the significance of the number "30" stamped on a fuse?

What is a magnet? Over 2000 years ago, men became acquainted with a material that attracted bits of iron. This was a natural magnet composed of magnetic iron oxide called *magnetite*, or *lodestone*. (See Fig. 8-15.) Later, they observed that when they stroked a steel needle or bar with this natural magnet, it too became magnetized. They soon learned to construct a *compass* by placing a magnetized needle on a pivot so that it could turn freely. The needle would swing around until it pointed in a general north and south direction. We call the end that points north a *north pole* (N) and the other a *south pole* (S).

Magnetic poles. You can easily prove there are two kinds of poles by

8-15. A lodestone is a natural magnet. (International Minerals and Chemicals)

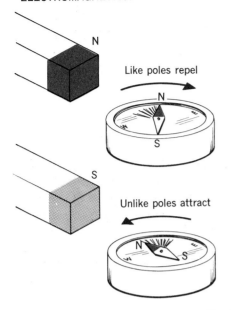

8-16. The N-pole of the magnet at the top repels the N-pole of the compass, while the S-pole of the magnet at the bottom attracts the N-pole of the compass.

bringing two compasses near each other, or by experimenting as in Fig. 8-16. When two north poles are close together, they *repel* each other. On the other hand, when the N-pole of one magnet comes near the S-pole of another, they *attract* each other. Hence, we have the basic principle: *magnetic poles repel each other if they are of the same kind, and attract each other if they are different.* In other words, *"likes repel—unlikes attract."*

You also find that the force between two poles rapidly gets less as you move them apart. Again, the familiar *inverse-square law* holds true. If you *double* the distance between the poles, the force becomes ¼th as much. At 3 *times* the distance, the force is only ⅑th, and so on.

How does iron become magnet-

ized? If you magnetize a bar of steel by stroking it with a magnet, it will have a north pole at one end and a south pole at the other. However, you *cannot* separate the N-pole from the S-pole of a bar magnet by cutting it in half. If you try it, you find that each half is still a complete magnet, each with both an N- and S-pole.

You can repeat this cutting process over and over again. No matter how tiny the pieces become, each is still a *complete magnet.*

The source of magnetism in any material is believed to come from spinning electrons within the atoms. Each electron generates a magnetic field as it *spins on its own axis* and also as it revolves in its *orbit around the nucleus* of an atom.

The atoms of most elements are not noticeably magnetized because about equal numbers of electrons spin in opposite directions, thus canceling their magnetic forces. In iron and a few other elements, however, these forces are not canceled and a magnetic field results.

In a magnetic material, the atoms group themselves into microscopic regions called *domains.* Within the domains, the atoms are lined up so that they all point in one direction. These magnetic domains, themselves, however, normally have a random, helter-skelter arrangement. However, stroking an iron bar with a magnet causes the domains to line up within the bar. The tiny N-poles point toward one end and the S-poles toward the other, and the bar is magnetized. An electric current can also be used to line up magnetic domains.

Can a magnet lose its magnetism? If you hammer a bar magnet violently,

Direction of lines of
force from north to south

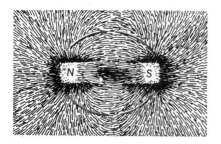

8-17. The iron filings indicate the presence of magnetic lines of force.

you break up this orderly pattern, and thus *demagnetize* it. *Heating* a magnet has the same effect. Can you explain why?

Some alloys tend to keep their magnetized pattern. It is difficult to magnetize them in the first place, or to demagnetize them later. They make excellent *permanent magnets.* One of the best of these alloys is *Alnico,* a steel alloyed with aluminum, nickel, and cobalt. Some Alnico magnets can lift over 1000 times their own weight.

On the other hand, some substances are very easy to magnetize and lose

their magnetism just as easily. These make good *temporary* magnets and are used as cores for electromagnets. Ordinary iron, and silicon steels, make good temporary magnets.

What is the magnetic field? When you sprinkle iron filings on a pane of glass placed over a bar magnet, you get a pattern of lines like that of Fig. 8-17. This shows that the magnetic force extends out into space around the magnet. *This space that exhibits the magnetic force is loosely described as a magnetic field.*

Because of the appearance of the iron filings, we describe the magnetism as existing in *lines of force* or *flux lines.* These lines *show the direction and strength of the magnetic field.* The more concentrated the flux lines, the stronger the magnetic field.

We define the **N**-pole as one from which lines of force leave and an **S**-pole as one where they enter. A glance at the iron-filing pattern of Fig. 8-18 shows that unlike poles attract and like poles repel.

Most substances are transparent to magnetism. Magnetic lines of force

8-18. Patterns formed by the iron filings indicate the forces of attraction between opposite poles (a) and repulsion between similar poles (b).

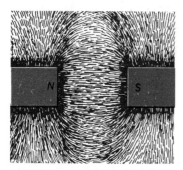

(a) Unlike poles cause attraction

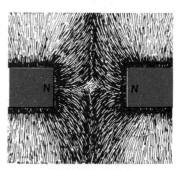

(b) Like poles cause repulsion

can go right through most substances. Try the experiment shown in Fig. 8-19 with various substances, such as cardboard, plastics, copper, aluminum, etc. The magnet picks up thumbtacks through any of them. Like the human body, they are transparent to magnetism.

However, your magnet will not pick up the tacks if you put a sheet of soft steel between them and the magnet. (A piece of a "tin" can, which is actually made of soft steel, works well.) As you will observe, the lines of force no longer go through and magnetize the tacks. Instead, they bend around and stay within the steel can.

The space immediately below the steel sheet is *shielded* from magnetism. Although there is no magnetic insulator, spaces can be shielded from magnetic effects. A magnetic compass is of little use inside a submarine because the space inside is shielded from the *earth's magnetic field* by the steel walls of the sub.

The earth acts like a huge magnet. Ever since the year 1600 when Sir William Gilbert experimented with magnets, we have known that the earth was magnetized. The *earth's magnetism* is much as it would be if a huge bar magnet were buried deep under the earth's surface. This imaginary buried magnet is slightly tilted from the polar axis of the earth; that is, the magnetic poles are not in line with the geographic poles. (See Fig. 8-20.)

The compass needle points to the *magnetic pole*, not to the geographic pole. In San Diego, for instance, it points about 15 degrees east of geographic north. Since the location of the magnetic poles is slowly shifting,

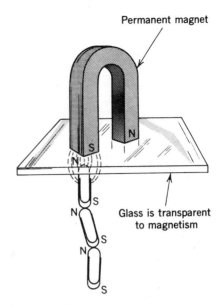

Permanent magnet

Glass is transparent to magnetism

8-19. Magnetic lines of force pass through glass and most other substances.

up-to-date navigation charts must be used for compass corrections.

The earth's magnetic field extends thousands of miles into space. This magnetism and that of the other planets and stars are being investigated by modern space science.

One source of the earth's magnetism is thought to be electric currents created by slow movements of electrically-charged liquid in the earth's interior.

The electric current produces magnetism. In 1819, a Danish scientist named *Oersted* noticed that a compass needle moved whenever a current flowed through a nearby wire. It was soon established that an *electric current always produces a magnetic field.* In other words, whenever a current flows in a conductor, a magnetic field always surrounds it.

When you remember that an electric current is a stream of electrons,

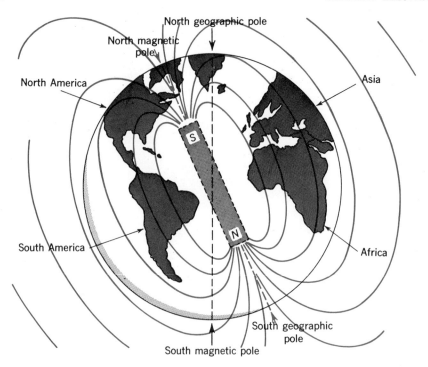

North geographic pole

North magnetic pole

North America

Asia

South America

Africa

South geographic pole

South magnetic pole

8-20. The earth acts as though a short thick bar magnet were buried deep under its surface. Actually the earth's magnetism is probably largely due to electric currents in the earth.

all of which produce magnetic fields, it is not surprising to realize that the current produces magnetism. The phenomenon makes possible electrical devices such as electromagnets, electric motors, and generators.

Electromagnets can be very powerful. An *electromagnet* is made by wrapping an insulated wire around a soft iron core, as shown in Fig. 8-21. We can do three things to make an electromagnet stronger: (1) use a stronger current, (2) increase the number of turns of wire around the coil, and (3) use a more *permeable* core, such as certain steel alloys. The greater the permeability of a material, *the stronger the magnetic field pro-*

duced. The electromagnets of some atom smashers weigh thousands of tons. (See Fig. 8-22.)

When the switch in the circuit of an electromagnet is opened, the magnetism rapidly dies away. When a crane operator, for example, has the load of scrap metal in place, he drops it by stopping the current flow in the magnetic coil.

Some electromagnets can be made supermagnetic. We have seen that when certain materials are cooled to near absolute zero ($-460°$ F) they become superconductors. Superconductors can produce magnetic fields hundreds of times more powerful than conductors at normal room temperatures. In addition to their high strength, they are also light in weight, have low power ratings, and take up little space. Such magnets may have important uses in the future.

How do you find the N-pole of an electromagnet? This is done by simply following the *left-hand rule* as shown in Fig. 8-23. Wrap the fingers of your left hand around the coil so they follow the electron flow. Your outstretched *thumb* will point toward the N-pole of the coil. This means that if you *reverse* the direction of the current, the *polarity* of the coil also reverses; that is, the *N- and S-poles exchange places.*

What is electromagnetic induction? Soon after scientists discovered that electricity could be used to produce magnetism, they wondered if it might not be possible to use *magnet-*

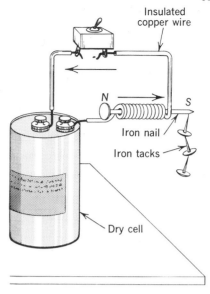

Insulated copper wire

Iron nail
Iron tacks
Dry cell

8-21. The principal parts of a simple electromagnet are shown here; a source of electric current, a coil of wire, and a soft iron core.

8-22. Thirty-two electromagnets go into the assembly of this atom smasher. (University of Wisconsin News Service)

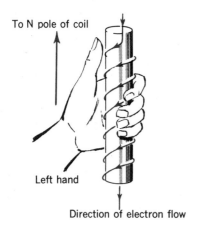

8-23. The left-hand rule for finding the north pole of an electromagnet. Note the direction of the thumb.

ism to produce an electric current. In 1831, both Michael Faraday in England and Joseph Henry in the United States found this could be accomplished. We can repeat some of their pioneering experiments.

Push a magnet into a coil connected to a galvanometer as shown in Fig. 8-24. The meter indicates that a current flows in the coil. But when you stop moving the magnet, the current also stops. When you pull the magnet out of the coil, a current flows briefly in the opposite direction.

This shows that *a magnet moving near a conductor produces a current in that conductor.* Of course, it doesn't

8-24. Current is induced only when there is motion between coil and magnet.

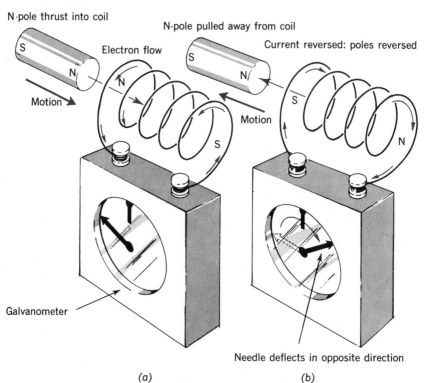

matter which moves, the magnet or the coil. This experiment seems so simple that you are apt to overlook its importance. Practically all of the electric energy we use today is produced in coils of wire spinning in magnetic fields, or in stationary coils of wire near rotating magnets.

Faraday called this process *electromagnetic induction,* and the currents that he produced were called *induced currents.* No matter how many times you repeat the experiment of Fig. 8-24, you do not weaken the magnets.

What is Lenz's law? This law states that the *direction* of an induced current is always such as to *oppose,* by its magnetism, the action that produced it. It is really the law of *conservation of energy* applied to electricity. This law explains why it is harder to turn a generator when you draw more current from it. Therefore, you are not getting something for nothing. *You cannot get electric energy without working for it.*

How do electric generators operate? Electromagnetic induction produces the currents in our huge *generators,* or *dynamos.* Coils of insulated copper wire in the *armature* cut through magnetic lines of force, inducing currents in them. Usually, in large dynamos, the *armature wires* form a cylindrical shell, inside of which spins a powerful electromagnet. *Electric generators* produce electric energy from mechanical energy. This is the opposite of what occurs in electric motors where mechanical energy is produced from electric energy. Generators and motors are very similar in construction and sometimes can be used interchangeably.

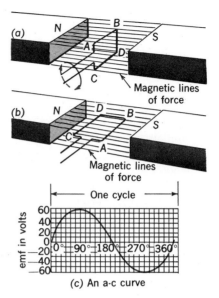

8-25. Current induced in a rotating loop of wire changes direction as the loop rotates. One full cycle is recorded on the graph.

Sometimes the armature coils are spun in a fixed magnetic field, as in Fig. 8-25. Note that in position (a) the armature wire **ABCD** is moving *parallel* to the lines of force. They are not being cut, and so there is no voltage induced, as shown at the 0° point of the curve in (c).

When the armature loop makes a quarter turn to position (b) it is cutting directly *across* the magnetic lines of force. Now *maximum voltage is induced,* as shown at the highest point in the curve. Halfway around, voltage again falls to zero. Now, as the loop continues to rotate, it cuts the magnetic field in the opposite direction, inducing a negative voltage shown at the lowest point in the curve. The induced current also reverses, along with the induced voltage.

The complete curve of diagram (c) illustrates *one cycle of an alternating current.* Practically all of our electric energy is in the form of *alternating current (ac)*.

When the armature wire passes both an **N**- and an **S**-pole, one cycle has been induced. The *frequency* of *ac* generated in most of the world is *60 cycles per second*. The armature of this generator would have to spin at a speed of 60 revolutions per second to generate this frequency.

Alternating current can be changed to direct current. Although ac is suitable for most uses, we do need *direct current* or *dc* for battery-charging, electroplating, and electrolysis in general. Some motors also require direct current for their operation.

Devices that change ac to dc are called rectifiers. The **commutator** of a generator acts as a rectifier. It maintains a direct current in the outside line by changing the brush contacts at the same time that the current in the armature reverses. (See Fig. 8-26.) Car generators were formerly of the dc type, but a-c generators (alternators) are now coming into use.

There are several other kinds of rectifiers. One of the newest types makes use of *semi-conductors* that act as one-way electron valves.

What are primary and secondary coils? We saw that electricity can be produced when a bar magnet is thrust into a coil of wire. Now we will see that the same results can be achieved when we use an electromagnet as our source of magnetism. We need to wrap two coils of wire around a common iron core as shown in Fig. 8-27. When we close the switch in the *primary coil*—that is, the one connected to the

dry cell—the iron core becomes magnetized. This has the same effect on the *secondary coil* as if you were to thrust a magnet very rapidly into it. Hence, a current flows briefly in the secondary coil, as shown by the galvanometer.

When the core becomes fully magnetized, no more current is induced. It is just as though you were holding a magnet at rest in the coil. A current is induced in the secondary coil only while *change* is occurring in the magnetic field of the primary.

When you open the switch in the primary circuit, note that the galvanometer needle again kicks over, but in the opposite direction. The core is now losing its magnetism, and the effect is just as though you were pulling out a magnet from the coil.

The induction coil can produce high voltage. The *more turns* of wire that you wrap on the secondary coil, the *higher is the voltage* of the induced current. In Fig. 8-27, the secondary coil has twice as many turns as the primary. Therefore, the voltage of the secondary is about twice that of the primary. However, the current in the secondary is less than half that in the primary.

Actually, the induced voltage depends upon the *number of lines of force cut per second by each turn of wire.* That is why we can get a very high induced voltage in the secondary by using many turns of wire in this coil.

The spark coil. The low-voltage current from the car battery goes through the *primary* of the auto's *spark coil.* This consists of a few turns of insulated wire wrapped around an *iron core.* Wrapped around the same

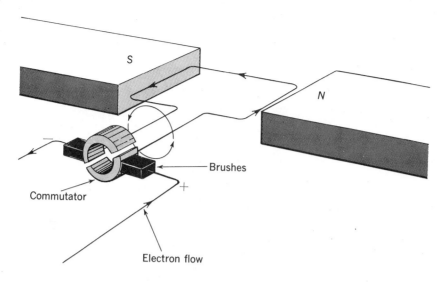

8-26. Alternating current from the coil is changed to direct current by a split-ring commutator.

8-27. Current is generated only while the switch is being opened or closed. The number of turns on the secondary coil determines the voltage of the induced current.

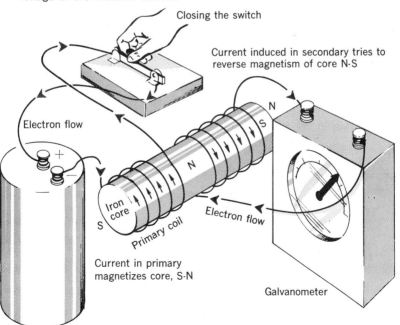

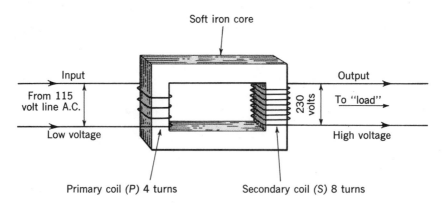

8-28. A transformer can be used to raise or lower the voltage of an alternating current, depending on the number of turns of wire in the coils.

core is the *secondary coil* with thousands of turns of wire. The voltage produced in the secondary is high enough to cause the induced current to jump the gap between the points of the spark plugs. This spark ignites the fuel-oxygen mixture in the cylinders.

In the *ignition system* of the car, a rotating *cam* turned by timing gears interrupts the primary circuit at the right moment. The high voltage is sent to the proper spark plug at the right time by the *distributor,* and the *rotor* of the distributor is turned by the same timing gears.

Spark coils produce high voltages for many purposes. They often have a magnetic type of timer to interrupt the primary circuit.

Transformers. *Transformers* contain two separate coils of insulated wire, usually wound around an iron core. Alternating current is fed into the *primary coil.* The ac produces a changing magnetic field because of its alternations. As this field cuts through the *secondary coil,* an alternating voltage is induced in it.

If, as shown in Fig. 8-28, there are twice as many turns in the S coil as in the P coil, the *voltage induced* will be twice the input voltage. If you plugged such a transformer into a 115-volt line, you would get a 230-volt output. This is called a *step-up transformer.* Notice that it acts much like the dc spark coil.

Transformers do not create energy. No machine can be 100 percent efficient. Hence, the output energy of a transformer must be *less* than the input energy. This means that if you *double* the voltage, you get *less than half* the current (power in watts = volts × amps.)

A *step-down transformer* has fewer turns on the secondary side, and thus reduces the voltage. If the secondary coil has $\frac{1}{10}$th as many turns as the primary coil, the output voltage will be only $\frac{1}{10}$th as much. However, the current becomes nearly 10 times as large.

How do we use transformers? Electric energy can be transported economically over *transmission lines* when voltage is high and the current is low. This is because transmission losses are proportional to the square of the current. Thus, high voltages permit the use of low amperages which, in turn, result in less heat loss in the transmission line. Hence, the current from the generators is sent to step-up transformers, where the voltage may go to 300,000 or 400,000 volts. At the other end of the line, other transformers step the voltage down for distribution to the consumer. (See Fig. 8-29.)

Step-down transformers may be used whenever low voltages are needed. On the other hand, you also may use one whenever a large current is desired. For example, the large current needed for *electric welding* is obtained from step-down transformers.

8-29. High voltage power lines like these make current available to most parts of the country. Practically every home and industry depends on the effects of electric currents. (Tennessee Valley Authority)

Quick Quiz

1. What are magnetic domains and how do they affect magnetism of materials?
2. State two laws that apply to magnetic poles.
3. What is meant when we say that certain materials are transparent to magnetic flux lines?
4. Describe the earth's magnetism. Suggest one cause of it.
5. What are two ways to weaken a magnet?
6. What is a magnetic field and how can you study it?
7. What three factors determine the strength of an electromagnet?
8. Is the spark coil like a step-up or step-down transformer? Explain.
9. Why is a magnetic compass of little value inside a submarine?
10. If atoms of a material have an excess number of electrons spinning in one way, what can you predict about the material's potential magnetism?
11. To make a permanent magnet would you use a substance that is easy or difficult to magnetize? Why?
12. Why should you avoid using Alnico as the core of an electromagnet?

C EFFECTS OF ELECTRIC CURRENTS

How many electric appliances are found in homes? It is likely that you are so accustomed to electricity that you take most of its uses for granted. Can you list the uses of electricity in your home? In addition to lights, did you include such appliances as a water heater, toaster, mixer, percolator, refrigerator, washer, waffle iron, television, food disposer, knife sharpener, can opener, clothes dryer, iron, and electric blanket? These are only some of the many different electric appliances that can be used in a home.

How does electricity produce heat? An electric current produces *heat* when it passes through a conductor. In typical electric wires, this heat is so small that we cannot notice it. Sometimes, however, it shows up in electric motors and represents a danger as well as a serious waste of energy. But at other times, as in the toaster and similar appliances, we want the current to produce a lot of heat.

Why is it that the same amount of current heats some substances very much and heats others very little? The answer is *resistance*. The frictional resistance to the passage of the current generates heat. The more resistance the electrons meet in being pushed along, the more heat is produced.

The wires in an electric toaster get red hot when we turn on the current, while the extension cord that leads to it does not get hot at all. Yet the same amount of current goes through both the toaster and the extension cord. The toaster heats up because its wires

Copper wire: low resistance, little heat

Wires tightly twisted together

Nichrome wire: high resistance, much heat

Dry cell

8-31. A high-resistance wire heats up when current flows.

are made of high-resistance *nichrome,* while the extension cord is made of low-resistance copper wire. Obviously, the high resistance of the nichrome makes the difference.

You can demonstrate that this is so by doing the following experiment. Twist together equally short lengths of copper and nichrome wires, about No. 24 in size. Connect them to a dry cell as shown in Fig. 8-31. The ni-

8-30. Appliances such as toasters and portable heaters have elements that put the heat from the electric current to advantageous use. (General Electric Co.)

chrome gets red hot, while the copper is only slightly warmed. (**Caution:** Do not leave the wires connected too long, or you will damage the dry cell.)

Here again, the same amount of current flowed through each wire. The heat produced in each wire depended upon its resistance. *The greater the resistance, the greater the heat.*

The amount of heat also depends on the current. When more current is forced through a conductor, it gets hotter. To show this, pass a current from a single dry cell through a thin nichrome wire. Use an ammeter to measure the current, as shown in Fig. 8-32. Now, instead of one cell, use several cells in series. Two things happen. The ammeter shows that more current is flowing, and the wire gets much hotter.

Exact measurements in the laboratory show that the *heat increases as the square of the current.* That is, when you *double* the current, you get *four times* as much heat.

Three factors determine the amount of heat produced. Two of these are the *resistance of the conductor* and the *size of the current.* The third is *time.* Obviously, the longer you leave the heater turned on, the more heat you get.

Experiments show that the number of calories of heat produced can be calculated by the following formula:

Calories of heat = 0.24 × amperes²
$$\times \text{ ohms} \times \text{seconds}$$

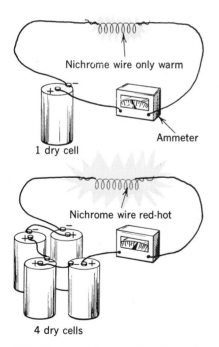

Nichrome wire only warm

1 dry cell

Ammeter

Nichrome wire red-hot

4 dry cells

8-32. The heat produced in the wires depends on how much current flows.

SAMPLE PROBLEM

How many calories of heat are produced when a current of 5 amps passes through a toaster of 20 ohms resistance for 2 minutes?

SOLUTION:
Step 1. Change 2 minutes to 120 seconds.

Step 2. Substituting in the formula: Calories of heat = 0.24 × amp² × ohms × seconds,
Calories of heat = 0.24 × 5² × 20 × 120
= 14,400 calories

Electricity produces light. The first type of electric light was the *electric arc.* An arc is obtained when a small gap is made in the circuit while the current is flowing through a suitable resistance. If there is enough voltage, the current "jumps" the gap, producing a *bright arc.*

Light from the electric arc is used when we want a very *bright and concentrated* source of light, as in some types of *searchlights* and *movie projectors*. However, although the arc gives a powerful and efficient light, it is *not practical* for most lighting purposes.

The incandescent light bulb. During the 1880's, Thomas Edison and others developed the familiar *incandescent light bulb*. The basic idea behind this type of electric lighting is the *heating* of a wire or filament to the point where it glows brightly. That is, it becomes *incandescent*. Therefore, the filament must be made of material that has a very high melting point. Why? The element *tungsten* has proved to be the most suitable for this purpose. (See Fig. 8-33.)

The air is pumped out of the bulb to keep the filament from burning. However, in its place is added a small quantity of an *inactive* or *inert* gas such as *nitrogen* or *argon*, which will not support combustion.

Even though it is widely used, the incandescent bulb is an extremely *inefficient* source of light. Less than 5 percent of the radiation is in the form of light waves. The rest is lost as heat. Large light bulbs are more efficient than small bulbs. For example, three 60-watt bulbs (totaling 180 watts) give about 10 percent more light than do five 40-watt bulbs (totaling 200 watts), and one 150-watt bulb gives *twice* as much light as five 25-watt bulbs (totaling 125 watts). *The wattage of a bulb indicates the power rating rather than the amount of light which is produced.*

Incandescent bulbs would be more efficient if we forced a larger current

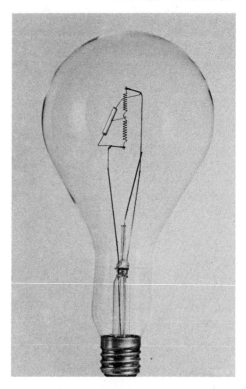

8-33. A photograph of an incandescent lamp showing the tungsten filament. (General Electric Co.)

through them. They would glow more brightly, like photoflood lamps, but would not last as long as they do now.

Neon lights are low-pressure electric arcs. At night, cities are brightly lighted with "neon" signs that produce light of many colors at low cost.

Gases at ordinary pressures act as insulators, but at low pressures they become fairly good conductors. A high voltage can force enough current through them to *ionize* the gases. The gas molecules then give off a luminous glow with a color that depends on the gas used. Sodium vapor produces a bright yellow light and neon gas produces a reddish color.

The *mercury-vapor* lamp, used in photography, produces light that acts strongly on photographic films. It has largely replaced all other types of lamps for the illumination of streets and highways with its bluish-green light. (See Fig. 8-34.)

What are fluorescent lamps? *Fluorescent* lamps operate somewhat like mercury-vapor lamps in that they use a high-voltage, low-pressure mercury vapor arc to produce *ultraviolet* light. This ultraviolet radiation strikes a coating of powdered minerals called *phosphors* on the inside wall of the light bulb. This causes these minerals to fluoresce; that is, to *radiate a soft light* whose color depends upon the kind of mineral powder used.

Fluorescent lamps are even more efficient than neon lamps and are more suitable for general lighting purposes. Sometimes it is important to have lamps that give "true color values" to objects they illuminate. Such a light must be much like sunlight if the objects are to look natural. Some fluorescent lamps give light of this quality.

Even our best lighting is still quite inefficient. There is much room for improvement, and research is being done in this field. One good prospect is lighting by panes of *luminescent* glass. This is glass that glows when a small electric current is passed through it. (See Fig. 8-35.)

Some uses of the electromagnet. Hundreds of different kinds of jobs can be done with electromagnets. You can slide the bolts of locks and latches, ring bells and buzzers, or tap out telegraphic dots and dashes. The rotors of all electric motors are spun by electromagnetism. You can open and close switches in distant electric circuits.

A simple relay. As shown in Fig. 8-36, when you close the switch at **A**, the distant electromagnet attracts a small block of iron, called an armature, **B.** This opens the switch **C** in a

8-34. Mercury vapor lamps are replacing other types of highway lighting in many areas of our country. (General Electric Co.)

8-35. This house of the future is illuminated by luminescent glass that absorbs light during the day and releases it at night by electric stimulation. (Westinghouse)

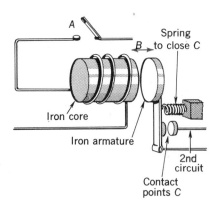

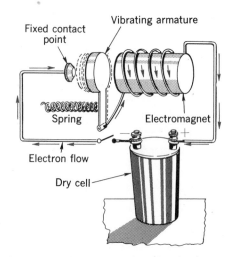

8-36. A simple electromagnetic relay, such as the one shown in the illustration, can operate a switch in a distant circuit.

8-37. The electromagnetic circuit interrupter has many uses, as in the buzzer.

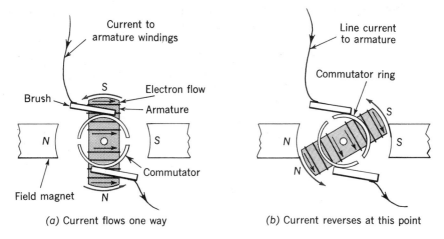

8-38. The armature rotates because of alternate attraction and repulsion by the poles of the field magnet.

different electric circuit. When you open switch **A**, the magnetism disappears and the spring again closes contact **C**. This is a very simple form of *electric relay*. The relay can operate even with a very small, and hence economical, current in the main line.

Electric doorbells and buzzers show how the electromagnet can be used as a rapid-fire interrupter of an electric current. The "make-and-break" of the circuit occurs between the fixed *contact* point and the *movable armature*. Can you see why the armature vibrates back and forth, opening and closing the circuit? This rapid vibration causes the familiar buzzing sound. (See Fig. 8-37.)

How does an electric motor work? Another effect of an electric current makes possible the electric motor. The electric motor is really a magnetic motor. Its rotor (movable magnet) is turned by the force of magnetism.

A movable electromagnet, called the armature, spins because of its changing attraction and repulsion by fixed magnets, called the *field magnets.* Magnetic forces cause the armature of Fig. 8-38 to rotate as shown. As the armature reaches "dead center," its current reverses. This in turn reverses the poles, as shown in the figure. This is done by contacts called *brushes* that slide over the segments of the split-ring called the commutator.

There are many types of electric motors designed for specific uses, but *they all use magnetism to change electric energy into useful mechanical energy.*

Quick Quiz

1. Explain why copper wire is used in extension cords and nichrome wire in electric toasters.
2. What three factors determine the total amount of heat that is produced when a current passes through an electric iron?

3. How much is the heat increased in a wire when you double the current flowing through it?
4. What type of electric light was the first to be used?
5. What gas is used in fluorescent lamps? What radiation does this gas first produce?
6. Explain why an electric motor can more truly be called a magnetic motor.
7. How does an electric current produce light in a neon tube?
8. Discuss the efficiency of incandescent bulbs.
9. Explain the operation of an electric buzzer.

SUMMARY

An electric current is a stream of electrons flowing through a conducting circuit. To keep the current flowing, a pressure, or electromotive force (emf), must be maintained. This is provided by electric cells, electric generators, static charges, nuclear action, or by thermoelectric, photoelectric or piezoelectric effects, all of which supply the necessary energy.

The circuits can be arranged in series, parallel, or in various combinations of these two types. The current in a series circuit is the same in all parts. In a parallel or branched circuit the total current is the sum of the currents in the branches. Lamps and other electrical appliances in your home are wired in parallel. A short circuit means a sudden large drop in the resistance of a circuit. To protect the circuit from damage by large currents, fuses or circuit breakers are used.

Magnetism is caused by the spinning and orbiting motion of electrons. Atoms of magnetic materials are grouped into regions called domains. Magnetizing consists of lining up the tiny domains of which a substance is made. Hammering or heating breaks this orderly pattern and demagnetizes the material. A magnet has two kinds of poles, north and south. Like poles repel; unlike poles attract.

An electromagnet consists of a coil of insulated wire, usually wound around a soft iron core. Its strength depends upon the current, number of turns of wire, and type of core. All electric motors use magnetism to change electric energy into mechanical energy. Electromagnetic induction occurs whenever a magnetic field is cut by a conductor. Generators, spark coils, and transformers operate by electromagnetic induction. Transformers step the voltage up or down depending upon the ratio of turns between the primary and secondary coils.

The first source of electric light was the electric arc. The incandescent lamp, an inefficient lamp in which the light comes from a white-hot tungsten filament, was the next to be developed. The glowing "neon-type" lamps are made by passing a high-voltage current through a gas under low pressure. Fluorescent lamps produce ultraviolet light that causes a mineral coating on the inside of the bulb to glow, or fluoresce.

CHAPTER REVIEW

Vocabulary

Match the words in Column A with the *best* response in Column B. Do not write in your book.

Column A

1. electric current
2. conductor
3. superconductivity
4. electromotive force
5. volt
6. ampere
7. ohm
8. kilowatt
9. electrolyte
10. galvanometer
11. battery
12. electric circuit
13. fuse
14. lodestone
15. domain
16. left-hand rule
17. generator
18. rectifier
19. transformer
20. electric motor

Column B

a. any substance that permits easy passage of electricity
b. property of certain materials when cooled to near absolute zero
c. complete path of electric current
d. device for changing alternating current to direct current
e. device for changing electric energy to mechanical energy
f. device for changing the voltage of alternating current
g. device for detecting very small currents
h. device that protects an overloaded circuit
i. dissolved substance that conducts electric current
j. flow of electrons along a conductor
k. method for finding the north pole in an electromagnet
l. natural magnet
m. device for changing mechanical energy to electrical energy
n. unit of electrical power
o. pressure that causes an electric current to flow
p. tiny magnetic region composed of atoms aligned in a common direction
q. two or more electric cells joined together
r. unit of electrical current
s. unit of electrical pressure
t. unit of electrical resistance

Questions: Group A

1. What is an electric insulator? Name two.
2. What is the source of thermoelectric current?
3. What is the unit of resistance?
4. Name the two factors that determine the size of the current.
5. Define "incandescent." How does an incandescent lamp operate?
6. What gases are used in incandescent bulbs? Why?
7. What is the difference between a volt and an ampere?
8. What are phosphors? How do they act?

9. Name three chemical elements that can be strongly magnetized.
10. How could you shield the working mechanism of a watch from magnetism?
11. Why must compass readings be corrected when they are used for navigation?
12. Why cannot all elements be strongly magnetized?

Questions: Group B

1. What is an electric relay and what is it used for?
2. When does electromagnetic induction occur?
3. How is Lenz's law related to the conservation of energy?
4. What one factor determines the amount of voltage produced by electromagnetic induction?
5. How can an ac current be converted to a dc current?
6. Discuss the construction and action of step-up and step-down transformers.
7. Explain the construction and action of a spark coil.
8. Discuss the use of transformers in power lines.
9. How do you charge a battery? What process occurs?
10. How do you test a battery to see if it is charged or discharged?
11. By what two processes does the automobile storage battery lose water?
12. What action produces the piezoelectric effect?
13. State Ohm's law.
14. What are the three essential parts of a simple cell?
15. What is the difference between a cell and a battery?
16. Who first made cells and batteries?
17. In what ways are series and parallel circuits alike? In what ways are they different?

Problems

1. How many volts are needed to push 7 amps through an electric heater that has a resistance of 16 ohms?
2. Four dry cells are connected in series to form a 6-volt battery. How many amps will it send through a 3-ohm circuit?
3. What is the resistance of a toaster if 110 volts produces a 5-amp current through it?
4. A light bulb draws 0.5 amp on a 10-volt line. (a) What is the resistance of the bulb in ohms? (b) If you plugged it into a 110-volt line, what current would flow? (c) How much extra resistance would you have to put in series with the bulb so that it would draw only 0.5 amp on the 110-volt line?
5. We have a circuit with four similar lamps in parallel, each drawing 1 amp on a 110-volt line. (a) What is the total current used by all four lamps? (b) What is the resistance of each lamp? (c) What is the total resistance of all four lamps?

6. About how much current is sent through 3000 ft of No. 10 copper wire by two ordinary dry cells joined in series?

7. An electric iron draws 5.5 amps on a 115-volt line. Calculate the watts.

8. A theater uses 50 light bulbs of 200 watts each for 4 hours. Calculate the cost at 2¢ a kwh.

9. How much does it cost to light your schoolroom for 5 hours at 3¢ per kwh? Assume 8 fluorescent fixtures of 200 watts each.

10. An immersion heater is dipped into a liter of water for 5 minutes. If the resistance of the heater is 40 ohms and it draws 3 amps, how much heat is produced? Can you calculate the rise in temperature of the water, remembering that 1 calorie warms 1 gram of water 1 C°?

9 ELECTRONICS

A ELECTROSTATICS

What is meant by electronics? So far, your study of electricity has been concerned with electric currents, and devices that generate and use these currents. *Electronics* is the branch of physical science concerned with the following four topics:

1. Electrostatics (*stationary electric charges*).

2. The motion of electrons through a vacuum, a gas, or a semi-conductor.

3. Currents of very high frequency.

4. Radiations given off by high-frequency currents.

In electronics, scientists are usually more interested in controlling the action of individual electrons than in producing large currents. However, in practical electronics, electric currents are usually involved in one way or another.

Early knowledge about electrostatics. Our early ancestors were acquainted with *static electricity*, or *elec-*

trostatics. They heard the crackle of little electric sparks produced when they stroked a cat's fur, or when they combed their hair. They saw the glowing discharge of static electricity from pointed objects on certain nights when the atmosphere was highly *charged*. They observed lightning, and saw the northern lights or *aurora*.

By 600 B.C. the Greeks had noticed that when they rubbed a fossilized resin, called *amber*, with wool, it would attract bits of fluff. These effects were given the name "electric" from the Greek word "electron," meaning amber. Little, if any, additional knowledge about static electricity was learned during the next 2000 years. Not until the 17th century was a careful scientific study of static charges made. After this date, however, research increased rapidly, and late in the 19th century, scientists finally discovered the electron itself. Now, electrostatics is explained almost entirely on the basis of electron behavior.

What are static charges? Unlike an electric current, which is a *stream of moving* electric charges, static charges are *stationary*. An object becomes *elec-*

9-1. Benjamin Franklin proved that lightning is caused by static electricity. (The Franklin Institute)

trically charged if it has *too many* or *too few* electrons.

We can better understand what happens by reviewing the structure of the atom. Normally, an atom contains equal numbers of positively charged protons and negatively charged electrons. Thus, the atom is considered electrically *neutral*. When an atom loses an electron, however, the charges are no longer equal. The atom, now called an *ion*, has a positive charge and the *free* electron has a negative

charge. This movement or transfer of electrons is what causes materials to become charged with static electricity. The material that gets the extra electrons becomes *negatively charged*, while the one that loses them becomes *positively charged*.

If you rub two objects together vigorously, the contact causes electrons to be transferred from one object to the other. If you rub hard rubber or almost any plastic with wool or fur, the rubber *picks up electrons from the wool*. This is how a fountain pen gets a negative charge when you rub it on your woolen sweater, and how your comb becomes charged when you run it through your hair. However, if you rub a dry glass rod with silk, the *silk removes electrons from the glass, thus leaving the glass with a positive charge*.

Static charges illustrate certain laws. Hang two toy balloons from a thread, as shown in Fig. 9-3. Charge them by rubbing them with wool or fur. Each is now charged negatively, and we see that they repel each other. As shown in the diagram, they are also repelled by a negatively charged rod. Similarly, we find that two positively charged objects repel each other also. From such experiments, we get the law: *like charges repel each other.*

Now charge a glass rod positively by rubbing it with silk. Notice that the positive rod attracts the negatively charged balloons. Hence the law: *unlike charges attract each other.*

Further experimentation shows that the balloons are *attracted* to both the positive and negative charges *even if the balloons are not charged*. Thus, we have another observation: *charged objects attract apparently neutral objects*. Note that the above generaliza-

9-2. Scientists can now study man-made bolts of lightning in the laboratory. (General Electric Co.)

9-3. The laws of electricity are similar to the laws of magnetism.

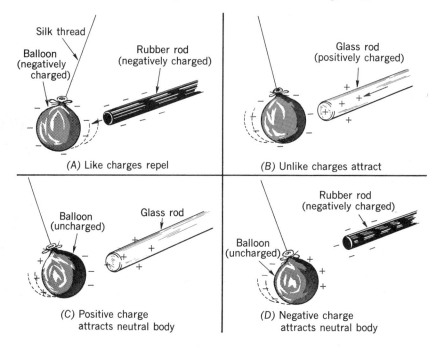

Silk thread

Balloon (negatively charged)

Rubber rod (negatively charged)

Glass rod (positively charged)

(A) Like charges repel

(B) Unlike charges attract

Balloon (uncharged)

Glass rod

Rubber rod (negatively charged)

Balloon (uncharged)

(C) Positive charge attracts neutral body

(D) Negative charge attracts neutral body

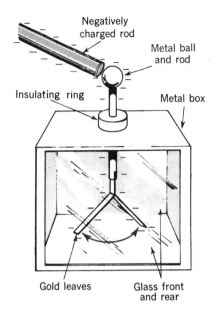

Negatively charged rod

Metal ball and rod

Insulating ring

Metal box

Gold leaves

Glass front and rear

9-4. The stronger the charge, the more widely the leaves of the electroscope spread apart.

tions are similar to those that apply to north and south magnetic poles.

Static charges also obey the *inverse-square law.* That is, when you move them twice as far apart, the force between them becomes ¼th as much. If the distance between them is made three times as great, the force will be only ⅑th as much. What will be the strength of the force if the distance is increased to four times its original distance?

Static charges also create a field of force in the space around them. You can map this *electric field* with short bits of hair, just as you mapped the magnetic field with iron filings.

Electroscopes detect electric charges. Any device used to *detect an electric charge* may be called an **electroscope.** The rubber balloons of Fig. 9-3 are one example. However, the *gold-leaf electroscope* is much more

sensitive than this, and can also be used to determine how strong the charge is. In Fig. 9-4, notice that the metal rod holding the gold leaf passes through an insulator at the top of the box. This prevents the electric charge that you put on the gold leaves from escaping to the box. The *leaves* may be made of aluminum or any thin metal foil, but gold is the most sensitive because it can be produced in thinner sheets. The leaves are mounted in a box or flask to protect them from air currents.

When you touch the electroscope with a negatively charged rod, some of the electrons crowded on the rod enter the electroscope. They spread all over the conducting metal by mutual repulsion, and some of them reach the gold leaves. The leaves are now charged alike and, hence, repel each other. The greater the charge, the greater the angle at which the leaves are spread apart.

What happens when you touch a *neutral* or *uncharged* electroscope with a positively charged rod? A positively charged rod has lost electrons, and so picks up electrons from the electroscope. Electrons leave the strips of metal foil. This gives each strip a positive charge, and again they repel and spread apart.

Charging by contact. Thus far, we have been charging objects by *touching* them with other charged objects. Fig. 9-5 shows what happens when a negatively charged object touches a neutral object. See if you can make similar diagrams using positive charges. Can you explain by the transfer of electrons how a positively charged object puts a positive charge on an uncharged object when they touch together?

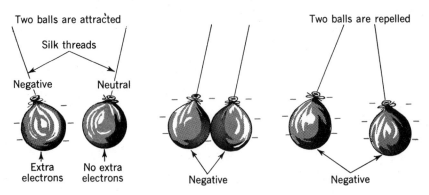

Two balls are attracted

Silk threads

Negative   Neutral

Extra   No extra
electrons electrons

Two balls are repelled

Negative   Negative

9-5. A neutral conductor touched by a charged object obtains the same kind of charge and is then repelled. This is an example of charging by contact.

Charging by induction. We stated earlier that a charged object, either positive or negative, attracts an apparently uncharged one. This occurs in Fig. 9-6 because some free electrons in the ball are repelled by the negatively charged rod. These electrons move to the far side of the ball leaving the positive charge on the near side. The unlike charges on the ball and the rod then will attract each other.

When the charged rod is removed, the displaced electrons return to their normal positions, and the ball again becomes neutral. This temporary *displacement of electrons results in induced charges,* and the process is called *temporary induction.* An *induced charge* is one that appears when a nearby charge *upsets the electron balance.*

Now suppose you "ground" the ball while the rod is close to it, as shown in Fig. 9-7. Just touching the ball with your finger will do, because your body makes a good ground for small charges. The rod's negative

charge repels the electrons from the ball to the ground. Why? If you now remove the ground connection (your finger), they can't get back to the ball. The ball is now charged *positively,* as it has lost some electrons. This process is called *charging permanently by induction.*

Notice that when an object is charged by induction, it always re-

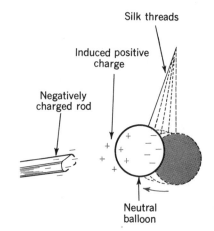

Silk threads

Induced positive
charge

Negatively
charged rod

Neutral
balloon

9-6. An uncharged object (balloon) is attracted to a charged object (rod) by induction.

ceives a charge that is *opposite* to that of the inducing charge. Here you started with a negatively charged rod, and induced a positive charge on the ball.

Where is the charge on a conductor? If you put a charge on an irregularly shaped object, such as the metal cup in Fig. 9-8, you find that the charge does not spread evenly over the entire surface. Most of it crowds together along the rim of the cup. The charge on the gently curving sides is much weaker.

Curiously enough, no charge is found on the *inside* of the cup. This is true even though you put the charge on the inside in the first place. The charge moves to the outside surface at once. This important behavior of charges is utilized in the *Van de Graaff generator* pictured on page 388.

If you place a sharp needle across the top of the cup before charging it, the charge quickly disappears. The charge is so *densely crowded on the sharp point that it leaks off into the air.* This *discharging effect of sharp points* is very important in the operation of many electrostatic devices. How does this principle apply to the functioning of a lightning rod?

You recall that there is no charge on the inside of the cup described in Fig. 9-8. Can you see how an area can be *shielded* from any effect of outside charges? Some electronic tubes in your radio are shielded in this way. For the same reason, you are relatively safe from lightning when in a closed metal car. Any conductor can act as a shield.

What causes lightning? In the days of Benjamin Franklin, lightning was a frightening mystery to most people. He believed, however, that it was the same as the sparks which he generated in his laboratory with his static-electricity equipment. His famous experiment with the kite and key proved that his theory was right. He proved that *lightning is caused by static charges.*

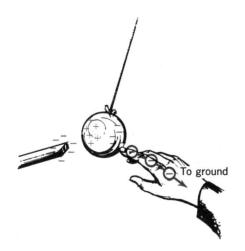

9-7. Electrons are repelled to the ground by a negative charge on the rod. The ball gets an induced positive charge.

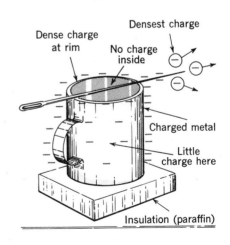

9-8. The charge is densest at sharp edges and points, and the charge will leak off fastest from the dense charge points.

9-9. Large bolts of lightning harmlessly strike structures like the Empire State Building. (UPI)

Sometimes a cloud, or mass of raindrops, becomes positively or negatively charged. When, for example, a positively charged cloud approaches the earth's surface, an equal and opposite charge is induced on the objects directly below. The electrical pressure between the two charges may rise to billions of volts. Under this great stress, the insulating effect of the air breaks down. *A discharge, called lightning, takes place* with shattering violence. The very high temperature causes the air to expand very suddenly, producing sound waves called *thunder*.

Lightning rods protect structures. Benjamin Franklin became aware of the peculiar ability of pointed objects to disperse a charge quickly. He believed, therefore, that buildings might be protected by well-grounded points "to draw off the electrical fluid." This practical suggestion resulted in the development of the *lightning rod*.

Suppose a house, as in Fig. 9-10, has a number of pointed metal lightning rods connected to the ground by good conductors. The charge that may be built up in an oncoming thunderstorm will be gradually and quietly neutralized by the charge induced from the earth. If the atmospheric charge is positive, the electrons may stream from the metal points so fast that they form *coronas* that *glow* visibly on a dark night.

The neutralization may not take place rapidly enough to prevent a stroke of lightning. In that case, lightning rods act as good conductors to carry the charge safely. However, lightning rods can be dangerous if they are not properly grounded. A steel skyscraper has no need of lightning rods. Why? *Your television antenna, however, is no substitute for a lightning rod.*

Static charges are found in many places. Static charges may lead to fires and explosions wherever flammable material exists. Static electricity has caused many disasters in the petroleum and dry-cleaning industries. Sparks from static charges have set fire to hydrogen balloons and to anesthetic gases used in surgery. Today, careful precautions have eliminated most of these hazards.

Did you ever get a shock on touching the door handle of an auto? A car may develop a static charge in several ways. For this reason, a car usually passes over vertical well-grounded wires just before it reaches a highway toll station. This neutralizes the static charge built up on the car and prevents you and the station attendant from getting a shock as you hand him the coins.

Some people seem to be more subject to static charges than others. Often they boast of being "full of electricity." Actually, it simply means that their clothing generates static charges, and they are well insulated from the ground.

Neutralizing charged objects. When a car is grounded to discharge it at a highway toll station, it is being *neutralized*. To *neutralize* a charge we must restore the normal *electron-proton balance*. In general, there are two ways to do this:

1. We can bring the charged object into contact with an object that has an equal opposite charge.

2. We can "ground" the charged object. The earth acts as a storehouse of free electrons, available to neutralize positive charges. The earth also acts as a "sink" into which excess electrons from negatively charged objects can flow. For this reason, conductors can be charged only if insulated from the ground.

Charged objects also lose their charge slowly while standing. We say the charge *leaks off* into the air. This is due to charged molecules, or ions, in the air. When the air is cold and dry, it contains fewer ions, and so is a better insulator. We get better results from electrostatic experiments on such days.

How are large static charges generated? By the 17th century, scientists

9-10. Properly installed lightning rods help to protect buildings from damage during electrical storms.

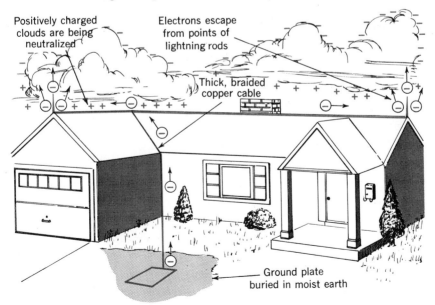

Positively charged clouds are being neutralized

Electrons escape from points of lightning rods

Thick, braided copper cable

Ground plate buried in moist earth

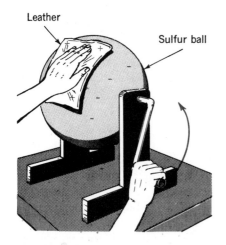

Leather

Sulfur ball

9-11. Static charges were obtained by friction in early generators.

could produce charges by rubbing various materials together. In 1672, Otto von Guericke, a German physicist and inventor, *built a machine to do the rubbing for him.* His machine looked

something like a grindstone except that he substituted a ball of sulphur for the stone. (See Fig. 9-11.) From that day on, scientists have built bigger and better machines to generate electrostatic charges.

The Van de Graaff generator. High voltage Van de Graaff generators are able to produce very large charges. To understand how it works, refer to Fig. 9-12. The rubber belt becomes charged as it passes over a fleece-lined pulley wheel. In large generators, the electric charges are first produced in another electronic device and are then "sprayed" on the belt.

At the top, the charge is removed from the belt by a set of points connected to the inside of a large metal chamber. The charge goes immediately to the *outside* of this spherical chamber. (Remember the experiment with

9-12. The pulley belt of the Van de Graaff generator carries electrons to the sphere at the top. The photograph on the left shows a modern classroom Van de Graaff generator. (Central Scientific Co.)

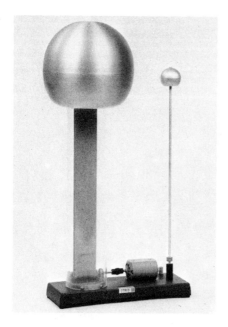

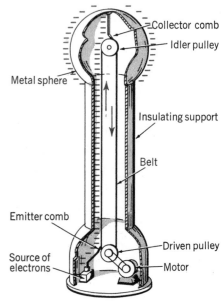

Collector comb

Idler pulley

Metal sphere

Insulating support

Belt

Emitter comb

Source of electrons

Driven pulley

Motor

the cup?) As the action continues, the sphere soon has a large charge.

How are electrostatic charges stored? In 1745, E. G. Kleist, German clergyman, and Pieter von Musschenbroek, from Leyden, Holland, each built a device in which static charges could be stored. Musschenbroek's device became known as the *Leyden jar.* They were astonished at the violent shocks they got from glass jars coated inside and out with metal foil, as shown in Fig. 9-13. These devices were called *condensers,* because they were capable of "condensing" the so-called "electrical fluid." Today they are called *capacitors.* They come in many shapes and sizes and consist essentially of two conductors separated by an insulator. Let us see how they work.

Suppose you put a small negative charge on metal plate **A,** shown in Fig. 9-14. The electroscope leaves spread wide apart, showing that the charge has produced a high pressure or voltage. Now if you bring a grounded metal plate **B** close to **A,** the electroscope leaves fall together. Only when you put a much larger

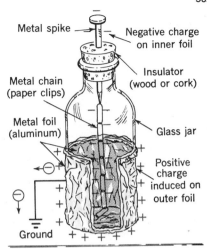

9-13. The Leyden jar was the first capacitor.

charge on **A** will the leaves again spread apart. As the diagram shows, the negative charge on **A** induces a positive charge on **B.** (Can you see how this happens?) This induced positive charge draws the electrons on **A** close together, making room for more electrons on **A.** In other words, you can put a larger negative charge on **A.** Without the capacitor effect, you

9-14. Plate A holds a much larger charge when it is part of a capacitor.

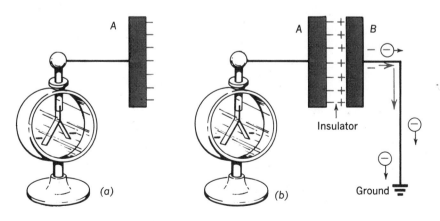

9-15. Electrostatic filters or precipitators clean up smokestack gases in many industrial communities. The smokestack on the left is also in operation, but its filter removes all visible impurities from the smoke. (Western Precipitation Div., Joy Manufacturing Co.)

could *not* put a larger charge on **A.** It would leak off as fast as you added it. Also, the closer **A** is to **B,** the *greater* the charge the plates can hold.

The capacitor has many uses. The capacitor is one of the most widely used devices in electronics. Sometimes we use them because of their ability to *store large charges.* But more often, they are used because each capacitor has its own definite frequency, just as a pendulum has. Electrons surge back and forth, in and out of a capacitor, at a rate dependent on its capacity. A small one, of low capacity, has a very high natural frequency. You tune your radio to any particular broad-casting station by adjusting a *variable capacitor.* Such a capacitor has two sets of plates that mesh together. As the plates open up, its capacity becomes less and the frequency rises. When you mesh the plates together, the capacity increases and the frequency becomes lower. In that way, you make the frequency of your set the same as that of the station you want to receive.

Capacitors are rated in *farads.* This is such a large unit of capacity that even most of the very large capacitors are only a few *microfarads* in size. (The prefix "micro" means *one-millionth.*)

Other applications of electrostatics. As our industries and cities get larger, the difficulty of supplying them with *fresh, clean air* becomes greater. *Smog* is already a serious problem in many areas. We must pay more attention to supplying our cities with pure air, just as we do with pure water.

One of the best ways of cleaning the air is by the use of *electrostatic filters.* These filters use high-voltage charges to ionize or charge the particles in the air. (See Fig. 9-15.) Then the air passes over plates or wires that are also highly charged, some positive and some negative. The ionized particles are attracted to the charged plates and removed from the air. The smokestack gases of many industries are filtered by this process.

We are now able to produce our best *vacuums* by ionizing the air or other gas and removing it by *electrostatic forces.*

Most loudspeakers produce sound waves by the vibration of membranes or cones. But *electrostatic speakers* cause charged air molecules to vibrate directly by electrostatic forces.

Electrostatics are also vital in the operation of many other electronic devices, such as the cathode-ray tube used in radar, television, and electrical test equipment.

Quick Quiz

1. What is the chief difference between electric currents and static charges?
2. What kind of charge does an electron possess?
3. What charge does an object have when it loses some of its electrons? Gains electrons?

4. Explain how like charges behave toward each other. Explain how unlike charges behave toward each other.
5. Name several ways in which magnetism and electric charges are similar.
6. Explain how an area can become shielded from electrostatic charges. Give an example of where such shielding is used.
7. In what two ways may lightning rods protect buildings from damage?
8. Explain how an insulated ball becomes charged when you touch it with a negatively-charged rod.
9. What happens when you ground a positively-charged conductor?
10. Where did we get the word "electric"?
11. What are some dangers of static charges?
12. Explain two methods by which you could charge an electroscope positively?
13. What happens to the leaves of a charged electroscope when you touch the knob with your finger? Explain.

B ELECTRONIC TUBES, TRANSISTORS, AND THIN FILM CIRCUITS

Electronics comes of age. During this century, we have seen a spectacular growth in electronics. This is due largely to the invention of the electronic tube and the more recent development of *transistors* and *thin film* circuits. Their development has made possible modern communication by radio, telephone, television, sound motion pictures, and public address systems. Computers, industrial *automation,* and automatic navigation of planes, rockets, and satellites also depend upon recent advances in electronics. In this section, we shall study the basic principles of electronic tubes, transistors, and thin films, as well as simple radio circuits.

Electric currents in low pressure gases. About 8000 volts are required to send a current through only 1 cm of ordinary air. This gap is shown between **A** and **B** of Fig. 9-16. However, when you pump most of the air out of the tube, the current finds the long path from **A′** to **B′** less resistant.

If this experiment is performed in a dark room, you first see a thin crackling arc jump from **A′** to **B′** as you pump out the air. Then the arc grows and spreads until the whole tube glows with a pale pink light. This is how "neon" lights work. The low-pressure gas is a fair conductor of electricity.

What are cathode rays? The discovery of the conductivity of low pressure gases was made in about 1875 by Sir William Crookes, a British scientist. He noticed that as he increased the vacuum beyond a certain point, the glow became fainter and fainter, finally disappearing altogether. He then found that a stream of *invisible* radiation was still coming from the negative electrode, or cathode. He called these radiations **cathode rays.**

It was soon discovered that cathode rays are *streams of negatively charged particles.* We now know that they are *electrons* traveling at high speeds. As the voltage is increased, the electrons go faster and faster, and finally approach the speed of light.

The Edison effect. In 1883, Thomas Edison was working on ways to im-

prove his newly invented electric light. He was trying to prevent the formation of a black deposit on the inside of the bulb. He tried putting a charged metal plate inside the bulb, as shown in Fig. 9-17.

He found that when this plate was positively charged, a current would flow to it from the *hot filament.* It is now known that this current is due to *electrons given off by the hot filament,* and this is called the **Edison effect.** Such currents, produced by electrons "boiled off" from hot substances, are called *thermionic* (*thur*-mee-*ah*-nik) *currents.*

Some years later an English scientist named Fleming found a use for the Edison effect. He made a vacuum tube like Edison's, with a *filament cathode* and a *plate.* Electrons were emitted from the hot cathode and attracted to the positively charged plate. This stream of electrons was an electric current, passing between the cathode and the plate. Thus, the first practical *electronic tube* was created. This tube permitted only one-way passage of electrons in a circuit. Tubes that contain only *two electrodes, a cathode and a plate,* are called *diodes* (*dye*-odes).

Discharge occurs through evacuated tube

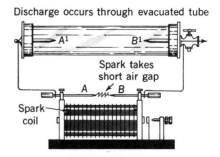

9-16. Electrons pass easily through the tube after the air has been removed.

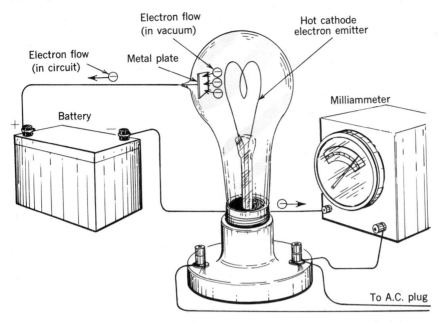

9-17. The Edison effect is obtained when a metal plate is introduced into the incandescent bulb.

The diode can rectify alternating current. *Diodes can be used to change alternating current to direct current.* You will recall that alternating current is a continuous succession of electrical surges flowing first one way then the other. A rectifier changes this back-and-forth succession of surges to a pulsating *flow of current going in one direction only.* Figure 9-18 shows how a diode can be arranged to charge a storage battery. The alternating current of the secondary coil of the transformer makes the plate alternately positive and negative. But alternating current *cannot* surge back and forth through the plate circuit; the diode will pass the current *only in one direction.* Only during the *half-cycle* in which the plate is positive can any current flow between the plate and cathode. Hence, you get a *pulsating direct current* through the plate.

The diagram shows that a diode is put into the circuit of the battery to be charged. Note that the cathode is heated by alternating current from a low-voltage tap on the secondary coil.

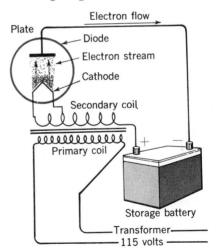

9-18. The diode can rectify alternating current to direct current.

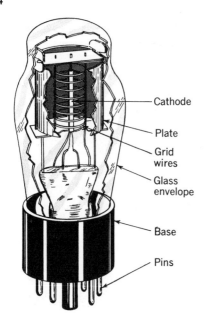

Cathode

Plate

Grid
wires

Glass
envelope

Base

Pins

9-19. Major components of a triode electronic tube.

Some diodes contain a small amount of gas, usually argon or mercury vapor. The gas ionizes to furnish a plentiful supply of electrons. This means that a *gas-filled tube* can carry a larger current than a high-vacuum tube. Hence, *gas-filled* diodes are used for charging batteries.

The diode can be replaced by a simple rectifier made of a *semi-conductor,* usually silicon or germanium. These also permit only one-way current flow.

What is a triode? In 1906, De Forest, an American inventor, put a *third electrode,* called a **grid,** in the diode. This new tube was called the **triode,** or three-element tube. The grid is usually a wire mesh placed between the cathode and the plate. (See Figs. 9-19 and 9-20.)

9-20. The charge on the grid controls the flow of electrons; that is, controls the plate current.

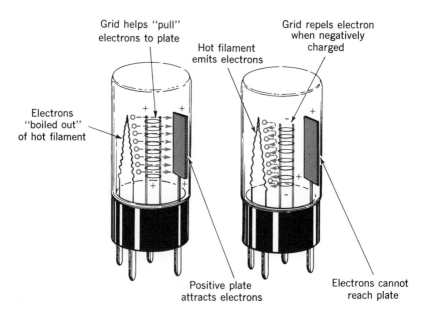

Grid helps "pull"
electrons to plate

Hot filament
emits electrons

Grid repels electron
when negatively
charged

Electrons
"boiled out"
of hot filament

Positive plate
attracts electrons

Electrons cannot
reach plate

When a negative charge is put on the grid, as shown in Fig. 9-20, the grid *repels* electrons, preventing many of them from reaching the plate. If the grid becomes negative enough, none of the electrons reach the plate. On the other hand, when the grid is made positive, a larger flow of electrons is *attracted* from the hot filament, as shown in Fig. 9-20. In other words, *the grid acts like a "valve" to control the amount of current passing through the tube.*

The number of electrons that can pass from the cathode to the plate depends upon three factors:

1. The number of electrons *emitted by the cathode*. The higher the temperature of the cathode, the more electrons are "boiled off."

2. The *positive voltage* on the plate. The higher the plate voltage, the greater is the *attraction* of electrons from the cathode.

3. The kind and amount of charge on the grid. Very *small voltage changes* in the grid have *very large effects* on the electron flow between the cathode and plate.

How does a triode amplify signals? Often in electronic circuits we must *amplify*, or *strengthen*, weak electric currents. In your radio receiver, a triode acts as an **amplifier.**

When radio waves from a broadcasting station strike your *antenna*, they induce very feeble electric currents in it. These currents are far too weak to operate the speakers on your radio or television set. These feeble currents, however, *are* sufficient to control the strong cathode-plate currents in a triode. The cathode-plate currents come from batteries or rectified ac, and supply the *power* for an *audible* signal, but the radio signals that strike the antenna supply the *controls*.

The feeble currents that result from the radio signals striking the antenna are connected to the grid or "valve." Thus, the flow of electrons between the cathode and plate fluctuates in the same manner as the feeble radio signals. Furthermore, as was stated earlier, *even slight changes in the charge on the grid produce large changes in the electron flow reaching the plate.* Hence, the output strength reaching the plate is many times greater than the strength of the signal picked up by your antenna. This is what is meant by *amplification.*

Several stages of amplification may be used in some radio circuits. That is, the current reaching the plate of the first tube is fed to the grid of the second amplifying tube, and so on.

More complex electronic tubes. There is the *tetrode,* so named because it contains *four electrodes*. It has an extra grid called the *screen grid*. The *pentode (five electrodes)*, as shown in Fig. 9-21, has still one more grid, called the *suppressor grid*. These tubes are more efficient in certain respects than the simpler triodes described above.

Still more complicated are the *triode-pentodes,* or *duo-diodes,* because, as their names imply, they actually contain the parts of two different tubes within the same shell.

Electronic tubes are designed to perform functions other than *rectifying* and *amplifying*. For example, they also act as *detectors,* to detect radio signals striking the antenna; they act as *mixers,* to combine several separate signals to produce different signals; as *oscillators,* to produce very high-fre-

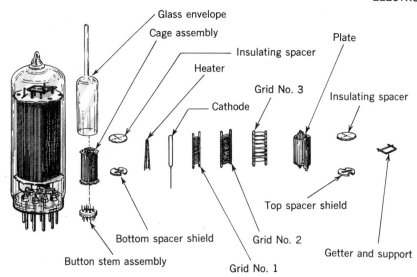

Glass envelope
Cage assembly
Plate
Insulating spacer
Heater
Grid No. 3
Insulating spacer
Cathode
Top spacer shield
Bottom spacer shield
Grid No. 2
Getter and support
Button stem assembly
Grid No. 1

9-21. The pentode has three grids.

quency alternating currents; and as *wave shapers* to change wave form into a desired shape for special use.

What are transistors? In 1948, an electronic device called the *transistor* was developed. Transistors soon proved to be very versatile and did the same jobs that vacuum tubes could do. In addition, transistors have a number of advantages over vacuum tubes. They are much smaller and thus require very little space and permit the building of miniature electronic devices. Transistors are also far more rugged, require less electricity to operate, and are more efficient than typical vacuum tubes. (See Fig. 9-22.)

The construction and theory of *transistors* are quite complicated, but basically they are made of thin *wafers* of *germanium* or *silicon* which are both *semi-conductors*. One type has a trace of impurity that causes free electrons to be emitted. This is called the *negative* or *N-type* germanium or silicon. *Positive*, or *P-type*, germanium or

silicon contains a trace of another impurity that causes it to be a *collector* of electrons. A transistor is made by placing a thin layer of N-type next to a thin layer of P-type to form what is called a *P-N junction*. You can use a P-N junction in place of an ordinary *diode as a rectifier*. It permits current

9-22. Germanium dice 99.99999 percent pure are the hearts of transistors. (Air Reduction Corp.)

to flow in only one direction. (See Fig. 9-23.)

By making N-P-N or P-N-P junctions, you can use transistors as triodes. Your transistor radio employs simple circuits containing P-N-P triodes.

Notice that the *emitter* of the transistor corresponds to the *cathode*, the *collector* to the *plate*, and the *base* to the *grid*. Like the vacuum-tube triode, this transistor can both rectify and amplify the current.

Solar batteries are constructed much like transistors, using the semiconductor *silicon*. They generate an electric current when light falls on a P-N junction.

What are thin film and integrated circuits? A great breakthrough in electronics has taken place in recent years with the development of *thin-film* and *integrated-circuit* techniques. In the thin-film technique, *microscopic (thin) layers (films) of material are deposited* on a base material. When this technique is used to build *active*

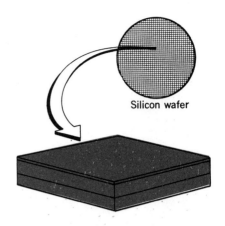

Silicon wafer

9-24. An integrated circuit begins as one of hundreds of tiny squares on a one-inch diameter disc of multilayered silicon.

components such as transistors, rectifiers, and diodes into a circuit, it is called an *integrated circuit*.

Refer to Fig. 9-24 to see how an integrated circuit takes shape. The base material is usually silicon or germanium shaped like a thin disc or wafer about one inch in diameter. Several layers of material are deposited on this

9-23. Free electrons of the N crystal pass into the P crystal (a). When battery connections are reversed (b), the free electrons in the N crystal are attracted away from the P-N junction and no current is conducted across the junction.

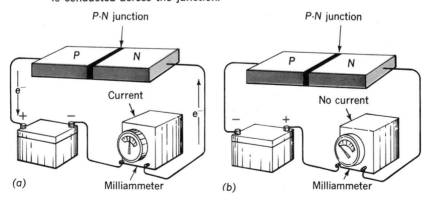

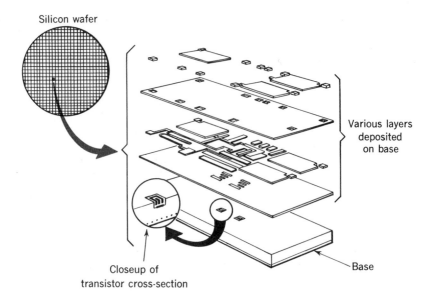

Silicon wafer

Various layers deposited on base

Closeup of transistor cross-section

Base

9-25. An exploded view of an integrated circuit developed as a result of depositing thin films of materials and of etching.

9-26. Integrated circuit is placed into a case, viewed under a microscope. (RCA)

disc after which it is divided into as many as 1000 squares. Each square is then developed into a highly complex electronic circuit with a great many *components*.

The wafers are then subjected to a number of complicated and exact processes during which microscopic layers of certain materials are *added* and other materials are *etched away*. An exploded view of the results of the adding and etching processes is shown in Fig. 9-25. After these processes are completed, each wafer is then cut apart into its separate circuits.

The building and etching of materials is controlled by a photographic technique. Thousands of circuits are built up simultaneously, but each circuit is then placed into individual cases by hand. This final assembly must be done under a microscope. (See Fig. 9-26.)

The finished product as shown in Fig. 9-27, gives you an idea of how small the thin film and integrated circuits are. The device shown in this photograph contains approximately 50 separate components. Compare this to a 5-tube radio which has between 20 and 30 individual components. Can you see why thin film and integrated circuitry are sometimes referred to as "the science of vanishing electronics"?

Radio signals are transmitted on selected frequencies. At every instant, waves from scores of radio transmitting stations are inducing complicated currents in your radio antenna. Commercial broadcasts, "ham" operators, police calls, etc., all are on the air at once. Why do not all these programs come from your radio in a meaningless jumble of sound? Why is it that you can "tune in" any particular program you want?

The reason is that every electric circuit has its own *natural frequency,* just as a tuning fork has. It does not respond to a radio wave whose frequency is not in tune with it. Remember how two tuning forks having the same frequency responded to each other? Here is another such example of *resonance.*

Each radio station sends out waves of one particular frequency. International agreement has set aside certain frequency bands for commercial broadcasters. Other frequency bands are reserved for the use of amateurs, police, airlines, military units, etc.

In order to pick up a certain station, you must adjust the frequency of your radio to match the frequency of

9-27. Final product of an integrated circuit contains up to 50 components and dwarfs conventional and transistor packages. (Westinghouse)

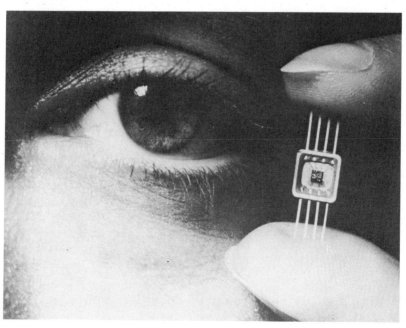

the waves sent out by the station. As discussed earlier, you *tune* your receiver by adjusting a variable capacitor.

Transmitters produce carrier waves. Every broadcasting station has a very complex radio device called a *transmitter*. The *transmitter* contains an electron tube called an *oscillator* that produces high-frequency alternating currents. These currents surge back and forth in the antenna of the transmitting station. As a result, high-frequency radio waves radiate out into space from the antenna. These are known as *carrier waves*.

Each station's carrier wave is kept at a constant frequency, one that is different from that of every other transmitter. Before the carrier wave is broadcast, however, it must be *modulated*.

What is meant by modulation? At the broadcasting station, the sound waves of the program, either voice or music, are picked up by the *microphone*. The "mike" produces a low-frequency current whose vibrations have the same pattern as that of the sound waves. In the part of the transmitter called the *modulator*, the carrier wave is made to "carry" this sound-wave pattern. (See Fig. 9-28.) *Modulation* is the process of *tailoring the carrier wave so that it "carries" the pattern of the sound waves.*

The usual method used in broadcasting is called *amplitude modulation*, or *AM*, as shown in the diagram. In this method, the carrier wave is changed in its amplitude to carry the pattern of the sound wave. A different method called *frequency modulation*, or *FM*, is also used. In transmitting by FM the amplitude of the carrier

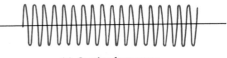

(a) Carrier frequency

(b) Sound pattern

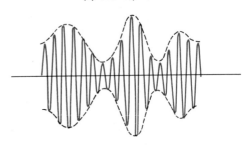

(c) Amplitude modulated carrier

(d) Frequency modulated carrier

9-28. A wave can be amplitude-modulated (AM) or frequency-modulated (FM).

wave is kept constant, but its frequency is changed in such a way that it carries the sound-wave pattern.

FM transmission is used for some radio programs and for the *audio* part of TV broadcasts. FM has the advantage of not being affected by "static" that sometimes disturbs AM transmission. However, FM, like television, uses a carrier wave of *very high frequency* which does not reflect off the *ionosphere*. For this reason, good FM reception is limited to a *line-of-sight distance* from the transmitting station.

What are audio- and radio-frequencies? The frequency of radio carrier waves runs from a low of about *30,000* cycles per second to a super-high of 30 billion cps. This range is known as radio-frequency, or r-f. The frequency of sound, also called audio-frequency, or a-f, ranges from about 20 to 20,000 cps.

The frequency range of the commercial broadcasting stations extends from about 550,000 to 1,700,000 cps, and is called the standard broadcast range. (See Fig. 9-29.)

You could not receive a radio program simply by amplifying the feeble currents that come from your antenna. If you sent these amplified currents to the earphones or speakers, you would not hear anything. Radio-frequencies are too high to be heard.

Therefore, your radio must separate the audio-frequency wave from the carrier wave, so that only the audio part goes to the speaker. This process of de-modulation is known as detection. The electronic tubes that accomplish this are called detectors.

Early radios used a crystal as a detector. The crystal diode is still used in some electronic circuits. In modern radios, the electronic tube or transistor triode is used as a detector.

How do radio receivers work? Figure 9-30 shows a simplified circuit of a one-tube receiving set. As explained earlier, you select a station by adjusting the variable capacitor. This puts an alternating voltage on the grid of the tube. This produces a pulsating direct plate current. The r-f carrier wave is by-passed through a capacitor, while the audio part discharges through the earphones.

The plate current of a one-tube circuit is not strong enough to operate a speaker. More powerful sets have several stages of amplification. As shown in the block diagram of Fig. 9-31, first there is r-f amplification, followed later by a-f amplification.

There are several kinds of microphones. As stated earlier, the purpose

9-29. The radio wave band of the electromagnetic spectrum.

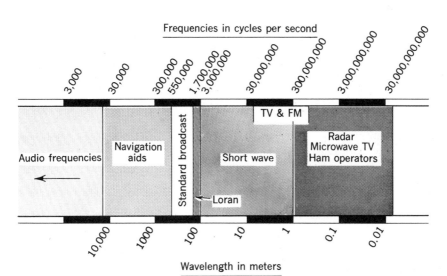

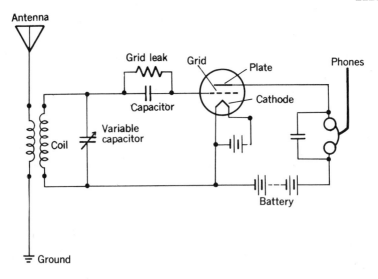

9-30. The simplified circuit of a one-tube radio.

of the "mike" is to pick up the sound waves and produce a current that fluctuates just as they do. *The microphone changes sound energy to electrical energy.* We shall discuss two of the ways of doing this:

1. *The resistance microphone.* The mouthpiece of your telephone contains a resistance microphone, as shown in Fig. 9-32. The sound waves cause a *diaphragm* to vibrate. This in turn vi-

brates a small box filled with *carbon granules.* The vibration changes the electrical resistance of the carbon. As the resistance changes, the strength of a current passing through the box changes also. Hence, the current is *modulated,* or given the same pattern that the sound waves have.

2. *The crystal microphone.* As already mentioned, one way of generating electric voltage is to put a *strain*

9-31. This block diagram shows a circuit with both radio-frequency and audio-frequency amplification.

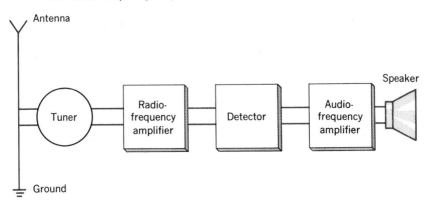

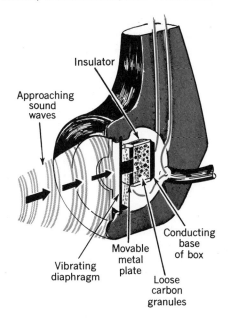

Insulator

Approaching sound waves

Conducting base of box

Movable metal plate

Vibrating diaphragm

Loose carbon granules

9-32. The resistance decreases and the current increases as the diaphragm presses the granules together.

on certain crystals. This is called the *piezoelectric effect.* In the crystal mike, the diaphragm presses against a tiny crystal wafer, usually made of quartz. The varying pressure on the crystal produces a *feeble* current that changes in strength and frequency just as the sound waves do.

Earphones and speakers. Speakers, or *loudspeakers,* act like the earphones of a telephone. As shown in Fig. 9-33, they contain *electromagnets.* The fluctuating current from the radio tube (or the telephone current, as the case may be) goes through the coils as shown. This strengthens or weakens the magnetic field, causing the iron diaphragm to vibrate and give off sound waves.

The ordinary loudspeaker uses a modification of this method, with larger coils and more powerful currents. (See Fig. 9-34.) The larger the

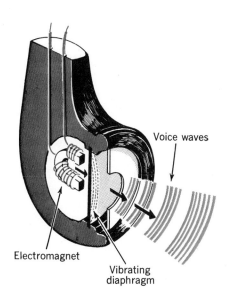

Voice waves

Electromagnet

Vibrating diaphragm

9-33. The telephone earphone contains an electromagnet. Variations in the magnetic field cause the metal diaphragm to vibrate and produce sound waves.

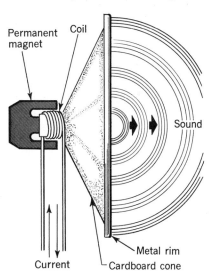

Permanent magnet

Coil

Sound

Current

Metal rim

Cardboard cone

9-34. As the current in the speaker coil fluctuates, the movable cone vibrates, producing audible sound waves which are transmitted to the ear.

diaphragm, the more intense the sound, so that in public address systems, very large diaphragms and powerful electromagnets are used.

Some loudspeakers produce sound waves by causing air molecules to vibrate directly by electrostatic forces instead of by the vibrating membranes. These speakers are called *electrostatic speakers*.

Crystal microphones can also be used as earphones, because the *piezoelectric effect* works both ways. That is, a fluctuating current applied to the crystal causes it to vibrate. The vibrating crystal in turn causes a diaphragm to start vibrating, which results in the production of sound waves.

Quick Quiz

1. Can you get a longer electric arc in gas under low pressure or high pressure?
2. Of what do cathode rays consist?
3. What is the Edison effect? How was it discovered?
4. How does a diode convert ac to dc?
5. In what way is the grid of a triode like a valve?
6. What three factors determine the amount of electron flow in a triode?
7. Briefly describe the differences between AM and FM.
8. How are integrated circuits made?
9. What is meant by tuning to a station?
10. What happens to the flow of electrons between the cathode and plate if you put a negative charge on the grid?
11. What kind of tube is a tetrode? A pentode?
12. What is sometimes referred to as the science of vanishing electronics? Why?

13. List some advantages of transistors over ordinary vacuum tubes.
14. Explain how a telephone receiver converts electrical energy into sound waves.

C TELEVISION AND OTHER MODERN ELECTRONIC DEVICES

Electrons are attracted to positive charges. The simple fact that electrons are attracted to positively charged plates is the basic principle used in such ingenious devices as *X-ray machines, electron microscopes, oscilloscopes, radar,* and *television*. Some atom-smashing machines also operate by causing high-speed electrons to crash into targets.

In the X-ray machine, X rays are produced when a beam of high-speed electrons strike a plate. In the atom-smashing machines, electrons are shot at high speeds into target atoms to obtain information about atomic structure. In oscilloscopes, radar, TV sets, and similar devices, electrons are "fired" at fluorescent screens to make them glow.

What is a cathode-ray oscilloscope? Until recently, the *cathode-ray oscilloscope* was of importance only to the radio engineer. Now it is an indispensable tool in most fields of science and engineering. For example, both the *radar screen* and *TV picture tube* are modified *cathode-ray oscilloscopes*. Refer to Fig. 9-35 as you read about the *oscilloscope*.

In the oscilloscope, a cathode ray is formed by a sort of "electron gun."

Electrons boil off the hot cathode and are pulled toward ring-shaped *positive anodes*. Thus, a thin beam of electrons "shoots" through the length of the tube. This beam is controlled by two sets of deflecting plates. Just as firemen can play a stream of water back and forth, so these plates direct the electron beam to-and-fro, only much more nimbly.

After passing by the plates, the cathode ray hits the mineral-coated end of the tube. The mineral glows, or *fluoresces*, when the electrons strike it. If there is no voltage on the deflecting plates the beam passes straight through, and makes a dot of light on the screen.

How is the beam controlled? A variable voltage is applied to the horizontal deflecting plates, sweeping the beam back and forth across the end of the tube. This produces a horizontal streak of light on the face of the screen. These horizontal deflecting plates are part of the *sweep circuit*. In a television set, the sweep circuit whips the beam back and forth in about 1/16,000 of a second.

The *vertical deflecting plates* control the up-and-down motion of the beam. The changing voltage of the incoming signal is applied to these plates. In the study of speech and music, the voltage produced by the sound waves in the microphone is applied to the vertical deflecting plates.

From the *combined* horizontal and vertical deflections a pattern of light is produced on the screen. This could very well be a sound-wave pattern, as was shown in Fig. 6-17.

Electrons can be deflected by magnetic fields as well as by electric charges. Hence, many oscilloscopes are provided with electromagnetic coils instead of electrostatic plates, to deflect the electron beam.

The television picture tube is a cathode-ray tube. Your television re-

9-35. This type of cathode-ray tube is found in the oscilloscope.

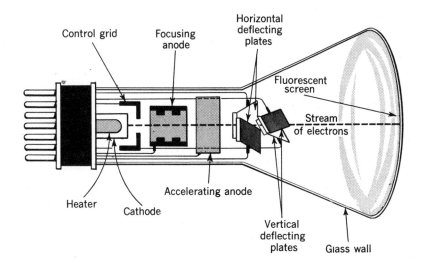

ceiver contains a large picture tube which is really a modified *cathode-ray oscilloscope*. The major difference is that the electron beam, thin as a pencil lead, sweeps back and forth across the end of a TV tube like a brush. It makes 525 strokes across the screen in 1/30th of a second. It "paints" 525 lines on the screen so rapidly that the first of them has not faded away by the time the last is drawn.

The strength of the electron beam, and hence the brightness of the spot of light, is controlled by the radio waves from your television antenna. As these waves have the same pattern as the light pattern of the original TV studio scene, you see an image of the scene on your TV receiver.

One of the many exacting problems of television is that the electron beam across the picture tube must be perfectly *synchronized* with the scanning beam of the TV camera. Also, the radio waves of the sound (*audio*) part of the program must be synchronized with the picture (*video*) part. This synchronization is accomplished by separate radio signals.

TV reception is limited to short distances. We can receive programs from TV stations only if they are no more than 50–100 miles away. Television uses *high-frequency waves that travel in straight lines, like light*. They *do not* reflect back from the upper atmosphere as do ordinary radio waves.

Hence, for long-distance transmission, the program may be carried by special cables from one city to another. It is also relayed cross-country by a series of stations mounted on high towers 20–100 miles apart. The waves then have to travel only the "line-of-sight" distance from the station of one tower to the station of the next.

Scientists are successfully using artificial earth satellites as TV *relay stations*. The satellite can be a huge reflecting balloon, such as the series of Echo satellites, or it can be an operating TV relay station that picks up, amplifies, and rebroadcasts the pro-

9-36. The basic three-gun color picture tube uses a mask to guide the beams.

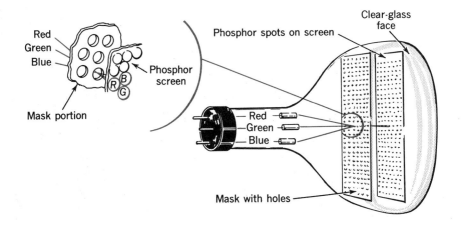

gram back to earth, such as the Early Bird and Syncom satellites.

How does color television work? Programs in full color are obtained by blending the three primary colors, red, green, and blue. Three cameras televise the scene. Each is provided with a *filter* that permits a different primary color to enter. Three separate signals, one for each color, are picked up by the cameras, and broadcast, or "telecast."

The color-TV picture tube has three electron guns, producing three electron beams. The inner face of the tube is coated with three different minerals, arranged in a series of tiny dots. Each mineral fluoresces to give a different primary color. (See Fig. 9-36.)

Each incoming color signal causes its electron beam to hit the proper dots. Your eye cannot see the separate dots, but instead sees the whole scene glow in natural color. The color TV system is *compatible*, which means that you can receive the color program in black and white on ordinary TV sets.

TV has many uses. TV is used for more than entertainment. In *closed-circuit* TV, the program is sent to TV sets through a special cable. Closed circuit television is used in industry, the military, schools, medicine, and oceanography. TV is also used in satellites and space probes for studies of the earth, the moon, and the stars. (See Fig. 9-37.)

What causes X rays? You have already learned that cathode rays are streams of high-speed electrons. While working with cathode rays in 1895, Wilhelm Roentgen (*rent-g'n*) noticed that a nearby mineral was glowing or fluorescing from the effects of these rays.

He covered the glass tube, from which the rays were coming, with a sheet of black paper so that no visible light could come from it. But the mineral still glowed. He gave the name "X rays" to this radiation that could penetrate the black paper. As we now know, *X rays are electromagnetic radiations similar to light, only of much shorter wavelength.* (See Fig. 9-29, page 401.)

When cathode rays strike a dense *target* such as the metal tungsten,

9-37. Closed-circuit television is used by this dentist to examine and study his patient's mouth. Note enlarged image of teeth on the screen. (Avco Manufacturing Corp.)

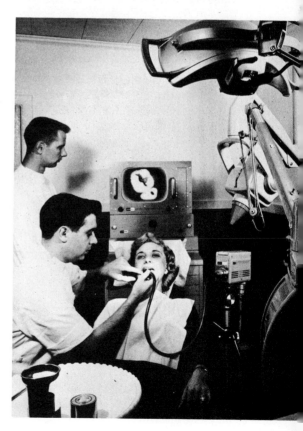

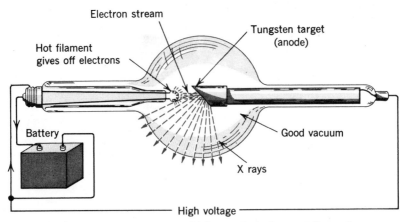

Electron stream

Hot filament
gives off electrons

Tungsten target
(anode)

Battery

Good vacuum

X rays

High voltage

9-38. X rays are formed when high-speed electrons strike a dense
target.

X rays are formed. (See Fig. 9-38.) If a higher accelerating voltage is used, the electrons strike the target harder, and more energetic X rays are produced. By using more than a million volts, we get X rays that will penetrate several inches of steel. For example, as shown in Fig. 9-39, metal castings can be tested for invisible flaws by using X rays.

9-39. A machine part is examined for flaws with X rays. (Eastman Kodak)

Doctors can look at bones in your body by placing the part of the body to be examined between an X-ray tube and a *fluorescent screen.* The bones, which are dense, strongly absorb the X rays, preventing them from reaching the screen. The rays are not as readily absorbed when they pass through muscle or other soft tissue. They strike the fluorescent screen, causing it to glow brightly. Thus, the familiar *X-ray shadow picture* is obtained.

If, instead of a screen, special photographic film is used, pictures like the one shown in Fig. 9-40 are obtained.

Are X rays dangerous? *Long exposure* or intense bursts of X rays can produce harmful effects on your body. Many pioneer experimenters suffered serious burns and even death before the danger was recognized. Recent studies have shown that in addition to burns and the destruction of body cells, exposure to X rays may produce undesirable *mutations.* **Mutations** are changes in the factors that control heredity. Hence, extreme care should be used to protect the body from an over-dosage of X rays.

As soon as scientists found that X rays could destroy body cells, they used this knowledge to produce a beneficial result. They found that certain types of *cancer* could be destroyed or checked by the proper use of X rays. This is still one of the chief methods of treating cancer today.

X rays are produced both by X-ray machines and by *radioactive elements*. X rays that come from radioactive substances are called *gamma rays*. Gamma rays are high-frequency X rays with extremely high penetrating power.

What is the photoelectric effect? The *phototube*, or *photoelectric cell*, is an ingenious electronic tube, sometimes called an "electric eye." It is capable of changing light energy into electric energy.

Many years ago it was noticed that certain metals became *positively charged* when they were struck by light. It was found that only metals whose atoms had very *loosely bound* electrons behave in this way. When a beam of light strikes atoms of such metals, electrons are ejected, leaving the metal with a positive charge. The energy of a single *photon* is enough to detach an electron from its atom. This is known as the *photoelectric effect*.

Figure 9-41 shows a circuit containing a phototube. No current flows until light hits the cathode. Then electrons go to the positively charged anode, or *collector*. *The brighter the light, the stronger the current.*

The tiny current from a phototube is amplified, and then usually used to trigger a sensitive relay. The relay may then act as a switch to control still more powerful currents.

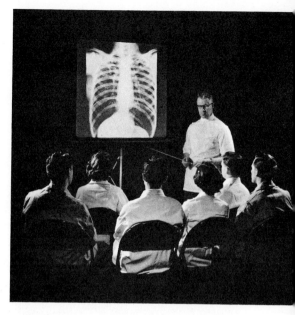

9-40. X rays are used in medicine for the diagnosis and treatment of many diseases. (Eastman Kodak)

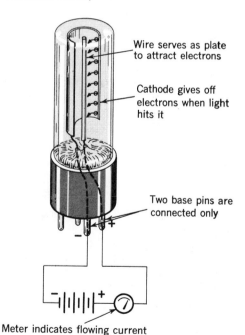

Wire serves as plate to attract electrons

Cathode gives off electrons when light hits it

Two base pins are connected only

Meter indicates flowing current

9-41. The brighter the light that strikes the phototube, the greater the current.

A phototube circuit may be arranged in such a way that a counting device operates each time that a beam of light is interrupted. Interruptions might be caused by traffic on the highway, coins in a mint, or packages on a moving belt. Doors can be automatically opened and closed by photoelectric cells. They can be used to turn on street lights and building lights as darkness approaches. Some cities are installing automatic electronic signals to control traffic at busy street corners. The foul lights on bowling alleys are also controlled by photoelectric cells.

Fire alarms and *burglar alarms* may also be operated by photoelectric cells. A burglar may break an invisible beam of infrared light, thus setting off the alarm.

Photocells made out of the semiconductor germanium are more sensitive than the phototube type. Also, they are only a hundredth as large, making them more advantageous.

How are sound movies projected? A beam of light throws an image of the film on a screen. Another beam of light goes through the film also, producing quite a different effect. It shines through the *sound track* of the film and causes music or speech to come from the loudspeaker.

Examine the irregular streak of light running along the right side of a section of sound-movie film. This is the photographic record of the sound and is called the sound track. The pattern of light and dark of this sound track is just like the pattern of the sound waves recorded by it.

A tiny pencil of light, shining through this sound track, falls on a phototube. The amount of light that gets through depends upon the optical density of the sound track at that point. This flickering light causes the phototube to produce a fluctuating current. After being amplified, it goes to loudspeakers located near the movie screen.

The television camera depends upon the photoelectric effect. For many years, scientists tried to master the baffling problems of transmitting moving images by means of radio waves. The perfecting of the photoelectric cell helped them achieve success.

Television is transmitted and received by a process similar to the one that we use in seeing with our eyes and brain. In fact, it is remotely possible that some blind people may someday be able to use a TV camera instead of eyes. In a way then, television is "seeing by electromagnetic waves."

An image of the scene to be televised is formed in the *television camera.* This camera may have an electronic tube called an *iconoscope* (eye-kon-oh-skope), which means "image-viewer." The camera may have a more sensitive tube called the image *orthicon* (or-thih-kon), or a *vidicon,* as shown in Fig. 9-42.

The iconoscope is used in TV studios, where very strong illumination is available, because it gives a sharper picture. The image orthicon is used where the light is dimmer, as at ball games. The vidicon is used in small, portable television cameras.

In an ordinary camera, the light produces a chemical effect on the film. In the TV camera, the light forms an image on a surface that is coated with thousands of particles of a *photoelectric substance.* Each sensitive particle acts like a tiny photoelectric cell, and

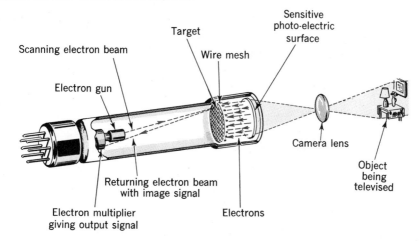

9-42. The image orthicon is a sensitive television camera tube containing an electron gun.

receives a varying charge, depending upon the brightness of the light. An electron beam rapidly scans this surface. This produces an electric current that varies just like the pattern of light from the scene being televised. This varying electric current is amplified and broadcast by shortwave radio.

Radar depends upon radio waves. The origin of the concept of radar goes back to 1922 when the U.S. Navy observed that high-frequency radio waves were cut off by ships passing through the line of transmission. In 1934, the U.S. Naval Research Laboratory bounced high-frequency pulses off an airplane 15 miles away. It wasn't until the early years of World War II, however, that radar was developed and used extensively. The word Radar was coined from the words "Radio Detecting and Ranging." Briefly, radar functions when a powerful radio *transmitter* sends out pulses of high-frequency waves and a *receiver* listens for the *echoes* that are reflected from surrounding objects.

The distance of an object is determined by measuring the length of time it takes for the pulse to hit the object and the echo to return. The direction of the object is determined by the direction in which the *rotating antenna* is pointing when the signal is received. (See Fig. 9-43.)

The continuous stream of reflected signals produces a glowing light on the *radar screen.* This screen is the fluorescent end of a cathode-ray tube that resembles the picture tube of a TV set.

What are some of the uses of radar? Today, scientists are probing millions of miles out into space with radar. They have bounced signals off the moon, sun, and some of the planets. By putting radar to use, we are learning much about our solar system.

Radar is important to our military defense. It can be used to locate enemy ships, planes, and rockets. Our defense department has set up radar systems to protect our borders. For example, the DEW-line (Distant Early Warning) and BMEWS (Ballistic Mis-

9-43. The radar pulse goes out and returns before the plane has noticeably moved.

9-44. Latest advances in radar include the development of the 50-ton "boxcar" antenna capable of detecting enemy air attack hundreds of miles away. (Raytheon Co.)

sile Early Warning System) are "radar fences" across the northern part of the continent. (See Fig. 9-44.)

Peacetime uses of radar are of great importance. Radar is used for the safe navigation of ships and planes during times of poor visibility. Radar also helps planes and ships detect hurricanes and storms so that they can be avoided. Radar is also used as an *all-weather landing aid* to aircraft. Surprisingly, radar is even used to make detailed studies of migrating birds.

The electron and field-ion microscopes give high magnifications. You have probably seen photographs of *viruses* or other objects that are too small to be seen with the ordinary microscope. These pictures are taken of enlarged images produced by the *electron microscope.* This device uses *beams of electrons instead of light rays.* An electron microscope is shown in Fig. 9-45.

The electron microscope is really a very large *cathode-ray tube.* At the top is the "electron gun." High-voltage *anodes* speed the electron beam downward. The beam strikes a very thin slice of the object you want to look at. The electrons that pass through are focused by a complicated set of *magnet coils.* Finally, they strike a fluorescent screen at the bottom, forming an enlarged image of the object.

The *field-ion microscope* operates in somewhat the same way except that instead of electrons being sped to the screen, *helium ions* are used. These ions are produced from a small amount of helium which is introduced into the high-vacuum microscope tube. The needle-like tip of the material being investigated is subjected to an extremely high positive charge. When a

9-45. The electron microscope is capable of magnifying objects 400,000 times. (RCA)

helium atom comes close to the positively charged needle, an electron is stripped from the atom and the resulting ion is repelled into the screen. The pattern which forms on the screen corresponds to the atoms on the needle tip over which the helium was ionized. The field-ion microscope can magnify up to 4,000,000 times, while the electron microscope magnifies up to about 400,000 times, and an optical microscope up to about 2000 times.

Electronics is important in modern telephone systems. The simple *telephone* as invented by Bell consisted of a microphone (transmitter) and an earphone (receiver) in a circuit with a source of current, such as you would find in a battery.

The modern telephone system is, of course, much more complicated.

For example, there are complex electronic *switching* devices that permit you to dial directly to any of millions of phones in the United States.

For long distance calls, the signal must be repeatedly strengthened by *electronic amplifiers.* Electronic equipment also handles the calculation of the toll charges automatically.

What are some other electronic devices? During the past decade or more, scientists have developed greater and better electronic devices called *computers.* These electronic devices are taking over many of the jobs that formerly demanded the use of man's mental skills. Computers can perform complex mathematical operations at lightning speed.

Our civilization is getting to be so extensive and complex that the prob-

9-46. This modern electronic computer computes and records data concerning the United States census on thousands of miles of magnetic tape (left). The tapes are then stored in huge libraries (right). (US Bureau of the Census)

lem of handling statistical records is becoming immense. We find a partial answer to this problem in electronic devices, including computers, that act as *data-processing machines*. These machines keep track of such data as the U.S. census, military rolls, and income tax statistics. They also make out utility bills, and figure out bank statements. With the use of these electronic devices, scientific research is accelerating at an ever faster pace. (See Fig. 9-46.)

In addition to all the electronic devices mentioned so far there are many, many more. Just a few additional devices include hearing aids, electrocardiograph machines, electric guitars, electronic stethoscopes, and lie detectors. Can you add more items to this list?

Quick Quiz

1. What kind of rays are identical to high-frequency X rays?
2. How are X rays produced?
3. What is the photoelectric effect?
4. In what way are the oscilloscope and a TV picture tube alike?
5. How does radar work?
6. What are the chief differences among the optical, electron, and field-ion microscopes?
7. Discuss briefly how color is shown on the screen of a color TV set.
8. How is the photoelectric cell used in a motion picture projector?
9. What is a fluoroscope? How is it used?
10. Name two biological effects of X rays.
11. What is the source of light in the picture tube of your TV set?
12. What causes the streaks in the picture that you see if you sit close to your TV set?

SUMMARY

Electrostatics is a branch of electronics that deals with stationary charges or charges at rest. Objects become negatively charged by gaining electrons and positively charged by losing them. These charges can be detected by the use of an electroscope.

A capacitor, or condenser, is made of two conductors separated by an insulator. It is used to store a large charge and to control radio frequencies.

Cathode rays are streams of high-speed electrons that travel through a vacuum from a cathode to a positively charged plate. This effect is used in a diode which can act as a current rectifier. De Forest added a grid to the diode creating a triode which can be used as a rectifier, amplifier, detector, and oscillator. When striking certain materials, cathode rays produce X rays.

Transistors are made of a semi-conductor, usually silicon or germanium. They are much smaller than conventional vacuum tubes, more rugged, and use much less power. Thin film and integrated circuits are extremely small electronic circuits and components that are produced by depositing thin films of certain substances on a base material.

Microphones change the sound-wave pattern to a corresponding pattern of electric impulses that can be used to modulate the transmitter. In radio broadcasting the sound pattern is put on a carrier wave and transmitted. Your radio receiver strips the audio wave from the carrier and reproduces the sound.

The operation of many electronic devices depends upon the control of electron beams that strike a variety of targets. The cathode-ray oscilloscope tube gives precise control to a beam of electrons that forms a pattern of light on a fluorescent screen. Modified forms of this tube are used as radar screens and television picture tubes.

When a beam of light hits the atoms of certain metals, it ejects electrons from them. This is called the photoelectric effect, and is used in such devices as sound movie projectors, automatic control devices, and TV cameras.

Radar stations send out pulses of high-frequency radio waves and receive the echoes which are reflected back from objects within its range. In this way it uses radio waves for detecting objects and determining their ranges.

CHAPTER REVIEW

Vocabulary

Match the words in Column A with the *best* responses in Column B. Do not write in your book.

Column A	Column B
1. electrostatics	a. adding a sound wave to a carrier wave
2. static electricity	b. adjusting the frequency of a receiver

3. electroscope
4. induction
5. lightning rod
6. neutralizing
7. capacitor
8. Edison effect
9. diode
10. triode
11. grid
12. amplifier
13. detector
14. transistor
15. tuning
16. modulation
17. X rays
18. oscilloscope
19. phototube
20. radar

c. branch of electronics dealing with charges at rest
d. cathode-ray device used to make wave forms visible
e. combining equal amounts of positive and negative electricity
f. device that separates the audio wave from the carrier wave
g. device "to draw off electrical fluid" from buildings
h. device used to detect electric charges
i. device used to store an electrical charge
j. device used to strengthen feeble electrical signals
k. device which produces an electric current from a beam of light
l. electricity at rest
m. electrode that controls the flow of electrons in an electronic tube
n. high-frequency radiation of great penetrating power
o. miniature semi-conductor that functions like a vacuum tube
p. name given to the passage of electrons from a hot cathode to a positive plate
q. process of producing a charge in nearby objects by a charged object
r. radio detecting and ranging
s. three-element electronic tube
t. two-element electronic tube

Questions: Group A

1. What four topics are included in the study of electronics?
2. What happens to an object that gets more than its normal quota of electrons?
3. When you rub hard rubber with wool, which kind of charge does each substance obtain? Explain.
4. What is the electroscope used for?
5. How does a charge become neutralized?
6. Which kind of a charge is induced by a positive charge?
7. What is a stroke of lightning?
8. What is a capacitor used for? How is it constructed?
9. Name the electrodes of the triode. What are their functions?
10. Name some functions that electron tubes can perform.
11. What is the purpose of a microphone?
12. What property of X rays makes X-ray pictures possible?
13. What is the sound track of a movie film? How does it function?
14. What is the dot of light that you see as the picture dies away when you turn off your TV set?
15. Why are relay stations necessary for long-distance TV transmissions?

Questions: Group B

1. Describe in detail what happens when you touch a positively charged rod to a neutral electroscope.
2. Explain why neutral objects are attracted by either positively or negatively charged objects.
3. Describe how you can induce a negative charge on an insulated conductor using a positively charged rod.
4. A gold-leaf electroscope has a positive charge. As you bring a charged rod toward it, the leaves spread farther apart. Which kind of charge does the rod possess? Explain.
5. Which has more need of lightning protection, a brick smokestack or a steel skyscraper? Why?
6. Why do you get a spark when you shuffle across a nylon rug and then touch a metal doorknob?
7. Explain why a capacitor can store up electric charges.
8. Explain how a triode can act as an amplifier.
9. What is meant by modulation? De-modulation?
10. Explain how a loudspeaker works.
11. Why do transistors require less power than ordinary electron tubes? Can you think of more than one reason?
12. Discuss the construction and operation of the cathode-ray oscilloscope.
13. Discuss briefly the action of the TV camera.
14. How can a radar set indicate the presence of a rocket 300 miles away, due north?
15. How does an electrostatic filter work?

10 NUCLEONICS

A NUCLEAR CHANGES

The nucleus is part of the atom. Let us review atomic structure. You learned in Chapter 1 that practically all the mass of the atom is the *nucleus*, its center.

Orbiting around the nucleus are negatively charged particles, called *electrons*. The neutral atom of one element differs from that of another in the number of these orbiting electrons. A model of the uranium atom is shown in Fig. 10-1. The hydrogen atom has one electron, helium has two, and so on up to element 104. Most of the elements occur in nature. However, elements 43, 61, and those that follow 92, do not occur in nature and are man-made. The atom is electrically neutral, because its nucleus contains as many positively charged *protons* as there are negatively charged electrons spinning about it. For example, the nucleus of uranium has 92 protons to balance its 92 electrons. In addition to protons, the nucleus also contains *neutrons*, which have about the same mass as protons, but have no electrical charge.

In other words, we believe that nuclei, like automobiles, are assembled from interchangeable parts. As far as we know, any one proton is exactly like all other protons, and any neutron is the same as any other neutron. The difference between nuclei of gold and silver, for example, is due essentially to the *number* of protons and neutrons that each atom contains in its nucleus.

Atomic masses are relative. You also learned in Chapter 1 that chemists do not use the actual masses of the atoms in their calculations. Instead they use *comparative* masses. They are interested in how the atoms of different elements compare with each other. They use *carbon-12 as their standard*, and arbitrarily assign it an atomic mass of *12 mass units*. (Naturally-occurring carbon is slightly heavier than carbon-12.) A magnesium atom, for example, is about twice as massive as the carbon atom, and so the atomic mass of magnesium is about 24. The hydrogen atom, on the other hand, is only about $\frac{1}{12}$th as massive as the carbon atom,

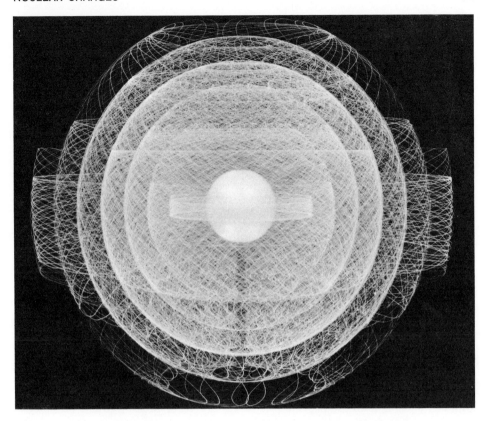

10-1. This photograph of a uranium atom model shows the complex arrangement of electrons orbiting the nucleus. Notice how the electron cloud decreases in density away from the nucleus. (Union Carbide Corp.)

and has an atomic mass of about 1. This gives uranium, the last naturally-occurring element, an atomic mass of about 238.

Scientists have determined atomic masses with extreme accuracy. For example, the atomic mass of hydrogen is 1.00797, and that of uranium is 238.03. Precise atomic masses must be used in calculating *nuclear reactions*.

The mass number of an element. The ordinary hydrogen atom consists of only one proton and one electron. If you neglect the very slight mass of the electron, the atomic masses of the proton and the hydrogen atom are both about 1 mass unit. Hence, you can find the approximate atomic mass of all other atoms by adding up the *number of protons and neutrons* in their nuclei.

For example, the helium nucleus contains 2 protons and 2 neutrons, and so its atomic mass is about 4. We call these approximate atomic masses **mass numbers.** Thus, the mass number of helium is 4. The oxygen nucleus contains 8 protons and 8 neutrons. What is its mass number?

The *mass number* of an element should mean two things to you: (1) *the sum of the number of protons and neutrons in its nucleus,* and (2) *the approximate atomic mass of the element.* That is, the mass number is the *same as the atomic mass* expressed to the nearest whole number.

Ordinarily, when we mention the atomic mass of an element, the approximate value, or the mass number, is given.

The atomic number. The *number of protons* in the nucleus of an element is called its *atomic number.* For example, the atomic number of hydrogen is 1, because its nucleus has only one proton. The helium nucleus contains two protons, and so its atomic number is 2. What is the atomic number of oxygen?

In the *Periodic Table,* at the end of this book, the elements are listed in the order of their atomic numbers. They go from hydrogen 1, to helium 2, and so on, each element having one more proton in its nucleus than the previous element had. The list builds up in this way to element-104.

The atomic number of an element is its chief identification or "name tag." Any atom whose nucleus contains 92 protons, for example, is an atom of uranium, no matter how many other particles it may contain.

Furthermore, even though a substance may have the same mass number as uranium, it is not uranium unless each of its atoms contains 92 protons.

Because each proton carries a single positive charge, the atomic number also represents the *charge on the nucleus.* For example, the helium nucleus carries a charge of +2, and the uranium nucleus a charge of +92.

The discovery of radioactivity. In 1896, a French scientist named Henri Becquerel (Bek-err-*ell*) made a startling discovery. By chance, he had left an unexposed photographic film near a sample of uranium. To his surprise, he found that upon development it was darkened just as if it had been exposed to light. After further study and experimentation, he concluded that uranium ore gave out a mysterious kind of energy by a process called *radioactivity.* This radiation was even more powerful than the X rays discovered by Roentgen just 3 months earlier.

Year in and year out, uranium and all its compounds send out this highly penetrating radiation. Nothing we can

THE CARBON ATOM IS THE STANDARD FOR ATOMIC MASSES

	Hydrogen atom	Carbon-12 atom	Uranium-238 atom
No. of protons	1	6	92
No. of neutrons	0	6	146
No. of electrons	1	6	92
Atomic mass	1.00797	12.00000	238.124
Mass number	1	12	238
Atomic number	1	6	92

do affects it in any way. We can toss it into a fiery furnace or into frigid liquid air. Unaffected, the uranium atoms just keep on giving off this radiation. *Radioactivity* is caused by spontaneous *changes that take place in the nucleus of certain atoms.*

In 1898, Madame Curie found that the element *thorium* was also radioactive. During that same year, she and her husband noticed that *pitchblende,* an ore of uranium, was more radioactive than pure uranium itself. This led them to conclude that pitchblende must contain an unknown element that was highly radioactive. Further investigations led the Curies to their discovery of *radium.* (See Fig. 10-2.)

Eventually, Madame Curie succeeded in separating about ⅒th of a gram of radium from many tons of pitchblende. She found that it was more than 100 *million* times more radioactive than pure uranium.

Radioactivity produces three kinds of radiation. The nucleus of a radioactive atom is made up of many particles held together by very powerful binding forces. But certain internal disturbances, or bombardment by a particle from the outside, can upset the balance within the nucleus. Then radioactivity occurs, with energy and matter flying off in the form of *alpha, beta,* and *gamma rays.*

The *alpha particles,* or *alpha rays,* consist of positively charged *helium nuclei. Beta rays* consist of *electrons* traveling nearly as fast as light. *Gamma rays,* the third type of radiation, are similar to powerful X rays.

The British scientist, Ernest Rutherford, showed that radioactivity occurs when an atom *disintegrates or decays;* that is, when changes occur in its nu-

10-2. Madame Curie and her husband were the joint discoverers of radium. (Bettmann Archive)

cleus. (See Fig. 10-3.) Whenever radioactivity occurs, the nucleus is *changed* into that of a *different element.* For example, the *uranium* atom disintegrates and eventually changes to *radium.* Radium atoms, in turn, disintegrate in a series of steps to form atoms of *lead.* In each case, we go from a heavier to a lighter element.

What is meant by "half-life"? The rate of decay or disintegration varies with different radioactive elements. However, all of them decay at a rate measured by the element's *half-life.* The *half-life* of a radioactive element is the time required for *half of the atoms of a sample to disintegrate.* For example, the half-life of radium is about 1600 years. This means that no matter how many atoms of radium there are to begin with, in 1600 years *only half* of them will be left unchanged. During the next 1600 years, half of the remainder will disintegrate,

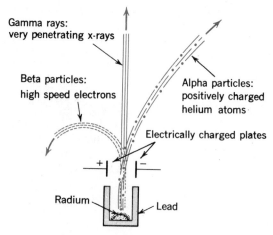

10-3. A radioactive element such as radium emits three types of radiation.

and the pattern repeats again and again. (See Fig. 10-4.)

For some radioactive elements, the half-life is less than a billionth of a second. For others, as shown in the table below, it is billions of years.

The amount of energy set free by radioactivity is tremendous. For example, the heat given off every hour by a pound of radium would be more than enough to heat a pound of water from freezing to boiling. This may not seem like much, but remember that this process continues for thousands of years.

Most nuclei are very stable. It is extremely difficult to *break up the nucleus* of an element that is not radioactive. For example, *nitroglycerin* is made of atoms of hydrogen, nitrogen, carbon, and oxygen. The explosion of nitroglycerin simply *rearranges* these atoms to form new molecules. The atoms just swap partners, forming new

HALF–LIVES OF SOME RADIOACTIVE ELEMENTS

Element or Nucleus	Symbol *	Half-life
Tin—124	$_{50}Sn^{124}$	1,700,000,000 billion years
Thorium—232	$_{90}Th^{232}$	14 billion years
Uranium—238	$_{92}U^{238}$	4.5 billion years
Carbon—14	$_{6}C^{14}$	5568 years
Radium—226	$_{88}Ra^{226}$	1622 years
Scandium—46	$_{21}Sc^{46}$	85 days
Barium—139	$_{56}Ba^{139}$	86 minutes
Nitrogen—16	$_{7}N^{16}$	7.4 seconds
Helium—5	$_{2}He^{5}$	2.4×10^{-21} second

* See page 424 for explanation of symbols.

compounds. The inner part of the atom, the nucleus, *is not* disturbed.

The explosion of nitroglycerin is a chemical reaction that sets free a large amount of energy. In comparison, radioactive *changes in the nucleus* may set free millions of times as much energy.

Rutherford was first to smash the atom. Until 1919, the nucleus defied our attempts to alter it in any way. But, in that year, Rutherford discovered a method of attacking it. By bombarding atoms with very high-speed atomic "bullets," he was able to hit the nucleus and cause a *nuclear reaction.*

His first success resulted in *changing nitrogen atoms to oxygen atoms.* The nucleus of the nitrogen atom was hit by *alpha particles* from radium. Hydrogen was given off and oxygen was produced.

Remembering that an alpha particle is the nucleus of the helium atom, we may summarize the results as follows:

helium + nitrogen →

oxygen + hydrogen

A helium nucleus, traveling at high speed, struck a nitrogen nucleus and was *absorbed* into it. The resulting nucleus became *unstable* and broke up, giving off a high-speed hydrogen nucleus (*proton*). This resulted in the formation of an oxygen nucleus. (See Fig. 10-5.)

This reaction represented man's first success in the **transmutation** (*trans-mew-tay*-shun) *of one element into another.* For centuries, the early *alchemists* had tried in vain to produce gold from other elements. Today, the

10-4. A half-life curve is used to illustrate how radium decays to lead.

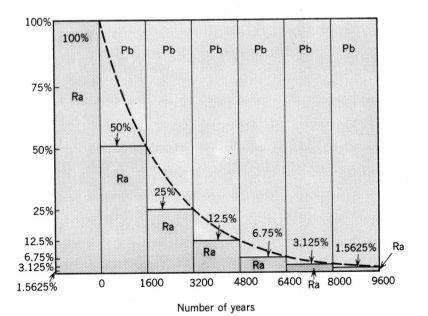

Number of years

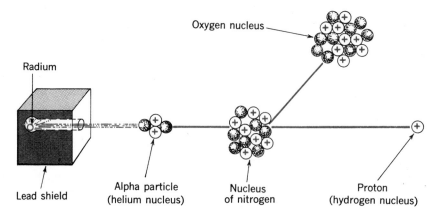

10-5. Nitrogen was changed to oxygen in the first nuclear reaction.

transmutation of one element into another by nuclear reactions is a routine operation.

Rutherford's work was important in showing that man could attack the nucleus. But it was not the final key needed to unlock *atomic energy.* Although the hydrogen was shot out with more energy than the helium bullet had, there were so few hits that energy was actually lost in the total process. Not until scientists split the uranium atom were vast quantities of energy released. This will be discussed in detail in the next section of this chapter.

What are nuclear equations? Nuclear physicists use *nuclear equations* that look much like chemical equations. Here is the one for Rutherford's pioneering *nuclear reaction* in converting nitrogen to oxygen

$$_2\text{He}^4 + {}_7\text{N}^{14} \rightarrow {}_8\text{O}^{17} + {}_1\text{H}^1$$
Helium   Nitrogen   Oxygen   Hydrogen

This means that a helium nucleus reacted with a nitrogen nucleus to give an oxygen nucleus and a hydrogen nucleus. The figure at the *lower left* of each symbol is the *atomic number* of the atom. It represents the number of protons in the nucleus. Notice that the number of protons adds up to 9 on each side of the equation. No protons were gained or lost in the reaction.

The figure in the *upper right* gives the *mass number* of the atom. This stands for the total number of protons and neutrons in the nucleus. The total of the mass numbers on each side of the equation must also be equal.

What are isotopes? Any atom whose nucleus has 8 protons is an oxygen atom. The ordinary oxygen atom also has 8 neutrons, making a total mass number of 16. However, some oxygen atoms contain an *extra neutron,* giving them the mass number of 17. The oxygen atom in the equation above has 9 neutrons in its nucleus.

Atoms whose nuclei contain the same number of protons, but which contain different numbers of neutrons, are called **isotopes.** Most elements have several natural isotopes, but some have none at all.

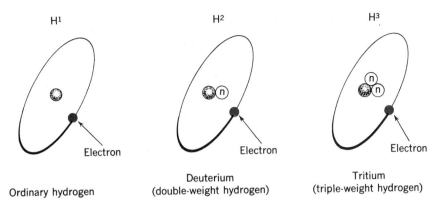

10-6. Three isotopes of hydrogen.

Why was it not until recently that we learned about isotopes and found out how to separate them from each other? Because chemically they are exactly alike, and so no chemical method can be used to separate them. Instead, some method that depends on their differences in mass must be used.

Five thousand parts of ordinary hydrogen contain about one part of an isotope called *heavy hydrogen,* or *deuterium* (dew-*teer*-ee-um). As shown in Fig. 10-6, the nucleus of deuterium contains a neutron in addition to the proton of the ordinary hydrogen nucleus. Hydrogen also contains a trace of another isotope called **tritium** (*trit-i-um*), which has two neutrons in its nucleus. These isotopes of hydrogen, $_1H^2$ and $_1H^3$, are of importance in nuclear reactions.

Nuclear energy. Rutherford used the natural radiations of radium to bombard nuclei. In 1932, two other British scientists bombarded lithium nuclei with protons, or positively charged hydrogen atoms. The protons were accelerated down a long tube by applying a high voltage. When the nucleus of a lithium atom was hit by a proton, it split into two helium atoms. At the same time, a large amount of energy was set free

$$_1H^1 + _3Li^7 \rightarrow _2He^4 + _2He^4 + energy$$

Scientists had known that the nucleus was a tremendous storehouse of energy, and were now learning how to set some of it free. Nuclear reactions soon proved that Einstein's prediction made in 1905 was right: *matter and energy are equivalent. Matter may be thought of as energy in a very concentrated form.*

During some nuclear reactions, matter disappears and an equivalent quantity of energy is released in its place. The relation between the two is given by Einstein's equation: $E = mc^2$. In this equation, **E** stands for the *energy,* **m** for the *mass* that is destroyed, and **c²** for the *square of the speed of light.* We can calculate from the equation that when 1 gram of matter is destroyed, about 25 million kilowatt-hours of energy are produced. (See Fig. 10-7.)

The above-mentioned reaction, in which lithium and hydrogen nuclei combine to form helium nuclei, may be expressed as

$$_1H^1 + _3Li^7 \rightarrow$$
$$1.0080 + 7.0160 \rightarrow$$
$$_2He^4 + _2He^4 + \text{energy}$$
$$4.0026 + 4.0026$$

The numbers below the symbols are the masses of the nuclei in atomic mass units. Notice that the left side totals 8.0240 mass units, while the right side adds up to only 8.0052. The difference,

0.0188 mass units, was converted into energy.

Nuclear physicists often use a very small unit of energy called the **electron volt,** or **ev.** This is the energy acquired by a single charged particle, such as a proton or electron, when it "falls" through an *electric potential of one volt.* **Mev** stands for a million electron volts of energy.

When one mass unit of matter is destroyed, 931 Mev of energy are produced. During the bombardment of lithium by protons, illustrated above, 0.0188 mass unit disappears and 17.5 Mev of energy are produced ($931 \times 0.0188 = 17.5$). This is an important verification of Einstein's energy-mass equation.

Atom-smashing machines. Once Rutherford had succeeded in breaking apart the nucleus of an atom, scientists began to build bigger and more powerful machines, so that higher and higher voltages could be applied to the *nuclear bullets.* This was because the higher the voltage, the faster the particles traveled and the harder they smashed into the target nucleus. This allowed scientists to study the nucleus in greater detail.

One device used to obtain high voltages is the **Van de Graaff generator.** You will recall how this works from your study on page 388. It produces very large charges to speed particles through a vacuum tube. The **linear accelerator** is a more powerful atom smasher. It applies many successive pulses of voltages that pull the particles through a long tube with ever-increasing speed. Accelerators may be thousands of feet long. (See Fig. 10-8.)

In 1931, Dr. Lawrence of the University of California invented the *cy-*

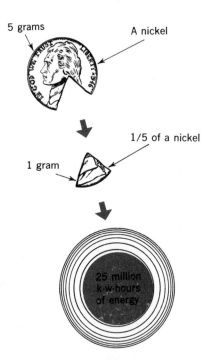

10-7. From the Einstein equation, $E = mc^2$, it is calculated that when one gram of matter disintegrates, twenty-five million kilowatt-hours of energy are produced.

clotron to speed up the nuclear bullets. The cyclotron uses a *powerful magnet* to bend the speeding particles into a spiral path. They are given voltage "kicks" many, many times as they whirl round and round. This causes the particles to attain great speeds.

One of the most powerful types of *particle accelerators* is called the **synchrotron.** Its magnets are arranged in a large circle, and cause the particles to follow a circular path. In 1960, a synchrotron nearly half a mile in diameter was built. It gives particles as much energy as if they had been speeded up by 32 billion volts. The particles are speeded up by a linear accelerator before being injected into the synchrotron. (See Fig. 10-9.)

Nuclear bombardment. Scientists use a variety of "bullets" to cause nuclear reactions. Usually the nuclei of the lighter elements, such as ordinary hydrogen, deuterium, and helium are used, although heavier nuclei are also used.

The newest, most powerful particle accelerators can duplicate most of the effects of cosmic rays. **Cosmic rays** are high-speed, *high-energy particles from outer space.* These particles are atomic nuclei, mostly protons. Cosmic rays act as natural atom-smashing bullets. They produce nuclear reactions when they strike atoms of our outer atmosphere.

Scientists found that many new kinds of particles resulted from violent nuclear bombardment. Some of these particles are lighter than protons, but heavier than electrons. Hence, we call them **mesons** (*mez*-ons), meaning "in-between" particles. Some of the new particles are heavier than protons, and so are called *hyperons*, or "over" par-

10-8. The linear accelerator is an atom smasher that produces high-speed atomic nuclei bullets that strike other target nuclei. (Lawrence Radiation Laboratory)

ticles. *Scientists believe that one type of meson is responsible for the tremendous forces that bind the protons and neutrons together in the nucleus.*

Of the many particles that are produced in nuclear reactions, one of the most interesting is the *neutrino.* Its existence was predicted in 1934 because something was needed to "balance the books" in certain nuclear equations. Some energy and momentum had to be accounted for. Hence, it was assumed that a neutral particle with practically no mass was escaping undetected. So elusive was the neutrino that its existence was not actually verified until 1955.

Many nuclear reactions give rise to neutrinos. For example, so many neutrinos reach the earth from nuclear reactions in the sun that millions pass

10-9. Thermonuclear reactions are studied with this modern particle accelerator or stellarator. (Project Matterhorn, James Forrestal Research Center, Princeton Univ.)

through our bodies every second. Neutrinos pass through the entire earth as easily as mosquitoes through chicken wire. Hence, we are always being bombarded by them, even at night when the entire earth is between us and the sun.

Neutron bullets. The neutron was discovered by Chadwick, a British scientist, in 1932. Neutrons occur tightly bound in atomic nuclei and can be freed only through nuclear bombardment. We cannot store up a supply of free neutrons. For one thing, they would pass through the walls of the container. Another reason is that the neutron is *unstable* when it is outside the atomic nucleus. Its average life

is only about 15 minutes, after which it disintegrates into a proton and an electron. Hence, scientists must produce neutrons when and where they want to use them. Here is one of the many nuclear reactions suitable for producing neutrons ($_0n^1$):

$$_4Be^9 \quad + \quad _2He^4 \quad \rightarrow$$
$$\text{\textit{beryllium} \quad \textit{alpha particle}}$$

$$_6C^{12} \quad + \quad _0n^1 \quad + \quad \text{energy}$$
$$\text{\textit{carbon-12} \quad \textit{neutron}}$$

The neutron makes a very good bullet for atom smashing. It has *no electric charge* and therefore is *not repelled* by the *positive charge* on the target nucleus. Instead, there is an attraction between the neutral neutron bullet and the positive nucleus when they are very close together. (See Fig. 10-10.)

Positively charged bullets such as protons can score hits only if they are traveling at high speeds. Otherwise they cannot overcome the repulsion of the positively charged nucleus. But even slow neutrons can enter target nuclei quite easily. (See Fig. 10-10.) When a neutron is absorbed by the nucleus of an atom, that atom becomes unstable, or radioactive. Such atoms make up what are called *radioisotopes* of the elements.

Beams of neutrons cannot be produced in the high-voltage particle accelerators. This is because neutrons, being electrically neutral, are not affected by electricity. Our principal source of strong beams of neutrons is the *nuclear reactor*, which will be discussed in the next section.

What are anti-particles? For every kind of nuclear particle there may exist a sort of "left-handed" twin, called an *anti-particle*. Many kinds of anti-particles have already been produced by

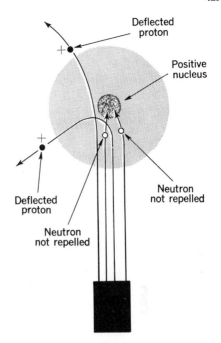

10-10. Neutrons make effective atomic bullets because they are not repelled by the positive nucleus of an atom.

nuclear bombardment. *When a particle meets its anti-particles, they are both destroyed* and, in their place, *an equivalent amount of energy appears.* (See Fig. 10-11.) *Anti-protons* are now

10-11. When a particle collides with its anti-particle, they both completely disintegrate into radiant energy.

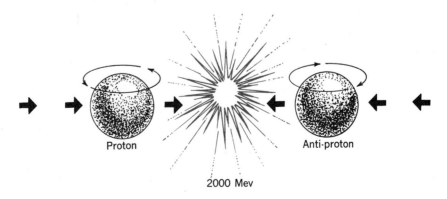

being produced in large quantities in our powerful synchrotrons. They are identical to protons except for having a negative charge instead of a positive charge.

The opposite, or anti-particle, of the electron is the *positron,* an electron with a positive instead of a negative charge. *When positrons meet electrons, they destroy one another to form gamma rays.*

Scientists now know that **anti-matter** can exist. Its atoms would have a *nucleus* made of anti-protrons and antineutrons, with positrons instead of ordinary electrons circling about it. If even a small amount of anti-matter should collide with the same amount of ordinary matter, it would all instantly convert into radiant energy, exploding like a super atom bomb. (See Fig. 10-12.)

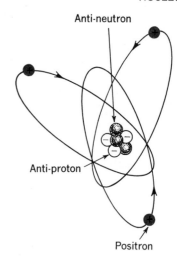

10-12. Anti-matter has a negative nucleus with positrons instead of electrons orbiting around it.

12. What electrical charge does an atomic nucleus have? Explain how it receives that charge.
13. Why is it impossible to accelerate neutrons in a high-voltage particle accelerator?

Quick Quiz

1. Who discovered radioactivity?
2. Name three elements that are naturally radioactive.
3. What is the final disintegration product of uranium?
4. What is meant by half-life?
5. Why do we give hydrogen the atomic mass of 1.008?
6. What is meant by the mass number of an element?
7. How does the nucleus of oxygen-16 differ from that of oxygen-17?
8. Why is it difficult to separate the isotopes of an element?
9. What is the nuclear structure of tritium?
10. Why are neutrons effective bullets for atom smashing?
11. Explain why an atom is electrically neutral.

B ATOMIC ENERGY

What is nuclear fission? By 1938, several scientists, including Enrico Fermi, Lise Meitner, Otto Hahn, and others were using *neutrons* to bombard different kinds of atomic nuclei. When they used *uranium* as the target, something completely unexpected happened. When the uranium nucleus captured a neutron, it became unstable and split apart, forming two smaller

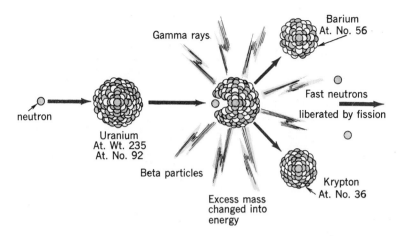

10-13. Neutrons produce fission of U-235 nuclei.

nuclei, a few free neutrons, and a great deal of energy. (See Fig. 10-13.)

Until then, radioactivity only produced slight changes in the nuclei of radioactive elements and released only traces of energy. But in this experiment the uranium nucleus actually split into two large fragments and a small number of speeding neutrons. In this process, great amounts of energy were released. This process is called *nuclear fission. Fission is the splitting of a heavy nucleus into two or more lighter nuclei.*

After fission occurs, the total mass of the pieces is less than that of the original uranium nucleus. The matter that disappears is changed into an equivalent amount of energy, in accordance with the Einstein energy-mass equation.

There were two reasons why the scientific world was excited by the discovery of fission. First, because of the large amounts of *energy* set free. The fission of a single nucleus of uranium liberated about 200 Mev of energy.

Second, because the fission process could lead to a *chain reaction.* That is, the neutrons set free by the fission of one uranium nucleus might, in turn, cause fission of neighboring nuclei of uranium. Thus, the reaction would spread and huge quantities of energy could be set free.

The separation of U-235. It was found that only the scarce uranium isotope, *U-235,* would undergo fission. Ordinary uranium consists of one part of *U-235* to 140 parts of *U-238.* A huge plant was built at Oak Ridge, Tennessee, to separate the isotopes. The Atomic Energy Commission of the United States is still operating this plant. (See Fig. 10-14.)

Uranium isotopes cannot be separated by chemical means. To separate them, a gaseous compound of uranium is first prepared. This gas is passed through acres of porous *barriers,* over and over again. The compound containing the lighter *U-235* passes through, or *diffuses,* more readily than the one containing the *U-238,* thus pro-

10-14. A gas diffusion plant at Oak Ridge, Tennessee. (USAEC, Wescott, Oak Ridge.)

ducing "enriched" *U-235*. The separation is completed by a magnetic device somewhat like a cyclotron.

What is "critical mass"? *U-235* will produce a chain reaction only when a sufficient quantity of it is brought together in one piece. *If the mass is too small, many of the neutrons that* *could produce fission escape without striking other nuclei.*

If, however, the block of *U-235* is sufficiently large, most of the neutrons set free by fission will strike other nuclei before they escape. The *minimum* mass of *U-235* necessary for an atomic explosion is called the **critical mass.**

10-15. The critical mass is assembled by shooting sub-critical masses at each other.

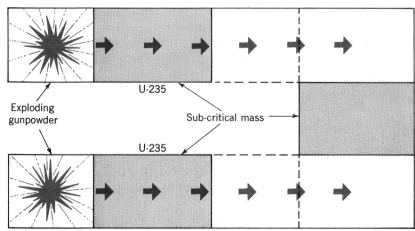

During storage, the fissionable material of an *atomic bomb* is kept in smaller parts, called *subcritical masses*. It is exploded by bringing these masses together very suddenly. (See Fig. 10-15.)

The first atomic bomb was exploded on July 16, 1945. The predictions of the scientists proved to be correct. The explosion produced a temperature of millions of degrees and a blinding glare brighter than the sun. The first atomic bombs were as powerful as 20 kilotons (20,000 tons) of TNT, a chemical explosive. Since then, both larger and smaller bombs have been produced.

What is a nuclear reactor? Most peacetime uses of nuclear energy require a slowed-down chain reaction. It must take place under complete control. Fermi and other scientists built a *nuclear reactor* for this purpose at the University of Chicago. On December 2, 1942, the first large-scale, controlled *nuclear reaction* was successfully accomplished there. (See Fig. 10-16.)

Only *slow neutrons* can produce a chain reaction in naturally-occurring uranium. The fast neutrons from the fission of *U-235* must be slowed down. Otherwise, most of them would escape or would be captured by the nonfissionable *U-238* nuclei. Too few of them would be available to hit other *U-235* nuclei and thus continue the fission chain reaction. The material used to slow down the neutrons is called the *moderator.*

Heavy water makes the best moderator. *Heavy water* is made from *deuterium*, rather than from ordinary hydrogen. *Graphite* and *ordinary water* are also good moderators. If graphite is used, small chunks of uranium are

10-16. The first nuclear reactor was built under the stands of an athletic field in Chicago. (US Dept. of Defense)

evenly distributed throughout it so that neutrons must pass through graphite before having a collision with a neighboring nucleus of uranium. (See Fig. 10-17.)

The first nuclear reactor was a large room-sized lattice made by piling up layers of graphite blocks and small "slugs" of ordinary uranium. Because of this construction, nuclear reactors were often called *atomic piles. Cadmium* and *boron steel* are good *absorbers* of neutrons. Hence, *rods* of these materials are used to *control* the reaction. When all of the control rods are inserted in the pile, the chain reaction stops. Most of the neutrons set free by the fission of *U-235* are absorbed by the control rods. Thus, the action of the pile may be slowed down or speeded up by moving the rods in or out. A very large lattice is needed for an atomic pile made with naturally-occurring uranium.

Many other types of nuclear reactors have been developed since the first one. Some use *enriched uranium*, containing a higher percent of *U-235* than is found in natural uranium.

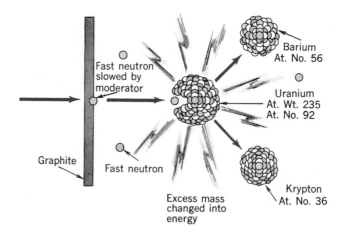

Fast neutron slowed by moderator

Graphite

Fast neutron

Barium
At. No. 56

Uranium
At. Wt. 235
At. No. 92

Krypton
At. No. 36

Excess mass
changed into
energy

10-17. As fast neutrons pass through the graphite moderator they are slowed down to the desired speed.

Some reactors use ordinary water as the moderator. In that case, the fissionable material may be immersed in a large tank of water called a "swimming pool." The water not only serves as the moderator but also as a *shield* to absorb dangerous radiations.

10-18. A 50-ton head is placed on the reactor vessel after a uranium core is placed inside. Twenty-five feet of water will then cover the reactor for added shielding. (General Electric Co.)

Reactors can also utilize a fissionable isotope of the element *thorium.* More often, they use a man-made element, *plutonium.*

Plutonium is also fissionable. It was discovered that if neutrons were slowed to a particular speed, many of them could be "captured" by the abundant U-238 isotope of natural uranium. If neutrons are going faster or slower than this *critical speed,* few of them are absorbed by the U-238 nuclei. The U-238 nucleus becomes the unstable or radioactive U-239 when it absorbs one of these slow neutrons. In two steps, as shown below, the U-239 changes into a new element, plutonium.

$$_{92}U^{238} + {}_{0}n^{1} \rightarrow {}_{92}U^{239}$$
$$_{92}U^{239} \rightarrow {}_{93}Np^{239} + {}_{-1}e^{0}$$
$$_{93}Np^{239} \rightarrow {}_{94}Pu^{239} + {}_{-1}e^{0}$$

This new element, plutonium, is even more fissionable than U-235. Because it is a different element, it can be separated from uranium by *chemical means.*

If a reactor contains the proper mixture of *U-238* and *U-235*, and if the neutrons are slowed to the critical speed, it may act as a "breeder" reactor. That is, it may produce more plutonium from *U-238* than the amount of *U-235* it uses as a fuel. By using breeder reactors, it is possible to convert most of our supply of natural uranium into fissionable material.

Uses for nuclear reactors. There are several basic uses for nuclear reactors. First, the tremendous amount of *heat* may be used as a source of *power*. Secondly, the *radiations* set free may be used to produce useful *radioisotopes*. Thirdly, the nuclear reactor is a very good source of *neutron beams,* which are used in nuclear *research.*

Several different types of nuclear reactors have been developed for power purposes. We shall discuss four of them:

1. The *boiling-water reactor.* In this system the water is heated to a temperature of up to 600° F, at pressures up to 1000 lbs per square inch. The steam resulting from the heated water is used to drive the turbine generator in a direct or "one loop" system as shown in Fig. 10-19. It can also be used in an indirect or "two loop" system as shown in Fig. 10-20.

2. The *pressurized-water reactor.* This is somewhat different from the boiling-water reactor although the temperature is about the same in each (600° F). With the pressure in this system increased to 2000 pounds per square inch, the water does not boil. The pressurized water offers a better means of transferring heat than does steam at the same temperature. The pressurized water does not drive the turbine generator directly, but heats water in a secondary loop which pro-

10-19. In a one-loop system, the liquid or gas heated by the core of the nuclear reactor is used to drive the turbine directly.

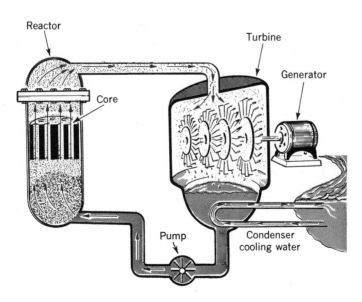

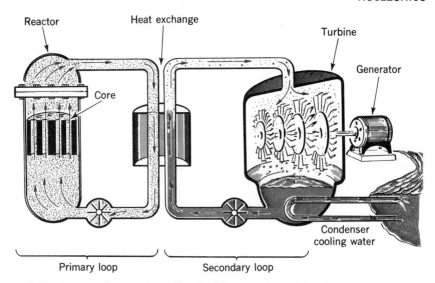

Reactor   Heat exchange   Turbine   Generator   Core   Condenser cooling water   Primary loop   Secondary loop

10-20. In a two-loop system, the liquid or gas heated by the core of the nuclear reactor is kept away from the turbine. Instead, it heats steam in a second loop. This system safeguards the power plant from radioactive contamination in case of accident.

duces the steam to drive the turbines. (See Fig. 10-20.)

3. The *high-temperature gas reactor. Helium* gas is circulated through the primary loop of this reactor. Helium is used because it can be heated to approximately 1400° F with a pressure build-up of only 300 pounds per square inch. Thus, very high temperatures are delivered to the secondary loop. In addition, helium virtually eliminates corrosion.

4. The *liquid-sodium reactor. Sodium,* when heated so that it becomes a liquid, is an excellent medium to transfer heat to the secondary loop because of its high heat conductivity. The use of sodium permits operating temperatures of about 1000° F, with pressures of only several pounds per square inch.

All these reactors are similar in that the atomic core generates the heat and the heat is then transferred by circulating either a gas or liquid through it.

Other uses of power reactors. Nuclear reactors can be used to power ships and large airplanes. The United States was the first nation to use atomic energy to power *submarines.* When an ordinary submarine is submerged, it cannot run on its diesel engines, for these quickly use up all the oxygen. Hence, electric motors powered by storage batteries are used when submerged. But the batteries soon run down, and the submarine has to surface and use diesel power to recharge them.

Since nuclear reactors do not use oxygen, a nuclear-powered submarine can remain submerged indefinitely. In early tests one of them cruised for over 2 months without surfacing. Our nuclear-powered subs have made extensive explorations under the ice of the Arctic Ocean. Every year or so, the fissionable material of the core must be replaced. Many of our old-fashioned submarines have been replaced by the newer and faster nuclear-powered type. Nuclear power is also being used to run surface ships.

Air-cooled nuclear reactors suitable for powering *aircraft* have been developed. Air is taken in at the nose of the plane and passes through the hot core of the reactor. It then shoots at high speed from the rear of the plane, just as does the hot gas from a regular jet plane.

Nuclear reactors produce dangerous radiations. The practical use of atomic energy to power passenger airplanes and rockets in the immediate future is still uncertain. The dangerous radiations set free by nuclear reactors are an ever-present problem. Thick, heavy *shielding* must be used to protect the passengers and operators. This cuts down on the useful payload.

10-21. A typical atomic power plant can be identified by its large dome-like structure which houses the reactor. (Atomics International)

Reactors must be surrounded by concrete, or immersed in water, or buried underground. For example, a power reactor near New York City has its core inside a vessel whose steel walls are seven inches thick. This is immersed in a water-filled steel tank, surrounded by a thick concrete wall. The whole unit is enclosed in a steel sphere, 160 feet in diameter. Another concrete shield surrounds this steel sphere. (See Fig. 10-21.)

We have sufficient experience with the operation of reactors to know they can be safely used even in populated areas. Safeguards are set up so that the chain reaction cannot get out of control and become explosive. Operating personnel and the surrounding communities are protected from excessive radiation by proper shielding and other operational safeguards.

Radioactive contamination. As more reactors are built and more nuclear energy is used, one serious problem demands more attention. Periodically, the radioactive uranium, plutonium, or thorium of the reactor core must be replaced. The spent or used-up core material is violently radioactive, giving off deadly radiations for years. The safe and cheap disposal of this material is an unsolved problem. The problem is to avoid widespread pollution of our planet with *radioactive wastes.* (See Fig. 10-22.)

Most of the waste is now stored in containers in caves and abandoned mines. Some containers are sunk in the sea. Since certain plants and animals, both on land and in the sea, tend to concentrate radioactive material in their bodies, we must use great care to prevent the contamination of our food supplies. (See Fig. 10-23.)

10-22. S.N.A.P. (System for Nuclear Auxiliary Power) generator uses heat produced by pellets made from radioactive wastes to supply continuous electric power for satellite instruments. (Aerojet-General Corp.)

Another source of dangerous nuclear radiations is in the testing of nuclear explosives. Unless such tests are carried out deep underground or far out in space, so-called *fall-out radiation* contaminates the atmosphere as well as food and water supplies. While the amount of the fall-out is at present very small, it is known that such radiations have harmful effects. Hence, we owe it to future generations to keep radioactive contamination of the earth's atmosphere as low as possible.

Atomic energy from nuclear fusion. Scientists have for some time known of another way of obtaining atomic energy. Instead of splitting large nuclei (fission), it is possible to make lighter nuclei combine to form heavier

ones. This process is called *fusion.* An outstanding example is the fusion of four hydrogen nuclei to form one helium nucleus. For billions of years, the energy of the sun has been generated by this process.

The single helium nucleus has *less* mass than the total mass of the four hydrogen nuclei. This difference in mass is converted into an equivalent amount of energy. (See Fig. 10-24.)

$$4_1\text{H}^1 \rightarrow {}_2\text{He}^4 + 2_{+1}\text{e}^0 + \text{energy}$$
(*4 hydrogen* (*1 helium* (*2 positrons*)
nuclei)   *nucleus*)

The *original mass* (4 hydrogen nuclei) consists of 4.0320 *mass units* (4 × 1.0080). The *final mass* (1 helium nucleus and 2 positrons) consists of 4.0037 *mass units* (4.0026 + 0.0011). As you can see, there is a *loss* of 0.0283 *mass unit* (4.0320 − 4.0037). The difference between the combined mass of its component parts and that of the final atomic nucleus is called the *mass defect*.

As 1 mass unit equals 931 Mev of energy, the energy liberated per helium nucleus is

$$0.0283 \text{ mass unit} \times 931 \, \frac{\text{Mev}}{\text{mass unit}}$$
$$= 26.3 \text{ Mev}$$

This is about 10 times as much energy as is set free by the *fission* of an equal mass of uranium.

All of the various ways of causing hydrogen nuclei to fuse into helium require temperatures in the millions of degrees. For this reason, they are known as *thermonuclear reactions.* At high temperatures and high densities the reactions go at explosive speed,

10-23. Radioactive wastes are buried deep in the ground (left) or encased in concrete for burial at sea. (Left: Oak Ridge National Laboratory; Right: Brookhaven National Laboratory)

10-24. When four hydrogen nuclei fuse to form one helium nucleus, some mass disappears. Add the four hydrogen weights and compare with the weights of one helium atom.

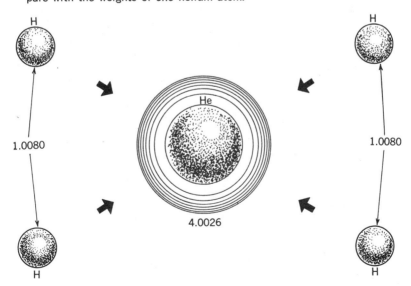

producing the *hydrogen bomb,* or *H-bomb.*

The hydrogen bomb is a product of fusion. One way of producing the H-bomb explosion is to subject a compound of lithium and heavy hydrogen (lithium hydride, $_3Li^6{}_1H^2$) to a very high temperature. The reaction is

$$_3Li^6{}_1H^2 \rightarrow 2\ _2He^4 + energy$$

(Note that this is practically the same as the first nuclear reaction produced in an atom smasher. See page 425.)

Unlike the atom bomb, whose size is limited by the *critical mass* of the fissionable material, the hydrogen bomb can be made as large and powerful as desired. The first ones that were detonated had the explosive force of many megatons (millions of tons) of TNT. In addition to the blast effect, the hydrogen bombs produce deadly radiations over an area of many hundreds of square miles.

A probable structure of an H-bomb is as follows. At the center is an ordinary fission bomb made of *U-235* or plutonium. It acts as a *fuse* to produce the very high temperature needed to start the thermonuclear, or fusion, reaction in the lithium hydride. The outside of the bomb could be a shell made of ordinary uranium metal. Earlier, we stated that ordinary uranium would not produce a chain reaction. However, under the influence of the extremely high temperatures produced by the H-bomb, individual fissions of the *U-238* nuclei occur, adding more energy to the explosion. This type of H-bomb is referred to as the fission-fusion-fission or triple-F bomb. (See Fig. 10-25.)

All mankind hopes that the world will be spared from devastation by H-bombs, and that instead we can learn how to harness the fusion process for useful power. Intensive research concerning this problem is beginning to look promising.

With the control of thermonuclear reactions, mankind will be in possession of unlimited supplies of energy. The oceans of the world can furnish all the heavy hydrogen needed for this purpose.

How are nuclear reactions studied? The particles and radiations involved in a nuclear reaction are far too tiny

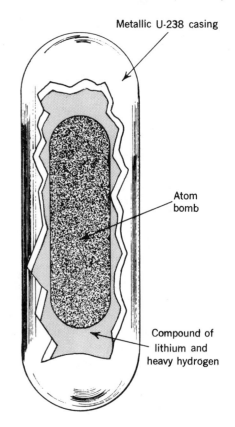

Metallic U-238 casing

Atom bomb

Compound of lithium and heavy hydrogen

10-25. An F–F–F hydrogen bomb may possibly be constructed in this manner.

to see directly. However, they do disturb electrons of the molecules of matter through which they pass. This permits the scientists to *track* them. The three effects of the nuclear particles and radiations listed below help scientists study their behavior.

1. They *ionize* molecules of gases and liquids.

2. They cause certain substances to *fluoresce*.

3. They affect *photographic films*.

The simplest device that makes use of the ionizing effect is the *electroscope*. When certain radiations pass through the air, they ionize it; that is, they knock electrons from the gas molecules of the air. The air then becomes electrically conductive. Hence, a charged electroscope is gradually discharged when exposed to ionized air. The *rate of discharge* indicates the strength of the radiations.

One kind of electroscope is used as a *dosimeter* (doe-*sim*-ih-ter), or "dose" meter, that is worn by workers in nuclear laboratories and industries. It is read daily to check each person's exposure to radiation. A careful record is kept so that the accumulated dose of radiation is kept within safe limits. (See Fig. 10-26.)

What is a Geiger counter? A more complicated device that also utilizes the ionization of gases is the well-known **Geiger counter.** This contains a thin-walled cylindrical metal tube with a fine wire running down its central axis, as shown in Fig. 10-27. The wire is insulated from the wall of the tube, and a voltage is maintained between the wire and the wall. The resistance of low pressure gas in the tube prevents a current from flowing until some ionizing radiation passes

10-26. The atomic scientist wears a pocket dosimeter and a sensitive film badge on his person to indicate radiation dosages he has been exposed to during his experimentation. (Brookhaven National Laboratory)

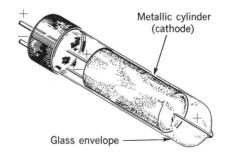

Metallic cylinder (cathode)

Glass envelope

10-27. The basic components of a Geiger tube.

through. This might be gamma or beta radiation from radioactive material or from cosmic rays. The small pulse of current that then flows is amplified, causing the instrument to click, or a light to glow. Specially designed electronic counters keep track of the number of radiations per second that pass through the tube.

A tiny Geiger counter, no bigger than a pencil, is made with miniature transistors. Worn by radiation workers, its flashing light warns of danger from overexposure.

Cloud chambers and bubble chambers detect radiation. When ionizing radiations pass through a gas that is supersaturated with a vapor, the atomic particles condense the vapor to form cloud-like streaks that show the paths taken by the rays. This is what happens in the **Wilson cloud chamber.** (See Fig. 10-28.) These cloud-chamber streaks are much like the large *vapor trails* often made by high-flying aircraft.

By surrounding the cloud chamber with a powerful magnet, the tracks can be made to curve. The scientist who is examining the tracks can then tell what kind of particles made the tracks, their electric charge, and their speed or energy.

A more recent improvement on this method is the **bubble chamber** developed by Dr. Donald Glaser, 1960 Nobel Prize winner, while at the University of Michigan. The bubble chamber is filled with a liquid that is just above its boiling point. However, the liquid cannot boil because it is kept under pressure. When the pressure is released quickly, the liquid is ready to boil. When an ionizing particle or radiation passes through it, a trail of tiny bub-

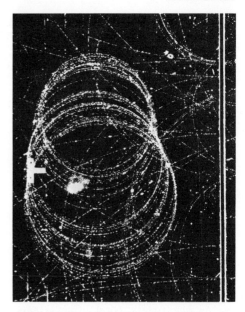

10-28. Positrons accelerated at 42 Mev produced these cloud-chamber tracks. (Lawrence Radiation Laboratory)

bles is formed. This makes a visible streak similar to the vapor trails.

Although it is very dangerous to handle, *liquid hydrogen* makes the best liquid for bubble chambers. When liquid hydrogen is used, there is only one simple kind of nucleus, that of hydrogen, for the particles to collide with. This makes it easier to interpret the results.

The bubble chamber is the best device currently available for studying nuclear changes.

The scintillation counter. High-energy radiations and particles cause certain chemicals to *fluoresce* or glow when they are struck. This flash of light, or *scintillation,* is picked up by a phototube, and electronically recorded. The **scintillation counter** is somewhat like the luminous dial of a watch face. If you examine such a dial with a magnifying glass in the dark, you can see the scintillations or sparkles of light.

Detection by photography. Radioactivity was first detected by Becquerel through the use of photography. Packs of special-emulsion *films* are now used to trace the effect of nuclear radiations. The film-packs may be exposed in high-altitude balloons or in rockets. When they are developed and studied, they provide a great deal of information about the nuclear reactions that occur in the laboratory or in outer space.

Nuclear workers often wear *film badges.* These are small pieces of photographic film shielded from ordinary light. Upon development, they reveal the amount of dangerous radiation to which the worker has been exposed while working with radioisotopes.

10-29. This radioautograph was made after the plant had absorbed a specific radioactive isotope that was added to the soil. With this technique, scientists can determine where certain elements are used and stored in the growing plant. (Brookhaven National Laboratory)

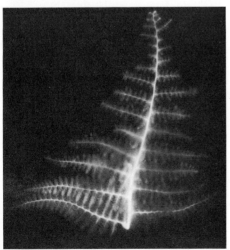

Radioisotopes. Scientists have now produced *radioisotopes* of all the elements by nuclear bombardment with *neutrons.* Moreover, new radioactive elements have been synthetically created with atomic numbers from 93 to 104.

Artificially created radioisotopes have become of great importance in modern life. By using these radioisotopes, scientists are learning the laws of nuclear structure. Other scientists use radioisotopes as "tagged atoms," or *tracers.* The chemist can easily follow their course, and can thus learn what is happening in complicated reactions. Tagged atoms act as important tracers in other fields also, such as in biological and medical research. (See Fig. 10-29.)

Radioisotopes are also used in the direct treatment of bodily ills. *Radioactive iodine* is used in the treatment of cancer of the thyroid gland. *Radiophosphorus* is used to treat certain types of bone cancer. There are many other applications of radioisotopes in medical practice. (See Fig. 10-31.)

When a neutron enters the nucleus of an atom of ordinary cobalt (atomic mass 59), it forms a radioisotope, *cobalt-60,* which is extremely radioactive. Its powerful gamma rays are used not only for medical treatments but also in industry, as a substitute for X rays, to test large metal castings for *flaws.*

Other uses of radioisotopes. Radioisotopes have been used for other specialized uses. For example, electric batteries operated by radioisotopes have been developed. The United States produces great quantities of radioisotopes, mostly at Oak Ridge, Tennessee. They are available to scientists all over the world. Your school can ob-

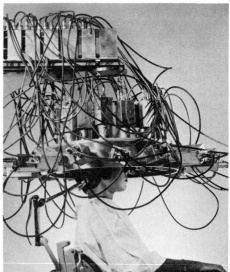

10-30. Mechanical hands or remote control manipulators are essential for handling highly radioactive materials. (Brookhaven National Laboratory)

10-31. A complicated device for locating brain tumors by means of positron emitters. (Brookhaven National Laboratory)

tain some of these materials for science experiments, provided that certain safety rules are followed.

In industries where large quantities of "hot" radioisotopes are handled, elaborate equipment for remote control must be installed. This may include very ingenious *mechanical hands.* As a result, the operator merely activates some mechanical or electrical controls, and never comes in direct contact with the radioactive materials.

Quick Quiz

1. What causes nuclear fission?
2. Why is it difficult to separate U-235 from U-238?
3. What is meant by a critical mass of U-235?
4. Name three fissionable elements.
5. What is the purpose of the moderator in the nuclear reactor? What

three substances are widely used as moderators?
6. Explain the use of control bars in nuclear reactors.
7. What is a breeder pile used for? Explain its action.
8. What is the purpose of the cloud chamber and the bubble chamber? How do they operate?
9. On what principle does the scintillation counter operate? To what everyday device can its action be compared?
10. How are radioisotopes prepared?
11. Explain the expression "Fission-Fusion-Fission" as applied to the thermonuclear bomb.
12. Why is the disposal of radioactive wastes an important problem?
13. What are the major advantages of a liquid sodium nuclear reactor over the pressurized water reactor?
14. What causes the current to flow between the cylindrical wall of a Geiger tube and the fine wire in its center?

SUMMARY

Radioactivity occurs when the nucleus of an atom disintegrates. Radioactive elements emit alpha particles or helium nuclei; beta rays or high-speed electrons; and gamma rays, high-frequency electromagnetic radiations. The half-life of a radioactive element is the time required for half of its nuclei to disintegrate.

In 1919, Rutherford produced the first nuclear reaction by causing alpha particles to hit nitrogen nuclei. We now use particle accelerators to speed up charged particles and shoot them at target nuclei to produce nuclear changes. There are several kinds of atom smashers, such as the linear accelerator, the cyclotron, and the synchrotron.

Forms of an element whose atoms are alike in all respects except in the number of neutrons in their nuclei are called isotopes. Radioactive isotopes are produced by bombarding nuclei of elements with neutron beams.

Einstein's equation, $E = mc^2$, tells us that when matter disappears in a nuclear reaction, energy appears. The source of atomic energy is this change of matter into energy.

When a critical mass of U-235 is brought together, a violent chain reaction occurs. Neutrons set free by the fission of one nucleus strike and split neighboring nuclei. This uncontrolled chain reaction was the basis of the early atom bombs.

Nuclear reactors control the fission process. The reactor contains a core of fissionable material, a moderator to slow down the neutrons, and control rods to adjust the reaction rate by absorbing excess neutrons. Nuclear reactors produce heat for power, beams of neutrons, and radioisotopes. Breeder reactors can convert ordinary U-238 into a new fissionable element, plutonium.

By the action of extremely high temperatures and pressures, hydrogen nuclei are fused into helium nuclei. This process is called a thermonuclear reaction, or fusion. An uncontrolled thermonuclear reaction takes place in the explosion of a hydrogen bomb.

Nuclear particles and radiations are detected by various devices including the electroscope, Geiger counter, cloud chamber, bubble chamber, scintillation counter, and photographic film.

CHAPTER REVIEW

Vocabulary

Match the words in Column A with the best response in Column B. Do not write in your book.

Column A	Column B
1. mass number	a. agent used to slow down neutrons in a controlled atomic chain reaction
2. radioactivity	
3. alpha particles	b. anti-particle of the electron

  4. beta rays
  5. gamma rays
  6. half-life
  7. isotope
  8. deuterium
  9. tritium
 10. electron volt (ev)
 11. cyclotron
 12. positron
 13. nuclear fission
 14. chain reaction
 15. critical mass
 16. nuclear reactor
 17. moderator
 18. nuclear fusion
 19. Geiger counter
 20. tracer

c. atomic mass of an element expressed to the nearest whole number
d. combining light atomic nuclei to form heavy ones
e. device for accelerating charged particles
f. device in which energy is produced by controlled nuclear reactions
g. electronic device used to detect ionizing radiations
h. form of an element whose nucleus differs in the number of neutrons
i. hydrogen atom with a neutron in its nucleus
j. hydrogen atom with two neutrons in the nucleus
k. high-speed electrons given off by radioactive elements
l. nuclear reaction that is self-perpetuating
m. positively charged helium nuclei
n. radioactive atoms used in research
o. smallest amount of fissionable material that will sustain a chain reaction
p. splitting of an atomic nucleus
q. spontaneous disintegration occurring in the nucleus of certain atoms
r. time required for 50 percent of the atoms of a sample of a radioactive element to disintegrate
s. unit of energy equal to that acquired by an electron in "falling" through an electrical field of 1 volt
t. very penetrating X rays

Questions: Group A

1. Name and describe three kinds of rays given off by radioactive elements.
2. What is the source of radioactivity?
3. What is the half-life of radium?
4. List three major uses of nuclear energy.
5. What is the common name for deuterium? What is the structure of its nucleus?
6. What happens when a nuclear particle meets its anti-particle?
7. What is the neutrino? Why was it so difficult to detect?
8. What is meant by Mev?
9. What is a power reactor?
10. Give an advantage and a disadvantage of using a nuclear reactor to drive a spaceship.
11. Give an example of nuclear fission.
12. What are dosimeters and film badges used for?

Questions: Group B

1. Why is nuclear physics a relatively "new" science?
2. Compare the amounts of energy obtainable from nuclear reactions and from chemical reactions.
3. Write the equation for the first nuclear reaction and explain its meaning.
4. Explain what is meant by the atomic weights of the elements.
5. Explain the meaning of all the numbers in the following equation:

$$_1H^1 + {}_3Li^7 \rightarrow {}_2He^4 + {}_2He^4 + energy$$

6. What was the source of the "bullets" for the first nuclear reaction?
7. How does a cyclotron differ from a linear accelerator?
8. How are radioisotopes produced?
9. State and explain Einstein's equation of mass-energy equivalence.
10. Explain how the fission of U-235 produces a chain reaction.
11. What is the source of the energy obtained from nuclear reactions?
12. Describe how plutonium is made.
13. Discuss the advantages of nuclear-powered submarines.
14. What is the amount of energy produced when four hydrogen nuclei fuse to form one nucleus of helium?
15. What is meant by a thermonuclear reaction?
16. Discuss some uses of radioisotopes.
17. List three effects by which nuclear particles and radiations may be detected.

Problems

1. How long would it take for one gram of radium to decay so that only ⅛th of the material is still radium? (Use 1600 years as the half-life of radium.)
2. How much barium-139 would remain in a 16-oz sample after a decay period of 7 hrs, 10 min? (Half-life of barium-139 is 86 minutes.)
3. Fill in the missing spaces in the chart below, just as has been done for phosphorus. (Use a separate sheet of paper for this exercise.)

Atom	Protons	Neutrons	Electrons	Atomic number	Mass number
Phosphorus	15	16	15	15	31
Hydrogen	1	—	—	—	1
Deuterium	1	—	—	—	2
Tritium	1	2	—	—	—
Helium	—	2	—	—	4
Carbon	—	6	—	—	12
Oxygen	—	—	—	8	16
Uranium	—	—	92	—	238

EARTH AND SPACE SCIENCE

11 GEOLOGY:
THE HISTORY AND STRUCTURE
OF THE EARTH

A
THE STRUCTURE
OF THE EARTH

Origin of the earth. To understand the structure of the earth, we should discuss how it was formed. According to one theory, the earth and other planets cooled and condensed from an enormous spinning cloud of gas and tiny particles of matter.

The crust of the earth is formed from relatively lightweight material floating on top of a denser and hotter inner mass. Some of the rocks in the crust are lighter than others and consequently were pushed up toward the surface. We know that today the rock under the ocean floor is mostly *basalt,* a denser and heavier rock than the *granite* bedrock that makes up most of our continents. All of these observed facts lead to the above theory.

As the planet continued to cool off, gases and moisture from the earth's interior escaped to form the *atmosphere.* The moisture cooled and fell as rain, and finally collected in the lower portions of the earth's surface. Thus, the lakes and oceans of the earth were gradually formed.

According to this theory, the gradual cooling and condensing process took millions of years. During that time, more water vapor was escaping from deep in the earth's crust, only to fall back into the oceans as rain.

The three main divisions of the earth. We have subdivided our planet into three main divisions: the *atmosphere,* the *hydrosphere,* and the *lithosphere* (*lith*-uh-sfeer). You will learn about the atmosphere when you study meteorology and the gases of the air in the next chapter. The earth areas that are covered with *water* make up the **hydrosphere.** We shall continue our study of the waters of the earth in Chapter 13, *Oceanography.* In geology, however, we are concerned mainly with the **lithosphere,** or the solid part of the earth.

What are the geological eras? Many changes have taken place in the earth's crust since it was first formed. These changes required billions of years to accomplish. As the mountains rose, seas developed where the land fell. Also, great sheets of lava or volcanic ash spread over half a continent and ice sheets covered large areas and then receded, only to form again.

After each such change and upheaval, new kinds of plants and animals flourished. We know this from the fact that certain distinct types of *fossils* are found in each layer of the earth's crust.

The following table lists the six main geological eras. Scientific names ending in *"zoic"* identify the eras that marked these geological changes. In addition to these eras, there are many subdivisions, called periods or epochs.

How old is the earth? The gradual but continuing change of the structure and life on the earth gives us some means of determining the planet's age.

Starting with evidences of early forms of life called *fossils*, which are remains of once-living things, scientists can work backward toward early periods of the earth's history. (See Fig. 11-1.) Geological evidence suggests that the earth is approximately four and a half billion years old and has existed with its present rocky crust for more than three billion years. Methods used in estimating the age of the earth are complicated, and theories pertaining to its age are subject to constant revision.

Radioactive minerals from the earth furnish the best clues to help geologists estimate the age of the earth. Atoms of uranium become *radium* through a natural release of energy. Radium continues to *decompose*, eventually becoming the stable element *lead*. Scientists have determined how long it requires for these changes to occur. Thus, they can estimate the age of the earth from the composition and rate of "decay" of uranium ores.

One method used to obtain a record of man's early history is through the decay of carbon-14, a radioactive isotope of carbon. All living matter ob-

TABLE OF GEOLOGICAL ERAS

Era	Events	Era began about
Cenozoic (modern life)	The age of mammals; the rise of man	60 million years ago
Mesozoic (middle life)	The age of reptiles; fishes; dinosaurs	200 million years ago
Paleozoic (ancient life)	Carboniferous period; coal and oil formations; amphibians	500 million years ago
Proterozoic (primitive life)	One-celled plants and animals	1 billion years ago
Archeozoic (earliest life)	Great mountain building; traces of life	2 billion years ago
Azoic (no life)	Continents and oceans formed	4.5 billion years ago

tinents is the **continental shelf,** which is covered with relatively shallow water. (See Fig. 11-3.)

What is the earth's crust like? As you have traveled over the earth's surface, you have become familiar with some parts of its crust. The upper surface of the lithosphere in most places is a layer of loose material composed of soil, sand, loose rock, large boulders, gravel, and clay. You have seen the thin layer of *topsoil* upon which our crops are raised and the thicker *subsoil* underneath. The subsoil contains little or no organic matter and is not fertile. It often contains pebbles and rocks that have broken away from the underlying *bedrock*. In some places, the soil layer is hundreds of feet thick. In other places, it has all been swept away, and you can see an *outcropping* of bedrock. (See Fig. 11-4.) Mountain peaks and their projecting ledges are good examples of these outcroppings.

The crust of the earth is comparatively light in weight when compared to the dense inner parts of the earth. The crust "floats" on the surface and varies in thickness from about 6 miles

11-1. The fossil imprint of this extinct aquatic organism was formed in sedimentary rock. (Smithsonian Institution)

tains carbon-14 from the air by photosynthesis. This process stops when the living matter dies. The *decay* of carbon-14 continues, however, and since its half-life is 5800 years, the approximate age of the material can be determined by comparing the degree of decay of this material with living samples. Carbon-14 dating was developed by Dr. Willard F. Libby, who was awarded the Nobel Prize in chemistry for this work. Carbon-14 is useful for making reliable age determinations only as far back as about 20,000 years. (See Fig. 11-2.)

The lithosphere. The lithosphere is a round ball slightly flattened at the poles, and nearly 8000 miles in diameter. A little more than three-quarters of its surface is covered with water. The low parts form the **ocean floor.** The raised parts form the **continents.** Between the ocean floor and the con-

11-2. The age of this fossil skull of a primitive man was determined by carbon-14 dating. (R. Solecki)

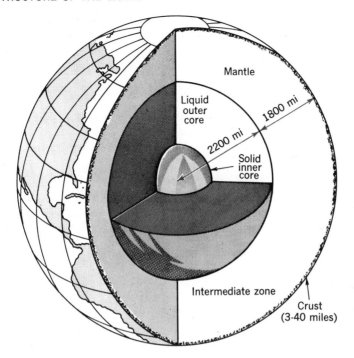

Mantle

Liquid outer core

1800 mi

2200 mi

Solid inner core

Intermediate zone

Crust (3-40 miles)

11-3. The interior of the earth.

to over 30 miles. The greatest thicknesses are below continental land masses while the thinnest parts are located below the ocean floor.

The deeper we go into the crust of the earth the hotter it becomes. Some oil wells have been drilled about 5 miles into the earth's crust, and at the bottom of these wells the temperature is about 400° F. On an average, for every 60 feet in depth, the temperature increases 1° F. For this reason, the depth of mines very seldom exceeds 6500 feet.

Probing the Moho. In 1909, a Yugoslav scientist, Andrija Mohorovicic, after studying the effects of earthquake waves, discovered that there is a "break," or *sharp boundary, between the earth's crust and the mantle.* This break is. known to geologists as the *Mohorovicic Discontinuity,* or **Moho.**

Recently, the National Academy of Sciences has undertaken a project to drill through the crust to the Moho in order to provide the first direct sampling of the mantle. This project is called the *Mohole.* Since the crust is thinnest below the ocean floor, the drilling is conducted there. (See Fig. 11-5.)

The problems of such an undertaking are many and severe. First of all, the drilling platform on the surface of the ocean is constantly affected by the up and down motion of the waves. Secondly, the platform must constantly be powered to keep the ocean currents from drifting it away. These two actions can cause the drill stem to bend, disengage, or break completely. Finally, the length of the drill stem is so great that its own weight places great stresses on the entire system.

The mantle. Below the crust of the earth is a deep layer of material about 1800 miles thick called the *mantle.* It is believed to be composed mostly of oxides and sulfides of magnesium, iron, and silicon. It is under extreme pressure and temperature, and is of a slightly plastic composition.

The core. The central *core* of the earth has a radius of approximately 2200 miles, or about the size of the planet Mars. It is under tremendous pressure and is extremely hot. This core, which probably is composed largely of nickel and iron, is believed to contain a *solid inner* core and a *molten* or *plastic outer core.*

The heat is caused by pressure estimated to be as high as 7500 tons per square inch. The pressure is caused by the forces of gravity, or in other words, the weight of the earth pressing toward its center. Heat is also produced in the earth's interior by radioactivity.

How do we know what it is like inside the earth? Scientists learn about conditions inside the earth by studying waves from earthquakes and from seismic explosions in the crust. Waves travel at different speeds through various materials. By observing what happens to these waves as they travel through the earth's interior, scientists can learn much about the materials through which they have passed.

We also get important evidence by studying the kinds of molten rocks or lavas that come from the upper mantle and pour through cracks in the earth's crust. In the laboratory, scientists apply heat and pressure to various rock specimens. They find that at certain definite pressures and temperatures these rocks change sharply into new forms, much denser than before. Thus, they have a possible explanation of the existence of a crust and a mantle. The Moho separation occurs where the pressure and temperature are just right to change the rocks to the new, denser forms.

You can see why there is so much interest in the Mohole project. It

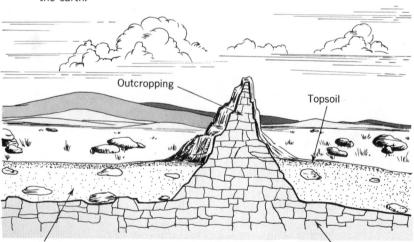

11-4. Subsoil and loose rock cover the bedrock in most parts of the earth.

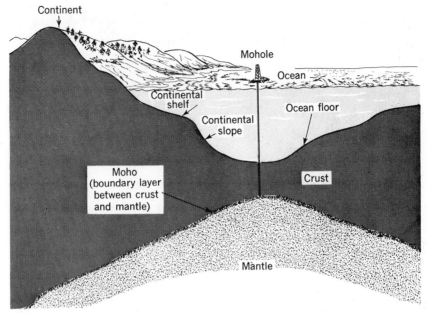

11-5. Project Mohole is designed to pierce the earth's thin crust under the ocean.

may help us to check our theories and to revise them when necessary. Thus, we expect to obtain a better "model" of the earth's interior.

What are rocks and minerals? *Rocks* are fairly large units of the earth's crust that can be of organic or inorganic origin. They include consolidated or random solid matter composed usually of two or more minerals. Rocks can also include organic matter such as coal. *Minerals are specific elements or combinations of elements that are entirely of inorganic composition.*

Rocks are divided into three classes. Any kind of rock belongs to one of the three general classes: (1) *igneous* (*ig*-nee-us); (2) *sedimentary* (sed-ih-*men*-tuh-ree); or (3) *metamorphic* (met-uh-*mor*-fik). *Igneous* rocks

come from *molten mixtures of minerals* that have been solidified. *Sedimentary* rocks are those formed from *mineral sediments* like sand and clay. The minerals have been moved by running water, wind, or ice from one place to another. Sedimentary rocks usually form in layers or *strata*.

Metamorphic means "changed in form." *Metamorphic* rocks were *originally igneous and sedimentary rocks* that were *acted upon by heat and pressure* deep below the earth's surface. These changes usually bring about a new crystalline structure. Sometimes these changes are so complete that it is not always possible to determine what the original rock was.

Common igneous rocks. Pressure deep within the lithosphere can force liquid rock through cracks toward the

11-6. Granite (left) is a tough igneous rock with visible crystals in it. Obsidian (right) is a glassy igneous rock. (Smithsonian Institution)

surface. Cooling changes this molten material into solid igneous rock. Igneous rocks are glassy and unstratified.

When the cooling occurs *slowly*, coarse crystals of different minerals are scattered throughout the mass. *Granite* is an example that shows this coarse, crystalline structure. We can identify granite by its speckled appearance. (See Fig. 11-6.) It is usually very easy to see particles or crystals of *quartz, feldspar,* and *mica* in a sample of granite.

Granite is hard and tough and is the chief rock of the great land masses of the earth. It is usually white or gray, but sometimes it is pink. You are familiar with granite as the stone used for making beautiful monuments and public buildings.

Another igneous rock is basalt. Here the cooling has taken place more *rapidly.* Basalt in the earth's crust often reaches the surface as molten lava. Basalt is the general term for a fine-grained, dark-colored igneous rock that occurs in many forms. One variety,

called *traprock,* is widely used for road building. Basalt is denser than granite, and we believe it to be the chief rock found under the ocean floor and under the granite of the continents.

Once the lava reaches the surface, it may cool rapidly and solidify as a kind of *volcanic glass* called *obsidian* (ob-*sid*-ee-un), which contains no crystals at all. Obsidian is very hard and brittle. Because of the sharpness of its edges, this rock was used by primitive peoples for making hatchets, arrowheads, knives, and other sharp implements.

If steam and other gases bubble through the lava as it comes from a volcano and solidifies, *pumice* (*pum-*iss) is formed. Pumice is a light, porous, sponge-like rock that can float on water and may be washed ashore far from the volcano from which it comes.

Sedimentary rocks are formed from deposited materials. Running water has the capability of carrying away particles of matter. Rocks, chips, sand, and other loose materials are ground finer and finer as the pieces rub over one another in a stream of water. Finally they drop to the bottom as layers of fine mud or clay. These deposits form *sedimentary* rocks. Sedimentary rocks are somewhat dull in appearance, with no regular crystalline form.

Limestone, sandstone, and shale are sedimentary rocks. Perhaps the most interesting of the sedimentary rocks is *limestone*. It is formed from the shells and skeletons of countless tiny water plants and animals. Sometimes you can see an outline of these fossil remains, like "fingerprints" in the rock. Shells and skeletons are sometimes dissolved by water containing carbon dioxide. Later the calcium carbonate of the material is re-deposited in a new location as limestone.

Another common sedimentary rock is *sandstone*. It is formed by grains of sand becoming cemented together over a long period of time. Oxides of iron frequently color this rock red.

A third kind of sedimentary rock is *shale*. It is formed from deposits of very fine sediment such as clay or silt. Its color is usually gray, but sometimes is black or dull red.

How are metamorphic rocks formed? *Metamorphic* rocks are those that have been changed by adjustments in the earth's crust. Pressure and heat inside the lithosphere are so great that in many places entire layers of rocks are bent and folded. (See Fig. 11-8.)

Folding of the earth's crust causes some layers of rock to be squeezed and

11-7. These layers of sedimentary rock were formed under water. (Union Pacific Railroad)

11-8. Heat and pressure produced these rock folds. (Standard Oil Co., (NJ))

made denser. The increase in pressure changes some sandstone to *quartzite. Limestone* can be changed to *marble; shale* to *slate;* and *bituminous* coal to *anthracite.* These are four examples of metamorphic rocks.

How can minerals be identified? Minerals vary greatly in abundance. Some, like quartz and feldspar, are found in such quantity that they are "dirt cheap." Others, like rubies, emeralds, and diamonds, are so rare that they are called *precious stones.* To identify a mineral, the geologist studies its physical properties such as color, luster, and hardness. He may also study its crystalline form, determine its specific gravity, and apply the *hardness test.*

The *standard hardness test* provides a rough indication that is useful in mineral identification. It is based on a scale of ten minerals: (1) *talc,* (2) *gypsum,* (3) *calcite,* (4) *fluorite,* (5) *apatite,* (6) *feldspar,* (7) *quartz,* (8) *topaz,* (9) *corundum,* and (10) *diamond.* These minerals are arranged in order of *increasing hardness.* A min-

eral is said to be harder than another if it will scratch the other. Diamond is the hardest because it will scratch any other mineral against which it is rubbed. We see that talc is the softest because all other minerals can scratch a sample of it.

You can compare this scale with a few well known materials. Your fingernails, for example, have a hardness of about 2 or 2.5. Thus, you should be able to scratch talc easily with your fingernails, and probably gypsum also, but with some difficulty. A penny has a hardness of about 3.5, a good quality carving knife about 5.5 and ordinary glass about 6.

Most minerals are crystals. The crystalline shapes of many minerals make up some of the wonders of nature. We have learned that crystals have a regular shape, with straight edges and flat surfaces or faces. Their outer shapes depend upon their inner structure. That is, they depend upon the regular order in which their atoms are arranged.

Some minerals crystallize in the form of *cubes.* Others form crystals that are like pyramids with their bases together. Six-sided crystals are common in specimens of quartz, as shown in Fig. 11-9.

Many of the naturally-occurring minerals can be readily identified by studying the shape of the crystals that they form. Several natural crystals, such as the diamond and amethyst, are valuable as gems, while other types of crystals are widely used in electronics.

The crystals used in the electronics industry are usually produced artificially because in this way their size and purity can be controlled.

Polishing rocks can be fun. You can set up an inexpensive rock polishing device known as a *barrel tumbler*. For your barrel you may use a capped fruit jar with a small hole in the lid. The pebbles you wish to polish should be put into the jar along with some abrasive material. The jar should then be constantly turned on an apparatus such as is shown in Fig. 11-10. In this way the rocks tumble over and over against the abrasive material and against themselves and gradually wear away the rough edges.

The debris should be removed from the jar every few days and as the

11-9. Quartz is a six-sided crystal. (Courtesy of the American Museum of Natural History)

11-10. A fruitjar rock tumbler operated on a tiny electric motor can polish pebbles and rocks in two to three weeks. Coupling of the bolt to the motor shaft should be aligned carefully to insure smooth spinning action of the homemade barrel tumbler shown here.

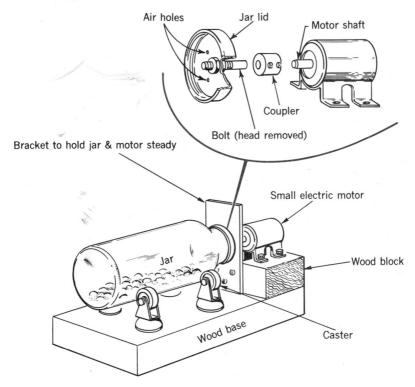

rocks become smoother and rounder, the size of the abrasive should be reduced until it is a fine powder which gives the final polish to the stones. *Silicon carbide* can be used as the abrasive and comes in many grit sizes. For the final polishing, *iron oxide* (or *jeweler's rouge*) can be used.

It is important that a hole is cut into the lid of the jar because carbon dioxide is released from many rocks and could build up enough pressure to explode the jar. The opening permits the gas to escape harmlessly.

What is contained in fertile soil? Fertile soil contains mineral substances, organic materials, and a variety of microscopic forms of plant and animal life. The weathering of rocks provides the complex mineral mixture found in soil. Decayed plant and animal substances account for the presence of organic compounds in the soil. Bacteria and other forms of simple plant life make up the greatest part of the "living" portion of fertile soil. It has been stated that there are more living things in a spoonful of fertile soil than there are people in the world. In addition to the organic and inorganic substances, soils also contain varying quantities of air and water.

The size of soil particles ranges widely. Inorganic particles more than 2.0 millimeters in diameter are classified as *gravel* or stones and are not usually included in an analysis of particle size. Particles between 0.05 mm and 2.0 mm in diameter are classified as *sand;* particles between 0.002 mm and 0.05 mm are classed as *silt* while particles less than 0.002 mm in diameter are *clays.*

The larger the particle, the smaller is the *surface area per unit mass.* Conversely, the smaller the particles, the greater is the surface area per unit mass. Thus, a pail of clay will have much more total surface area than will a similar pail of sand.

Since most of the important chemical or physical-chemical reactions in soil take place at the surface of particles, the silts and clays are well suited for these reactions. However, the larger sands and gravels can transmit moisture and air easily to the roots. Thus, a good soil will have a proper blend of particle size to promote both chemical reactions and the transmission of air and water. In addition, it will also contain the organic materials and microscopic plant and animal life discussed previously.

Since most life depends on soils, you can understand why it is necessary to conserve our topsoil and carefully manage its use.

Quick Quiz

1. What are the main divisions of the earth?
2. Name the geological eras.
3. Why is the Mohole project an ocean-based rather than a land-based project?
4. How do we know what it is like inside the earth?
5. What are the three general types of rocks?
6. Are the rock formations beneath the ocean floor heavier or lighter than the rock formations of the continental land masses? Explain.
7. About how many years did the Mesozoic era last?
8. About how many years ago did the Proterozoic era end?

9. What are some of the advantages of clay in a soil mixture? Sand?
10. What class of rock is traprock? What is it used for?
11. How hot would it be at the bottom of a mine shaft 6000 feet deep if the surface temperature is 60° F (assuming that there is no artificial heating or cooling)?
12. How do ocean waves and currents affect attempts at deep drilling of the ocean floor? Explain.

B PHYSIOGRAPHY: THE STUDY OF SURFACE FEATURES OF THE EARTH

Our shrinking and expanding earth. Ever since the earth was formed it has been subject to constant stresses caused by the action of internal forces. These forces are responsible for earthquakes and volcanoes, the formation of mountains, and the rising and falling of land masses. According to one theory, some of these forces are believed to be caused by a constantly shrinking planet. Billions of years ago when the planet cooled, the surface contracted and the earth gradually shrank. The shrinking earth caused the large land masses to squeeze together and become "wrinkled" much like the skin of a prune. These wrinkles are the many chains of mountains on the surface of the earth.

Despite this cooling of the planet, there is evidence that some sections of the earth's interior seem to be getting hotter. This heating, largely caused by radioactivity, may cause movement in the plastic mantle and contributes to the mountain-building process.

There are several types of mountains. Masses of rock that are folded or forced together may produce rock layers as shown in Fig. 11-8. When these layers become large enough, they may form mountains. The Jura Mountains on the border between France and Switzerland are *folded mountains* that were formed in this manner.

Mountains may develop in somewhat different ways also. Sometimes these adjustments in the earth cause pressures so great that large rock masses rise or fall to new levels. These huge breaks or fractures are called *faults.* (See Fig. 11-11.) At these faults, large masses of rocks may slide up or down considerable distances. The Appalachians were formed this way and are called *complex folded mountains.*

A third general formation called *block* mountains, also developed. These mountains were formed by tremendous faults which caused great blocks of

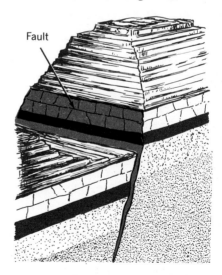

11-11. Rises or drops in rock layers bring about the formation of a fault.

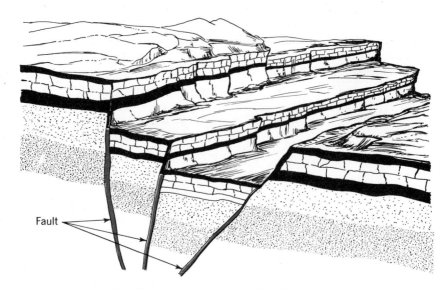

Fault

11-12. The typical formation of block mountains.

rocks to be pushed up above normal ground level. You can recognize these mountains by "hogbacks" or formations of rock and land with almost vertical faces on one side, with gentle slopes on the others. Mountains of this type are common in southern Oregon. (See Fig. 11-12.)

Rising and falling land masses. In addition to the folding and faulting of land forms caused by the shrinkage and expansion of different parts of the earth, there are other forces affecting the lithosphere. One of these is the rising and falling of land masses due to their constantly changing weights. As mountains erode and wear away, the materials are eventually deposited on the ocean floor. This adds weight to the ocean floor and reduces the weight of mountains. Thus, the ocean floors have a tendency to sink while the mountains have a tendency to rise. This displacement is called *isostatic adjustment*. The isostatic pressures

probably do not create mountains, but they tend to keep existing mountains from disappearing as fast as they normally would.

Isostatic and other forms of pressure cause land masses to rise and fall. (See Fig. 11-13.) Some of these changes in the earth's crust thousands of years ago caused the shore line to sink in many places. For example, we know that the Hudson River once extended out into the sea a hundred miles farther than it does now. When the land area sank, the sea crept in. This sinking of the land area formed the deep harbor of New York City.

The Sacramento River in California flows into San Francisco Bay. Here again the sinking of the land formed a deep bay that makes one of the finest harbors in the world. (See Fig. 11-14.)

Faulting sometimes causes earthquakes. Faults are still occurring, particularly in regions where *earthquakes* are observed. In fact, the chief cause of earthquakes is thought to be a sudden slip of rock layers *along a fault line.* The movement of the rock layers against each other creates violent vibrations that can shake large land masses for several minutes.

Earthquakes, and sometimes volcanoes, tend to occur in regions where the earth's crust is under great stress. This is often the case where high mountain ranges are close to ocean deeps. One such area stretches along the entire west coast of North and South America. Many disastrous earthquakes have occurred there.

One of the most famous of these was the San Francisco earthquake of 1906. The 600-mile-long San Andreas fault passes along the west coast of the United States through this city.

The strongest earthquake ever recorded in North America took place on March 27, 1964, in Alaska. It caused the land to shift more than 20 feet in some parts of Anchorage. (See Fig. 11-15.) Fortunately, the accompanying sea wave, though destructive, was comparatively small and the loss of life was kept to approximately 200. Earthquakes of less intensity have been catastrophic in other parts of the world. Over 100,000 lives were lost in an earthquake which hit Japan in 1923, and an estimated 800,000 lives were lost in a massive quake which hit China in 1556.

Earthquakes produce several types of shock waves. Earthquakes produce *primary, shear,* and *surface* shock waves. *The **primary wave** is a compression or longitudinal motion that exerts a push-pull type of force and passes through all parts of the earth including the liquid core.* It travels about five miles per second and can pass through the entire earth in about

11-13. Isostatic adjustment causes mountains to rise and ocean floors to sink when weight is transferred from the mountains to the sea.

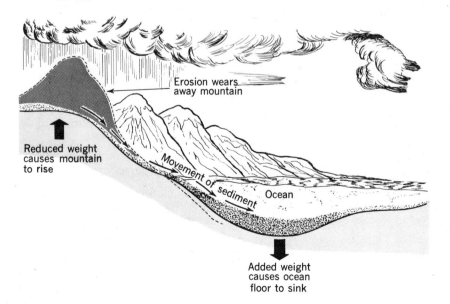

Erosion wears away mountain

Reduced weight causes mountain to rise

Movement of sediment

Ocean

Added weight causes ocean floor to sink

11-14. This excellent harbor is the result of the sinking of the shoreline. (San Francisco Chamber of Commerce)

11-15. Earthquakes caused this destruction in Anchorage, Alaska, in 1964. (UPI)

26 minutes. This is similar to a sound wave. (See Chapter 6.)

The shear wave is a transverse wave in which particles of matter travel at right angles to the direction of the shock itself. This snake-like wave travels at about two-and-a-half miles per second through the crust and mantle of the earth. It is reflected, however, by the earth's liquid core which does not transmit the side-to-side motions. Thus, the shear waves do not reach those portions of the earth which lie on the opposite side of an earthquake. (See Fig. 11-16.)

The *surface waves* are similar to the shear waves but are confined mainly to the earth's crust. One type of surface wave has a horizontal side-to-side motion while another type may have a vertical or up-and-down motion as it speeds along the earth's surface.

The eruptions of volcanoes can be violent. *Volcanoes* develop from openings in the upper crust of the earth and are of many types. In some cases, the melted rock, or *lava*, wells up quietly. It may flow out from cracks or *fissures* in the ground. At the other extreme is the *explosive* type. Its eruption is often accompanied by local earthquakes. The explosive type of volcano produces great quantities of ash, hot poisonous gases, and steam. (See Fig. 11-17.)

Famous volcanic eruptions took place on Krakatao in the East Indies, Mt. Pelee in the West Indies, and Mt. Vesuvius in Italy. In 1883, the explosion of Krakatao produced giant sea waves that killed over 36,000 peo-

ple. Vesuvius, the famous volcano near Naples, Italy, exploded violently in 79 A.D. Pompeii and other towns were completely buried under tons of hot ash. Then again in 1631, after several milder eruptions, there was a violent lava flow that killed some 18,000 people. Vesuvius still continues to be in a mild state of activity.

In some places, notably Yellowstone Park, Iceland, and New Zealand, beds of hot lava give rise to *hot springs* and *geysers*. The superheated steam below the surface of the earth blows out the water above it to form a geyser. Old Faithful, in Yellowstone Park, is the most famous geyser in the world.

Volcanoes occur chiefly in belts around the ocean basins where young mountains meet the sea. This is also the zone of violent earthquakes. Where the earth's crust is under great stress

11-16. The primary shock wave of an earthquake travels through all parts of the earth. The shear wave travels only through the solid part of the earth, while the long surface waves remains near the surface.

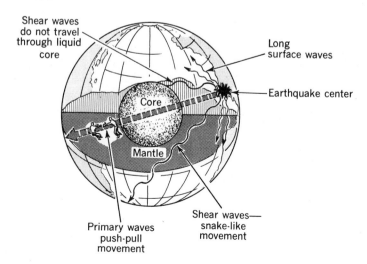

Shear waves do not travel through liquid core

Long surface waves

Earthquake center

Core

Mantle

Primary waves push-pull movement

Shear waves— snake-like movement

11-17. An eruptivg volcano throws great billows of smoke, ashes, and dust into the atmosphere. (UPI)

and faults are developing, molten rock finds its way to the surface.

Weathering. Weathering is an important factor in the gradually changing surface of the earth. *Weathering is the gradual physical and chemical decomposition of rocks.* Even hard rocks are weathered. They are broken into fragments, and even ground into fine powder by natural processes. Wind, rain, snow, ice, frost, temperature changes, and running water each help in this decomposition process.

Chemical action of the oxygen and carbon dioxide of the air helps, too. The acids formed by growing plants and by the decay of organic matter also cause weathering of rocks. The process is extremely slow and hardly noticeable in a lifetime. But do not forget that these weathering agents have been working for millions of years.

Expansion and contraction due to temperature changes produce cracks in even the hardest rocks. When water freezes in these cracks, the expansion splits the rock into pieces. Loosened fragments topple and fall to the bottom of a cliff. Perhaps you have seen a pile of rock fragments at the base of a cliff. This is the result of weathering over long periods of time.

A demonstration of weathering can be performed in the laboratory. Heat a few rock samples strongly with a Bunsen flame or in a hot oven. Then drop the rocks into cold water. Some of them will crack or split open. This shows, on a small scale, what happens in nature as rocks are heated and cooled.

Ground water forms many beautiful caves. In some areas, water dissolves minerals that are below the surface of the ground. Where the water is hot, it may dissolve many minerals. Later, as the water cools and evaporates, it may redeposit these minerals as beautiful crystals.

The ground water often contains acids. This may be carbonic acid (H_2CO_3) formed by the reaction of water with the carbon dioxide of the air, or it may be other acids formed by the decay of plant life. When such water seeps through layers of limestone, it slowly dissolves the rock, leaving a hollow region underground. Thus, great *limestone caves* may be formed. The Mammoth Cave of Kentucky and Carlsbad Caverns of New Mexico are two well-known examples.

In such caves, you see pillars of stone called ***stalagmites*** (stuh-*lag*-mites) *standing upright* on the floor of the cave. As the limestone solution drips from the ceiling, some of the

11-18. These unusual limestone formations (stalactites and stalagmites) occupy the Cave of the Winds in Colorado. (Chamber of Commerce, Colorado Springs, Colorado)

sion than the deeper one. This is because the shallow river is wider and affects more surface area.

A large river carries away huge quantities of material. The Mississippi River, for example, carries away an estimated 600,000,000 tons of material to the Gulf of Mexico annually. Some of this material is dissolved in the water, and the rest is carried in suspension or is rolled along the river bottom. The sediment that is deposited at the mouth of the river forms a *delta.*

Sheet erosion. When water falls on a smooth land surface, it may run off slowly in a sheet. This erosion of a smooth surface, called *sheet erosion,* occurs especially in nearly level fields.

Sheet erosion washes away valuable topsoil from rich farmlands. This is

water evaporates, causing the dissolved limestone to *crystallize* out. Often other stony "icicles" called *stalactites* (stuh-*lac*-tites) *hang down* from the ceiling as shown in Fig. 11-18.

Erosion is a continuous process. *The wearing away of the crust of the earth is called erosion.* (See Fig. 11-19.) Erosion is caused chiefly by running water and to some extent by wind, glaciers, and temperature changes. The amount of erosion produced by running water depends upon three factors: (1) the nature of the earth's surface; (2) the speed of the water; and (3) the depth of the stream.

Measurements show that when a stream doubles its speed, its capacity to carry suspended matter increases 64 times. If two streams carry the same volume of water at the same speed, the shallower one will cause more ero-

11-19. Wind, rain, snow, and temperature changes cause rocks to erode. (Union Pacific Railroad)

why farmers like to see a slow, steady rain that soaks in, rather than a heavy downpour that washes away topsoil.

Floods. Evidences of the loss of topsoil can be seen in the "muddy" appearance of some rivers clogged with sediment. The load of sediment in a river is especially heavy when watershed and runoff areas are unprotected by grass, trees, or other forms of vegetation. These rivers carry away countless millions of tons of topsoil annually. As rivers approach the ocean, the land through which they flow usually becomes more and more level. Thus, the speed of the water is constantly slowing down, and its ability to carry sediment is reduced. Therefore, heavy loads of sediment are deposited on the river beds and banks. Over a long period of time, these deposits have built walls called *natural levees* (*levees*). At many places, *artificial levees* have been built by man to keep the water contained in the channel. Sometimes the pressure of the high water causes a break in the levee. When this happens, the water floods a wide area. An example of this devastation was the great flood of the Hwang Ho (Yellow) River in Honan Province, China, in 1887. Sediment had built up the river bed and banks so much that the *bottom* of the river was actually higher than the surrounding land areas. When the floods did come that year, they broke out of the levees and inundated over 50,000 square miles of lowland. This is equal to the combined areas of Connecticut, Delaware, Maryland, Massachusetts, New Hampshire, New Jersey, and Vermont. An estimated 1,000,000 people lost their lives in that disaster. Since the Hwang Ho often built up its bed to a higher elevation

than the surrounding lowlands, it changed its course frequently. During floods, the waters simply cut a new channel through the lowlands whenever the existing river bed became too high. (See Fig. 11-20.)

Wind erosion. When unprotected soil is sufficiently exposed to wind action, it is easily picked up and carried away. Such *wind erosion* can quickly strip away the fertile topsoil to expose unproductive layers of rocks and sand. Arid regions are especially susceptible to wind erosion because of the lack of plant life to cover and hold the ground. During the late 1800's and early 1900's large areas of southwestern United States were plowed and seeded to crops. These lands, however, were too arid to support crops of grain, especially during slight reductions in the already low annual rainfalls. Thus, the plowed and bare lands were gradually abandoned and later were the cause of the serious "dust bowl" conditions of the 1930's

Antarctica is almost entirely covered by ice and snow. Most of the earth's ice is located in Antarctica. It has about five million square miles of ice packed to an average depth of 7500 feet. This is approximately 90 percent of all the ice on the earth. Geologists have discovered that the glacial ice cap has internal pressures similar to those pressures found in the earth's crust itself. For example, ice is pushed into upward and downward folds, fault lines are developed, and crevasses are formed. These phenomena are similar to those found on land masses.

If all the ice of Antarctica should melt, it is estimated that ocean levels would be raised more than 250 feet.

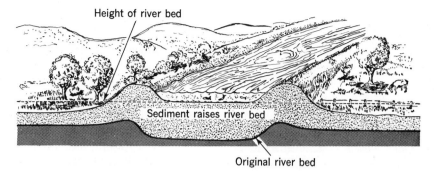

Height of river bed

Sediment raises river bed

Original river bed

11-20. Some rivers build up their channels until the stream bed is higher than the surrounding countryside. When floods come, the destruction is often severe, and the river cuts a new channel to the sea.

Think of what this would do to the coastal cities and communities of the world!

There have been several Ice Ages. Several times during the past million years large areas of the earth have been covered with great sheets of ice. The last *Ice Age* ended about 10,000 years ago. The huge mile-deep sea of ice spread down from the Arctic region, covering Canada and northern United States nearly as far south as St. Louis. These large masses of ice are continental glaciers.

Glaciers are formed when more snow falls during the winter than melts during the summer. Year after year, new layers of snow pile up, and finally the snow is compressed into ice and the pressure of the ice becomes so great that it begins to flow slowly like tar.

During this Ice Age there were periods during which the ice melted. Right now many scientists think we are in the midst of an *interglacial* or warming up period. Glaciers once covered about 32 percent of the surface of the earth. They now cover about

10 percent of it, mostly in the Arctic and Antarctic regions.

Just what caused the Ice Ages of the past is still not completely known. One theory is that the earth's climate got colder due to the more rapid radiation of heat into space. This happens when the amount of carbon dioxide in the air decreases. Another theory suggests the cause to be the slight changes in the earth's orbit due to the gravitational attraction of the other planets. Excessive volcanic dust in the air, which has the effect of cooling the earth's surface, may also have played a part.

Glaciers can form lakes and plains. As the great North American ice sheet melted away during a warming period, great changes in the land areas took place. As the ice sheet moved south over our north central states, it gouged out the Great Lakes. The bottoms of four of these lakes are below sea level, indicating that they could not have been dug by running water. Thousands of hollows were formed by *glacial erosion* and, as the glaciers melted, these holes were filled with water. Many of the lakes of Minnesota, Wisconsin, Michigan, and New York were formed in this way.

The ice sheets scraped most of the valuable topsoil from eastern Canada and deposited it in the northern parts of the United States. This formed some of our best agricultural lands.

Glacial plains were formed as glaciers passed over an area. (See Fig. 11-21.) In places, the glacier melted away as fast as it advanced. In these places, the soil, sand, gravel, and rock that had been carried along in the glacier fell out and formed rubble deposits, called *moraines.* Moraines account for much stony soil in New England and in North Central States.

How do glaciers move? The movement of glaciers is not too well understood. It is assumed that the pressure of ice on top causes some of the ice at the bottom to melt. This lets the ice mass move forward. Glaciers travel slowly, usually only a few feet a day. As they descend to lower altitudes, they may melt and result in glacier-fed streams. Sometimes they slide into the ocean and break up, becoming huge *icebergs.*

Exposed granite core

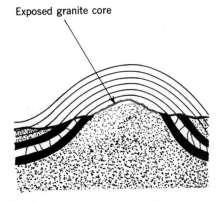

11-21. Erosion by glaciers can remove entire mountains of sedimentary rock.

One of the earliest scientists to study glaciers was Louis Agassiz, a Swiss zoologist and geologist. He proved that glaciers actually moved. He drove iron stakes into the ice in a straight row across a valley glacier. (See Fig. 11-22.) The following year he returned to find that the stakes were no longer in a straight line. The stakes in the middle of the glacier had been carried farthest downstream while stakes near the sides of the glacier moved very little. He not only proved that glaciers were moving masses of ice but later produced convincing evidence that glaciers have been important factors in shaping the face of much of the planet.

Land tides. In addition to weathering, erosion, and glaciers, there is at least one other external force acting on the earth's surface. It is the gravitational force of the sun and moon. It causes *land tides* of a few inches just as ocean tides of greater dimensions are formed.

How does a valley start? No land is absolutely flat, and so water always flows toward a low spot, gaining speed as it moves.

The flowing water collects in a streamlet that continues to flow to lower ground. As it travels along, it digs into the ground, producing a channel, or *gully.* The gully grows wider, longer, and deeper with each rain. Water flowing in from the sides washes down material. This action makes the gully wider. Gradually it becomes longer as the head of the gully works up the slope, and deeper as it erodes the bottom.

Throughout all of these travels, the flowing water washes away and erodes the surface over which it flows. It

11-22. This valley glacier was photographed in Canada. (B. M. Shaub)

widens and deepens its channel until a broad *valley* results. A *valley* is a lowland area with higher land on both sides. It may be caused also by the action of rivers or glaciers or by faulting or folding in the earth's upper crust. Valleys may be long or short, shallow or deep.

There are four stages of valley growth. Erosion causes a river and its valley to go through a series of four gradual changes called *infancy, youth, maturity,* and *old age.* At the start, when the smooth surface is cut by a gully, we say that the valley is in its *infancy.* The gully soon cuts into its bed and has V-shaped, almost vertical sides. We say that the valley is now in its *youthful* stage. (See Fig. 11-23.) Of course, successive rains over a long period of time carry water and suspended matter from the sides of the valley. Thus, the valley becomes wider and the sides less steep. The flowing water erodes the ridges and hills, changing the area to one that approaches a flat surface. (See Fig. 11-24.) The valley and the river that flows through it are now *mature.* During maturity, the river that flows through

11-23. A typical youthful river valley. (Lee, W. T., US Geological Survey)

a valley flows less swiftly than in youth. A mature river has a broad valley with a gentle slope.

In old age, a river is sluggish. Further erosion may change a river valley into a plain that is nearly at *base level*. **Base level** is the level of

the ocean or the body of water into which the river flows. Of course, it is this level that limits the depth to which a valley can be eroded.

When all of the high surfaces are nearly worn down, the river and its valley are said to be in **old age.** In old age, rivers flow sluggishly most of the year. But spring rains and melting snows may produce a flood stage. This will make the river spread over a wide area. The flood waters bring with them a great deal of sediment. As the flood waters recede, this sediment forms *sand bars* in the old channel. These bars may turn the water to one side. This makes the water cut into the sides of the banks, which widens the valley still more. The *twists* and *turns* of a river in old age are called **meanders** (me-*an*-ders). (See Fig. 11-25.)

An old river may become young again. The river may grow old, eroding the surrounding land down to base

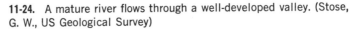

11-24. A mature river flows through a well-developed valley. (Stose, G. W., US Geological Survey)

11-25. An older river valley with a meandering river. (Pierce, W. C., US Geological Survey)

level. But then if the land is *uplifted* or *tilted,* the stream immediately becomes young again. It rushes down its new slopes and it starts actively digging a new channel. Many of our present rivers have gone through this change. The Colorado River is a good example of this. Though young in its present erosion stage, it follows the meanders of the old river bed.

Also, different parts of the same river may be young, mature, and old, all at the same time. The Mississippi-Missouri is a good example of this. It is a young river in its upper reaches near the source, but is a very old river during the later part of its course, nearing the mouth. Of course, neither a river nor its valley is a living thing. The terms infancy, youth, maturity, and old age are arbitrary. They do not have the same meaning as when you are speaking of plants or animals.

What makes a canyon? The canyons cut by the Colorado River into the Colorado Plateau have exposed to view different layers of rock. These horizontal layers show that this area

was a smooth plain before it was pushed up. Before that it was under water for several million years. Layers of sediment nearly a mile thick were laid down.

Ever since then, for millions of years, the Colorado River has been cutting its channel through this rising plain. The river has cut its *canyon,* or narrow channel, all through the sedimentary layers and is now digging its way into the igneous rock below. (See Fig. 11-26.)

Meanwhile, weathering and erosion have worn away so much material that now the Grand Canyon is hundreds of miles long, up to 12 miles wide, and as much as a mile deep. In all, approximately 2000 cubic miles of soil and rock have been eroded away. Where has all this material gone? Much of it formed a land bridge across the Gulf of California cutting off the northern part of the Gulf from the sea. Most of this northern part has evaporated and is now the Salton Sea and Imperial Valley, California, situated as much as 100 feet below sea level.

Some waterfalls are caused by rivers eroding their valleys. A look at Fig. 11-27 reveals how the Yellowstone Falls were formed. As the river wore down its valley, it came to a place where there was a *dike*, a layer of hard *basalt*. This barrier acted like a dam across the stream. The soft rock downstream wore away quickly. This made an even deeper valley into which the river now plunges.

The Niagara River was formed after the last Ice Age. The bed of the river is a hard, horizontal limestone layer. This washes away more slowly than the softer shales below. The churning water in the gorge at the bottom of the falls erodes the shale. This undercuts the limestone, making an overhang. Occasionally great blocks

11-26. The erosion of a plateau resulted in the formation of these canyons in Grand Canyon National Park. (National Park Service)

of limestone are loosened so that they drop into the gorge below the falls. In this way, the falls have "traveled" about seven miles upstream toward Lake Erie during the last 9000 years.

Other falls are not caused by water erosion but by glaciers. Thus, Yosemite Falls in California plunges over a cliff to the bottom of a glacier-made valley 2600 feet below. Faulting and uplifting of the earth's crust may also produce waterfalls.

What is a river basin? An imaginary line joining the tops of a chain of mountains forms a divide. The divide determines the direction that the water will follow when it falls on the mountains. The Rocky Mountains form a very important divide in this country. The rain that falls on the western slopes flows west into such rivers as the Columbia and the Colorado. The rain that falls on the eastern slopes is carried off by the Missouri, Platte, Arkansas, and other rivers.

The area drained by a stream forms a watershed. Rain falling on the watershed usually collects in a stream or river at the bottom of the valley. On a larger scale, the *drainage area between two widely separated mountain chains* is called a **river basin.**

The land between the Appalachians and the Rockies forms the Mississippi River basin, as shown in Fig. 11-28. It extends from western New York to western Montana, and from the Canadian border to the Gulf of Mexico. Other large river basins are those of the Columbia, Colorado, Rio Grande, and the St. Lawrence.

Plains are level areas. Stretches of land that are level, or nearly level, are called *plains.* Some extend for hundreds of miles, like the Great Plains

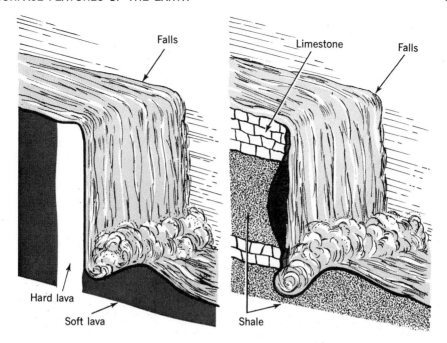

11-27. The rock formations underlying Yellowstone (left) and Niagara Falls (right).

11-28. This map shows the river basin of the Mississippi River system.

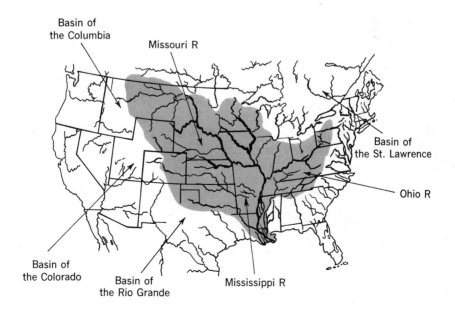

between the Mississippi and the Rockies. The *prairies*, or *grasslands*, between the Appalachians and the Mississippi form another extensive plain. You can easily see the plain on a *relief map*. A *relief map* is a map that shows the *irregularities of the earth's surface.*

Most plains are flat and level because they are formed by layers of sediment. Often you can see the different layers in the side of a cliff. In any one layer, the coarser material lies underneath with the fine sand above it. Then there is still finer clay or slit on top. As these sediments dropped out from the water in which they were suspended, the larger and heavier particles settled out first.

What is the Atlantic Coastal Plain? There is a broad *coastal plain* along the Atlantic seaboard running south from Cape Cod in Massachusetts to include the peninsula of Florida. A continuation of this plain, known as the Gulf Coastal Plain, extends around the Gulf of Mexico, as shown in Fig. 11-29. In most places, this plain is 50 to 100 miles wide.

The Atlantic Coastal Plain was formed by the erosion of the ancient Appalachian Mountains. It does not end at the present shore line but extends out to sea as the *continental shelf*. Rivers flowing from the high ground cut through the coastal plain on their way to the sea.

Waterfalls and rapids along the rivers mark the beginning of the coastal plain. They also show where the shore line was before the coastal plain existed. A line joining points along the border of the coastal plain and the adjacent higher land is called the *fall line*.

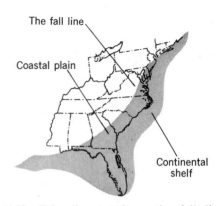

11-29. This diagram shows the fall line, coastal plain, and continental shelf of the Atlantic coast.

Flood plains and uplifted plains. Plains formed from sand, mud, and clay that a river deposits are called *alluvial* (uh-*loo*-vee-al) *plains.* When its soil contains large quantities of decaying organic matter, such a plain is very fertile. Excellent crops grow on this kind of land. The flood plains of many rivers provide fertile "bottom land."

The forces that push up mountains often raise nearby plains, too. That is how plateaus are formed. The Appalachian Plateau extends westward from the Appalachian Mountains at an altitude of about 2000 feet. The Great Plains area extending eastward from the Rockies is really a *plateau*, or *uplifted plain*. Its elevation is nearly a mile above sea level. Between the Rockies and the Sierra Nevada Mountains is a high plateau more than a mile above sea level.

How are plateaus eroded? After a plain has been elevated into a plateau, rivers cut valleys into the surface. Where there is plenty of rainfall, the

11-30. A butte is an impressive feature of our western plains. (Hunt, C. B., US Geological Survey)

valleys are broadened so that the plateau loses its flat appearance. Portions of the Appalachian Plateau have been so deeply cut away by rivers that what is left no longer looks like a flat surface at all. However, the level skyline along the ridges shows that the area was once a flat plateau.

Plateaus in dry regions are worn away slowly, and the wind may be the principal eroding agent here. In a dry climate, the wind picks up dust and grains of sand. Have you ever seen men smooth off iron castings by sandblasting? If so, you can see why such a wind over a long period of time is a very good eroding agent.

Often a flat, table-like surface of hard rock remains after the wind has eroded the surrounding land. This is called a *mesa* (*may*-suh). A small mesa is called a *butte* (bewt). Formations of this kind are often seen on our dry, western plateaus. (See Fig. 11-30.)

The earth is still changing. Areas along the Atlantic seaboard are sinking about one foot every 100 years. The same thing is happening along the coast of Holland. On the other hand, parts of Canada and of Sweden, for example, are slowly rising.

Mountain-building goes on steadily. Some geologists believe that most of our mountains were built in the past by slow changes just like those taking place today. It is certain that the face of the earth will look different a few million years from now.

Soil conservation is important to the nation. Only the top 6 to 12 inches of soil is suitable for providing food for the peoples of the world. In this topsoil, roots of food plants find the necessary nourishment and moisture that they need for growth. But suppose that this valuable topsoil is washed or blown away. Then only barren ground, or the subsoil, remains, and this soil will not grow good crops.

Once started, water erosion becomes worse with each succeeding rain. Deep gullies form over the surface of the land. Eventually the area must be abandoned as unproductive.

11-31. Contour plowing and strip cropping help to reduce erosion. (USDA Photo)

The erosion of topsoil has ruined millions of acres of land in some parts of our country.

Intelligent use of such natural resources as petroleum, minerals, forests, topsoil, and water is one of our most important goals today. *The proper use of our natural resources is called conservation, and is the responsibility of all citizens.*

How can we slow down erosion? Perhaps the most important of all soil conservation practices is the planting of trees, grasses, or some other form of vegetation to cover and hold the topsoil. Plants hold the soil with their roots and root hairs. The proliferation of root systems in some plants is almost unbelievable. According to a

11-32. Gullies can be converted to grassed waterways that hold the soil. (Soil Conservation Service—USDA)

study reported by the U.S. Department of Agriculture, a single rye plant grown for four months in one cubic foot of loam soil developed an astounding root system. The cubic foot of soil contained 13,800,000 roots with a combined length of more than 385 miles and a surface area of over 2500 square feet. It also contained 14,000,000,000 root hairs with a combined length of more than 6600 miles and a surface area of over 4000 square feet. Figures such as these suggest that plants have effective soil-holding characteristics.

Other methods of reducing erosion include contour plowing, terrace farming, strip cropping, selective cutting of trees, building grass waterways, and building small check dams on streams running through farmlands. (See Figs. 11-31 and 11-32.)

In addition, the building of large flood-control dams cuts down the amount of erosion. Each of these methods helps to save fertile topsoil. By using proper methods to control erosion, we can be assured that our farmlands will remain productive.

Quick Quiz

1. What is isostatic adjustment?
2. What types of shock waves are produced by an earthquake?
3. What is erosion?
4. How are glaciers formed?
5. How is a valley formed?
6. What is meant by conservation of natural resources?
7. Write a brief explanation of the difference between stalagmite and stalactite formations.
8. Explain how limestone caves are formed.
9. Why is there so much stony soil in New England?
10. Why is the transverse shock wave of an earthquake usually a great deal more destructive than the primary shock wave?
11. Explain why a river carries away soil in one place but deposits it in another.
12. How did Louis Agassiz prove that glaciers moved?
13. Why are exposed boulders and rock formations in dry, barren regions usually rounded and smooth instead of jagged or broken?

SUMMARY

Geology is the study of the structure and composition of the earth, and of its history as recorded in rocks. Scientists estimate the age of the earth at about 4½ billion years. They divide this time into six great geological eras. The earth is divided into three divisions: the atmosphere, the hydrosphere, and the lithosphere. The lithosphere, or the solid part, is again divided into three major parts: the crust, the mantle, and the core. The crust is very thin, made up mostly of bedrock. The mantle makes up most of the earth, and the core probably contains an inner solid part and an outer liquid part.

All rocks may be grouped in three classes: igneous, sedimentary, and metamorphic. Igneous rocks are those that have solidified from hot, molten minerals. Sedimentary rocks formed from layers of sediment deposited mostly under water. Metamorphic rocks are those that have been changed by the effects of heat and pressure on other rocks within the earth. Granite, basalt, obsidian, and pumice are examples of igneous rocks. Shale, limestone, and sandstone are sedimentary rocks. Marble, slate, and anthracite are metamorphic rocks.

Minerals are specific elements or combinations of elements that are entirely of inorganic composition. A method useful in mineral identification is the standard scale of hardness.

The study of the surface features of the land forms of the earth is called physiography. These surface features have been affected by internal and external forces. The shrinking and expanding masses of rock, isostatic pressures, earthquakes, and volcanoes are some of the internal forces constantly shaping the earth's surface. External forces affecting the earth are the forces of weathering and erosion. The chief eroding agents are wind, water, and glaciers. The amount of erosion produced by running water depends upon three conditions: (1) the nature of the surface; (2) the speed of the water; and (3) the depth of the stream. Sheet erosion is the wearing away of the land on a nearly smooth surface. The running water tends to flow toward low spots, washing away the surface to form a gully. The gully soon deepens to form a valley.

A river and the valley through which it flows go through a series of changes called infancy, youth, maturity, and old age. Rivers in old age are characterized by twists and turns called meanders. The area drained by a stream is called a watershed. The drainage area between two mountain chains is called a river basin. Sinking shore lines form deep harbors. Waterfalls may form from river erosion or glacial action.

Plains are level stretches of land. Plateaus are uplifted plains formed by changes in the earth's crust.

Large masses of ice formed during the Ice Age have changed the surface of the earth.

The proper use of our natural resources is called conservation, and is the responsibility of all citizens.

CHAPTER REVIEW

Vocabulary

Match the words in Column A with the *best* response in Column B. Do not write in your book.

Column A	Column B
1. geology	a. alluvial deposits built up at the mouth of a river
2. crust	
3. outcropping	b. an area drained by a stream
4. fossils	c. an uplifted plain

5. Moho
6. Mohole
7. mantle
8. core
9. metamorphic rock
10. sedimentary rock
11. igneous rock
12. faults
13. erosion
14. delta
15. levee
16. glacier
17. moraine
18. watershed
19. plateau
20. conservation

d. boundary between the earth's crust and mantle
e. innermost zone of the earth
f. intermediate zone of the earth's structure
g. large mass of ice slowly creeping over the land
h. layer of rock material forming the outer surface of the earth
i. mass of rocks not covered by soil
j. mixture of sand, soil, gravel, and rock material left by a receding glacier
k. project to drill through the earth's crust
l. remains of early forms of life
m. rock formed by the effects of heat and pressure
n. rock formed from layers of sediment usually deposited by water
o. rock formed from molten mixtures of minerals
p. study of the composition, structure, and history of the earth
q. vertical or horizontal cracks in the earth's surface along which rock masses slip, rise, and fall
r. wall along a riverbank to prevent flooding
s. wearing away the crust of the earth
t. wise use of our natural resources

Questions: Group A

1. About how old do scientists think the earth is? Explain one method scientists use to estimate the age of the earth.
2. What is the approximate radius of the central core of the earth? Of what materials, perhaps, is it composed?
3. How thick is the mantle? Of what mineral may the mantle be composed?
4. Describe the Mohorovicic Discontinuity. How may it be explored?
5. What is meant by the continental shelf?
6. What are some ingredients of fertile soil? What factors contribute to its formation?
7. How is marble formed?
8. Discuss one cause of earthquakes.
9. What causes volcanoes? Where do they chiefly occur?
10. Name five ways of reducing soil erosion.
11. Discuss the difference between a watershed and a river basin.
12. Explain why alluvial plains have rich soil.
13. What information can we obtain from a relief map but not from an ordinary map?
14. How were the great lakes formed?
15. State one theory of the cause of the Ice Ages.
16. How was the Atlantic Coastal Plain formed?
17. Name three ways in which waterfalls are formed.

Questions: Group B

1. In what way is the decay of radioactive carbon-14 an aid to our study of man's early history?
2. Discuss one problem that limits the depth we can drill into the earth.
3. What do basalt, obsidian, and pumice have in common? Explain their formation.
4. Name six properties by which minerals can be identified.
5. What causes the various shapes of crystals?
6. What is the scale of hardness? Name the softest and hardest mineral on the list.
7. What effect does doubling the speed of a river have on the amount of erosion that takes place?
8. Name two characteristics of a youthful valley.
9. Why is the Mississippi River forming such a large delta?
10. Why does New York City have such a fine harbor?

12 METEOROLOGY

A WEATHER AND CLIMATE

Meteorology is the scientific study of weather and climate. When you look outside, you may see that it is raining, clear, snowing, sunny, windy, or foggy. If you glance again an hour or so later you may find that some changes have taken place in the atmosphere. You are able to recognize these changes and describe them in familiar terms. You make remarks such as "it was raining today" and "it was warm yesterday." When you make descriptive statements about the atmosphere at a particular time and place, you are actually referring to the weather. *Weather is the temporary condition of the atmosphere at a particular time and place.*

Climate, however, is a less temporary condition of the atmosphere. It is weather over a long period of time and is sometimes referred to as "average weather." In studying climate we consider such factors as total yearly rainfall and average seasonal tempera- tures. "The summers are hot" and "the winters are wet" are typical remarks describing climates. Weather and climate are caused by such elements as air pressure, wind, temperature, humidity, clouds, and precipitation.

The study of weather, weather patterns, climate, and other phenomena of the atmosphere is called meteorology. This term was first used over 2300 years ago by the ancient Greeks and today it describes the scientific study of the atmosphere.

Factors which control weather and climate. Although weather is temporary and climate is far more general, both are similarly affected by certain physical conditions of the earth. Some of them are outlined below.

Land areas near large bodies of water have smaller variations in temperature than do areas farther inland. This variation occurs because water gains and loses heat very slowly compared to land. Thus, water gains heat slowly in the summer months and, conversely, loses it slowly in the winter, thus keeping yearly temperatures moderate. Inland areas, on the other hand, generally have greater daily and sea-

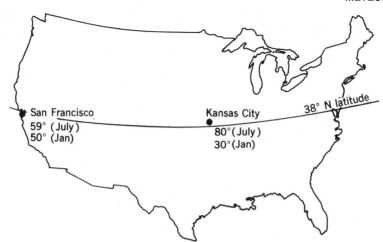

12-1. Large bodies of water have a moderating effect on climate. Notice the average January and July temperatures of these two cities located in similar latitudes.

sonal temperature changes. Examples of these differences can be seen by comparing the average January and July temperatures of San Francisco, California, on the shores of the Pacific Ocean, with Kansas City, Missouri, located over 1000 miles from the nearest large body of water. (See Fig. 12-1.) Both cities are located at approximately the same latitude, yet the temperature *averages* differ widely. San Francisco has an average January temperature of about 50° F, while Kansas City has about 30° F during the same month. During July, however, Kansas City is much warmer with an average temperature of 80° F compared to San Francisco's 59° F. Notice that the temperature *range* (or the differences between the high and low temperature) of the seacoast city is only 9 degrees F while it is 50 degrees F in the inland city.

Weather and climate also vary with latitude. As you move from the equator toward the poles, the temperature generally decreases. This decrease is caused by a gradual reduction of solar radiation, or sunshine, as the latitude increases.

Another factor which affects temperature is altitude. The temperature decreases from 3 to 5° F per 1000 feet up to an altitude of about eight miles. Thus, in some extremely high lands of the earth such as Mt. Kilimanjaro in Tanzania, Africa, the surface of the earth is covered with snow the year around even though located near the equator.

Mountain ranges affect the climate in other ways than by the cooling influence of elevation. Large mountain ranges act as barriers to air masses and divert the normal patterns of prevailing winds.

Finally, ocean currents greatly affect the climate in certain parts of the world. Warm currents bring moderate temperatures to lands normally in very cold latitudes while cold currents produce the opposite effects. For example, the Gulf Stream brings warm water to the western coast of Europe. Bergen, Norway, located near 60° North Latitude has an average January temperature of 34° F while coastal areas of Greenland and northern Canada seldom reach these warm temperatures even during the summer months. (See Fig. 12-2.)

Is the climate of the earth changing? Five thousand years ago the cradle of western civilization flourished in the bountiful lands of the Tigris-Euphrates Valley in what is now Iraq. Today, most of this land is semiarid and capable of supporting only a meager population. Baghdad, for example, now receives only about 7 inches of rain annually. *To support the beginnings of our civilization, annual rainfall in that area was probably much greater.*

Even greater changes have taken place in the climate of the earth as we look farther back into the past. Much of the northern hemisphere was covered by deep fields of ice thousands of years ago. At other times, however, tropical climates have extended far into northern latitudes. Thus, the climate of the earth has changed considerably in the past, and it is likely that it will change again in the future.

12-2. Ocean currents warm up some lands while they cool off other lands. For example, the Atlantic seacoast of Europe is warmed by the Gulf Stream while northern and northeastern coasts of Canada are cooled by the Labrador Current.

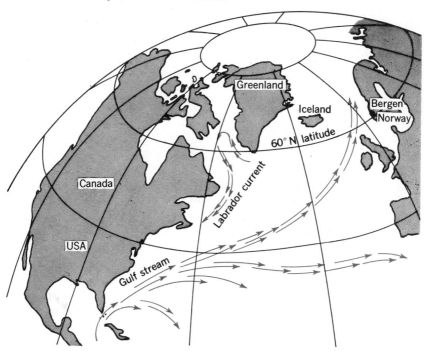

The changes in climate probably proceeded very slowly over thousands of years. Scientists today are searching for evidences of these tiny and gradual changes. During recent years there has been an increase of about 2 percent in the amount of the sun's radiation that reaches the earth. This warm up may be due to the vast quantities of carbon dioxide added to the atmosphere in recent years. The carbon dioxide gas resulting from combustion and decomposition of various fuels, acts as a *heat trap* for the sun's rays. At the present rate, the carbon dioxide content of our atmosphere will be increased 70 percent by the year 2000.

With a continuous, gradual, warming effect, huge masses of ice about the poles could melt, resulting in a rise of the level of the oceans. This could bring disastrous results for many coastal communities of the world.

Effects of climate on man. Climate has greatly affected man's history on earth and has modified the course of his civilizations. Man appears to thrive best in regions of the world in which extremes in temperature and in moisture are avoided.

Farmers in a particular region need to know the length of the growing season for the kinds of crops they can grow. The total seasonal or yearly rainfall and the temperature extremes are additional factors to be considered.

Industry needs to have an understanding about climatic conditions in a region. The probable demand for heating appliances and air-conditioning units are determined by such information. The kinds of clothes we wear, the sports we engage in, the houses we live in, and even the foods we eat

depend in large measure on climate.

What is the atmosphere? As we learned in Chapter 1, the atmosphere is a mixture of several gases, forming an ocean of air around the earth. The atmosphere has no definite height; that is, it does not suddenly end at one place as does an ocean of water. Instead, it gets thinner and thinner the higher you go. About half of our atmosphere is below an altitude of 18,000 feet and about 99 percent is below 18 miles. Traces of atmosphere extend much higher, however. At an altitude of 60 to 80 miles there is still enough air to transmit sound. Above that there is total silence. Also at this height, space capsules reentering from earth orbits begin to be affected by air resistance. Air molecules extend still higher, up to 600 and 1000 miles during major solar disturbances, but this area is often not considered part of the atmosphere.

Divisions of our atmosphere. For purposes of study, scientists have divided the atmosphere into four divisions, or layers: (1) the *troposphere*, (2) the *stratosphere*, (3) the *ionosphere*, and (4) the *exosphere*. (See Fig. 12-3.)

The *troposphere* is the layer of air nearest the earth's surface. It extends from the surface of the earth to a height of approximately 5 miles at the poles to about 11 miles at the equator, for an average height of about 8 miles. Nearly all of the water vapor and about three-fourths of all the air in the atmosphere is in the troposphere.

The word troposphere comes from a Greek word meaning *to turn and twist*. In this layer, air turns and twists, moving up, down, and sidewise to form air currents we call *winds*.

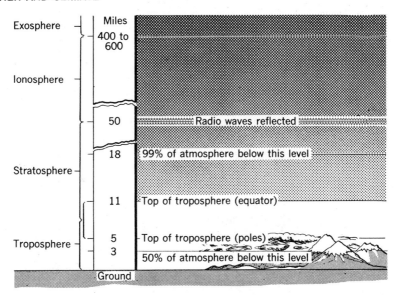

12-3. This diagram shows the divisions of the atmosphere into its various component layers. Notice that the troposphere is approximately twice as thick at the equator as it is at the poles.

Nearly all clouds, rain, snow, and hail occur in the troposphere. *Our weather occurs here.* The troposphere is the part of the atmosphere that supports life.

The stratosphere. The *stratosphere* is a deep layer that extends above the troposphere to 50 miles above the earth. Except for its low density, the air in the stratosphere is similar to the air in the troposphere.

Here, the weather is not so changeable. A few high clouds are in its lower levels, and there are traces of water vapor. The temperature in the lower stratosphere is about −70° F and, as we go higher, it rises and then falls again.

There are high-speed winds in the stratosphere. Sometimes these currents travel over 300 miles per hour and extend over half the country. They are called *jet streams* and usually blow from west to east. Jet streams are used to aid high-speed travel in the stratosphere.

The ionosphere affects radio waves. The third division of the atmosphere is the *ionosphere.* This layer extends from about 50 miles above the surface of the earth to about 400 miles. Some of the air in this zone is ionized, or electrically charged. These ions are produced by powerful cosmic rays and ultraviolet radiation from the sun. The lower part of the ionosphere acts like a mirror, reflecting radio broadcast waves back to earth. Other regions in the ionosphere have a similar effect on radio waves. The ability of the ionosphere to reflect radio waves makes it possible for you to hear distant radio stations. The temperature in the ionosphere rises steadily as the altitude increases whereas in the troposphere it decreases.

Beyond the ionosphere the region almost free of air is identified as the *exosphere.* This region is the space that is now being actively investigated by scientists. It is the frontier of *outer space.*

The atmosphere has many uses. We depend upon air for many other purposes besides the oxygen it provides us for breathing. For example, the air acts as a blanket to protect us from *meteorites.* Millions of these tiny chunks of matter from outer space crash toward the earth daily. Fortunately, most of them are burned to dust and ashes by the friction of the atmosphere and never strike the earth.

Air also absorbs most of the deadly *ultraviolet rays* from the sun. Enough of these rays pass through the atmosphere to cause sunburn and suntan; however, we could not survive exposure to the full dose of the sun's ultraviolet radiations. The effects of cosmic rays are also reduced considerably by the protective atmosphere.

Furthermore, light rays are scattered by our atmosphere. The sun's rays are scattered by our ocean of air so that a brightly-lighted sky is produced. Without an atmosphere there would be no sky light and we would see things in extremes of light and dark rather than in the gradual shadings so familiar to us. In other words, any spot not in direct sunlight would tend to be in almost total darkness were it not for the light scattering effect of the air.

The atmosphere also distributes heat. As you know, the regions near the equator are strongly heated by the sun. The great planetary winds or moving air currents are constantly carrying some of this heat by convection to the other parts of the earth. The atmosphere also acts like a blanket in preventing large amounts of heat from leaving the earth during the night.

The atmosphere actively distributes water over the whole earth. Can you imagine life in a world with no clouds and no rainfall? There could be no rivers or even streams.

Another important function of the atmosphere is to provide the *air to carry sound waves.* Without an atmosphere, the earth would be a silent planet.

Finally, the thick blanket of air extending hundreds of miles high has a substantial weight. The weight of air produces air pressure, which measures about 15 pounds per square inch at sea level. This means that the total weight of the many miles of air pressing down on this open book is over 1600 pounds! Why don't we "feel" this weight? Because air also pushes up with the same force. Thus, the final weight of the book is just its gravitational force.

This may seem a bit perplexing at first glance. First we say that the weight of the air is very great, but then we say that it is equalized so that it is not noticed. So why is it mentioned? The truth of the matter is that although it generally is taken for granted, air pressure is essential to us. Without this pressure our blood and other bodily fluids would boil. In space, astronauts must be constantly protected from a reduction in air pressure. Thus, capsules are pressurized and astronauts wear special suits to maintain pressure.

Air pressure is measured in many ways, but is usually based on the standard units derived from the mercury barometer. An inverted tube of mercury is placed with its open end in a dish of mercury. At sea-level, the atmospheric pressure will support a 760 millimeter column of mercury. Other instruments are calibrated with reference to this and thus usually have units of mm of mercury, or sometimes inches of mercury.

Air pressure is important in another way. Gradual variations in pressure build up over different parts of the earth. These variations cause movements of large masses of air as they seek to equalize; and thus they become important forces in our weather patterns.

How do these changes in air pressure occur? Why do they occur? These changes are due primarily to the heat of the sun. When air is heated it expands and rises. You have evidence of this every time you see smoke rise from chimneys. You can even see evidence of the rising currents of warm air from a lighted match or candle. The heated air rises because colder and heavier air displaces it, pushing it upward. Other examples of rising warm air and descending cold air can be seen by viewing bonfires, fireplaces, stoves, and any other source of heat. Another dramatic example can be seen in very cold climates. When a window is opened slightly at both the top and the bottom, you will notice that the cold air rushes vigorously into the room through the bottom opening of the window. At the same time the warm air of the room rushes out of the top opening with equal strength.

The movements of rising warm air and descending cold air are called *convection currents*. These are extremely important to weather patterns around the entire world. It is this cycle of rising and falling convection currents that produces most of the world's rain.

What causes winds? The movements of air rising from the heat of a burning match are duplicated on a gigantic scale all over the world. You know that the land surface heats up wherever the sun shines strongly for a long time. The land, in turn, warms the air above it. Another region may receive slanting, weaker rays from the sun, and the air above this cooler land will not be warmed as much. This heating and rising of the warmed air creates a constant movement of air. *Horizontal movements of air caused by the unequal heating of the earth's surface by the sun are called winds.*

Prevailing winds. General winds blow over large areas of the earth. They are caused by the sun's heat and are deflected by the earth's rotation. These are known as the *prevailing winds* and are shown in Fig. 12-4. Direct rays of the sun heat the land areas near the equator, causing the air above to warm up. This heated air slowly rises for several miles in the same manner that air rises over a hot stove.

Cool air from both sides comes in to replace the heated equatorial air. This entrance of cooler air creates the *trade winds* on both sides of the equator. Because of the earth's rotation, they are deflected so that they move in a westerly direction.

The gentle rising of warm air near the equator creates a zone of general calm or shifting winds called the *doldrums*. During the early days of sailing vessels, sailors feared the doldrum region because there was no dependable wind.

Heated air rises over the equator and then separates into two sections. Each section moves at high altitudes toward opposite poles. As the air moves, it becomes cooler and more dense. By the time it reaches about 30° north and south latitude, it is heavy enough to come down to earth again. This downward, vertical movement of air results in a high pressure area on the surface of the earth. Sea captains called this zone the *horse latitudes.*

As this downward movement of air hits the surface, it separates again. The flow toward the equator joins the trade winds that blow back toward the equator. The flow away from the equator becomes the *prevailing westerlies.* These are the prevailing winds in the United States; they "carry" our weather from west to east.

Here again, the rotation of the earth deflects the prevailing westerlies as shown in Fig. 12-4. These winds move in a northeasterly direction in the northern hemisphere until they meet the colder air moving from the polar regions toward the equator. The cold polar winds, called *polar easterlies,* force the westerlies to rise to higher altitudes. The meeting of the air masses takes place about 60° north and south latitude. After the upward move-

12-4. A map showing the prevailing winds of the world. The earth's rotation causes the winds to be deflected and move in different directions on different parts of the planet.

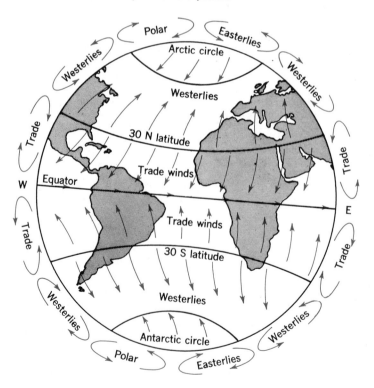

12-5. The three-cup anemometer records wind speed (left), while the arrow of the wind vane points into the wind. (US Weather Bureau)

ment continues for some time, the air mass divides. Some of this air moves back toward the poles and the rest returns southward at high altitudes.

How is wind speed measured? An instrument used to measure wind speed is called an *anemometer* (ann-eh-*mom-eh-ter*). This instrument is mounted on a tower so that local disturbances due to buildings and trees do not affect its reading. (See Fig. 12-5.) Many anemometers have automatic recording devices so that a permanent record of the wind speed can be made. Portable anemometers are often used at important track meets.

The wind direction is also important. A *wind vane* is usually mounted close to the anemometer and the wind direction is electrically transmitted to recording devices in the weather room. The *direction of wind* is the direction *from* which the wind is blowing. A north wind, for example, blows from north to south and causes the vane to point north.

What is a radiosonde? The Weather Bureau uses large plastic balloons filled with helium to obtain information from the upper atmosphere. They carry instruments called *radiosondes.* Pressure, wind speeds, temperature, and humidity are obtained and transmitted by radio to a ground receiver.

Eventually, the expansion of the gas inside the balloon resulting from reduced outside air pressure causes the balloon to burst, and the radio transmitter and weather instruments are lowered safely to the earth by a parachute. (See Fig. 12-6.)

Measuring air pressure. We have seen that air pressure is measured by an instrument called a *barometer.* The *mercury barometer* is simple to construct, but is bulky and easily broken. A more practical instrument, the *aneroid* (*an*-er-oid) *barometer* is smaller, less fragile, and more convenient to use. The aneroid barometer, which contains no liquid, looks much like an alarm clock. (See Fig. 12-7.) An increase in air pressure squeezes in the sides of a shallow, thin-walled metal box. The slightest change in the air-tight box is magnified by a series of levers, as shown in Fig. 12-7, causing the pointer to move across the scale on the face of the barometer.

When the atmospheric pressure decreases, the side of the shallow box bulges out again. This movement is transferred by the levers, and the pointer turns in the opposite direction.

Weathermen use the barometer in weather forecasting by taking barometric pressure readings at regular intervals. A gradual decrease in the air pressure often indicates that stormy or unsettled weather is approaching. The faster the pressure drops, the more

12-6. This weather observer releases a balloon and radiosonde. (Bendix Aviation Corp.)

violent the storm could be. A rise in air pressure usually indicates clear weather.

Altimeters are aneroid barometers. Barometers are also used to determine approximate altitudes. For each one-thousand feet increase of altitude in the lower troposphere, the barometer reading decreases by about 22 mm of mercury. By using an aneroid barometer, we can determine the height above sea level by merely reading the scale marked in thousands of feet instead of mm of mercury. Aneroid barometers used for this purpose in aircraft are called *altimeters*. Electronic altimeters that operate like radar and show the actual height above the earth's surface are also used in larger planes.

The amount of water in the atmosphere varies. Except for clouds and precipitation, the moisture of the atmosphere is not liquid, but a gas and is referred to as *water vapor*. The amount of the water vapor varies considerably from time to time and from place to place. In some of the hot tropical rain belts as much as 5 percent of the atmosphere's total volume may be water. Usually, however, the atmosphere contains considerably less and has almost no water vapor at all in some of the cold climates and great deserts of the world.

Where does the water come from? The water of the air comes mostly from the oceans which cover about 70 percent of the earth's surface. Other sources of moisture are the lakes and rivers of land areas, and also the water given off from plants and animals.

The change of water from a liquid to a gas is called *evaporation*. You can see evidence of evaporation by mois-

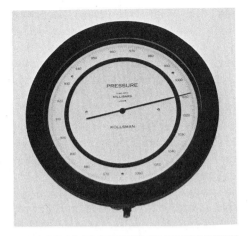

12-7. An external and internal view of the aneroid barometer. Pressure changes on the partial-vacuum container cause the pointer to move. (US Weather Bureau)

called *humidity*. Humidity changes with the weather, because warm air "holds" more water than cold air. Actually the presence of air makes little difference in how much water vapor can exist in a given space. At a particular temperature, only a certain maximum amount of water vapor can occupy a given amount of confined space. *As the temperature increases, more water vapor can occupy the space.* This is what we mean when we say that "warm air can hold more water vapor than cold air."

When a quantity of air contains all the water vapor that it can at a certain temperature, we say that it is *saturated* and has a *relative humidity* of 100 percent. *Relative humidity* is the amount of water vapor in a certain volume of air compared to the maximum amount that it can hold at that temperature.

If the air has only half the moisture that it can hold at that temperature, the relative humidity is 50 percent. At normal temperatures, people

tening the blackboard with water and watching the moisture dry off. Another way of seeing evidence of evaporation is to boil water in a kettle and hold a cold mirror or glass over the spout. Fog and tiny droplets of water soon condense on the glass. The moisture you see is not the vapor itself since that is invisible, but the tiny droplets of water that have condensed from the vapor. (See Fig. 12-8.)

What is meant by humidity? The amount of vapor found in the air is

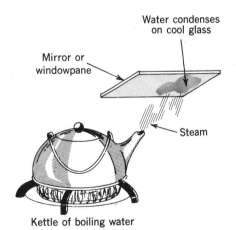

Water condenses on cool glass

Mirror or windowpane

Steam

Kettle of boiling water

12-8. Rapid evaporation and condensation. Water vapor escapes from a boiling kettle and condenses on a cool mirror or window pane.

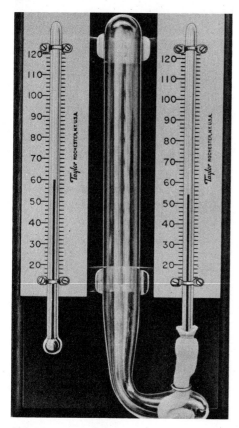

12-9. At low relative humidity, moisture evaporates from the wet bulb more rapidly, causing the wet bulb to have a lower reading than the dry bulb. (Taylor Instrument Co.)

The dry-bulb thermometer indicates the actual temperature of the air. The wet-bulb thermometer has a cloth wick surrounding its bulb. This wick is moistened with water. When the air is dry, the rapid evaporation of the water from the wick cools it. This makes the wet-bulb thermometer read less. The lower the relative humidity, the more rapidly the water evaporates and the greater will be the difference between the two thermometer readings. Relative humidity is read directly from prepared tables such as the one on the following page.

Let us consider an example in order to make use of the table shown. If the reading of the dry-bulb thermometer is 70° F, and the difference in readings between the dry-bulb and wet-bulb thermometers is 5 degrees, then the relative humidity is 77 percent.

Relative humidity is also determined by using a *hygrometer* (high-*grom*-eh-ter). One kind of hygrometer contains a human hair that shrinks or stretches as the air gets dry or moist. This motion is magnified mechanically and is indicated by a pointer on the dial.

What causes dew? Dew is formed by the condensation of water vapor on cold objects. At night the surface of the ground may lose heat rapidly. If the air near cold surface objects becomes sufficiently cool, its relative humidity becomes 100 percent. Further cooling causes the water vapor to form dew on cold objects. When the temperature is below freezing, the vapor condenses as frost instead of dew.

If we slowly add crushed ice, piece by piece, to water in a metal can, as shown in Fig. 12-10, and stir the wa-

are most comfortable when the relative humidity is between 40 percent and 60 percent. At a relative humidity above 60 percent, perspiration evaporates more slowly and we feel uncomfortable. High relative humidity on a summer day may make us more uncomfortable than the high temperature does.

How is relative humidity measured? One way of measuring the relative humidity is by using two thermometers, one having a *dry bulb* and the other a *wet bulb*. (See Fig. 12-9.)

DIFFERENCE BETWEEN DRY– AND WET–BULB THERMOMETERS

Degrees—F°	1	2	3	4	5	6	7	8	9	10	11	12	13	14	15
Reading of dry-bulb thermometer °F						*Percent humidity*									
63	95	89	84	79	74	69	64	60	55	51	46	42	38	33	29
64	95	89	84	79	74	70	65	60	56	51	47	43	38	34	30
65	95	90	85	80	75	70	65	61	56	52	48	44	39	35	31
66	95	90	85	80	75	71	66	61	57	53	49	45	40	36	32
67	95	90	85	80	76	71	66	62	58	53	49	45	41	37	33
68	95	90	85	81	76	71	67	63	58	54	50	46	42	38	34
69	95	90	86	81	76	72	67	63	59	55	51	47	43	39	35
70	95	90	86	81	77	72	68	64	60	55	52	48	44	40	36
71	95	91	86	81	77	72	68	64	60	56	52	48	45	41	37
72	95	91	86	82	77	73	69	65	61	57	53	49	45	42	38
73	95	91	86	82	78	73	69	65	61	57	53	50	46	42	39
74	95	91	86	82	78	74	70	66	62	58	54	50	47	43	40
75	95	91	87	82	78	74	70	66	62	58	55	51	47	44	40

ter with a thermometer, a film of water appears on the outside of the can. The temperature at the instant the moisture occurs is the *dew point.* This is the temperature at which *water vapor from air condenses into dew.* This explains why water appears on the outside of a glass of ice water. The air near the outer surface of the glass reaches the dew point and condensation occurs.

Knowledge of the dew point is important in predicting fog, rain, and snow. The relative humidity can also be determined from the dew point.

Cloud formations. The formation of clouds depends largely on humidity and temperature. Clouds usually result when masses of warm, moist air

12-10. The dew point is reached when the water vapor from the air first condenses on the surface of the metal container.

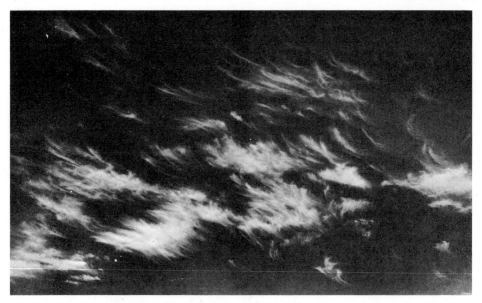

12-11. Cirrus clouds are usually the highest in the sky and appear as thin wisps. (US Weather Bureau)

become cooled. The invisible water vapor condenses on dust particles in the atmosphere to form visible water droplets. *A cloud is a mass of these droplets of water suspended in the atmosphere.* If the mass is close to the ground, we call it *fog.*

Cooling may take place in several ways. The air may lose some of its heat through *radiation.* Sometimes a cold mass of air mixes with warm, moist air. As the warm air is cooled, vapor condenses to form clouds. Or, the cooling takes place because of expansion of a warm air mass as it rises.

There are three basic cloud types. Clouds are classified according to the *altitude* at which they form and according to their *shape* and *appearance.* The U.S. Weather Bureau in agreement with the International Classification System lists 27 different cloud types. However, clouds are commonly grouped into a few basic systems. On the basis of altitude, clouds are classed as *high clouds,* which exist generally between 16,000 and 45,000 feet, *middle clouds,* from 6500 to 23,000 feet, and *low clouds* below 6500 feet. As the overlap in altitude suggests, these are general zones rather than specific.

Another method of classifying clouds is according to their shape, of which there are three basic types:

1. The *cirrus* (*seer*-us) or "curl" clouds are the *highest* in the sky. They are from three to seven miles above the surface of the earth and are considered to be *high clouds.* They look like thin, wispy curls, as shown in Fig. 12-11. Cirrus clouds are always made of ice crystals, because the air is so cold at these altitudes. These clouds indicate how the air of the upper troposphere moves as they go across the sky.

12-12. Cumulus clouds form large wooly puffs at moderate heights. (US Weather Bureau)

2. The *cumulus* (*kew*-mew-lus) clouds are heaped-up masses, flat at the bottom but piling up to a great height in large woolly puffs. For the most part, they are in the *middle* and *lower* troposphere, from one to four miles up. Sometimes, though, they extend from a lower to a much higher altitude. They often result from the condensation of moisture as currents of air rise upward. The updrafts from heated surfaces can bring about tremendous masses of cumulus clouds. Figure 12-12 shows typical cumulus clouds. These clouds are usually associated with fair weather.

3. *Stratus,* or "layer" clouds, are flat and are usually found in the *lower* troposphere. They are the clouds nearest the earth. Figure 12-13 shows a typical stratus cloud formation.

Other cloud names. The prefixes *alto-* (high), *nimbo-* (rain), and *frac-* to- (broken) are other words used to describe clouds. For example, an *alto-stratus* is a high cloud of the stratus type. The kind of cloud that brings thunderstorms is a *cumulonimbus.* A *nimbostratus* is the common, flat, gray, rain cloud from which rain is already falling.

Some clouds are a combination of two types, such as the *cirrocumulus* or the *stratocumulus.* Try watching clouds each day and see if you can recognize the different types.

What happens to accumulated water in the atmosphere? We have followed the movement of the water from the oceans and land areas into the atmosphere. If the water moved only from the surface of the earth into the air, the atmosphere would soon be saturated. There must be a place for the accumulated moisture to go; there must be an outlet. This outlet is a re-

12-13. Stratus clouds form thin flat layers and are closest to the earth. (US Weather Bureau)

12-14. The hydrological cycle (or water cycle). Moisture moves from the earth into the atmosphere by evaporation, and by transpiration from vegetation where it accumulates as clouds and finally condenses to fall back to the earth.

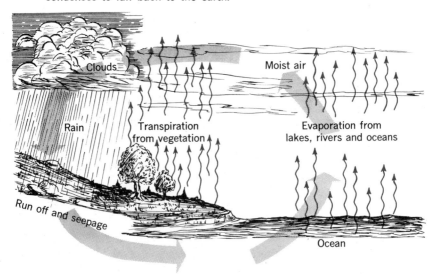

lease of moisture, usually in the form of rain, snow, sleet, or hail. This completes the path of moisture: first evaporating into the atmosphere, then forming clouds, and finally condensing into rain to return again to earth. This path forms a cycle which continually repeats itself. (See Fig. 12-14.)

What is precipitation? Now let us look at the returning moisture falling to earth. Meteorologists refer to this as *precipitation.* If the temperature is below freezing, the moisture in the air may crystallize directly into a solid instead of condensing into a liquid as rain. These crystals sometimes cling together and form *snow.* The crystal structure of snow depends upon the temperature during its formation. Larger snowflakes are formed just below freezing, while smaller flakes form at a much lower temperature.

Sleet results when raindrops falling through a very cold layer of air freeze into small pellets. During violent thunderstorms, chiefly in summer, updrafts and downdrafts cause raindrops to pass through many layers of warm and cold air, thus building up ice particles in onion-like layers. These ice particles are called *hail.*

How is precipitation measured? A *rain gauge* is commonly used by weather men to measure rainfall. It consists of an outer cylinder in which a smaller collecting tube is placed. A funnel is attached to the smaller tube supported by the larger container. (See Fig. 12-15.) The mouth of the funnel has an area that is 10 times larger than the inner collecting tube. This means that the rain collected in the tube is 10 times that of the actual rainfall. A narrow measuring stick measures the rainfall directly in inches.

12-15. The parts of a rain gauge include a support, overflow can, measuring tube, and a funnel that has an area ten times as great as that of the measuring tube. (US Weather Bureau)

The term "inches of rainfall" represents the thickness of the water layer the rain would leave on a level area if none of the rainfall were lost.

A depth of ten inches of snow is usually considered to equal one inch of rain.

Quick Quiz

1. What is the effect of a large body of water on climate?
2. Is there evidence that the climates of the earth have changed during recorded history? Explain.
3. What are the four major divisions of the atmosphere?
4. Name some of the ways in which the atmosphere is useful to us.
5. Describe the water cycle.
6. Name some of the components that make up weather.

7. Explain several factors that control climate.
8. Does the statement "It is cloudy today" refer to weather or climate?
9. Would you expect greater seasonal temperature variations in Minneapolis or in New York? Explain.
10. In what way is air pressure essential to our existence?
11. What causes doldrums?
12. What does a declining barometric reading indicate about probable future weather conditions?
13. Would you expect the relative humidity of a cool ocean air mass to increase or decrease as it travels over a warm land mass? Explain.
14. Would you expect the relative humidity to be high or low in the desert? Along the ocean? Explain.
15. Would you expect more rain on the eastern slope of the Rockies or on the western slope? Explain.

B AIR MASSES AND FRONTS

Characteristics of air masses. We have looked at some of the components of weather and climate such as air, its movements, its changes in temperature and pressure; and the function of wa-

ter vapor in the atmosphere. Now we will see how they combine and interact to produce the major weather and climate patterns all over the world.

A mass of quiet air takes on the temperature and humidity characteristics of the surface of the earth over which it lies. For example, an air mass over northern Canada in winter is very cold and dry because of the low temperature and low humidity in this region. Air masses over tropical regions are moist and hot. Hence, the atmosphere is made up of large portions of air having fairly uniform characteristics. These are called *air masses.*

As the air masses move away from a region, they tend to retain their temperature and moisture characteristics and affect the weather of the area over which they pass. An air mass, in turn, is gradually modified by surface conditions over which it moves.

The air masses which influence most of the weather of the United States are shown in the table below and Fig. 12-16.

Storms usually occur when a *tropical* air mass meets a *polar* air mass. Let us now examine the movements of these large air masses and see how they affect the weather.

Cold fronts. Air masses do not usually mix unless they are very similar in moisture content and in temperature. When a cold dry air mass, for

Air Mass	Characteristics	Weather Map Symbol
maritime polar	cold and moist	mP
continental polar	cold and dry	cP
maritime tropical	warm and moist	mT
continental tropical	warm and dry	cT

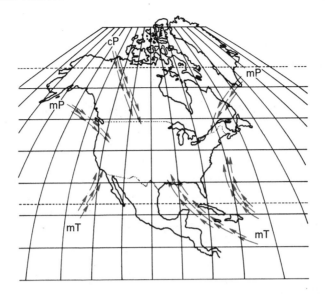

12-16. These air masses influence most of the weather in the United States.

example, meets a moist hot mass, the boundary between them is called a *front.*

If the cold mass pushes back the warm air, the boundary is called a *cold front.* The sloping edge of a cold front is very steep and produces an *abrupt* lifting of warm air. As the cold air pushes up the lighter warm air, thick cumulus clouds form above the boundary. (See Fig. 12-17.) Rain or snow may fall as this rising moist air mass cools. As the front passes and the cold mass moves over a region, scattered patches of cumulus clouds may appear. Clear, cooler weather is often found to follow the passage of a cold front.

At times in many parts of the United States, a cold front may be accompanied by a series of thunderstorms making a boundary called a *squall line.*

Cold fronts may extend over several hundred miles in length. They advance at a speed of about 20 miles per hour, traveling faster in winter than in summer.

Warm fronts. When a mass of warm air advances, replacing the colder air, a *warm front* is formed. The lighter, warm air tends to ride up over the cold air wedge, as shown in Fig. 12-18. The slope between the warm and cold air is much less steep than it is in a cold front.

You can see a warm front approaching an area by watching the sky. First, you observe cirrus clouds high up across the sky. Then altostratus clouds follow at lower altitudes, and finally nimbostratus clouds as the front reaches the area. A drizzling rain lasting for hours is typical of the passage of a warm front. Warmer weather follows as the warm air moves in over the re-

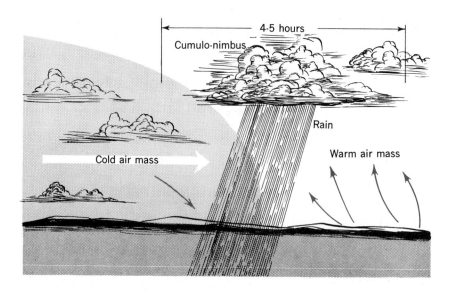

12-17. An approaching cold front pushes up masses of warm air. Rain usually falls from the cumulonimbus clouds that form at the front.

12-18. A warm front, which forms when a mass of warm air displaces a cold air mass, may extend 300 to 600 miles. Rain usually will form in front of the warm air mass, and the cirrus and stratus clouds form the front separating the warm and cold air.

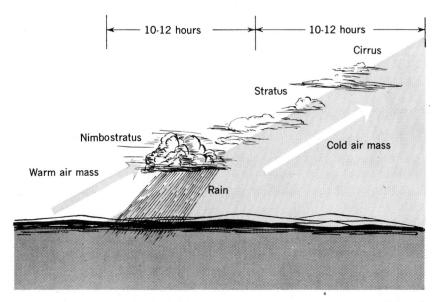

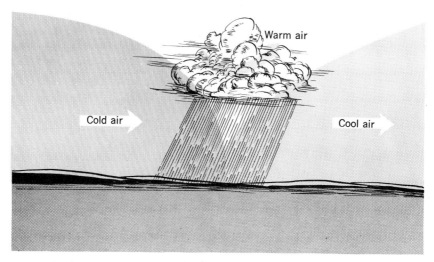

12-19. An occluded front is formed when two cold fronts overtake a warm front. The cold air forces the warm air up above the cool front. The resulting occluded front may take on the characteristics of either a cold or a warm front.

gion. Warm fronts usually advance much more slowly than cold fronts, moving at about 15 miles per hour, or less.

What are some other fronts? Sometimes neither the warm nor the cold air mass is able to push back the other. When this happens, we say that a *stationary front* has developed. Weather conditions at a stationary front are similar to that of a warm front.

At times, two cold air masses and a warm air mass meet. If the *warm air mass is lifted between the two cold air masses,* a "closed in," or *occluded front,* is formed. Occluded fronts may take on either warm front or cold front characteristics. (See Fig. 12-19.)

Weather maps indicate frontal systems by a series of symbols as shown in Fig. 12-20.

Anticyclones are "highs." The large world-wide masses of air don't move down from the poles in neat straight paths. The rotation of the earth as well as unequal heating and cooling of the land and sea masses set up a series of large swirling pressure systems. A high pressure area, or "high," may develop at any place where the upper cool air, being heavier than the warmer air near the earth's surface, tends to sink. As the cool air moves outward, it slowly develops a spiral motion because of the earth's rotation. In the northern hemisphere, its winds revolve in a *clockwise* motion away from the center, as shown in Fig. 12-21, and may cover an area several hundred miles in diameter.

A rising barometer reading usually indicates that an *anticyclone* (high) is approaching, bringing generally fair weather, light winds, and cooler temperature conditions over a relatively long period of time.

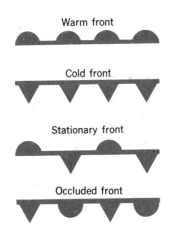

Warm front

Cold front

Stationary front

Occluded front

12-20. These symbols are used on weather maps to identify fronts.

Cyclones are "lows." A *low* is usually formed when a mass of warm moist air near the earth's surface rises. This upward movement of the warm air creates a *low pressure area* that is filled by surrounding air moving in toward the center. This air rotates in a *counterclockwise* motion in the northern hemisphere, as shown in Fig. 12-21. As the moist air continues to rise, it becomes cooler and finally loses its moisture as rain or snow.

A falling barometer reading usually indicates that a *cyclone* (low) is approaching. We can generally expect cloudy weather with some precipitation, strong winds, warmer and unsettled weather conditions.

"Highs" tend to follow "lows" across the United States in a more or less easterly direction. A shift in the wind may indicate that a high has followed a low over a given region.

Notice that, to the meteorologist, the word "cyclone" does not mean a violent storm, but just a low-pressure area. A *destructive* cyclone is called a *hurricane* or *typhoon*.

12-21. Anticyclones are "highs" and cyclones are "lows." The "high" does not refer to altitude but to pressure caused by the cooler, heavier, air. The "low" being warm and light may actually attain a greater altitude. The movement of air masses is generally from the "high" to the "low."

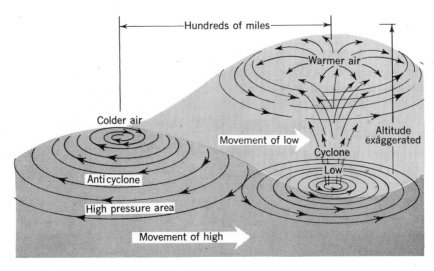

Hundreds of miles

Warmer air

Colder air

Movement of low

Altitude exaggerated

Cyclone

Anticyclone

Low

High pressure area

Movement of high

Warm air cooling

Air heated over land moves toward water

Cooler air over water moves toward land

Warm air cooling

Cooler air over land

Warmer air over water rises

12-22. Sea breezes (left) occur when the land heats up more rapidly than the water. Land breezes occur when the land cools more rapidly than the water (right).

Continental and maritime air. *High mountains* and large *bodies of water* tend to change prevailing winds. Air that has moved over the ocean is called *maritime air*. Air that has passed over a continental land area is called *continental air*. As you can see, maritime air picks up more water vapor than air traveling across a comparatively dry continent. When the moist air reaches a mountain, it may lose a great deal of moisture as precipitation. A good example of this is the large amount of rainfall in Washington and Oregon, where the prevailing westerlies bring in maritime air from the Pacific. In some of these mountain areas, 100 or more inches of rainfall annually is not uncommon.

Sea, land, valley, and mountain breezes. Places near the shores of large bodies of water have gentle winds known as *sea breezes* and *land breezes*. (See Fig. 12-22.) When the sun is shining on a shore line, the land heats up faster than the water. One reason for this is the fact that the *specific heat* of water is high compared with that of land. The air above the land becomes warmer than that over the water. The warmer air over the land is forced upward by the cooler air coming from over the water to give a *sea breeze.*

During the night, a breeze in the opposite direction develops. Water warms up more slowly, but it also cools off more slowly than the land. As the land cools off rapidly at night, the air above it becomes cooled faster than the air above the water. The cooler land air forces upward the warmer air over the water. This movement of air from the land area to water area is called a *land breeze.* Perhaps you have noticed a breeze from the land when out in a boat at night. Sea and land breezes do much to make the climate at shore resorts pleasant during hot weather.

During a warm, sunny day, the heating of the mountain slopes causes the air near the surface to rise by convection. Air from the valley below moves up the slope producing a mild *valley breeze* along the mountain slope.

At night, the same mountain slopes cool off quickly, causing air near the ground to cool, also. The cool, heavier air then "flows" down from the mountain tops into the valley as a *mountain breeze.* If the valley is very narrow, the mountain breeze is likely to be much stronger than the valley breeze. (See Fig. 12-23.)

What are monsoon winds? A *monsoon wind* is a huge land or sea breeze that changes direction with the seasons instead of with day and night. The cause of the monsoon winds is much the same as that for land and sea breezes. Instead of shallow layers of air moving on the surface, large masses are involved. These winds blow *from the sea* to the continent during the hot *summer* and *from the land* to the water during the *winter.* The summer monsoon winds from the sea are

responsible for the greatest deluges in the world. The greatest recorded rainfall during a 12-month period occurred in Cherrapunji, India, between August 1, 1860, and July 31, 1861. During this time over 1040 inches of rain fell. This represents over 100,000 tons of water per acre, and is 36 times greater than the annual average rainfall in the United States.

Monsoons also occur in other parts of the world, notably in the tropics and parts of Asia close to the China Sea and the Arabian Sea.

What is a storm? A *storm is a natural disturbance in the atmosphere.* It may be violent, having strong winds that bring rain or snow, or it may be a gentle movement of a large mass of air that you hardly notice. Sudden changes in temperature over a local area cause some of our most violent storms.

Previously we used the terms *cyclone* and *anticyclone* describing a condition for a *low* and *high,* respectively. The word "cyclone" is applied to a low-pressure area with its rotating winds.

Thunderstorms are local storms. They are characterized by gusty

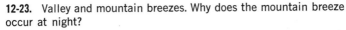

12-23. Valley and mountain breezes. Why does the mountain breeze occur at night?

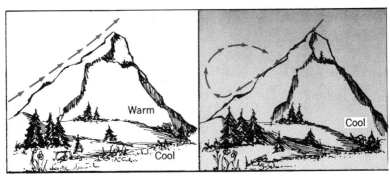

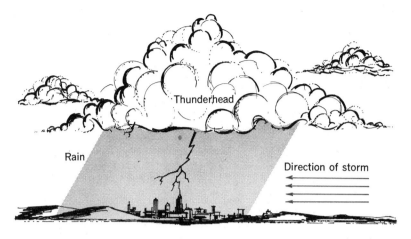

12-24. The cumulonimbus cloud is a regular "storm factory." The moist air rising rapidly through the cloud gives rise to thunderstorms.

winds, lightning, thunder, and, usually, rain and sometimes hail. Strong currents of moist air are also typical. *Thunderstorms* occur most frequently in spring and summer when a local area is strongly heated. Rising currents of warm, moist air are rapidly cooled as they go up. Condensation occurs, forming thick masses of huge cumulonimbus clouds called *thunderheads.* (See Fig. 12-24.) Within the cloud there may be columns of air moving violently up and down, subjecting water and ice particles to much friction with the air. This activity, in turn, helps to produce positive and negative charges of electricity. Often one part of the cloud becomes negatively charged while another part carries a positive charge.

When these masses become sufficiently charged, the electricity may discharge as *lightning* from one cloud to another or from the cloud to the earth. (See Fig. 12-25.) Most discharges take place between clouds.

The very hot bolt of lightning causes the air to expand suddenly as it passes through, producing the strong pressure wave that we hear as *thunder.* Thunderstorms are a hazard to flight chiefly because of the strains in the aircraft caused by sudden updrafts and downdrafts of air. They may also disturb radio communication.

The approach of a thunderstorm may be signaled by a strong wind which precedes the storm by several minutes. This is called a *squall wind,* and it is extremely dangerous to small boats in open water.

Tornadoes are violent storms. *Tornadoes* are the most violent of all storms, but fortunately occur only over small areas. They are made up of a whirling mass of air revolving at speeds of hundreds of miles per hour. These storms vary in diameter from several hundred feet to about a mile. Tornadoes follow twisting paths that are unpredictable. The most impressive part of a tornado is its *funnel-*

12-25. Lightning strikes somewhere on the earth about 100 times every second. It is common in many parts of the United States. (H. Armstrong Roberts)

shaped cloud, laden with dust and rain, that moves as fast as 50 miles per hour. (See Fig. 12-26.)

Tornadoes are caused by the sudden heating of a small area, which creates a low pressure. Air rushing in to replace the rising air at the region of low pressure enters with a violent whirling motion. *Extremely low pressures* exist in the interior of a tornado. Conditions best suited for the formation of tornadoes are found ahead of a cold front. Our Weather Bureau can now usually predict when and where tornadoes are likely to occur.

These violent storms destroy almost everything in their paths, killing many people. Tornadoes occur most frequently over the lower Mississippi Valley. Their great forces are capable of driving straws into a piece of wood, destroying buildings, and lifting and dropping frogs, fish, and other small animals from one location to other nearby areas. Similar storms occurring over the ocean are called *waterspouts.*

Hurricanes are tropical cyclones. *Hurricanes* are storms that originate in late summer and early fall over seas and oceans in the tropical areas. Most hurricanes that affect North America occur in August, September, and October.

While there is no satisfactory explanation for the formation of hurricanes, it is likely that considerable heating of the water causes a spiraling updraft stretching across hundreds of square miles. As this very humid air rises, it cools rapidly. Large quantities of heat are given off as the water vapor condenses. This further warms the air as it continues to rise and gives it the energy needed for violent activity. Its violence diminishes as it travels over land because of the friction offered by trees, hills, and buildings. (See Fig. 12-27.)

The "eye" is the center of the hurricane. This is a circular area of very low pressure. It may vary from a few miles to about 25 miles in diameter, and is a region that is rather calm, with no rain.

As the center of the hurricane approaches an area, the wind first blows violently in one direction. Then there is a calm and clear skies as the

12-27. Notice the counterclockwise wind direction of this typical hurricane path over our Atlantic coast.

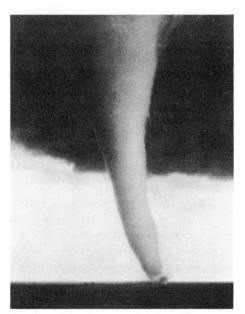

12-26. A funnel-shaped tornado cloud is a mass of air revolving at high speeds. (US Weather Bureau)

eye passes. A wind blowing in the opposite direction soon follows the calm as the other side of the *low* passes. Hurricanes cause great destruction because of wind speeds that may reach more than 150 miles per hour. Destructive winds may cover an area 500 miles wide and more than a thousand miles in length. Considerable amounts of rain fall in this area. The storm itself moves very slowly at first, usually a few miles a day. As the storm moves over land, its speed increases to about 100 miles per day. Tropical storms must attain wind speeds of at least 75 miles per hour before they are called hurricanes. Barometer readings as low as 28.00 inches of mercury are fairly common in well-developed hurricanes. The lowest barometer reading ever recorded in a hurricane was 26.35 inches in Florida in 1935.

Hurricanes usually originate in the Caribbean, West Indies, or the Gulf of Mexico. Hurricanes do not occur on the equator. They usually form between 6° and 15° north or south latitude on the western sides of the oceans.

The southwestern part of the north Pacific has more hurricanes than any other place on earth. Hurricanes formed between the Philippines and the Marshall Islands are called *typhoons*. These travel northward toward Japan.

Weather signs and superstitions. In some parts of the country you can become fairly expert at predicting the weather by observing certain "weather signs." In other parts of the country, even meteorologists, using their scientific instruments and skill, have a hard time trying to forecast the weather.

It is usual for the air pressure to fall and the humidity to rise as a storm (low) approaches from the west. Some of the following rain signs result from these atmospheric changes:

1. Rheumatic pains in arm and leg joints, or in corns or bunions.

2. Smoke sinking, instead of rising, as it leaves the chimney.

3. High, wispy "mare's tail" clouds in the western sky.

4. "Evening red and morning gray help the traveler on his way; Evening gray and morning red bring down rain upon his head."

Some so-called weather signs, however, are pure superstition. For example, in some places it is said that if the groundhog (woodchuck) sees his shadow on February 2, he will return to his den, and six weeks of bad weather will follow. Another is that rain on St. Swithin's Day (July 15) will be followed by rain during the next 40 days.

The beginning of scientific weather observation and forecasting. Although the Greeks used the term "meteorology" over 2300 years ago, it wasn't until relatively recent times that scientific weather observations and predictions were begun. In the United States the first national effort toward gathering weather data was begun in 1870 when the National Weather Service was organized by the Army Signal Corps. In 1890, the Weather Bureau was organized to continue and expand the functions of the National Weather Service. The Weather Bureau was originally under the jurisdiction of the Department of Agriculture, but in 1940 it was transferred to the Department of Commerce.

Gathering weather data. One of the most important functions of the Bureau is to gather weather data. Local weathermen record information about the winds and cloud formations, changes in barometric pressure, and changes in temperature and humidity. These observations help in predicting what the weather is likely to be a few hours later.

However, these local observations alone are not sufficient to reveal the movement of large air masses and the accompanying weather changes. To get such data, the United States Weather Bureau obtains reports from hundreds of stations throughout North America and other continents. Instruments on ships, in aircraft, balloons, rockets, and satellites are used.

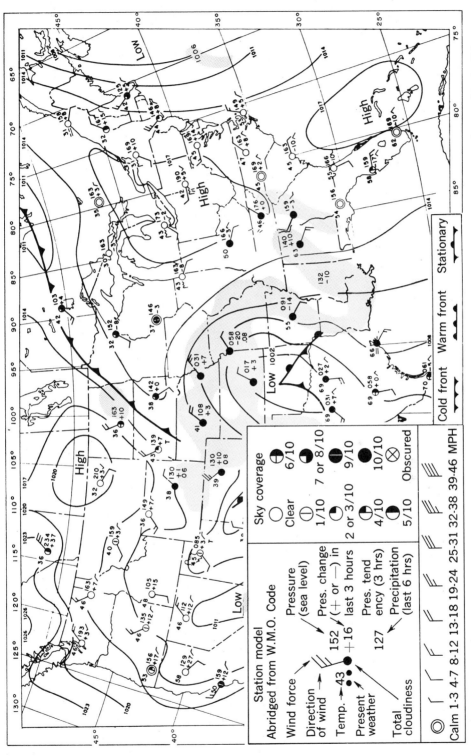

12-28. Our daily weather map contains data received from stations all over the country. From the map, discuss the weather in Chicago.

Reports are centralized. Over 600 Weather Bureau stations send reports by telegraph, teletype, radio, and telephone four times each day to the central weather station at Washington, D.C. Some stations send reports more frequently, particularly when the weather is unusual.

From the information received from all these sources, the Weather Bureau compiles the *Daily Weather Map* and issues predictions for various regions of the country. *A weather map shows actual weather conditions at a given time at a particular place.*

If you look at a copy of a Daily Weather Map, you will see that each location, or station, has a code system for conveying various information. This information makes up the *station model*. A **station model** is a convenient way of placing a great deal of information on a weather map. (See Fig. 12-28 insert.)

Electronic machines are now being used to make routine *forecasts*. These "electronic brains" are fed the observed weather data. Then they issue the prediction and print *forecast maps*. These maps are then modified to accommodate local conditions. Machine forecasting saves many man-hours of routine work.

Weather maps help forecasters. After the station information is recorded on a map, lines called *isobars* are drawn. *Isobars* are lines on a weather map that connect *points of equal barometric pressure,* as shown in Fig. 12-28. The isobars on weather maps give the pressure in *millibars.* Standard atmospheric pressure (760 mm of mercury) equals 1013 millibars.

Highs and *lows* are marked and labeled, as are areas of rain or snow. In addition, *air masses* and *fronts* are located and marked with symbols. *Isotherms* are also usually included

12-29. The movement of cyclones (lows) across the United States in an easterly direction.

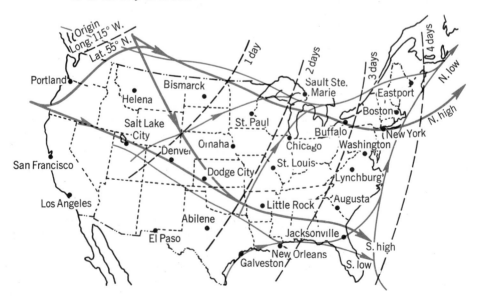

on a weather map. *Isotherms* are lines drawn through *places of equal temperature.*

A meteorologist studies the weather map and other charts and compares them with those of the past few days. With past and present information, and taking into consideration other local factors, he forecasts the weather for the next 24 or 36 hours.

The rate of movement of weather fronts *averages* about 500 miles per day in summer and about 700 miles per day in winter. In general, this motion is in a northeasterly direction. Benjamin Franklin was one of the first to become aware of this, when he noticed that the weather he experienced in Philadelphia often arrived in Boston about a day later. (See Fig. 12-29.)

Forecasts for the local weather are provided by each weather station throughout the country. Weather reports are given by radio and television stations. Simplified weather maps with fewer details are compiled from the larger map and are often printed in your newspapers. A copy of one such simplified weather map is shown in Fig. 12-28.

Besides the daily map, the Weather Bureau provides special forecasts of changed conditions as needed.

Hurricane warning system. One of the special functions of the U.S. Weather Bureau is to maintain a constant watch for signs of developing hurricanes.

Special *weather planes* are sent into hurricane centers to obtain weather data. Bulletins are issued every 6 hours giving the warning and the probable path. In this way, people

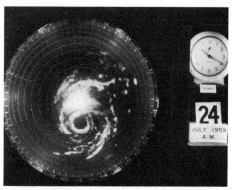

12-30. This photograph on the radarscope was taken during the formation of the eye of the hurricane. (Dow Chemical Co.)

have time to take necessary precautions for the preservation of life and property.

Radar stations along the eastern United States provide a considerable amount of information regarding the location and direction of the storm path. (See Fig. 12-30.) A very sensitive *micro-seismograph* is used to pick up disturbances caused by storms at sea and to locate and track the path of a hurricane. *Seismographs* are instruments that have long been used to record movements of the earth's crust, such as earthquakes and other disturbances. You may recall that they were used by geologists in searching for petroleum. Violent storms cause slight movements of the surface of the earth that may also be detected by these super-sensitive instruments.

Other functions of the Weather Bureau. Besides preparing the daily reports, the Weather Bureau performs many other services. Pilots are briefed by military and civil agencies on the weather to be expected before take-off and during flight. Advance information of hurricanes, thunderstorms, and tornadoes helps people to take proper precautions and permits travelers to avoid these storms.

During World War II, the original date for the invasion of France was postponed until meteorologists could predict more favorable landing conditions for the invasion of Normandy.

Fishermen and mariners avoid trouble by using weather reports. Special reports are issued to warn of dangerous floods and of "fire weather." Farmers study weather reports to be prepared for frost or other bad conditions. Contractors plan their construction work with weather predictions in mind. Railroads, utility and bus companies plan for emergencies when storm warnings are issued. This service is all of great value in protecting life and property. Other agencies, both private and public, supplement Weather Bureau information.

Progress in meteorology. Great advances have been made in collecting weather data during recent years. In addition to the use of radar, seismographs, specially equipped aircraft, and computors, the Weather Bureau uses *space probes* and *satellites*. *Sounding rockets* are launched to altitudes which are normally inaccessible to the balloons. These rockets gather data about wind, temperature, density,

12-31. The complex electronic system of a Tiros weather satellite includes magnetic tape recorders sealed in under the glass domes and a television lens housed in a cylinder below the platform. (RCA)

12-32. Nimbus, a second-generation weather satellite. (NASA)

and pressure at heights usually of 20 to 100 miles.

Perhaps the greatest recent advance in weather prediction has been the use of weather satellites. The first weather satellite, called *TIROS*, was launched on April 1, 1960. (See Fig. 12-31.) Although it was simple compared to the satellites now in orbit, it doubled the amount of the earth's surface under observation by weather stations. After a series of TIROS satellites, the NIMBUS was launched. (See Fig. 12-32.) It is a much more sophisticated satellite than TIROS and scans all of the earth's surface each day. A satellite's-eye view of the earth is shown in Fig. 12-33.

Ultimately, a still more advanced weather satellite will travel above the equator in a "stationary" or synchronous orbit. It will travel like the Syncom Communications Satellite at the same speed and direction that the earth turns. Thus, to an observer on earth, it will appear to be stationary in the heavens. In this way the satellite pro-

vides continuous surveillance of a given portion of the earth below its cameras. The system of high altitude rockets and satellites is shown in Fig. 12-34.

Controlling the weather. Some day scientists will be able to control weather. In some small ways this control has already begun. For example, freezing temperatures in citrus and cranberry-growing regions are often controlled by the use of such devices as smudge pots and wind machines. By these methods, temperatures are increased by a few degrees in order to avoid frost damage to the crops.

Another means of controlling weather has been the use of heat to disperse fog over a closed-in airport. If conditions are right, the heat causes

12-33. This photograph was taken from a meteorological satellite orbiting over the Great Lakes region of the United States and Canada. (NASA)

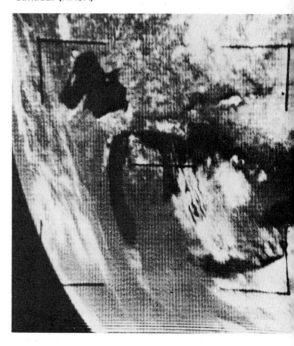

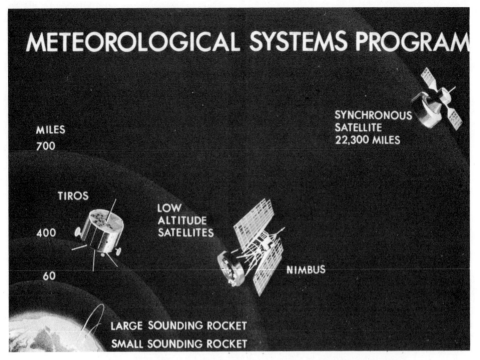

METEOROLOGICAL SYSTEMS PROGRAM

MILES
700

SYNCHRONOUS
SATELLITE
22,300 MILES

TIROS

LOW
ALTITUDE
SATELLITES

400

60

NIMBUS

LARGE SOUNDING ROCKET
SMALL SOUNDING ROCKET

12-34. The US meteorological systems program includes sounding rockets and orbiting satellites. (NASA)

the fog to evaporate sufficiently to improve visibility.

Rainmaking has been the subject of man's concern for many centuries. Now it seems that to some slight degree man can finally exercise some 'control. Rain or snow can often be formed by a process known as "seeding" clouds. As early as 1946, pellets of dry ice were dropped into clouds and caused precipitation to occur. More recent versions of cloud-seeding use a smoke made of very fine silver iodide particles on which water droplets can condense. The major drawback of cloud-seeding is that it seems to work only in certain types of clouds that are likely to produce rain anyway. Thus, there is no positive way of

determining whether the rain was man-made or natural.

Surprisingly, the real benefits of rainmaking may not be in the attempts to create rain where there is a lack of water, but in encouraging rain where there already is a great abundance of it. Great hurricanes often carry torrential rains over the south and east coasts of the United States causing floods and destruction. If these hurricanes can be induced to drop some of their rain into the ocean *before* they reach land, much destruction might be averted. Also the amount of heat released when water condenses may help reduce the storm's intensity.

Effective control of the weather will probably take centuries to accomplish.

Quick Quiz

1. What is an air mass?
2. What factors determine whether a front is to be called a cold front or a warm front?
3. How is continental air different from maritime air?
4. Outline the history of the development of the U.S. Weather Bureau.
5. List and describe some of the recent developments in meteorology.
6. What are some examples of controlling weather?
7. Is a sea breeze comparatively warm or cold? Is a land breeze comparatively warm or cold?
8. Explain what happens to the air between the horse latitudes.
9. What kind of weather is generally associated with a stationary front?
10. What are mountain and valley breezes?
11. What is the difference between sea breezes and monsoons?
12. How does high relative humidity affect the evaporation of water?

SUMMARY

Weather is the condition of the atmosphere at a certain place and time. Climate is the general condition of the atmosphere over a long period of time. The components that make up weather include air pressure, humidity wind, temperature, clouds, and precipitation. The factors that control climate are altitude, latitude, prevailing winds, mountains, and large bodies of water.

Traces of the atmosphere extend up to 1000 miles during major solar disturbances. There are four atmospheric layers: (1) troposphere; (2) stratosphere; (3) ionosphere; and (4) exosphere.

Water vapor causes clouds, humidity, and precipitation. Clouds are grouped by altitude into (1) high clouds, (2) medium clouds, and (3) low clouds. They are also grouped by form or shape into (1) cirrus, (2) cumulus, and (3) stratus. Cloud types and formations give us important weather information.

The unequal distribution of the sun's heat and the earth's rotation cause the prevailing winds of the earth. The differences in the heating and cooling of land and water regions give rise to sea and land breezes. Regions of high pressures are called anticyclones, or highs. These air masses revolve in a clockwise direction away from the center in the northern hemisphere and usually bring clear weather. Regions of low pressure are called cyclones, or lows. These masses of air revolve in a counterclockwise direction toward the center in the northern hemisphere and usually bring unsettled weather.

Air masses move across a region, carrying the temperature and moisture characteristics of their origin. They affect the weather in the regions over which they pass. The boundary between an advancing mass of cold air and a mass of warm air is called a cold front. A warm front is formed where a mass of warm air displaces a cold air mass.

A storm is a disturbance in the atmosphere. Thunderstorms occur after a local area has been strongly heated. Thunderheads, or cumulonimbus clouds, are storm factories. Tornadoes are very violent storms over a narrow path, with a whirling mass of air forming a funnel-shaped cloud. Hurricanes and typhoons are violent whirling masses of air, several hundreds of miles in diameter, originating over tropical waters.

Weather forecasts are based on information contained on weather maps and other charts. Cloud patterns observed by the United States Tiros and Nimbus weather satellites help meteorologists in improving forecasts.

CHAPTER REVIEW

Vocabulary

Match the words in Column A with the *best* response in Column B. Do not write in your book.

Column A	Column B
1. weather	a. a large portion of air having uniform characteristics
2. climate	
3. winds	b. a large whirlpool of air at low atmospheric pressure
4. humidity	
5. relative humidity	c. a large whirlpool of air at high atmospheric pressure
6. cirrus	
7. cumulus	d. amount of water vapor in a certain volume of air compared with the total amount that it can hold at that temperature
8. stratus	
9. precipitation	
10. air mass	e. boundary between air masses that are not in motion
11. cold front	
12. warm front	f. boundary formed where a warm air mass is lifted between two cold masses
13. stationary front	
14. occluded front	g. boundary formed where a warm air mass displaces a mass of cold air
15. anticyclone	
16. cyclone	h. boundary formed where a mass of cold air displaces a mass of warm air
17. tornado	
18. isobars	i. condition of the atmosphere at a particular time and place
19. isotherms	
20. seismograph	j. instrument used to record movements in the earth's surface
	k. large wooly clouds found at moderate heights
	l. lines of equal barometric pressure on a weather map
	m. lines of equal temperature on a weather map
	n. moisture falling to the earth in the form of rain, snow, sleet, hail, or drizzle
	o. movements of air caused by unequal heating of the earth's surface
	p. the amount of water vapor in a given volume of air

q. the general condition of the atmosphere over a long period of time
r. thin flat layer clouds close to the earth's surface
s. thin wispy clouds, consisting of ice crystals, and occurring at high altitudes
t. very violent whirlwind that occurs over a narrow path

Questions: Group A

1. How deep is the troposphere at the equator? At the poles?
2. About how deep is the ocean of air?
3. Are there any temperature changes in the stratosphere?
4. What effect does temperature have on the amount of water vapor air can "hold"?
5. In what way does relative humidity affect our comfort?
6. In which direction is a south wind traveling? In which direction does it make a vane point?
7. What are the three main cloud *forms*?
8. What causes winds?
9. Why are prevailing winds deflected?
10. What important changes usually occur when saturated air is cooled?
11. What is the name given to the zone of calm air near the equator?
12. What kind of climate do the monsoons bring?
13. What kind of weather is associated with a squall line?
14. Explain the formation of a low.
15. In what type of clouds do thunderstorms usually develop?
16. What is the difference, if any, between a hurricane and a typhoon?
17. What land instrument is used to detect violent storms far away at sea?
18. What space vehicle is used to detect weather conditions on the earth?

Questions: Group B

1. We say "Most weather occurs in the troposphere." What does this mean?
2. Where are the jet streams located?
3. What effect does the lower part of the ionosphere have on radio broadcast waves?
4. What is the difference between a hydrometer and a hygrometer?
5. How does an mT air mass differ from a cP air mass?
6. What type of warning system is provided for hurricane warning?
7. Explain the meaning of the expression, "Clouds are tattletales about our weather-to-be."

13 OCEANOGRAPHY

A THE OCEANS AND THEIR CONTENTS

What is oceanography? We have just begun to understand the importance of our oceans and how little we really know about them. Although oceans cover over 70 percent of the earth's surface, until recently they were practically an unexplored frontier. Today the investigation of the ocean is becoming more and more intense. Oceanographers study the organic and inorganic contents of the ocean, the physical and chemical properties of the water, and the movements of waves and ocean currents. They also investigate the sediment in the ocean floor and the structure of the earth's crust under the ocean. Broadly speaking, *oceanography is the scientific study of the ocean.* It covers biology, physics, chemistry, and geology. (See Fig. 13-1.)

How big are the oceans? There are four great oceans on the earth. They are the Pacific, Atlantic, Indian, and Arctic Oceans. The water areas around the Antarctic do not constitute a separate ocean as is sometimes mistakenly believed, but are parts of the Pacific, Atlantic, and Indian Oceans. The table on page 521 contains further information about the area and average and maximum depths of each of the oceans.

The average depth of all the oceans combined is approximately 12,000 feet, and if the land areas of the earth were flattened out, the water would cover the entire globe to a depth of over 1½ miles. The greatest depth of the ocean is located in the Marianas Trench near the island of Guam in the Pacific Ocean. The highest point of the earth, Mt. Everest, which reaches 29,000 feet above sea level, could be placed into this trench with room to spare. The top of the mountain would still be more than a mile below sea level.

Obtaining information about the ocean floor. We map the bottom of the ocean by a method called *sounding.* (See Fig. 13-2.) Formerly the only way of measuring the varying depths of the ocean floor was to lower a weighted line to the bottom. To-day, more reliable and faster depth measurements are made with a *fathometer* (fath-*om*-ih-ter). This instrument sends out sound impulses that are reflected from the ocean floor (see SONAR, page 291). By taking many continuous soundings, scientists are able to map a profile of the ocean bottoms. (See Figs. 13-3 and 13-4.)

Sampling the ocean bottom is done with a *coring tube.* This device is a hollow tube that is lowered until it hits the bottom in an upright position. The tube is then driven into the earth, forcing a core of the ocean bottom into the tube. From such samplings, we not only learn a great deal about the materials that make up the ocean bottom but also something of the past history of the oceans.

New machines and instruments are being developed for a more detailed study of the ocean floor. Powerful searchlights and television cameras are used in bathyscaphs. Manned and unmanned vehicles for roaming the ocean floor and collecting specimens are being devised. New oceanographic ships and land stations are being built. Even data collected by skin divers contribute to our knowledge of the oceans.

13-1. Oceanographers prepare to lower a special underwater camera. (Woods Hole Oceanographic Institution)

What does the ocean floor look like? At one time it was thought that the ocean floor was rather flat, sloping gently upward to the shorelines of the world's land masses. Today, however, we know that much of the ocean floor is very rugged and contains mountains, valleys, and cliffs. Some of the mountains rise from the ocean floor higher than Mt. Everest stands above sea level. Scientists have also found chasms deep enough to hide many

SIZE AND DEPTH OF THE OCEANS

Name of Ocean	Area to nearest million square miles	Average Depth to nearest 100 feet	Maximum Depth to nearest 100 feet
Pacific	64,000,000	14,100	35,800
Atlantic	32,000,000	12,900	30,200
Indian	28,000,000	13,000	26,300
Arctic	5,000,000	4,000	18,000

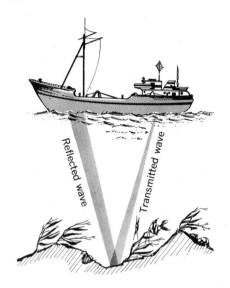

13-2. The ocean bottom is scanned with sound waves.

Grand Canyons and a mountain range that winds around the earth.

The more gently sloping plains of the oceans are usually found near the continental land masses. These broad submerged plains are called *continental shelves* and extend from a few miles to several hundred miles from the shore. Along the eastern coast of North America the continental shelf is 50 to 100 miles wide and up to 600 feet deep. It is covered with sand and mud which has been washed down from the land. At the outer edge, the shelf drops off sharply to depths of thousands of feet.

Underwater movements of land. The slipping and faulting of rock layers takes place in the ocean just as it does on land. There are volcanoes on the ocean floor which sometimes erupt violently as molten lava and heated gases come in contact with the cold ocean water. Earthquakes and huge landslides of muddy sediments also disturb the ocean bottom. Other than these violent activities, the features of the ocean floor are generally much better preserved than similar features on land. This is because the ocean formations are protected from such forces of erosion as temperature changes, wind, and running water.

Why is the ocean salty? For millions of years, rain has fallen on land areas of the earth and has run off into streams and rivers, and finally

13-3. This profile of a cross-section of ocean bottom was recorded by a fathometer.

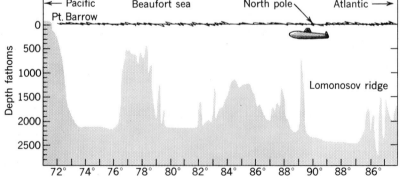

into the oceans. The rain water dissolved solid materials, mostly salts, from the land and carried them along to the sea. Thus, *for millions of years salts have been added to the oceans.* The water which evaporates from the oceans, to return to the land as rain, leaves the salt behind. Therefore, the remaining ocean water becomes more and more salty as time goes on.

The salt content of the ocean varies from place to place. The oceans contain, on the average, about 3.5 percent by weight of dissolved solids. It tends to be somewhat more salty in areas of great evaporation such as the Red Sea and Persian Gulf. The concentrations also are greater at the North and South Poles because of freezing. When water freezes, it forms ice crystals relatively free from salt leaving the remaining water more saline. In these areas, the salt content may reach 4 percent. The salt content is even higher in a few lakes which have no outlet to the sea. Can you guess why? For example, the dissolved salt content in the Dead Sea and the Great Salt Lake is over 20 percent.

The ocean is a storehouse of raw materials. As the waters run from the lands to the oceans, they bring with them not only common salt but also many other dissolved solids. Thus, the ocean is a storehouse of a wide variety of resources. For example, a single cubic yard of sea water contains 730 ounces of sodium chloride (table salt), 32 ounces of magnesium, 10 ounces of calcium, 10 ounces of potassium, and 1½ ounces of bromine. In addition to these there are many other minerals in smaller amounts. The ocean's resources become more impressive when we compute the dissolved solids con-

tained in a larger quantity of water. A cubic mile of sea water contains approximately 125,000,000 tons of sodium chloride, and over 4,000,000 tons of magnesium. The water also contains over $90,000,000 worth of gold and $8,000,000 worth of silver. Since there are hundreds of millions of cubic miles of sea water on the globe, the oceans are truly a tremendous resource. In addition to the dissolved salts, there are solid nodules or pellets, which contain manganese, copper, cobalt, iron, and other metals, found on the deep ocean floors.

The great resources remain relatively untapped because they are very difficult and expensive to extract from the water. At the present time sodium chloride, magnesium, bromine, iodine, and some phosphorites are about the only products commercially extracted from the sea. (See Fig. 13-5.)

The oceans also have resources that are not mineral. Perhaps the most abundant of these is *fresh water* which is reclaimed from salt water. Government and private agencies are actively

13-4. The observer reads a profile on the fathometer aboard a Navy survey ship. (US Dept. of Defense)

13-5. This plant extracts bromine from salt water. (Dow Chemical Co.)

pursuing methods of *desalting* ocean water. Some of these methods include *distillation, ion exchange, reverse osmosis,* and *freezing.* Some of the most promising projects utilize atomic energy and a combination of desalting techniques. Research in sea water conversion during the past ten years has sharply reduced the cost of purifying sea water. In the next ten years it is likely that the price of desalinated water, in many parts of the country, will be competitive in cost to water distributed by aquaduct. In some parts of the world, desalinated water is already more economical than any other source of pure water, but at present these are restricted to areas which have serious shortages of pure water. Kuwait, in Arabia, for example, has had a sea water conversion plant for a number of years.

Ocean life. Plant and animal life are extremely abundant in the ocean. Here you find both the smallest one-celled animals and the largest mammals in the world. Tiny plant and animal forms of life in the ocean are called *plankton.* (See Fig. 13-6.) These are the most numerous of all forms of sea life and exist in millions of fascinating forms. Plankton is the principal source of fish food. Contrasting in size with the plankton are the huge whales. Some large whales weigh as much as 150 tons and are as long as a ten-story building. Huge plants grow in the ocean, too. The *giant kelp* grows to a length of about 100 feet.

In tropical waters, the rapid growth of the *coral,* a simple form of animal life, forms **coral reefs.** The reefs are built up from the bony skeletal remains of tremendous numbers of these creatures.

Often at night you can see a beautiful glow, called *phosphorescence,* where the sea surface is disturbed by waves. This has nothing to do with the small amount of the element phosphorus in the sea water. Instead, it is due to the action of tiny sea organisms. It is like the light produced by fireflies, and is produced by a similar *chemical reaction.*

Food from the ocean. The oceans have for centuries been an important source of food. Today, with the earth's rapidly increasing population, this source is even more important. The countries of the United States, Japan, Peru, Red China, USSR, Iceland, Norway, and England all have important fishing industries. Important fish include salmon, cod, herring, tuna, sardines, and haddock. Other sea animals are also caught, including whales, turtles, seals, lobsters, and even squid. In addition, *seaweed* is now being made into *flour,* and tiny sea plants and animals are being used in soups. In some countries, such as Japan, sea food is now the chief source of all proteins being consumed.

Despite the extensive sea food industry now in existence throughout some parts of the world, many experts believe that we have barely begun to tap the ocean's harvest of food. Our fishing techniques have been compared to the hunting methods used by nomadic tribes of long ago. In both cases the "hunters" roam about searching for food. In the future, we may do more than merely *hunt* or *gather* food. Instead, we may *farm the ocean* as we now farm the land. *"Aquaculture"* may become as important as agriculture. Properly managed, it is believed that the ocean will supply far more food than all of the land areas of the world. Experts have estimated that the oceans could supply all the protein requirements for up to 30 billion people, or ten times the present day population of the earth.

13-6. Oceanographers sweep up plankton for study. (Woods Hole Oceanographic Institution)

1. What are the names of the oceans?
2. Describe the appearance of the ocean bottom.
3. Where are most of the gently sloping ocean floors located?
4. Why are physical formations on the ocean floor better preserved than similar formations on land?
5. What effect does the water cycle have on the salt content of the oceans?
6. What are some of the commercial products other than food extracted from the seas?
7. What are some methods of desalting water?
8. Are the oceans a good source of protein? Explain.
9. Why are gold and silver not commercially extracted from ocean water?
10. What is the principal form of fish food?
11. Explain why the Great Salt Lake is salty while most inland lakes are not.
12. In what way are our fishing techniques like the techniques of early hunters on land?

B WAVES, CURRENTS, AND TIDES

How are waves formed? Waves on water are caused primarily by the action of wind. When a wind arises on a comparatively calm sea, the movement of the air imparts a motion to the water because of friction. As soon as ripples develop, the wind also im-

parts a push to the back slope of the waves, thus encouraging wave formation still more. The final size of waves is governed primarily by the speed of the wind and the duration of the time that the wind acts upon the water. Greatest wave action is generated when strong winds are maintained for long periods of time over large expanses of water.

We have seen in Chapter 6, on sound, that the top of a wave is called its *crest* while the space between two crests is called the *trough*. A wave's height is measured vertically from the top of its crest to the bottom of its trough. The length of a wave is measured horizontally from crest to crest (or from trough to trough). Each ocean wave also has a *root* or *base* which is about one wavelength in depth. (See Fig. 13-7.) On the high seas the base does not affect the action of a wave, but once it approaches the shore it begins to exert an influence. First of all the base comes in contact with the shallow bottom usually some distance offshore and is slowed down by friction. The wave above the wave root continues on, however, and begins to "pile up" on top of its base. The wave face becomes more and more steep and finally breaks into a cascade of foam and spray called a *"breaker."* (See Fig. 13-8.) At this point the wave action is transformed into the actual forward motion of water as it surges onto the shore.

How do waves move? It is important to keep in mind one significant fact about the motion and movement of waves. *The movement of waves does not mean that there is a corresponding movement of water.* In fact, the ocean water may be traveling one way while

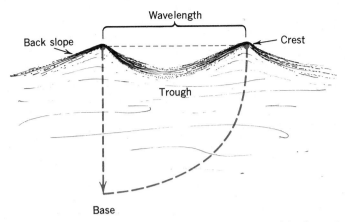

13.7 An ocean wave is composed of a number of basic parts.

the waves travel in another. A floating object on the surface of the ocean merely bobs up and down and moves in more or less a circular path as the waves pass along. (See Fig. 13-9.) One way in which wave action can be demonstrated is to tie an end of a rope to a solid object and "snap" the other end vigorously with a motion of your arm. This snapping action, or up-and-down motion, of your arm introduces a wave which travels the length of the rope. The wave moves along the rope, yet any particular part of the rope merely bobs up and down.

In addition to surface waves there are also *internal waves* below the ocean's surface. These internal waves

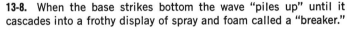

13-8. When the base strikes bottom the wave "piles up" until it cascades into a frothy display of spray and foam called a "breaker."

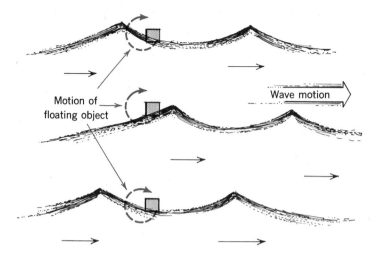

13-9. The movement of the ocean's water remains independent of the movement of the waves. A floating object merely bobs up and down in a circular path as the waves pass by.

are caused by currents that may exist between separate layers of water of different density. Internal waves are considerably longer than surface waves and are more gently curved. (See Fig. 13-10.)

What causes ocean currents? Just as we have air currents in our atmos-

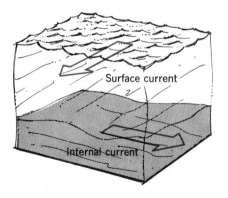

13-10. Surface and internal waves as well as surface and internal currents are often present at different levels of the same part of the ocean.

phere, so we have currents of water in the oceans. In Fig. 13-11 some of the important ocean currents of the world are indicated.

Ocean currents are produced by one or more of the following causes: (1) the *difference in density* of the sea water due to the amount of salt ·in the water; (2) the *unequal heating* of the water by the sun's rays, forming convection currents; and (3) the *prevailing winds* blowing on the ocean surface.

The rotation of the earth affects the currents also. The general movement of the currents is clockwise in the northern hemisphere and counter-clockwise in the southern hemisphere.

It is believed that in ancient times there were some instances in which people traveled thousands of miles on the ocean currents to bring mankind to uninhabited lands. Testing this possibility in 1947, Thor Heyerdahl and his companions on the raft "Kon Tiki" were carried over 4000 miles from South America to South Pacific islands on ocean currents. (See Fig. 13-12.)

In addition to surface currents there are currents below the surface of the ocean called *counter currents*. For example, a surface current travels through the Straits of Gibraltar into the Mediterranean Sea from the Atlantic Ocean, while near the sea floor, at the same place, the current is moving rapidly in the opposite direction. Similarly, the cold and saline waters of the Arctic and Antarctic regions sink and travel along the ocean floor toward the equator while the surface currents may be traveling in different directions.

How do the oceans affect our climate? The great ocean currents carry heat from the tropics to the poles. The balance between ice and sea water acts to keep the temperature more uniform. Excess heat is used up in melting the great ice-sheets, rather than in "warm-

ing up" the world. The balance between evaporation of sea water and the rainfall that follows is another great temperature regulator, helping to keep our climate more even. The oceans of the world act like a great heat-exchange engine.

By regulating the amount of carbon dioxide in the air, the oceans control the amount of heat that radiates off into space. Our civilization has shifted the carbon dioxide-oxygen balance maintained by plants and animals. By greatly increasing combustion, we have poured excess carbon dioxide into the atmosphere. We have already mentioned that our climate may be getting warmer. If the carbon dioxide were not largely absorbed by the oceans, the atmosphere would warm up even more.

In Labrador, north of Newfoundland, lies a vast tract of land that is extremely cold and barren in winter.

13-11. This world map shows some of the major ocean currents.

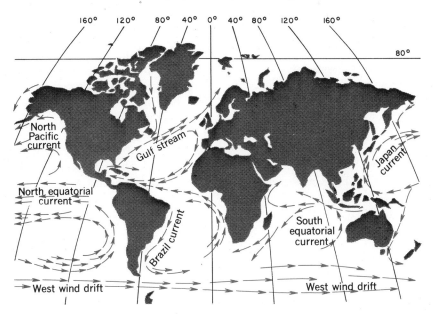

13-12. These scientists traveled 4000 miles on this balsa raft. (UPI)

Yet in England, which is as far north as Labrador, the winters are quite mild. Why?

The relatively warm water of the *Gulf Stream* warms the air above it. This Gulf Stream originating in a tropical climate, has a *warming* effect on England. Then, too, Labrador is affected by the cold ocean current coming from the north. If it were not for these ocean currents, the climate of England would probably be cooler, and that of Labrador would be warmer than it is now.

What causes tides? *Tides are the regular rise and fall of large bodies of water due to the pull of the moon and sun upon the earth.* The moon is much nearer to the earth than the sun is. Therefore, its tide-producing effect is greater.

Notice in Fig. 13-13 that when the sun and moon are in line with the earth, they cooperate with each other and cause tides that are *higher* than normal, called **spring tides.** At what phases of the moon would you expect them?

But twice a month, as you can see in Fig. 13-13, the sun and moon are competing with each other. Because it is nearer, the moon is more effective and causes the tide. However, this tide is not as high as before, and is called a *neap tide.*

If you live near the ocean, you know there are two high tides every day. As you can see in Fig. 13-13, there is a high tide on the side of the earth away from the moon, too. This second tide comes from the fact that the moon does not revolve about the center of the earth. Instead, both the earth and the moon revolve around each other, somewhat like a drum-major's baton thrown through the air. This rotation produces a tide on the far side of the earth.

At any one place, you usually find that the high tide comes about 50 minutes *later* each day. This is because the *moon lags behind the sun,* rising about 50 minutes later each day.

You cannot predict the time of the high tide by noticing where the moon is in the sky. Many other factors affect the size of the tides and the time they occur. One such important factor is the shape of a *tidal basin.* Certain shapes of the sea bottom and surrounding land forms tend to accentuate tidal activity. It is similar to carrying water in a shallow pan; the water tends to surge forward and backward and slosh over the sides. This surging action helps produce some of the world's highest tides in the Bay of Fundy, between Nova Scotia and New Brunswick. They sometimes exceed 40 feet.

Giant sea waves. In Japanese, *tsunami* (tsoo-*nah*-mee) means "large waves in harbors." The tsunami is commonly called a "tidal wave" although it has *nothing* to do with the tide. *Tsunamis are set up by underwater earthquakes, landslides, and volcanic disturbances.*

From this action, a huge volume of water is set in motion, forming waves that may be 100 to 600 miles long (*measured from the top of one wave to that of the next*). They travel across the ocean with speeds of hundreds of miles an hour. The destructive powers of these dangerous giant waves are tremendous.

In May, 1960, a series of volcanic eruptions and earthquakes in southern Chile caused considerable property damage and brought death to about 6000 persons. This disturbance also caused several violent tsunamis. Even after traveling 6800 miles across the Pacific to Hawaii, the waves were powerful enough to cause millions of dollars in property damage and the

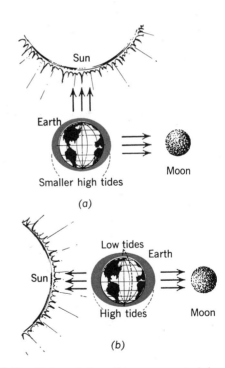

13-13. High and low tides are caused by the gravitational attraction of the sun and the moon; (a) neap tides and (b) spring tides.

death or injury of many people along the coast. Waves 30 feet high were reported in Japan, some 10,000 miles away from the original disturbance.

What is SCUBA? Human divers explore the shallow parts of the ocean with the aid of *Self-Contained Underwater Breathing Apparatus (SCUBA)*. Until the middle 1940's a swimmer with a tank of air was restricted to the top forty to sixty feet of the ocean. Below this depth he ran into serious trouble with *oxygen poisoning,* caused by inhaling too much oxygen. Oxygen poisoning resulted when the high pressures of the ocean water compressed the air taken into the body. A single breath of air contains far more oxygen underwater than on the surface. In Scuba diving this problem is corrected by a device which automatically substitutes a harmless gas such as helium for the excess amounts of oxygen.

An experienced diver with Scuba equipment can regularly go to depths of 150 feet, and in rare cases as deep as 300 feet for short periods of time. Under experimental conditions some divers have gone even deeper but sometimes with tragic results. A record depth of 1000 feet was reached by two men off the coast of California, but one died shortly after returning to the surface. At these great depths and pressures, divers are faced with such problems as *nitrogen narcosis,* a drowsy trance-like condition, and *air embolism,* a condition where air is forced into the blood stream causing death. When they return to the surface from great depths, divers are also in danger of suffering from the expansion of dissolved gases in their body fluids. This condition is often called *the bends.*

Experimental studies are also being undertaken to keep divers under water for periods of weeks and months, living in underwater "apartments" in which the pressure is the same as the surrounding ocean. In this way the divers become accustomed to great pressures and are then able to descend safely to greater depths than divers who come directly from the surface. It is hoped that eventually divers will be able to perform useful work and gather important information on the bottom of the continental shelf in depths up to 600 feet.

What vehicles and equipment are used in ocean exploration? Modern equipment and methods now make it possible to photograph the ocean bottom and to gather samples from it. Special vehicles have also been developed to help study the oceans. One unusual vehicle designed to study surface and internal waves is called *FLIP (Floating Instrumented Platform).* As it is towed to its research station, it looks like a long, low ship. Then the ballast tanks on one end of the vehicle are flooded and it is "flipped" to a vertical position. In this position, 300 of its 350 feet descend into relatively calm waters below the surface waves and it rides calmly even in a rough sea.

Another ocean vehicle is the deep diving bathyscaph (*bath*-eh-skaf) *Trieste.* (See Fig. 13-14.) The bathyscaph is sort of an underwater dirigible carrying a thick-walled sphere that holds two passengers. The "balloon" part of this underwater dirigible contains gasoline, instead of a gas such as helium. A liquid is used because it compresses very little under the tremendous pressures of the deep ocean. Gasoline is

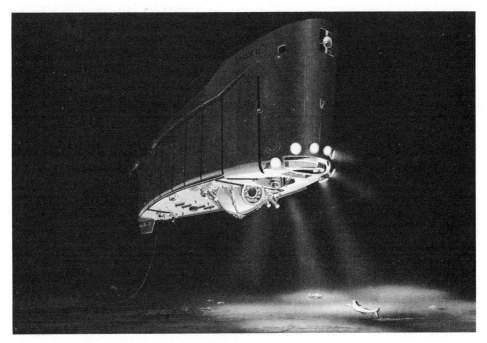

13-14. The bathyscaph Trieste is capable of descending to the deepest parts of the ocean. (Official Photograph, US Navy)

used because it is much lighter than ocean water and provides the vehicle with lift. There is no limit to the depth this vehicle can go. It has already descended 35,800 feet to the bottom of the Marianas Trench in the Pacific Ocean, believed to be the deepest part of any ocean. At that depth it sustained a pressure of over eight tons per square inch, or a pressure equivalent to four large automobiles pressing down on an area no larger than a postage stamp.

Other vehicles which ply the ocean depths include the *Aluminaut*, the *Alvin*, the *Deep Star*, the *Turtle*, and the *Cubmarine*, and include some made with steel, aluminum, and fiberglass. These vehicles will help in the study of plant and animal life, sediments, crust, and magnetic and gravitational conditions deep in the earth.

Quick Quiz

1. How are surface ocean waves formed?
2. Explain the formation of "breakers."
3. What are internal waves?
4. What causes tides?
5. Why do the Arctic and Antarctic waters sink to the ocean floor?
6. What causes ocean currents?
7. What governs wave size?
8. Why does FLIP remain stable in a choppy sea?
9. Why is liquid used in the Trieste's float instead of a gas?
10. What effect does pressure have on the amount of oxygen that can be inhaled in a single breath?

SUMMARY

Oceanography is the scientific study of the ocean. It makes use of biology, chemistry, physics, and geology. There are four oceans on the earth: the Pacific, Atlantic, Indian, and Arctic. Their waters cover about 70 percent of the earth's surface. Oceans have been an important source of food and a means of travel since the days of unwritten history. Modern oceanography, however, did not begin until the 19th century.

The ocean floor contains mountains, valleys, cliffs, and other formations. Many areas of the ocean floor have been mapped. Land masses shift in the ocean because of earthquakes and volcanic eruptions.

The ocean is a huge source of raw materials, fresh water, and foods. The ocean is filled with all forms of life, especially tiny plant and animal life called plankton. The ocean is salty because minerals from the land are washed into the ocean. Some of these minerals are now being extracted from sea water.

The oceans are constantly in motion. Wave motion is caused primarily by winds. Waves often move independently of the movement of the water or currents. There often are internal waves below the surface of the ocean separating two levels or zones of water. Ocean currents have an important effect on our climate. These currents are caused by (1) the difference in density of sea water due to the amount of salt in the water; (2) the unequal heating of the water surface by the sun's rays, forming convection currents, and (3) the prevailing winds blowing on the ocean surface. Destructive giant sea waves called "tsunamis" are caused by earthquakes or other violent disturbances on the ocean floor. Tides are caused by the gravity of the moon and sun on large bodies of water and by revolution of the earth around the earth-moon axis.

Divers use SCUBA to explore shallow water in the ocean. Scientists use the bathyscaph and other vehicles to explore the ocean bottoms. The greatest depth of the ocean is about 7 miles. The fathometer is an instrument that uses sound waves to determine the depth of water. Sampling of the ocean bottom is done with a coring tube.

CHAPTER REVIEW

Vocabulary

Match the words in Column A with the *best* response in Column B. Do not write in your book.

Column A	Column B
1. oceanography	a. a drawing showing a vertical cross-section
2. sounding	b. broad submerged plain off the shores of large land masses
3. fathometer	

  4. profile
  5. coring tube
  6. continental shelf
  7. plankton
  8. kelp
  9. coral reefs
 10. phosphorescence
 11. aquaculture
 12. breaker
 13. ocean current
 14. spring tide
 15. neap tide
 16. tsunami
 17. SCUBA
 18. bends
 19. FLIP
 20. bathyscaph

  c. condition in the human body where dissolved gases form bubbles
  d. deep-diving vessel to explore ocean floors
  e. large ocean research vessel
  f. device used to obtain samples of the ocean floor
  g. farming of the ocean
  h. flow of large stream of water in the ocean
  i. glow produced by tiny sea organisms by chemical reaction
  j. large ocean plant life
  k. weak high tide
  l. strong high tide
  m. huge ocean wave usually caused by an earthquake
  n. instrument used to measure depth of water
  o. method used to determine depth of water
  p. self-contained underwater breathing apparatus
  q. scientific study of the oceans
  r. stony skeletal remains of a simple form of animal life
  s. tiny plant and animal life drifting in the ocean
  t. wave that destroys itself as it moves onto the shore

Questions: Group A

  1. Why is oceanography becoming a more important science?
  2. What is the average salt content of the ocean?
  3. Of what use is plankton?
  4. What causes the formation of coral reefs?
  5. Why do parts of the ocean's surface occasionally phosphoresce?
  6. Where is the greatest known ocean depth found? How deep is it?
  7. How can we investigate the sedimentary layers on the ocean floor?
  8. Which is greater, ocean depths or mountain elevations?
  9. What is the fathometer used for? How does it operate?
 10. What governs the size of ocean waves?

Questions: Group B

  1. Explain how the oceans affect our climate.
  2. Why is the climate of England warmer than that of Labrador?
  3. What is the most abundant chemical dissolved in the ocean?
  4. Are the oceans of the world becoming saltier? Explain.
  5. If you evaporated 100 lb of sea water, how many pounds of solid material would you expect to obtain?
  6. What relationship is there between wave travel and the movement of water?

7. Explain the existence of internal currents.
8. Explain the excessive high tides in some parts of the world.
9. What gives the bathyscaph *Trieste* its "lift" in the water?
10. From a study of Fig. 13-11, would you expect the coast of Chile to have warm or cold winters? Explain.
11. What evidence is there to support the belief that ancient man traveled thousands of miles on ocean currents?

14 ASTRONOMY

A EARTH AND MOON

Our planet is called Earth. In Chapters 11, 12, and 13, we studied about the structure of the earth, its atmosphere and its oceans. Now we will examine the earth as a heavenly body, or as one of the nine *planets. A planet is a body which revolves around the sun, and shines by reflected light.*

Ancient people believed that the earth was flat. However, as early as 350 B.C. Aristotle, a Greek philosopher, reported that the earth's shadow on the moon during an eclipse was round. Less than one hundred years later, another Greek scientist, Eratosthenes, calculated the distance around the earth. Even at that early date, he obtained a figure very close to 25,000 miles. This was an amazing achievement considering the primitive apparatus with which he had to work.

Much more information about the earth has, of course, been gathered since that time. The earth is a sphere, with a very slight bulge at the equator and is slightly flattened at the poles. The bulge and the flattening are caused by the spinning of the earth on its axis.

The earth's rotation—how long is a day? If you had no clocks, watches, or other such devices, how would you be able to tell time? Exact time measurements would be difficult, but everyone would be able to tell time in a limited way. Everyone would surely notice the difference between night and day. In addition, most people could tell that it was morning, noon, afternoon, or evening. This observation shows that *our basic form of time measurement comes from the turning of the earth.* This turning is called *rotation.* The earth rotates on its axis once every day in a counterclockwise direction as seen from above the north pole. It rotates from west to east, but to an observer on the ground, the earth seems to be motionless and the sun appears to be doing the moving. Viewed this way, the sun, of course, rises in the east and sets in the west.

One complete turn of the earth on its axis gives us one *sidereal day.* In this type of timekeeping the day is not measured by the sun but against a reference star. The sidereal day is four minutes shorter than the more common *solar day* and is used primarily by astronomers for their special scientific purposes. By the more common *solar day* we mean the time from one noon to the next. In this case the sun is the reference point instead of a star.

The interval between times at which the sun is directly overhead varies slightly from day to day and may be off as much as 16 minutes during certain times of the year. This is caused by the slightly changing speeds of the earth in its orbit around the sun. Because of this slight variance, our clocks are adjusted to the **mean solar day.** This is the time from noon till noon, averaged for a whole year. For convenience, however, we begin our day at midnight instead of at noon.

Time depends on longitude. In our early history, people set their clocks at 12 o'clock noon when the sun was highest in the sky. Since the sun is highest above different localities at different times, it meant that each town had a different local time. This custom became a nuisance as roads and railroads developed. Travelers could not determine conveniently the arrival and departure of trains because the clocks were set differently from locality to locality. In 1878, Sir Sandford Fleming, a Canadian civil engineer and scientist, proposed that this problem be solved by dividing the earth into 24 different zones to represent the 24 hours in a day. Since there are 360° in a circle, each of these zones were 15 degrees wide. They were measured from Greenwich, England, in meridians of *longitude*. **Longitude is the distance** *in degrees measured east or west from prime meridian.* In 1883 at a General Time Convention, this plan was accepted by United States railroad companies and was quickly adopted by the entire world. (See Fig. 14-1.)

What are our standard time belts? As shown in Fig. 14-2, the conterminous United States is divided into four standard time belts. Within any one zone, all the clocks are set to read the same time. You may use Fig. 14-2 to answer the following questions. What time is it in Los Angeles (PST) when it is noon in New York (EST)? What time is it in New York when it is 11 A.M. in Chicago (CST)?

In many cases, *Greenwich Mean Time* (GMT) is used. Radio programs, cablegrams, and world news events carry GMT datelines. You can convert GMT to local time by dividing the mean meridian of a zone by 15 and subtracting the quotient from GMT. For example, if it is 11 A.M. GMT, it

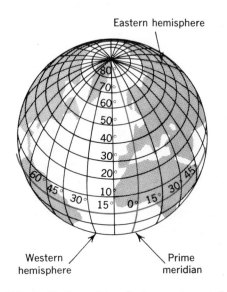

14-1. Latitude and longitude are represented as imaginary lines on the earth.

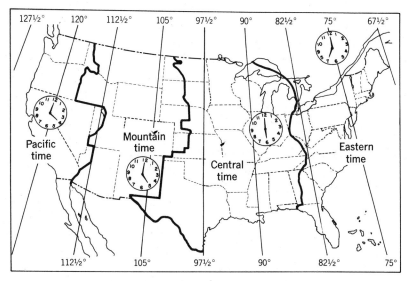

14-2. How many degrees apart from one another are the four standard time belts in the United States?

is 5 A.M. Central Time. The mean meridian for Central Time zone is 90 degrees West Longitude. This figure is divided by 15 degrees (the width of a zone), resulting in a quotient of six (the number of hours from GMT). This figure subtracted from 11 A.M. shows that Central Time is 5 A.M. For lands which lie east of Greenwich, the same process is used except that to arrive at local time, the quotient is added to GMT instead of subtracted.

The International Date Line. Since the earth is divided into 24 time zones, you can see that if you start with a certain time, say 1 P.M., Monday, in the one zone, and successively mark off one hour in each of the 24 zones around the earth, you would reach 12 o'clock noon, Tuesday, in the last zone. If you continued you would arrive again at your starting point and change time zones abruptly from 12 noon, Tuesday, to 1 P.M., Monday. The di-

viding line where this 24 hour change occurs so abruptly is called the *International Date Line* and is located on the 180th meridian. Actually, as you can see in Fig. 14-3, the date line zigzags a little to avoid passing through land areas. Why is this desirable?

What determines the length of a year? As you know, a *year* is the time it takes the earth to make one *revolution* about the sun. Hence, in one sense, life is a merry-go-round. Your life span is measured by the number of trips you make about the sun. Each trip is about 600 million miles long. To travel this distance in a year, the earth must speed around the sun at the rate of *18½ miles per second.*

The planets revolve about the sun in a *counterclockwise* direction. That is, if you were in the sky looking down on the north poles of the planets, you would see them revolve about the sun opposite to the direction of the hands of a clock. (See Fig. 14-4.) A German astronomer of the 17th century, Johannes Kepler, was the first to determine the orbits of the planets.

Why do we have seasons? The seasons of the year are very closely related to planetary motion. Seasons are caused by (1) *the tilting of the earth on its axis,* and (2) *the movement of the earth around the sun.* The tilt causes one part of the earth to receive direct rays of the sun while the other part receives more slanting rays.

The rays are more direct during the summer season than they are during the winter. Also, the seasons are reversed north and south of the equator. While it is summer in the northern hemisphere, it is winter in the southern hemisphere. Several other factors increase the intensities of the seasons.

During the summer months, for example, not only are the sun's rays more direct, but they pass through the layer of the atmosphere in a more-or-less short route reaching the earth with considerable strength. During the winter, however, the rays are slanted and go through the atmosphere in a longer diagonal path, thus reaching the earth in reduced intensity. Finally, there are more hours of daylight during the summer than during the winter.

The changes in the distance between the earth and sun are not significant factors in causing the seasons. Curiously enough, as you can see in Fig. 14-4, we are about three million miles closer to the sun during our winter than we are during summer.

Hold a globe with its axis tilted and move it around a lamp representing the sun. (See Fig. 14-5.) See how

14-3. Can you explain why the international date line is not a straight line and why it was established in the area of the world shown below?

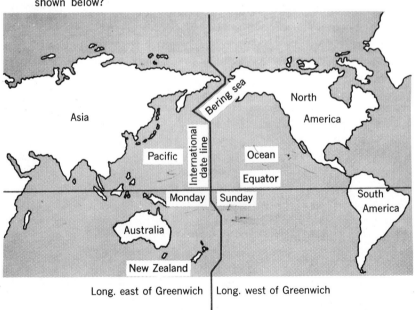

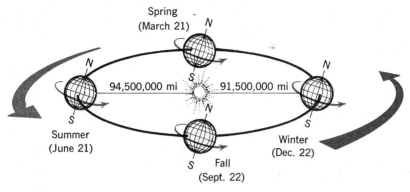

14-4. The earth revolves around the sun in a counterclockwise direction and rotates on its own axis in a counterclockwise direction, viewed from above the north pole.

the sun's rays fall on the earth when it is in the position labeled December 22. With the axis tilted 23.5° away from the sun, notice the lack of daylight at the north pole as you spin the globe. Note the few hours of daylight in the northern hemisphere. Notice also that the rays of the sun hit the earth on a slant. This causes the energy from the sun to be spread over a larger area and thus to be weaker.

If you are observant, you have noticed that the sun does not always rise and set due east and west. As winter approaches, the sun rises and sets farther and farther to the south. Finally, about December 22, it reaches its most southerly point. We call this

14-5. The seasons are caused by the tilting of the earth on its axis and by its revolving around the sun, over the course of a year.

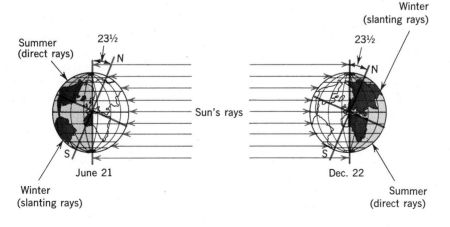

date the *winter solstice* (*sol*-stiss), meaning "sun stops." After this date, the sun appears to start north again. By March 21, it is rising and setting due east and west. The days and nights are of equal length, and we call this date the *spring equinox* (*ee*-kwih-nox). *Equinox* means "equal nights." Later, about June 21, the sun has moved farthest to the north. We call this date the *summer solstice.* This is followed by the *autumnal equinox* about September 22, when you again see the sun rising due east.

How did we get our calendar? From very early times, man has made *calendars* to keep track of the passing of days and seasons. You have already learned how he measured the length of the day and the year. The time from one new moon to the next he called a *month* (that is, a *moon*-th). He named the seven days of the week after the sun and the moon and the five planets that were known at that time. When he tried to keep track of time by using both the moon and the sun, he got into trouble. There are more than twelve moons in a year, and spring festivals based on the moon would gradually creep into the winter season.

Our calendar developed from an old Roman version, as revised by Julius Caesar in 45 B.C. This provided a leap year of 366 days every four years. By 1582 this was out of step by ten days, and was again revised by Pope Gregory. In our present *Gregorian calendar,* the even hundred years 1800, 1900, 2000, etc., are not leap years unless they are divisible by 400. This calendar will last about 3000 years before getting out of step by one day. But it is a patched-up affair with the months varying from 28 to 31 days each. People are debating the adoption of a modern **World Calendar.** (See Fig. 14-6.)

This calendar would retain the 12 months of the present calendar, but the lengths of the months are slightly different. The year is divided into four quarters of three months each. Each of these quarters begins on a Sunday and ends on a Saturday. In this way, January 1 would always fall on a Sunday and most holidays would always fall on the same day of the year.

The extra day for leap year is inserted between June 30 and July 1. This would be called *Leap-Year-Day,* and it would be an additional holiday between Saturday and Sunday, with no week-day name. In the same way, a *World Day* would be inserted between December 30 and January 1 every year.

The World Calendar would have the *same* number of workdays for each of the 12 months, or a monthly total of 26. This is accomplished by assigning four Sundays to the months with 30 days and five Sundays to the months which have 31 days.

What is the moon like? The moon has a diameter of about 2100 miles, and it is less than a quarter of a million miles away. As we go around the sun, the moon keeps up with us, going about the earth at the same time. The moon requires a little less than a *month* to go around the earth *once. It turns once on its axis while revolving once about the earth.* Hence, we always see the *same side* of the moon.

Because of its smaller mass, the pull of gravity on the moon is only about ⅙ as much as on earth. Therefore, on the moon, a 180-lb person

FIRST QUARTER		
JANUARY	FEBRUARY	MARCH

S	M	T	W	T	F	S	S	M	T	W	T	F	S	S	M	T	W	T	F	S
1	2	3	4	5	6	7					1	2	3	4					1	2
8	9	10	11	12	13	14	5	6	7	8	9	10	11	3	4	5	6	7	8	9
15	16	17	18	19	20	21	12	13	14	15	16	17	18	10	11	12	13	14	15	16
22	23	24	25	26	27	28	19	20	21	22	23	24	25	17	18	19	20	21	22	23
29	30	31					26	27	28	29	30			24	25	26	27	28	29	30

SECOND QUARTER		
APRIL	MAY	JUNE

S	M	T	W	T	F	S	S	M	T	W	T	F	S	S	M	T	W	T	F	S
1	2	3	4	5	6	7			1	2	3	4							1	2
8	9	10	11	12	13	14	5	6	7	8	9	10	11	3	4	5	6	7	8	9
15	16	17	18	19	20	21	12	13	14	15	16	17	18	10	11	12	13	14	15	16
22	23	24	25	26	27	28	19	20	21	22	23	24	25	17	18	19	20	21	22	23
29	30	31					26	27	28	29	30			24	25	26	27	28	29	30
																				** W

THIRD QUARTER		
JULY	AUGUST	SEPTEMBER

S	M	T	W	T	F	S	S	M	T	W	T	F	S	S	M	T	W	T	F	S
1	2	3	4	5	6	7			1	2	3	4							1	2
8	9	10	11	12	13	14	5	6	7	8	9	10	11	3	4	5	6	7	8	9
15	16	17	18	19	20	21	12	13	14	15	16	17	18	10	11	12	13	14	15	16
22	23	24	25	26	27	28	19	20	21	22	23	24	25	17	18	19	20	21	22	23
29	30	31					26	27	28	29	30			24	25	26	27	28	29	30

FOURTH QUARTER		
OCTOBER	NOVEMBER	DECEMBER

S	M	T	W	T	F	S	S	M	T	W	T	F	S	S	M	T	W	T	F	S
1	2	3	4	5	6	7			1	2	3	4							1	2
8	9	10	11	12	13	14	5	6	7	8	9	10	11	3	4	5	6	7	8	9
15	16	17	18	19	20	21	12	13	14	15	16	17	18	10	11	12	13	14	15	16
22	23	24	25	26	27	28	19	20	21	22	23	24	25	17	18	19	20	21	22	23
29	30	31					26	27	28	29	30			24	25	26	27	28	29	30
																				* W

* The Year-End World Holiday, W or 31 December (365th day), follows 30 December every year.
** The Leap-Year World Holiday, W or 31 June (an extra day), follows 30 June in leap years.

14-6. The proposed World Calendar.

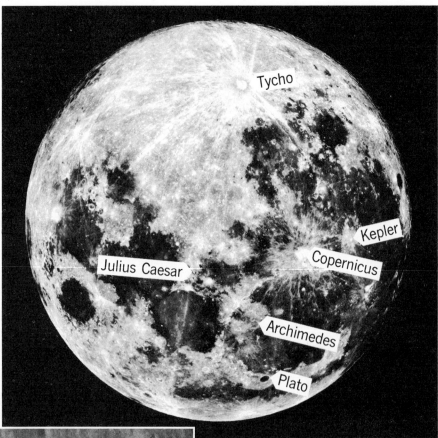

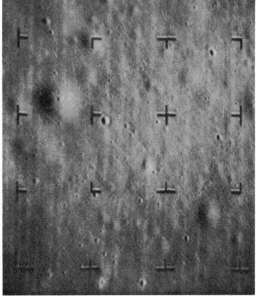

14-7. The inset shows that the surface of the moon is not as rugged when viewed from close range as it appears from earth-based telescopes. The inset photo was taken by the Ranger moon probe and shows about 1 square mile of the lunar surface.

would weigh only about 30 pounds. Since he would still have as much strength as on earth, imagine what his athletic ability would be under those conditions.

There is no atmosphere on the moon and as a result temperature changes are severe. During the moon's day the temperature rises to about 250° F. At night the heat radiates rapidly out into space because there is no atmosphere to hold it, or clouds to reflect it back. The temperature then drops to −200° F.

What is the moon's surface like? A telescope, or even a pair of good binoculars will reveal the surface of the moon in sharp detail. As shown in Fig. 14-7 you can see that the surface of the moon is covered with craters, rills, volcanoes, rays, and mountains. Before the discovery of the telescope and during the early years of its use, people thought that the large dark areas of the moon were covered with water, and even named these areas as seas and oceans. Later, however, as telescopes were improved and our observations became better, it was determined that the moon contained no water, but was a barren dry sphere. Not only does it lack water but because of its feeble gravity, the moon has no appreciable atmosphere. That is why we see its surface so clearly. There is no atmosphere to blur the view. As we look at the moon through our large telescopes, only our own atmosphere reduces the visibility.

The lack of air and water means that there is no wind or water erosion. The only forms of erosion are caused by temperature changes and meteorite bombardment. The uppermost layer of the moon's surface is composed of very finely pulverized material. It is light in weight and a very poor conductor of heat. Thus, it heats up rapidly when exposed to the sun and cools rapidly when in the shade.

The lunar land features appear fairly rugged as viewed from the earth, even through our largest telescopes. However, because of the distorting effects of our atmosphere, no object smaller than one mile in size can be seen on the moon's surface with earth-based telescopes. Photographs from satellites and moon probes (see Fig. 14-7), and studies by radar show that instead of these rough features most of the moon's surface is fairly smooth. Steep slopes over 15 degrees account for not more than about 1 percent of the lunar surface.

It is now believed that most of the large craters on the moon, called *primary craters,* were caused by meteor impact. These include such well known craters as Copernicus, Tycho, Kepler, and Eratosthenes. A large number of smaller craters are called *secondary craters.* They were caused by chunks of rock and debris thrown out by the meteors which created the large craters. These chunks were sometimes blasted hundreds of miles, but impacted with much less force than meteors, and dug shallow craters all over the moon. Primary craters are characterized by deep pits with sharp sides, while secondary craters have rounded, gently sloping sides.

In addition to primary and secondary craters, there are also some craters that show evidence of having been formed by volcanic action. For example, the crater Alphonsus is believed by some scientists to be of volcanic origin. Several incidents of volcanic

14-8. The Surveyor is an advanced lunar vehicle capable of analyzing lunar surface material, measuring meteorite bombardment and moonquakes. (NASA)

activity have been reported there in recent years.

Thus, the moon is dotted with craters of all kinds. Covering all this may be a layer of powdery substance. This substance is "ruddy" in appearance and scatters the sunlight which strikes it. The scattering effect can be deduced by noting that the moon has very little *limb darkening.* In other words, the moon's edges appear just about as bright as does its center. If the surface were smooth and did not scatter the sun's light, the moon would appear bright in the center but considerably darker at the edges.

Why is the moon of interest to space scientists? Many people look at the moon with new interest during these early days of the *Space Age.* The scientist thinks of the moon as a good *observation post* to study conditions on earth. The astronomer knows he could learn more about the distant universe if he could set up his instruments on the moon. There would be no air to absorb light and distort telescope images. The astronaut looks to the moon as his first big step in *space travel.* As explained in the next chapter, the moon could be a "jumping-off" point for the exploration of other planets in our solar system.

Visitors to the moon must wear space suits to pressurize their bodies and to supply oxygen for breathing. If unprotected, they would be pelted with meteorites and burned by ultraviolet rays from the sun. Preceding man are instrumented lunar probes such as Ranger, Surveyor (see Fig. 14-8), and Prospector.

The phases of the moon. A study of Fig. 14-9 shows why the moon goes through its well-known *phases,* from *new* to *quarter* to *full* each month. The new moon is not visible to an observer on earth for two reasons: (1) the shadow side of the moon is facing the earth, and (2) the moon is close to the glaring light of the sun. Shortly after the **new moon,** however, it is possible to see a *thin crescent,* which grows larger as the moon moves out of line with the sun. When the moon is in its *quarter phase,* it can be easily seen. At this time part of its sunlit side is outlined even against the daylight sky. The moon is, of course, brightest during its *full phase.* During this time the side facing the earth is fully lighted by the sun. Full moon can only occur when the moon is opposite to the sun as viewed by an observer on earth. Thus, a full moon rises when the sun sets.

Solar and lunar eclipses. A *solar eclipse occurs when the moon passes directly between the sun and the earth. This causes the shadow of the moon*

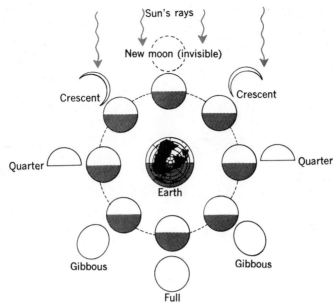

14-9. The inner circle shows that one-half of the moon always receives light. The other diagrams indicate how much of the lighted area we can see from the earth.

to fall on a small strip of the earth's surface. This shadow is never more than 170 miles wide, and usually much narrower. A solar eclipse never lasts more than seven minutes at any one place, and usually much less than this. (See Fig. 14-10.)

Eclipses do not occur every month because the moon usually does not pass directly between the sun and the earth. They are more or less in line at new moon and full moon, but not exactly. Although there may be as many as five partial eclipses a year, we usually have fewer than one total solar eclipse a year. The moon's shadow strikes any one spot on the earth only once in every 500 to 600 years.

14-10. Eclipses occur when the moon or the earth cast shadows.

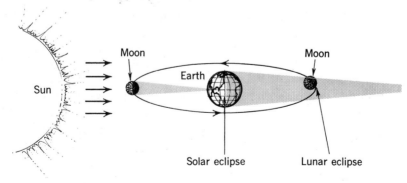

14-11. The progressive changes during a lunar eclipse. (Yerkes Observatory)

Lunar eclipses are more common. *A lunar eclipse occurs when the moon passes through the shadow of the earth.* There are several reasons why you are apt to see many lunar eclipses in your lifetime.

First of all, there are more lunar eclipses than solar, and they last much longer. This is because the shadow of the earth is larger and longer than the shadow of the moon. Then, too, you can see a solar eclipse only if you are living in the right place—that narrow strip of earth covered by the moon's shadow. On the other hand, more than half the people of the world can see any lunar eclipse if the sky is clear.

As a lunar eclipse starts, you can see the curved shadow of the earth darkening the moon. But even when the moon is entirely in the earth's shadow, you can still see it reflecting dull red. This is because sunlight is bent into the earth's shadow, and because of fluorescence of the moon's surface. (See Fig. 14-11.)

A solar eclipse is a thrilling spectacle. It can occur only when the moon is new. As the moon moves between the sun and the earth, twilight descends upon the land. You can see the brighter stars shining in the sky. Just as the sun becomes completely covered, the pearly light of the great *corona* flashes out into space. (See Fig. 14-12.)

Astronomers travel great distances to study eclipses. During an eclipse they can measure more accurately the orbits of the earth and moon. They

14-12. The corona can be studied during a solar eclipse. (Yerkes Observatory)

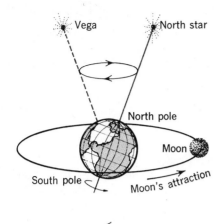

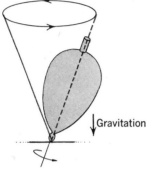

14-13. Precession can be compared to the wobbling of a spinning top. The earth completes one wobble or cycle every 25,800 years.

can also check on the size, shape, and rotation of the earth. They learn more about the corona.

What are some other effects of the moon? We have seen in Chapter 13 that the moon is a major cause of tides. Because of tidal friction, the earth's *rotation* is slowed down about 14 seconds per century. We think that four billion years ago the earth rotated once every four hours. At the present rate of change, in about one billion years, the earth will rotate only once every year. In other words, the same side of the earth would always face the sun.

The gravitational pull of the moon on the bulge of the earth at its equator tends to reduce the angle of tilt of the earth's axis. This has the effect of making the earth "wobble," like a spinning top. At present the axis of the earth points toward the north star, *Polaris.* But in 12,000 years, because of this wobble, our north pole will point toward the bright star called *Vega.*

This slow change in the pointing of the earth's axis completes its cycle once every 25,800 years. The spinning earth acts very much like a spinning gyroscope. (See Fig. 14-13.) The *wobbling motion* is called **precession.** You may find it interesting to read further on the cause of precession in astronomy books.

Quick Quiz

1. Describe the planet earth, giving its size, shape, and general appearance.
2. Explain what is meant by a mean solar day.
3. What is the origin of the word month?
4. What are the two causes of our seasons?
5. What are some of the reasons for our cold weather in winter?
6. Name the standard time belts in the United States.
7. What is the prime meridian? The International Date Line?
8. What is meant by the winter solstice? When does it occur?
9. Why don't the mountains on the moon erode as quickly as mountains on earth?
10. What causes a solar eclipse? A lunar eclipse?
11. What is the chief cause of tides on earth?

12. What can we conclude about the moon's surface from its lack of limb darkening?
13. Where in the sky do you see the full moon at midnight? Explain.

B THE SOLAR SYSTEM

The earth belongs to the solar system. The planets, their moons, and the sun are all in a group called the *solar system*. *Solar system* means a system belonging to our sun. As the sun speeds through space, the earth and other planets "follow" along, spinning around it. All the planets go around the sun in the same *counterclockwise* direction as seen from above the north pole. All except Pluto revolve in about the same plane; that is, as if they were part of a flat wheel.

The planet *Jupiter* is larger than all the others put together. However, the planets are only tiny chunks of matter compared with the sun. The sun contains 750 times as much material as all of the planets combined.

Despite the fact that most people have probably often seen figures telling about the sizes of the sun and planets, they still have difficulty gaining a true understanding of the actual differences. A better understanding can be obtained by showing the size relationships on a two-dimensional scale such as shown in Fig. 14-14. If you wish to obtain a better understanding of distance as well as size, you may want to set up a scale model of the solar system accurate according to both *size and distance*. Using the same scale as shown in Fig. 14-14, Mercury is 30 feet away from the sun; Venus is 55 feet; Earth, 80 feet; Mars, 120 feet; Jupiter, 400 feet; Saturn, 740 feet; Uranus, 1565 feet; Neptune, 2330 feet; and Pluto, 3085 feet. How much of this scale model solar system could you get onto a football field?

The sun is the center of the solar system. During the early years of recorded history, people believed that the earth was the center of the universe, and that the sun, moon, and stars all revolved around our planet. Then, however, some early scientists discovered that the sun was the center of our solar system and that this system was only a tiny part of the universe. Aristarchus, a Greek scientist, in 270 B.C., discovered that the sun was considerably larger than the earth and concluded, therefore, that the sun must be the center of the solar system.

Other scientists, notably Ptolemy, believed that the earth was the true center of the universe. The false theory prevailed even among scientists until after the death of Nicolaus Copernicus in 1543. Even such a great astronomer as Tycho Brahe, who was born after the death of Copernicus, refused to believe the Copernican theory of the sun-centered solar system. He thought that if the earth traveled around the sun, the stars would be viewed from different angles at different times of the year. Since no change could be seen in the star pattern, he concluded that the earth was stationary. It was difficult to realize at that time that the stars were so far away that the viewing angles would be practically identical

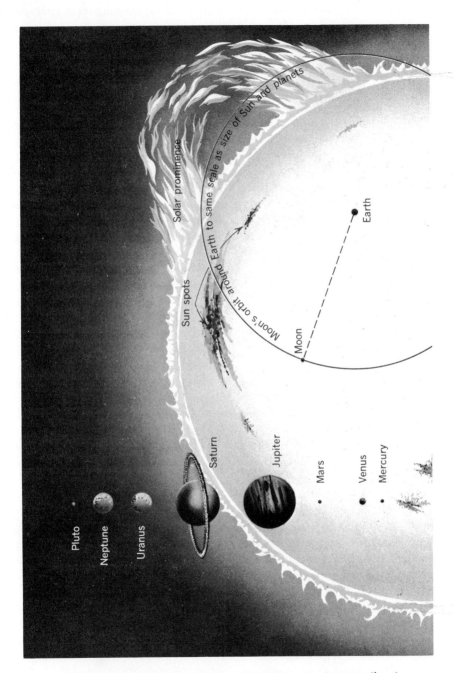

14-14. The sun and the planets are shown to scale according to their sizes. On the same scale the size of the moon is shown, as well as its proper distance from the earth. Notice that the moon can easily orbit the earth in an area as large as the sun.

despite the 186,000,000-mile-diameter of the earth's orbit. Johannes Kepler and others, in 1609 and later, added to the evidence to indicate that Copernicus and Aristarchus were right.

What is the sun like? The sun is one of billions of stars in the universe. It looks bigger and brighter than the others merely because it is closer to us. *Rigel* (*rye*-jel), for example, a bright star in the group called *Orion* (oh-*rye*-un), is more than 20,000 times as bright as the sun. Of course, the sun looks much brighter because it is only 93 million miles from the earth, compared with Rigel's distance of more than *3000 trillion* miles.

The diameter of the sun is 865,000 miles, compared with 7900 miles for the earth. Its surface temperature is about 10,000° F, but the temperature deep inside is about 20 million degrees. We get energy from the sun at the rate of five million horsepower per square mile or 1 horsepower per square yard. If we were to pay for this power at the rate of 1¢ per kilowatt-hour (a very inexpensive rate), the earth's bill for sun-power would be about a quarter of a billion dollars per second. Yet our tiny earth picks up only one half-billionth of all the energy radiated by the sun.

Where does the sun's energy come from? Scientists had long puzzled over the source of the sun's heat and light. They knew that the sun contains huge amounts of combustible hydrogen. However, if the sun's energy came from burning, the sun would have been completely burned up long ago.

They had no satisfactory explanation until Einstein, in 1905, showed by his famous equation, $E = mc^2$ (energy equals mass times the square of

the speed of light), that matter could be changed into energy. This formula shows that when one gram of the sun's mass is turned into energy, about 33 million horsepower-hours of energy are formed.

You may think of the sun as a huge atomic reactor that produces energy by *atomic fusion*. Hydrogen is converted into helium and, in this process, about four million tons of the sun are turned into light and heat each second. Yet the sun is so big that, even at this rate, only 1 percent of the hydrogen of the sun will be used up in 150 billion years.

The solar atmosphere is divided into three layers. The layer closest to the sun's surface is called the *photosphere.* It is a few hundred miles deep and is very dense. We receive almost all of the sun's visible radiation from this zone. (See Fig. 14-15.) The second layer is called the *chromosphere.* It is about 9000 miles thick and much less dense than the photosphere. The temperature of this layer ranges from the "cool" 10,000° F of the photosphere to the "hot" 2,000,000° F of the *corona.*

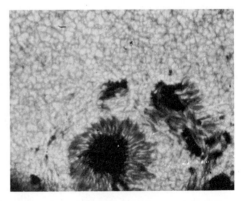

14-15. This close-up of the sun's surface shows the granular appearance of the photosphere. (Princeton University)

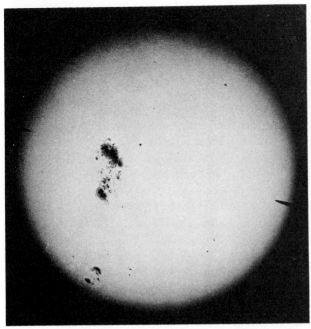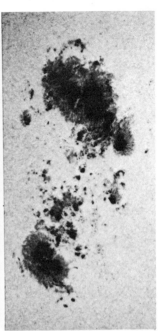

14-16. Sunspots are violent eruptions on the surface of the sun. (Mount Wilson & Palomar Observatories)

The *corona* is the outermost layer of the sun's atmosphere and appears as a white or pale yellow glow that completely surrounds the sun. It extends outward for millions of miles and is visible during a total eclipse of the sun. Its temperature reaches 2 million degrees F during active sunspot and solar-flare activity. Fortunately, the corona's atmosphere is so thin that it radiates almost no heat to the earth. If it were as dense as the photosphere, its high temperature would send out so much heat that it would rapidly vaporize the entire earth.

Sunspots and their effect upon us. Sunspots are an indication of some *great disturbances* that are occurring *in the sun's photosphere.* Astronomers believe that sunspots are caused by the buildup of powerful localized magnetic fields which retard the flow of hot gases from the sun's interior. This, therefore, leads to a localized cooling of the sunspot, a region which may be as much as a hundred times larger than the earth. These spots have a temperature of over 7000° F, hotter and brighter than an electric arc. They appear dark only by comparison with the rest of the sun's surface, which is at a temperature of about 10,000° F. (See Fig. 14-16.)

The number of spots on the face of the sun comes and goes in a cycle of about 11½ years. That is, the number and size of the spots increase and then decrease about every 11½ years. The next maximum is expected about 1970.

Unusual sunspot activity causes disturbances on the earth. *Radio reception* is upset. Electric currents generated in the crust of the earth affect *telegraph* circuits. Even *television* sig-

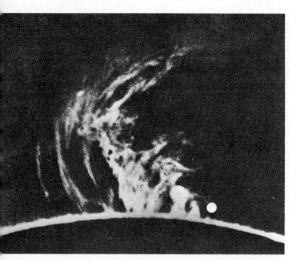

14-17. The flaming clouds of a solar prominence. (Mount Wilson & Palomar Observatories)

nals, which normally pass through the *ionosphere,* may be reflected back from it and sent around much of the world during a maximum of the sunspot cycle. Other changes include the earth's magnetism and our weather. These disturbances are actually caused more by solar flares that are sometimes associated with sunspot activity, rather than by the spots themselves.

Solar flares and prominences. The activities of sunspots look small when compared to the large *solar flare.* The solar flare is a region of intense brilliance covering hundreds of millions of square miles. It appears to develop with great suddenness and may become ten times as bright as the surrounding sun's surface. Flares usually last only a few hours and give out intense streams of electrified particles. The more highly charged particles strike the earth in a matter of minutes, while streams of less energetic particles take a day or two to reach the earth. When they strike the upper atmosphere of

the earth, they usually intensify the *aurora borealis* (bor-ee-*ah*-liss), more commonly known as *northern lights.* As mentioned above, they also produce many of the disturbances associated with sunspot activity.

Other mysterious occurrences on the sun include **solar prominences.** These are streamers of glowing gases that swirl up at fantastic speeds for hundreds of thousands of miles above the surface of the sun. The violent movement of the solar prominences tells us of seething activity in the solar atmosphere. (See Fig. 14-17.)

Why does each planet have a different year? By a year we mean the time it takes a planet to go around the sun once. As you will notice in the table on page 555, the farther away the planet is from the sun, the longer is its year. Note that Mercury makes about four trips around the sun to our one. It is pulled strongly inward by gravity which prevents it from flying off in a straight line as its *inertia* tends to make it do. By contrast, we see that to survive even one full year on Uranus, you would have to live to a ripe old age. Neptune has not made even one full trip about the sun since it was discovered in 1846.

Mercury is the innermost planet. In the table on page 555, you will find a few vital statistics about our family of planets. You might find it interesting to be able to name them in their proper order from the sun. The innermost planet is Mercury. It is so close to the sun that it is too hot for known forms of life. Besides, it is too small to have enough gravity to hold an atmosphere. Because it is so close to the sun, Mercury is very difficult to see from the earth. The only time it can be spotted is immediately before sunrise or after sunset.

Venus is covered with clouds. Except for the moon, Venus is the brightest object in our sky at night. Sometimes Venus is the *"evening star,"* shining in the west after sunset. Sometimes it is the *"morning star,"* shining in the east before sunrise. If you study Venus with a telescope, you will find that it seems to change shape, just as the moon does. It goes from crescent shape, to quarter, to full, in phases much like those of the moon.

Much information about Venus was gained by the *Mariner II spacecraft* in 1962. From that flight we learned that Venus has a very dense cloud layer about 15 miles thick with the bottom of the layer about 45 miles above the surface and the top of the layer about 60 miles high. The atmosphere consists mostly of carbon dioxide, nitrogen, and other gases with only a trace of oxygen. The atmospheric pressure of this planet is estimated to be about 300 pounds per square inch, or 20 times as great as sea level pressure on earth.

Because of the thick clouds a "greenhouse effect" is created and temperatures reach 800 degrees F. You may have noticed this greenhouse effect in a car left standing in the sun with the windows closed; as the temperatures become quite high. (See Fig. 14-18.)

Temperature differences may cause winds estimated to be up to 400 miles per hour. Thus, because of the high temperatures, great winds and lack of oxygen and water, Venus does not appear to be capable of supporting any form of life. The planet has very little, if any rotational motion. Therefore, it gets its day-night sequence mostly from its movement around the sun, and each is half a Venus's year in length. The long night does not, however, have much effect on the temperature. The blanket of clouds and the winds distribute the heat to both the sunlit and dark side of the planet. If the sun could be seen through the

FACTS ABOUT THE PLANETS

	Approximate diameter in miles	Approximate distance from sun in miles	Period of revolution (Year)	Period of rotation in earth days and hours	Number of moons
Mercury	3,100	36,000,000	88 days	88 days	0
Venus	7,850	67,000,000	225 days	225 days(?)	0
Earth	7,930	93,000,000	365¼ days	1 day	1
Mars	4,270	142,000,000	687 days	24½ hours	2
Jupiter	89,300	483,000,000	12 years	10 hours	12
Saturn	75,000	886,000,000	30 years	10 hours	9
Uranus	33,200	1,780,000,000	84 years	11 hours	5
Neptune	30,900	2,795,000,000	165 years	16 hours	2
Pluto	3,600(?)	3,700,000,000	250 years	6⅓ days (?)	?

(?) = unconfirmed

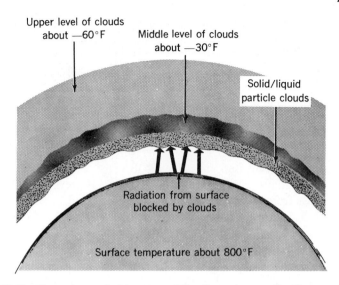

Upper level of clouds
about —60°F

Middle level of clouds
about —30°F

Solid/liquid
particle clouds

Radiation from surface
blocked by clouds

Surface temperature about 800°F

14-18. Venus is very hot because of the "greenhouse effect" caused by the dense layer of clouds. The height of the clouds is not drawn to scale.

clouds from the surface of Venus, it would appear to rise in the west and set in the east once each year.

Mars is known as the red planet. Mars is generally red in appearance with small areas of green and white. These areas change during the seasons of a Martian year. (See Fig. 14-19.)

Mars comes nearest to the earth about every two years. (The closest possible approach is about 35,000,000 miles.) These are the best times to study it with telescopes or to send space probes to it. In July, 1965, the Mariner IV spacecraft flew to within 5500 miles of the Martian surface.

About 1877, an Italian astronomer noticed markings on its surface. These were called *canals* (due to a mis-translation from the Italian). Photographs taken by Mariner IV, however, show no evidence of actual canals. Instead, Mars has a desert-like surface covered with many craters. It has very little air,

oxygen, or water. Thus, living on Mars would be very difficult for humans.

Jupiter and Saturn are the largest planets. Even though it is over 450 million miles away, Jupiter shines like a bright star in the sky because of its great size. When you look at Jupiter through a small telescope or good field glasses, you can usually see the outer four of its 12 moons. Of course, if one of them happens to be behind Jupiter, you cannot see it.

Through a large telescope we can see that Jupiter is covered by a dense cloud-like atmosphere, composed mostly of *hydrogen*. The clouds are not made of water droplets but of ammonia and methane. Certainly such an atmosphere would not support life as we know it.

Unexplained markings, including a massive *red spot*, occur at various intervals. (See Fig. 14-20.)

An interesting feature of Saturn is its three large bright rings. These are

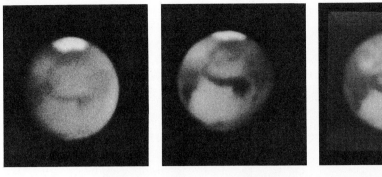
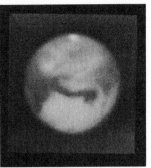

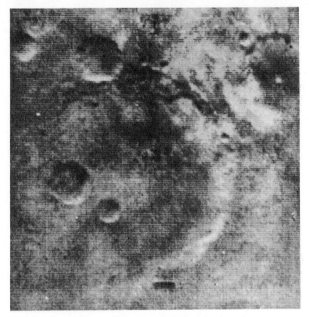

14-19. The planet Mars during seasonal changes (top). Notice the variations in the polar ice cap and dust clouds. (Lowell Observatory) Bottom: one of the remarkable Mariner IV photos of the Martian surface, showing craters and other features. (Wide World Photos)

very flat, thin bands that revolve about the planet's equator. Each one is made up of billions of small particles of rock, dust, and ice. These rings sometimes appear on edge and at other times in full view. (See Fig. 14-21.)

The atmosphere of Saturn is very deep. Like Jupiter's, it is not suitable for breathing. Saturn, of course, is even colder than Jupiter. (Can you think of a reason why this might be so?)

The outer planets. You can sometimes see Uranus as a very dim star, but usually you need a telescope. William Herschel discovered Uranus in 1781.

It was soon noticed that Uranus did not follow exactly the path pre-

14-20. Markings such as the giant red spot are visible on Jupiter, our largest planet. These markings are not fully understood. (Mount Wilson & Palomar Observatories)

dicted for it. Astronomers became convinced that there must be another planet out beyond it, pulling it out of its normal path. Mathematicians calculated where this new planet must be. In 1846, the astronomers trained their telescopes toward this location in the sky and observed the planet Neptune. This was a remarkable triumph for Newtonian mechanics!

14-21. This photograph shows the ring system around the planet Saturn. (Mount Wilson & Palomar Observatories)

Much later, and for the same reasons, some astronomers began to suspect the existence of still another planet. After a long search of the skies, Pluto was found in 1930. Pluto, probably about the size of Mars, has a path about the sun quite different from those of the other planets. Its orbit is more eccentric than any planetary orbit. At its closest approach to the sun, Pluto is inside Neptune's orbit, but most of the time it is millions of miles beyond Neptune. Pluto's orbit is also different in that it is inclined or tilted at about 17 degrees from the plane of the other orbits. Many astronomers believe Pluto to be a former moon of Neptune.

Most of the planets have moons. A *moon* is a smaller body that circles about a planet. *Moons* are also called *satellites,* and so we often use the term *artificial satellite* for the small bodies we put into orbit about the earth.

Note that Saturn possesses nine regular moons in addition to its rings. One of these, *Titan,* is much larger than *our* moon, and has an appreciable atmosphere, not suitable for breathing, however. Two of Jupiter's 12 moons, *Ganymede* and *Callisto,* are larger than *our* moon. While the earth has only one moon, *our* moon is larger, compared with the size of the earth, than any other moon compared with its planet. *All moons, like planets, shine by reflected sunlight.*

The orbit of each planet about the sun is oval-shaped, or *elliptical.* The moons also revolve about the planets in elliptical orbits. As each planet, like earth, spins on its own axis, so does each moon spin on its axis.

Was there a tenth planet? Besides the *nine* major planets, there are many

14-22. Halley's comet streaks across the sky with exciting beauty. (Mount Wilson & Palomar Observatories)

smaller masses called *planetoids,* or *asteroids,* in the solar system. Each circles about the sun in its own orbit, just as the planets do. Nearly 200 of them have already been discovered and named. The largest asteroid, Ceres, 1/800 the size of earth, was found in 1801. It is known that there are many thousands more.

About two-thirds of the planetoids are found in an orbit between Mars and Jupiter. They are located just where a mathematical formula suggests another planet should be. Possibly these asteroids are the remains of a single large planet that once occupied this orbit. Another theory is that they are the "raw material" of a planet that never formed.

What are comets? The head of a *comet* is composed of a loose collection of particles of mineral matter and ice, together with dust and gases. Many comets are much larger than the earth, but less dense. When it is near the sun, a comet usually has a glowing tail millions of miles long as shown in Fig. 14-22. This tail is made of low-density gas that is driven from the head of the comet by *radiation pressure* of the sun. For this reason, the tail of a comet points away from the sun. Comets circle around the sun as the planets do, only in *long, elliptical orbits.*

Although there are thousands of comets in the solar system, the chances are that you will see only two or three bright ones during your lifetime. The orbits of a few of them have been calculated, and we can predict when they will return.

The most famous comet is Halley's comet. Its appearance about every 76 years has been traced back to 240 B.C. It last appeared in 1910, and many of you who are reading this will see it during its next return in 1986. (See Fig. 14-23.)

It is now believed that a small comet struck the earth in 1908. Landing in a remote part of Siberia, it demolished everything over an area of 10,000 square miles.

Meteors and meteorites. Probably you know that "shooting stars" are

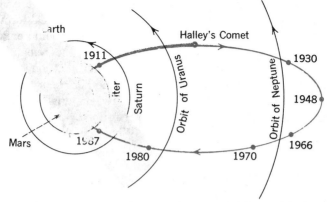

14-23. The orbit of Halley's comet is compared here with the orbits of the planets.

not real stars at all. They are *meteors,* small particles of metal and stone that speed about in space. When they hit the earth's atmosphere, friction causes them to glow white-hot, and you see a streak of light. Actually, the hot particles ionize the upper air, starting about 70 miles up. This makes the entire column of air glow like a neon sign.

Meteors are closely related to comets. Not all of the comet is contained in its head. Many particles of the comet are strung out along its entire orbit.

14-24. The surface of this huge metallic meteorite was eroded by oxidation as it penetrated the earth's atmosphere. (Courtesy of the American Museum of Natural History)

Objects that pass through the orbit of a comet collide with some of these particles. Sometimes a comet breaks up and, on the date of the expected return of the comet, a *shower* of meteors appears instead. Your parents may remember such a shower that occurred in October, 1946. It is calculated that the earth will cross its orbit again in 1972. At this time, it is quite possible that there may be a similar meteor shower.

Most *meteoric* material is about the size of dust particles. Some are as large as grains of sand. They burn out while still 30 to 60 miles above the earth. A very few are big enough to reach the surface of our planet.

Meteors that do *reach the earth* are called *meteorites.* Most of them consist of rocky minerals, but a few are made of a nickel-iron alloy. (See Fig. 14-24.)

A large meteor may be bright enough to be seen even in daylight, and is often called a *fireball*. It may explode into many pieces before hitting the ground. After one of these fell in Iowa in 1877, 774 pounds of fragments were collected. The 600-foot deep meteor crater in Arizona was formed by a large fireball many thousands of years ago. (See Fig. 14-25.)

Today we can detect meteors in the sky, day or night, by *radar*. Millions of them approach earth every day, but because the atmosphere acts like a protective blanket, relatively few ever hit the ground. One possible hazard of travel in outer space is the danger of collision with meteors. Possibly a thin metal jacket (meteor bumper) can be used to deflect the small ones. Radar can be used to locate and avoid the larger ones. The *Pegasus* satellite was orbited in 1965 to study meteor dangers, and found that they were not too severe.

How do we obtain information about heavenly bodies? The chief instrument for obtaining information about the sun, planets, and stars is the *astronomical* or *optical telescope*. Ever since Galileo's first use of the telescope, astronomers have set up observatories to chart the skies. Mt. Palomar Observatory in California has a *reflecting telescope* with a mirror of Pyrex glass 200 inches in diameter. This telescope and other reflectors ranging from 36 to 120 inches, located in many countries of the world, have greatly extended man's knowledge of the universe. (See Fig. 14-26.)

Much of the information about the heavens is obtained by attaching a *spectroscope* to a telescope. A **spectroscope** is used to tell what elements produced the light which shines on it. In addition, scientists can determine the speed, temperature, chemical composition, and sometimes the spin of the body producing that light.

Another means of learning about the sun, planets, and stars is to *photograph* them through filters permitting

14-25. This large crater in Arizona was caused by a meteor weighing ten million tons that fell over 50,000 years ago. It is one mile in diameter and 570 feet deep. (Fairchild Aerial Surveys, Inc.)

the passage of only *selected types of radiation*. For example, a photograph of X-ray emissions shows the sun as a relatively dim body but the corona, normally invisible, as quite bright.

14-26. The observer sits in the prime focus cage and reflecting area of the 200-inch mirror of the Hale telescope. (Mount Wilson & Palomar Observatories)

14-27. The world's largest fully steerable radiotelescope is in Cheshire, England, at Jodrell Bank. The telescope is constructed of steel and weighs 2,000 tons. The reflector bowl alone weighs 750 tons and is 83 yards in diameter. The complicated controls are seen in the foreground. (British Information Services)

The camera, with various filters, along with the spectroscope can see much more than the human eye. That is the reason why an astronomer rarely looks through the large telescope. "Seeing time" is too precious to be wasted in that way.

Radio astronomy. Since 1942, this new branch of astronomy, using radio telescopes, has been growing in importance. Huge disk-like antennas, or radio "ears," hundreds of feet in diameter, are in operation today, as shown in Fig. 14-27. They are used to "listen" for radio signals coming from the solar system and outer space. We often hear some of these signals as static in our radios. To the astronomer, however, these signals are very impor-

tant, because our optical view of the universe is limited by several factors. Light waves cannot pass through the great clouds of gases and dust in outer space. Many radiations are also absorbed by our own atmosphere. Radio waves do not have these handicaps. Hence, by means of radio waves, we can "see" many parts of the universe that were formerly hidden from us.

With the help of radio waves, we learn more of the nature of solar activity. We can study the center of our Milky Way system of stars. We can measure the motions of distant stars. With their radio telescopes, astron-

14-28. The top panel shows how the Cygnus portion of the sky appeared to optical astronomers. Strong radiations coming from that area led radio astronomers to concentrate on this area and identify two gigantic galaxies in collision (bottom). (National Radio Astronomy Observatory)

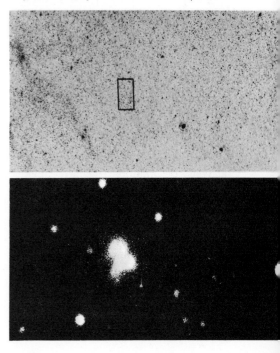

omers are locating many *dark stars* that are completely invisible with the ordinary telescope. It is possible that radio telescopes can probe space to the very edge of the observable universe, about *ten billion light years away*. (*One light year equals about six trillion miles*.) The present limit, with optical telescopes, is *several billion light years*. (See Fig. 14-28.)

Sources of radio waves in space. Radio waves come from the sun and planets, and from the distant stars. The strongest sources of radiation occur when there is a collision between two galaxies, from the *exploding stars*, or *novas*, and *quasars*. A fourth interesting and important source is *hydrogen gas*. Hydrogen is the chief raw material of the universe. Most stars, such as our sun, are composed largely of hydrogen, and hydrogen is also widely scattered throughout space. Excited hydrogen atoms in space emit radiation of one particular *wavelength*, about *21 cm.* Hence, this *universal wavelength* is used to listen for radio messages from intelligent beings who may live on planets of other stars. In *Project Ozma*, radio telescopes were tuned to 21 cm, and were trained on nearby stars for this purpose.

14-29. The orbiting astronomical observatory (OAO) is designed to help astronomers gain information about the universe from a place free of the interfering effects of our atmosphere. (Grumman Aircraft Engineering Corp.)

14-30. Mariner is a spacecraft designed for the exploration of the planets. (NASA)

Radar astronomy is also yielding important information about the sun, moon, and other planets of our solar system. Powerful *radar* beams are transmitted to, and reflected from, these objects.

The difference between radar and radio astronomy is that in radio astronomy we use natural radiation, or radio signals from nature, while in radar astronomy we generate our own signals and study their reflection from celestial bodies.

Another improvement in the techniques used to study astronomy is achieved by sending up rockets and satellites. Telescopes and other instruments are now or soon will be orbiting the earth in satellites such as the Orbiting Solar Observatory (OSO), the Orbiting Astronomical Observatory (OAO), and the Orbiting Geophysical Observatory (OGO). (See Fig. 14-29.)

Finally, the lunar and interplanetary probes such as *Ranger, Surveyor,* and *Mariner* have done much to increase our knowledge about the moon and planets. They have also been very helpful in obtaining information about conditions in the void of space as well as in giving scientists experience in ultra long-range electronic transmission. As time goes on, the program of space research will sharply increase man's knowledge of the universe. (See Fig. 14-30.)

Quick Quiz

1. Name the planets in order outward from the sun.
2. Name the planets in order of their size from the smallest to the largest.
3. Why is Venus sometimes called the morning star and sometimes the evening star?
4. Why is it impossible to see Mercury at midnight?
5. Why does the sun look bigger and brighter than other stars?
6. Describe the atmosphere of the sun. What are its parts?
7. How do you account for the fact that the dark side of Venus has approximately the same temperature as the sunlit side?
8. What are some differences between sunspots and solar flares? How are they alike?
9. Why do astronomers seldom actually look through their large telescopes?
10. What are some advantages of radio telescopes over optical telescopes?
11. Why is it unlikely that life as we know it can exist on any other planet of our solar system?
12. Why were some famous astronomers unwilling to believe that the earth revolved around the sun, even as late as 1600, fifty years after the death of Copernicus?

13. Why is there so little heat transmitted from the sun's corona although it is far hotter than the sun's surface?

C THE UNIVERSE

What is the stellar universe? The *physical universe* includes all *space, time, matter,* and *energy.* In this section, you will read about the **stellar universe,** the universe of stars. You will learn something of the nature of stars and how they are distributed through space. You will be called upon to stretch your imagination to the very limit. You will think of space and time measurements much greater than those of your everyday experience.

Stellar distances are measured in *light years.* You know that the stars are glowing hot masses of gas, similar to our sun. These stars are so far away that even when you look at them through the most powerful telescope they still look like tiny points of light.

Light from the sun, 93 million miles away, reaches us in about 8 minutes. But it takes 4.3 years for light from the next nearest star to reach the earth. That is what we mean when we say that this star is 4.3 light years away. A *light year* is the *distance* that light travels in a year, about six trillion miles.

Stars are large, heavenly bodies. All stars that we can see are *hot enough to shine* by their own light. The nearest star, our sun, is a relatively small star. Many stars are hotter, and many are larger. We believe that millions of other stars may also have planets like ours. But all of the other stars are so far away that we could not see their planets even with the most powerful telescope.

How many stars can you see? On a clear, moonless night, the sky seems to be studded with millions of stars. This is especially true if you are on a high mountain. Actually, without a telescope, even on a clear night, you can see fewer than 3000 stars at any one time.

Ever since the days of the ancient Greeks, the apparent brightness of stars has been measured in **magnitudes.** The Greeks classed the 20 *brightest stars* as stars of the *first magnitude.* These stars are about 2.5 times as bright as those of the second magnitude. Similarly, stars of the second magnitude are about 2.5 times brighter than those of the third. Under ideal conditions you can see stars as faint as the fifth or sometimes even the sixth magnitude. Usually, however, viewing conditions are diminished by lights around us or by a hazy sky.

Of course, there are many more stars than just those that are visible to the unaided eye. The number is so great that it defies the imagination. There are probably more stars than there are grains of sand on all the seashores and deserts of the world.

How are the stars classified? You have learned that ordinary matter is made of different kinds of atoms. Astronomers have learned that the universe is made of larger particles (stars), of which there are also different kinds. You learned that all atoms are alike in certain ways but differ in others. In the same way, although all the stars are somewhat alike, we can divide them into several different classes.

We may classify stars according to their *temperatures.* Some stars are cold and dark. Others, like Antares (an-*tair*-eez), are red-hot. Antares has a surface temperature of 5000° F. At the other extreme you find blue-white stars such as *Rigel* with a temperature of 36,000° F. The sun is between these two extremes. It is a yellow star with its surface temperature of about 10,-000° F.

Compared with the sun, some stars are *giants* in size. *Antares, a supergiant, is 70 million times as big as the sun!* As shown in Fig. 14-31, all the planets up to Mars could revolve about the sun in their present orbits and still fit inside this star.

Some stars are smaller than the sun. *Sirius* (*seer*-ee-us) is the brightest star in the sky. It is a *double star.* This means that it is made up of *two stars* that are fairly close together, *revolving about each other.* The smaller of the two stars is a *dwarf star.* It is only about 1/30,000 as big as the sun.

Curiously enough, although the stars vary so much in size, the difference in their *masses,* or the amount of matter they contain, is much less. This means that the giants have a very low density, while the dwarfs have amazingly high densities.

Matter is so rare in some supergiants that the density can be compared with the vacuum inside a television tube. On the other extreme, some little *white dwarf* stars are so dense, or closely packed, that a single teaspoonful of this material would weigh thousands of pounds on earth.

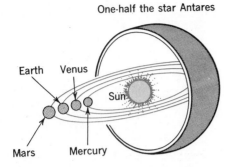

One-half the star Antares

Earth Venus

Sun

Mars Mercury

14-31. The tremendous size of the star Antares is shown by the above comparison.

How can we measure star distances? We can find out how far away the nearest stars are by using a surveying method called *parallax*. **Parallax is the apparent shift of an object observed, due to a change in the position of the observer.** Since the diameter of the earth's orbit around the sun is 186,000,000 miles, this certainly constitutes a change in the position of the observer. Thus, the objects observed, the stars, should appear to shift when viewed from different positions in the earth's orbit. The distances to the stars are so great, however, that no shift in the positions of the stars was detected until 1830. Now, with highly refined methods using telescopes, photographs, and microscopes, we can detect a shift equal to one inch in an object 100 miles away. Even with these refinements, only a few thousand stars, all less than 100 light years away, can be measured in this way. All the rest of the billions upon billions of stars are too far away.

Why are variable stars important? Certain stars have regular periods of growing brighter and dimmer. This may be because they are double stars, one less brilliant than the other. Every so often, the dimmer one will get in front of the other and hide its brightness. These are called *eclipsing variables*.

Other stars change in brightness because they go through a regular *pulsating* period. We call these *Cepheid* (*sef-ee-id*) *variables* because the first one was noticed in the constellation *Cepheus* (*see-*fee-us). The time or period of pulsation may be anywhere from one to sixty days. The brighter the star actually is, the longer a period of pulsation it has. Hence, by observing the pulsation period, we can measure the *actual brightness*. If a star is twice as far away as another but gives off just as much light, it will seem to be only *one-fourth* as bright. Thus, because we can estimate great distances this way, the cepheid variables act as important "yardsticks" of the universe.

Stars rise and set. If you watch the stars for any period of time, you can see that most of them rise in the east and set in the west, like the sun. The ones near the *north star* circle about it once every 24 hours. This motion can be seen by pointing even a simple box camera at the north star and taking a time exposure. In two or three hours you get bright, curved *star trails* like the ones in Fig. 14-32. Choose a moonless night away from city lights.

This *apparent motion* of the stars is due to the same cause that makes the sun seem to rise and set. It is the *daily rotation of the earth* with its axis pointed toward the north star. The stars "stay put," but your camera turns with the earth.

What are constellations? *Constellations are groups of stars that seem to form patterns when viewed from earth.* Some constellations represent true clus-

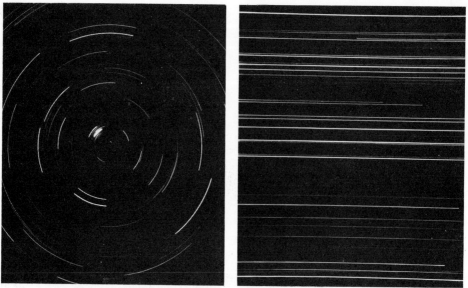

14-32. These star trails were photographed with the camera aimed at the North Star (left) and at stars above the equator (right). (Yerkes Observatory)

ters of stars but in most cases, they just appear that way and are not grouped together at all.

Some constellations, such as the *Big Dipper* and the *Northern Cross*, are named because of their shape. Many are given names of characters in Greek mythology. These include *Perseus* (pers-ee-us), and *Orion* (oh-*rye*-un). If you know the constellations, you can quickly locate different stars. Astronomers and navigators use the positions of the stars to help find direction, location, and time on the earth. With the help of a star map, learn to know a new constellation each month. You will soon learn the names and locations of many stars and constellations.

Many of the early stargazers were *astrologers. Astrology* (as-*trol*-uh-jee) teaches that your daily life, or your fate, depends upon the stars and planets. Astrology is not a science—it is a superstition.

What is the Milky Way? The Milky Way is a pale, irregular band of hazy light extending across the night sky. When you look at it through a telescope, you can see that it is made up of swarms of stars. They are too far away for you to see them as separate points of light without a telescope.

This vast swarm of billions of stars is the particular *star group,* or *galaxy,* that the sun belongs to. The galaxy is roughly disk-shaped, something like a watch or a fried egg. The sun is located about 30,000 light years away from its center. When you are looking out into space in the direction toward the center, you can see many more stars than when you look in the opposite direction. There are so many stars in the center that they give the faint glow of light that we call the Milky Way. The word "galaxy" comes from a Greek word meaning "milk."

The few thousand stars that you can see in the sky are all a part of this vast galaxy. The diameter of our galaxy is about 100,000 light years. Its thickness at the center is nearly 20,000 light years.

On the outskirts of the central part of our galaxy we find tightly clustered groups of stars called *globular clusters*. Each globular cluster is about 200 light years across and contains tens of thousands of stars.

Some galaxies have spiral shapes. In the constellation *Andromeda*, you can just barely see a dim, hazy star. But, when you look at it through a telescope, you discover that it is not a star at all. It is another system of billions of stars like our own galaxy.

As you can see in Fig. 14-33, this star cloud is in the form of a spiral, like a pinwheel. Because of its shape, it is called a *spiral galaxy*. This spiral galaxy is about as large as our own Milky Way galaxy. Although it is one of our nearest neighbors in space, it is nearly two million light years away. *This means that we see it as it was about two million years ago!* If we could go to this distant star-swarm and look back, we should find that our galaxy, too, would look like a spiral. Figure 14-34 shows how a spiral galaxy looks when it is seen from the side.

With the aid of huge telescopes, astronomers have found that there are billions of these spiral galaxies, or "island universes." They vary somewhat in shape. The most distant one observed with the 200-inch Mt. Palomar telescope is several billion light

14-33. The spiral nebula shown above lies far beyond our Milky Way. (Mount Wilson & Palomar Observatories)

years away. Like our own galaxy, each one is made up of millions or billions of stars.

As you would expect from their appearance, the spiral galaxies are spinning like giant pinwheels, or like the cream in half-stirred coffee. Because of this motion alone, our sun has a speed of about 170 miles per second. Yet, so huge is our galaxy that, even at this speed, it takes the sun about 230 million years to go around only once.

Besides rotating about their own centers, the spiral galaxies seem to be rushing away from each other at terrific speeds. And the farther away the

14-34. This spiral nebula is shown here on its edge. (Mount Wilson & Palomar Observatories)

14-35. A gaseous nebula in the constellation Orion. This great cloud of gas glows because it receives light from a nearby star. (Mount Wilson and Palomar Observatories)

galaxy, the faster it goes. The most distant ones seem to be fleeing at a speed of over 90,000 miles per second or about half the speed of light. According to one theory of the *expanding universe*, this motion is due to the expansion of space itself.

Galaxies form supergalaxies. Just as the stars are clustered together to form galaxies, so *galaxies seem to be grouped into systems called supergalaxies.* There are over a dozen galaxies in our own cluster, in which Andromeda galaxy and our own are the largest. Some supergalaxies contain more than a hundred galaxies.

What is a nebula? *Nebula* is a Latin word meaning "vapor" or "mist." It is a great mass of gas, mixed with dust. If there are one or more stars near this kind of nebula, it will glow as shown in Fig. 14-35. On the other hand, if this gaseous nebula is not lighted up by a nearby star, it will appear as a *dark nebula* against a background of stars. Then it blocks from view anything that may lie behind it, as shown in Fig. 14-36.

Before the construction of our large telescopes, distant galaxies were often confused with nebulae. Great galaxies with billions of stars are sometimes so far away that they appear as hazy clouds. Examination through powerful telescopes, however, show these to be galaxies composed of billions of individual stars.

A star has a life history. Apparently, stars pass through a life history, from youth to old age. Gravitation may pull a thinly scattered mass of gases and dust into a great ball. This becomes a *newborn star*. It becomes heated by compression and turns into a *young red-giant star*.

In time, this mass becomes hot enough for nuclear reactions to produce atomic energy which is radiated as light and heat. The star then becomes a *mature star,* such as the sun. As you have already learned, the star's energy comes mostly from the conversion of hydrogen to helium. Most stars contain so much hydrogen that this can go on for billions of years. A balance is set up between the inward pull of gravitation and the outward pressure of heat and radiation.

A more massive star lives faster and dies earlier. Its temperature rises higher and the nuclear reactions go on more rapidly.

Eventually, when a great deal of the hydrogen fuel is used up, the life cycle of the star ends.

What is a supernova? Occasionally a star in the sky suddenly grows much brighter than it was. We call such a star a *nova* (*no*-vuh). If it becomes *exceedingly bright,* we call it a *supernova.*

A supernova seems to be the result of a giant explosion. We might say that the star "blows its top" as the whole outer part is blown off. If the star happens to be one in our own galaxy, it becomes so bright that we may be able to see it in broad daylight. Three supernovas have been reported in our galaxy during the past 900 years. Figure 14-37 shows the expanding gas cloud from a supernova reported by the Chinese in the year 1054. Since this star is 5000 light years away, it actually exploded 5000 years before that date.

14-36. The dark nebula in the constellation Orion, commonly called "Horsehead," hides the stars behind it from view. (Mount Wilson and Palomar Observatories)

14-37. The "Crab" nebula in the constellation Taurus is the remains of a supernova that exploded in the year 1054 A.D. (Lick Observatory)

Quasars are immense sources of light and radio waves. *Quasars,* or *quasi-stellar sources* as they are sometimes called, *are newly discovered heavenly phenomena.* Their characteristics are so amazing that even astronomers, accustomed to the greatness of the universe, are awe-struck by their size and power. A single quasar may be more than ten light years in diameter. (Compare this to our sun which is about five light-seconds in diameter.) And a single quasar generates up to 100 times more light and radio waves than does an entire galaxy of over 100 billion stars. (See Fig. 14-38.)

There is no conventional explanation that accounts for either its size or power. Stars, theoretically, cannot attain even a tiny fraction of this size, and entire galaxies of billions of stars

fall far short of matching the quasar's brilliance and radio activity. Thus, new theories are being proposed to explain the phenomena. One suggestion is that a *chain reaction of exploding stars* is taking place much like the *chain reaction of atoms* in a nuclear explosion. An entirely different theory is that of *gravitational collapse.* It is believed that a body which is as large as a quasar could have such a powerful gravitational force that it could collapse its matter in upon itself, creating unprecedented amounts of radiation. Under gravitational collapse, for example, it is estimated that the entire earth would be compressed to a sphere less than one inch in diameter.

No quasars have been found in our galaxy. It is believed that they are located between 2 and 6 billion light years away and would then be the most distant objects that can be seen. They were discovered recently because of an improvement in radio telescopes which permitted astronomers to pinpoint the source of radio emissions. This made it possible to find and identify these "stars" with optical telescopes and to measure their distances, brilliance, and sizes.

It is important to realize that the quasar displays we are now observing took place two to six billion years ago, because it has taken that long for the light to reach us. It is also important to realize that the quasars probably were in the heavens, visible to the earth for millions of years before they were discovered. This is because there are so many stars that it is difficult to study even a tiny fraction of their number.

How did it all begin? Most scientists believe that we cannot explain creation and existence by scientific study alone. However, we are impressed by the complexity and orderliness of the universe. We see changes taking place, and we realize that the universe will be different many years from now. Looking backward, we wonder what it was like a few billion years ago.

There are several theories that try to explain how the universe came to be as it is today. One suggestion is that the galaxies resulted from the explosion of a single huge "atom" of matter and energy. This theory is called the *"big bang"* theory. The stars represent the "shell fragments" from the explosion while the earth is like one of the "dust particles." There is evidence that this explosion took place 10 to 25 billion years ago and is still going on. Therefore, we are living in *an expanding universe.*

A rival *theory* proposes *a steady state universe.* It states that new matter, in the form of hydrogen, is being *continuously created,* together with space. This furnishes the raw material out of which new galaxies are always being formed. As space steadily expands, the old galaxies move farther away, beyond the edge of the observable universe. According to this theory of "continuous creation," there is *no beginning and no end to the universe,* either in time or in space.

How did the sun get its solar system of planets? Do other stars also have planets? One famous theory, called the *nebular hypothesis,* was developed by the 18th century French astronomer, Laplace. According to his theory, what is now the solar system was once a vast gas cloud. Rotation gave it a disk-like shape. Parts of the nebular, or gas cloud, captured other

14-38. Quasars, such as 3C 273 in the constellation Virgo, are the most distant objects known to astronomers. (Mount Wilson & Palomar Observatories)

parts. The effect "snowballed" and the planets and other bodies of the solar system were formed.

Several other theories have been suggested. However, a modification of the above theory is in favor today. If this theory is at all true, it is probable that billions of other stars in our galaxy alone also have planets. Millions of these may be suitable for life as we know it.

Of what use is astronomy? Some of you may say, "But what earthly good is astronomy? It is all right as a hobby, but it has no practical value." You would be wrong. Most of today's astronomers are really physicists. Stars are their laboratories. In the stars, there is matter at temperatures and pressures far greater than they can obtain on earth.

By studying what happens in the sun and other stars, they learn more about the structure and behavior of matter. They learn more about the control and beneficial application of atomic energy.

We have already spoken of the importance of astronomy in navigation and in the measurement of time. With artificial satellites, and intercontinental rockets, astronomy becomes still more important. They are guided by astronomical observations. And, as man reaches out toward the moon and planets, he turns to astronomers to guide his spaceships.

But astronomy has an interest for us far beyond its practical importance. One way in which we differ from other animals is in our eagerness to learn more about the world we live in. We want to know all about life and its meaning, and we want to know about the whole of creation.

This striving for a fuller understanding of the universe is the goal of astronomy. It is one of the greatest challenges to the human mind.

Quick Quiz

1. About how many miles is a light year?

2. About how many stars can you see on a clear night, from one spot, without using a telescope?

3. What is meant by a star of the first magnitude?

4. Why do most stars seem to rise in the east and set in the west?

5. Why are Cepheid variable stars so important?

6. How large is our galaxy? About how many stars does it contain?

7. Describe a popular theory that explains the creation of the universe.

8. Explain how galaxies were confused with nebulae.

9. What causes the difference between a bright and dark nebula?

10. Describe a theory which might account for the light and radio activity of a quasar.

11. Since quasars are believed to have been in existence for at least 2 to 6 billion years, why is it that they were just recently discovered?

12. What is a supernova?

SUMMARY

The earth is a planet about 7900 miles in diameter. It rotates on its axis once every 24 hours, causing day and night, and revolves around the sun once a year. Because the time when the sun is highest in the sky comes earlier and later in places of different longitudes, standard time belts and the International Date Line were adopted.

The seasons are caused by the tilt of the earth on its axis and by the earth's annual path around the sun. Summer is typified by strong direct rays of sunshine and long days, and winter is characterized by weak, indirect rays and short days.

The half of the moon that is lighted by the sun shines brightly. As the moon circles the earth, we can see more or less of this bright face. Thus the moon passes through its phases from crescent to quarter to full. The moon is the chief cause of tides on the earth. When the shadow of the moon hits the earth, a solar eclipse results. When the moon enters the earth's shadow, we see a lunar eclipse.

The sun is one of billions of stars. Its atmosphere is composed of layers called the photosphere, chromosphere, and corona. All of the energy used on the earth, except for atomic energy, comes from the sun. The sun maintains its great output of light and heat by fusing hydrogen into helium.

In radio astronomy, the natural radio waves of the sun, planets, and stars are used to identify them. In radar astronomy, man-made radio signals are used to identify and study heavenly bodies.

The universe of stars stretches out in time and space beyond our imagination. All of the billions of stars of the Milky Way make up the one galaxy to which we belong. Billions of other such galaxies are known to exist. Many of them, from their shape and appearance, are called spiral galaxies. Even the nearest one is nearly two million light years away.

Some stars are smaller and hotter and denser than the sun. Others are giants in size and are cooler. Occasionally a star will suddenly grow in magnitude, or brightness, as if it had exploded. Such a star is called a supernova.

A quasar is a heavenly body of such brilliance that it eclipses the total brightness of entire galaxies of hundreds of billions of stars, and produces more radio signals than many galaxies combined.

Galaxies may have formed after the explosion of a huge single "atom" of matter and energy about 10 to 25 billion years ago. On the other hand, creation of new galaxies may still be going on.

CHAPTER REVIEW

Vocabulary

Match the words in Column A with the *best* response in Column B. Do not write in your book.

Column A	Column B
1. planet h	a. condition when the moon passes between the sun and the earth
2. longitude c	
3. latitude d	b. dark spot on the sun caused by disturbances in the sun's atmosphere
4. prime meridian k	
5. equinox s	c. distance in degrees measured east and west from the prime meridian
6. solstice t	
7. eclipse a	d. distance in degrees measured north and south from the equator
8. precession m	
9. corona l	e. distance of about six trillion miles
10. sunspot b	f. groups of millions or billions of stars
11. satellite n	g. hazy, glowing, cloud-like area in the heavens which may be glowing gas
12. comet i	

13. meteor
14. radio astronomy
15. light year
16. radar astronomy
17. star
18. constellation
19. galaxy
20. nebula

h. heavenly body that revolves around the sun and reflects the light of the sun
i. heavenly body, orbiting the sun, having a long tail and hazy, gaseous body
j. large heavenly body that gives off its own light and heat
k. line of zero-longitude, drawn through both poles and Greenwich, England
l. outermost layer of sun's atmosphere
m. slow wobbling motion of the earth's axis
n. object, such as a moon, that revolves around a larger object, such as a planet
o. small particles of matter that burn up in our atmosphere
p. stars that are grouped so they appear as a pattern in the sky
q. study of the heavenly bodies by bouncing radio frequencies off them
r. study of heavenly bodies by means of radio waves they emit
s. time of year when the sun rises due east and sets due west
t. time of year when the sun rises farthest to the south or north

Questions: Group A

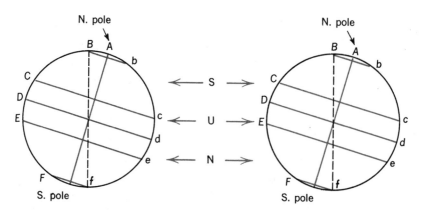

Figure I: June 21   Figure II: Dec. 22

Use the diagram to find the answers to the questions. Read the diagram carefully. Do not write in your book.

Use the figures on page 576 to answer questions 1–10.

1. What season of the year is it at "E," figure II?
2. What season of the year is it at "F," figure I?
3. What season of the year is it at "C," figure II?
4. What season of the year is it at "A," figure I?
5. What season of the year is it at "e," figure I?
6. What season of the year is it at "F," figure II?
7. What season of the year is it at "b," figure II?
8. What season of the year is it at "f," figure I?
9. What time of day is it at "E," figure I? (Morning, noon, evening, or midnight?)
10. What time of day is it at "B," figure II? (Morning, noon, evening, or midnight?)

Questions: Group B

1. What do you think would happen if the earth collided with a comet's head? With its tail?
2. What is meant by a year? Why does every planet have a year of different length?
3. Give two explanations of the fact that so many asteroids are found between the orbits of Mars and Jupiter.
4. Why is it so hot on the planet Venus?
5. Explain the difference between radio and radar astronomy.
6. What is the chief advantage of having an observatory in space?
7. Describe the size, orbit, and surface of the moon.
8. Why are the standard time belts 15 degrees wide?
9. Explain why the moon's appearance changes from new to quarter to full.
10. Why are lunar eclipses much more common than solar eclipses?
11. How far away is the nearest galaxy?
12. Explain how star brightness is measured in magnitudes.
13. Explain two methods of finding star distances.
14. In what way do the densities of dwarf stars and supergiants differ?
15. Explain the theory of continuous creation.
16. In what way does the atmosphere affect the intensities of our seasons?
17. Why is it impossible to measure distant stars by using parallax?
18. Compare the apparent brightness of a star with another that is twice as far away but gives off just as much light.
19. What is the importance to our seasons of the slight differences in earth-sun distance throughout the year?

Problems

1. One night in 1946, the U.S. Army Signal Corps sent radar pulses to the moon. The echoes came back 2.56 seconds later. Radio waves travel at the same speed as light—about 186,000 miles per second. (a) How long

did it take for the radio waves to travel from the earth to the moon?
(b) How far away from the earth was the moon that night?

2. When it is 2 P.M. in St. Louis, 90° W longitude, what time is it in Greenwich? When it is noon in Greenwich, what time is it in your town?

3. If it is Wednesday noon in Greenwich, what time would it be in Sydney, Australia, 150° east longitude? In Tahiti, 150° west longitude?

4. If Mars were 50 million miles away, and you traveled at 10,000 miles an hour, how many hours would it take you to reach Mars? About how many days is this? (Actually, on a trip to Mars, you would not follow this straight-line distance. You would spiral outward from the earth's orbit to Mars, and cover a much greater distance.)

5. Calculate the speed of the earth in its orbit around the sun by answering these questions. (a) What is the average distance from the earth to the sun? (b) What is the diameter of the earth's orbit in miles? (c) What is the circumference of the earth's orbit in miles? This is the distance the earth must cover in a year. (d) How many seconds are there in a year of 365 days? (e) Then to travel around the sun once every year, the earth's speed must be about how many miles per second? Show all calculations.

6. The nearest star beyond the sun is 4.3 light years away. About how many miles is this?

7. If a star at one side of our galaxy should explode, about how long would it be before the explosion could be seen at the other end of the galaxy? About how many miles would the light have to travel?

15 AVIATION AND ASTRONAUTICS

A
FLIGHT THROUGH AIR AND SPACE

Flight brings together many sciences. To understand why an airplane stays in the air, how it operates, and its source of power, we need to know about such things as pressure, forces, engines, fuels, and buoyancy. In space flight these topics are encountered in addition to astronomy, and the laws of gravity, and motion. Be sure to refer to earlier chapters in this book when some scientific principle about air and space flight needs to be more fully understood.

When did men learn to fly? For centuries, as they watched birds soar through the sky, men dreamed of flying. But all their attempts to imitate birds ended in failure. Leonardo da Vinci in the 15th century designed flying machines, parachutes, and helicopters. His flying machines, some designed with flat panels that flapped like birds' wings, were not successful.

Although some Frenchmen had flown in balloons before 1800, and gliders were flown frequently before 1900, no one flew a powered airplane until 1903. In that year, Orville and Wilbur Wright made their first successful flights at Kitty Hawk, North Carolina. (See Fig. 15-1.)

The reason why balloons were flown so much earlier than airplanes is that balloons rise by the simple force of buoyancy. Airplanes, however, must use other forces.

Forces in flight. Airplanes use different forces than do balloons. These forces include *lift, thrust, weight,* and *drag.* Lift and thrust combined form the *resultant force* **R** as shown in Fig. 15-2. The wind that strikes the airplane has two effects. First, it tends to push the plane backward. This effect is called the *drag.* Second, it tends to force the wing upward, overcoming the *weight.* This is the *lift.* In a well-designed wing, the lift may be many times as great as the drag.

The *push* or *pull* of the propeller or the jet is the *thrust.* The thrust overcomes the drag and causes the plane to move forward through the air. The propeller of a plane acts like the screw

15-1. The first flight of the Wright Brothers in 1903. (NASA)

propeller of a ship. The bigger the "bite" it takes of the air, the more vigorously it is thrust forward. This is another example of action and re-action.

How can lift be increased? Naturally, if the weight is greater than the lift, the plane will fall. To prevent this, the pilot opens the throttle and "guns" the engine. This speeds the propeller or jet engine to increase the thrust, making the plane go a great deal faster.

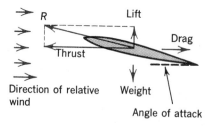

15-2. An illustration of balanced forces on a plane in straight and level flight at constant speed.

The air now hits the wing harder, increases the lift, and the plane stops falling. Meanwhile, because of the higher speed, the drag also increases. When the drag again equals the thrust, the plane no longer accelerates but keeps flying at its new speed.

As shown in Fig. 15-2, the angle of attack is the angle between the *relative wind* and the lower wing surface. The *relative wind* is caused by the motion of the plane and always blows in the direction opposite to the direction of the plane.

Instead of speeding up the engine, a pilot may get more lift by raising the nose of the plane. This increases the *angle of attack*. Up to a certain point, a greater angle of attack gives more lift. It also increases drag, causing the plane to fly along at a lower speed.

What makes a plane stall? Lifting the nose of the plane too high at low speeds causes a *stall*. A *stall* is the result of losing the speed necessary to keep control of the plane. The air no longer flows smoothly over the wing. Instead, it breaks up into little whirlpools shown in Fig. 15-3, creating *turbulence*. When this happens, lift is suddenly lost and the plane stalls.

If a plane stalls it falls rapidly and will crash unless the speed of the aircraft and the angle of attack are brought back into working balance. This is usually easy to do if the stall occurs at high altitudes. Can you tell why?

Most planes are designed so that they can be controlled even if the engine fails. In this event, it is possible to land safely by putting the plane into a *glide*. Part of the pull of gravity now takes the place of propeller thrust.

There are two sources of lift. One source of lift comes from the "*kite ef-*

15-3. Air turbulence above the wing increases as the angle of attack increases.

fect." The air that hits the under surface of a kite forces it up. In the same way, the wind pressure under a wing produces lift. This is the same sort of lift that you get when you ride on water skis behind a rapidly moving motorboat.

There is another source of lift. When the airstream hits the leading edge of the wing, it divides, part going above and part going below, as you would expect. However, the air flowing above must travel up and around the curve of the wing. In other words, it has farther to go than the air flowing below the wing. As a result it travels faster, creating a partial vacuum, and thus produces a substantial amount of lift.

Explanation for this effect is found in *Bernoulli's* (ber-*noo*-lees) **principle,** first stated by Daniel Bernoulli early in the 18th century. This principle states that *whenever the speed of a liquid or gas (fluid) is increased, its internal pressure is decreased.* The passing of air over the upper surface of the airplane wing exerts *less* pressure than the air beneath the wing.

To demonstrate this effect, blow across the upper surface of a sheet of paper. The rising of the paper as the air passes over it is an illustration of Bernoulli's principle. If you blow against the underside of the paper, the paper also rises. This illustrates the kite effect. The wing of a plane gets its lift from a combination of these two forces, as shown in Fig. 15-4.

Suppose that on top of the wing the normal air pressure of 14.7 pounds per square inch is reduced to 14.5 pounds per square inch. Also, suppose that the pressure below the wing is increased to 14.8 pounds per square inch

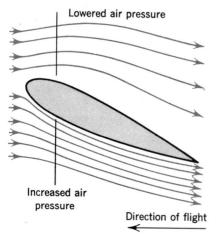

Lowered air pressure

Increased air pressure

Direction of flight

15-4. The difference between the lower pressure above the wing (Bernoulli effect) and the increased pressure below the wing produces lift.

by the kite effect. Subtracting 14.5 from 14.8, you have a net upward pressure of 0.3 pounds on each square inch of the wing. On each square foot this amounts to more than 43 pounds ($144 \text{ in.}^2 \times 0.3 \text{ lb/in.}^2 = 43.2 \text{ lb}$).

If the wing is 50 feet long and eight feet wide, its area is 400 square feet. Hence, the total lift is $43 \text{ lb/ft}^2 \times 400 \text{ ft}^2$, or 17,200 lb. The total lift of a B-52 jet bomber is about 175 tons! Most of the lift comes from the region of low pressure above the wings, with some coming from the kite effect.

The shape of the airfoils is important. Any surface of the plane that produces lift or other useful force is called an *airfoil.* The wings are the chief airfoils, but the propellers and tail surfaces are also airfoils.

The lift produced by an airfoil depends largely on the shape of its *cross section.* A thick wing with a lot of curvature has great lifting power but much drag. This design could be used

on big cargo and transport planes. High-speed planes must have thin wings that create little drag.

The shape of propellers is important. The propeller is not a fan that blows air against the wing. It is actually an *airfoil* with a cross section like that of a wing. As it slices through the air, a low pressure is formed in front of the blade and a high pressure at the rear. This produces a forward thrust.

The *efficiency* of a propeller depends on the *angle of the blades,* which is termed *pitch.* There must be a proper balance between the pitch of the propeller, the rate at which it turns, and the forward speed of the plane. Most light planes have propellers with a fixed blade angle. These always take the same bite of air and so are not efficient under all flying conditions.

Variable pitch propellers, however, change the *blade angle* automatically to suit conditions. High aircraft speeds are achieved by regulating the blades on the hub to make a large blade angle. For low aircraft speeds, the angle is made small. Changing the pitch of a propeller is like shifting gears in your car.

Propellers are efficient only at subsonic speeds. As the aircraft nears the speed of sound, the efficiency of the propeller decreases. At the speed of sound, the propeller would actually *retard* the forward speed of an aircraft. Thus, *no propeller-driven plane can fly at supersonic speeds.* Even if a propeller-driven plane were to dive straight down from a high altitude, it could not reach the speed of sound. It can actually reach a higher speed with the power *off* and *propeller stopped* than at full power. Therefore, supersonic speeds are reached only by jet and rocket driven craft.

Airflow changes at supersonic speeds. The air flowing above and below a wing travels faster than the airplane itself. Thus, the airflow reaches supersonic speeds before the airplane travels that fast. As an aircraft approaches supersonic speeds, a high pressure supersonic shock wave builds up first on the upper surface, and then on the lower surface of the wings. These high pressure waves compete with the low pressure usually found there and cause *buffeting* and *drag*. Modern supersonic aircraft, however, are now designed to minimize these problems as they pass from *subsonic* to *supersonic* speeds.

What is Mach number? Supersonic planes are provided with a panel instrument that shows the **Mach** (mahk) number, a figure giving *the ratio of the plane's speed to the speed of sound.* For example, Mach 1 means as fast as sound, and Mach 2 is twice as fast.

At supersonic speeds, powerful shock waves are produced by the plane which often reach the ground with a crash called the *"sonic boom."* The boom is caused by a jump of air pressure due to the shock waves originating from the supersonic aircraft. A pressure jump of 0.3 pound per square foot is hardly noticed and a jump of up to one pound is not objectionable, but a jump of over one pound sounds like a thunderclap and can cause damage to windows in buildings on the ground.

The intensity of the shock wave builds up rapidly as the speed increases above Mach 1, but levels off at speeds above Mach 2. The size of

the plane and the altitude at which it flies also influence the intensity of the sound.

A large commercial airliner traveling at Mach 2 would create a pressure jump of about 0.4 pound per square foot when traveling at 80,000 feet, 1.0 pound at 50,000 feet, 2.6 pounds at 30,000 feet, and 8.7 pounds at 10,000 feet.

Supersonic aircraft have "coke bottle" shapes. If you look closely, you will notice that most supersonic airplanes have a pinched-in fuselage or *"coke-bottle"* shape. The fuselage is narrowed by an amount equal to the area of the cross section of the wing. This discovery is known as the *"area rule."* The use of the coke-bottle shape reduces drag by about 25 percent at supersonic speeds. (See Fig. 15-5.)

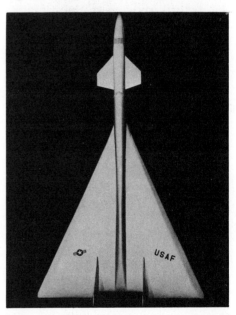

15-5. The RB-70 Valkyrie designed to fly faster than 2000 miles per hour shows the characteristic "coke bottle" shape of supersonic aircraft. (North American Aviation, Inc.)

How is an airplane controlled? A car has only two basic movements that can be controlled by the driver. One is the movement forward and backward, and the other is the ability to turn left or right. An airplane has many more controls than a car. An airplane cannot travel backward like the car but it can (1) travel forward, (2) turn left or right, (3) move up or down, and (4) roll clockwise or counterclockwise.

The *forward* speed of the airplane is controlled by the speed and pitch of the *propeller*, or by the thrust of the escaping gases of the *jet engine.*

Up and *down* movements of the airplane are controlled by moving the *elevators.* To dive the plane *downward* the elevators are moved downward. The wind blowing back against the bottom surface of the elevators pushes the tail up. This causes the plane to swing about so that its nose drops.

When the pilot pulls back on the control wheel, the elevators tip *up* and the wind blows against their top surfaces. This forces the tail down and *lifts* the nose of the plane.

The rudder is used to turn the plane left or right. Pushing the *right* rudder pedal swings the rudder to the *right.* The air blast now *blows the tail to the left.* The plane swings about, with its *nose pointing to the right,* and heads in that direction.

However, because of *inertia,* the plane keeps moving forward in the direction in which it was going. We say that the plane is **skidding.** In other words, it is pointing one way but moving another. This is very similar to what happens when a car skids on a slippery curve.

To avoid skidding, the pilot must *bank* the plane or roll it over on its side by turning the control wheel. When he does this, the *aileron* (*ay*-ler-on) on one wing moves up and the other tips down. This makes one wing fall and the other wing rise. The plane now turns smoothly as your car does on a banked highway curve.

Most planes also have control surfaces called flaps. Additional control surfaces called *flaps* are also hinged to the rear edge of the wing. The flaps on each wing dip *down* at the same time, and so they do not make the plane bank as do the ailerons. The pilot uses the flaps as airbrakes to increase the drag when he desires to land. This helps high-speed planes land on short runways. The flaps are also used on take-off to provide some additional lift to help raise the plane off the runway. (See Fig. 15-6.)

Many instruments are used in aircraft. If you have ever looked into the cockpit of a large plane, you must have been impressed by the large number of controls and dials on the instrument panel. These instruments help the pilot to navigate safely and accurately, and inform him of the performance of the plane and engines.

The *tachometer* (tack-*om*-et-er) indicates the number of revolutions per minute made by each engine. With the tachometer and other instruments, the pilot can be sure that each engine is delivering full power.

The *altimeter* is an aneroid barometer *calibrated* to measure elevation in feet. Altimeter readings are corrected for temperature and ground pressure. Actually, this instrument does not tell how far above the ground the plane is, but indicates altitude above sea level.

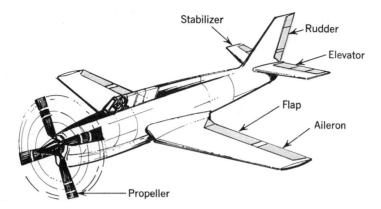

Stabilizer

Rudder

Elevator

Flap

Aileron

Propeller

15-6. Can you explain the function of each of the control surfaces on this light plane?

The *radio-altimeter* uses *radar* to indicate to the pilot how far above the ground he actually is. The height of the plane is determined by the time that it takes for a radio beam to reach the ground and for the signal to bounce back to the plane.

Below a certain air speed, or flying speed, a plane starts to lose lift and begins to fall. Hence, the pilot must be aware of his *air speed* at all times. His *air-speed indicator* does not reveal ground speed. It reads the same when he is flying at 100 miles per hour in still air as when he is flying at 50 miles per hour into a 50-mile-per-hour headwind. In each case, the air is hitting the plane with a net speed of 100 miles per hour.

Other aircraft instruments. The pilot must be able to determine his flight direction accurately in order to reach his destination. *Magnetic* and *gyro compasses* are often used for this purpose. The magnetic compass is a simple device to indicate direction. It must be corrected, however, to com-

pensate for the magnetism of the plane. The gyro compass is more complex but operates independent of magnetic forces.

Another aircraft instrument is the *turn indicator*. It is run by a small gy-

15-7. The instrument panel makes the pilot aware of flying conditions. (Trans World Airlines, Inc.)

roscope and shows any turn the airplane may be making. The *bank indicator* is an instrument used in some light planes. It contains a ball that rolls back and forth in a curved tube and informs the pilot if the plane is properly banked in a turn.

The actual flying of large planes is often turned over to *automatic pilots.* These controls are complicated gyroscopic devices that maintain the plane on a desired course.

Radios are essential to flight. Most aircraft today are provided with a two-way radio, which is used for several purposes. The *radio beam,* transmitted by *radio beacons* along the airway, helps the pilot keep his course and avoid collisions with approaching planes. Civilian planes use a system of radio navigation called *omnirange* which works as follows: Transmitting stations, about 100 miles apart, send out very high frequency waves in all directions. The radio tells the pilot whether he is heading toward or away from an "omni" station. By noting the direction from any two stations, he can tell his exact location.

Besides permitting pilots to "fly the beam," there are other reasons why planes should have radios. They receive reports on weather conditions and corrections for altimeter, compass, and clock. Besides this, a radio is required for landing at many airports, where instructions from the *control tower* must be received. Large passenger planes carry *radar sets* to help the pilot avoid thunderstorms and collisions with other planes and dangerous obstacles.

How are wind tunnels used? Engineers use *wind tunnels* to test models or parts of air and space vehicles.

Some wind tunnels are large enough to hold full size planes or space capsules. Others can blow air many times faster than the speed of sound. Automatic balances measure the forces acting on the models being tested. The chief purpose of a wind tunnel is to measure *aerodynamic forces;* that is, forces caused by airflow. They also use wind tunnels to test the power and efficiency of engines and propellers, and to test atmospheric heating on space capsules re-entering our atmosphere. (See Fig. 15-8.)

VTOL and STOL. Aircraft that can take-off or land vertically, but otherwise fly like regular airplanes, are known as **VTOL** (Vertical Take-Off and Landing) planes. (See Fig. 15-9.) Aircraft that require very short runways are known as **STOL** (Short Take-Off and Landing) planes. These planes

15-8. A hypersonic wind tunnel capable of producing speeds greater than nine times that of sound is used here to test a model. (NASA–JPL/Caltech)

15-9. VTOL planes are not affected by limited take-off and landing space. (US Dept. of Defense)

have a great advantage in that they do not need the long two-mile runways customary in large city airports. They require only small unimproved places to land and take-off which could be located conveniently in populated areas. You can probably recognize the value of VTOL and STOL planes in military operations.

The major disadvantage in developing these aircraft is that they require extremely powerful engines to overcome the force of gravity. At take-off and landing the entire lift must come from the propeller or jet thrust. None of it can come from the wings until the craft is traveling horizontally through the air.

The helicopter can take-off and land vertically. Since helicopters do not fly like regular airplanes when in

horizontal flight, they are not usually classed as VTOLs. The idea of *helicopters* dates back to the days of Leonardo da Vinci who, in the 15th century, designed and built models of helicopters. Instead of wings, they have large horizontally-rotating blades. The angle of the rotors can be tilted to make the helicopter go in different directions.

The turning of these big blades makes the body of the helicopter tend to rotate in the opposite direction. (Here is Newton's law of action and reaction again.) One way of stopping this is to use two sets of blades rotating in opposite directions. Sometimes a small propeller is mounted sidewise on the tail to keep the body of the craft from turning. A third scheme is to run the main propeller by ramjets mounted

15-10. The rotor blades of this helicopter are driven by ramjet engines located at the blade tips. (US Dept. of Defense)

at the tip of each blade. (See Fig. 15-10.) Then there is no reaction on the body of the helicopter. Instead, the reaction is between the exhaust gases and each blade tip.

Helicopters are widely used in short flights for carrying mail, rescue operations, police work, and, more recently, for commuting between cities.

The search for power. For many years man looked for enough power to make successful flights in the air. Not until this century, however, was enough power available to do this. The Wright brothers' success in making their historic flight was due largely to an improvement of the reciprocating engine. (This is an engine in which the pistons move in a back-and-forth motion inside cylinders.) The reciprocating engine was used to power aircraft until near the end of World War II. Then a new form of power, *jet propulsion,* began to be used.

Jet propulsion gives more thrust. Jet planes get their thrust from the "kick" of high-speed *exhaust gases.* As they are pushed violently from the rear of the exhaust, their reaction pushes the plane forward, in accordance with Newton's third law of motion. The surrounding air does *not* give thrust to the jet plane. This air is used only to burn the fuel and to supply lift.

Jets can fly at very high speeds because jet engines give much more thrust than do ordinary propeller-type engines of the same weight. These engines deliver tremendous power, especially at high speeds.

The jet plane most used at present is the *turbojet,* run by a gas turbine. Large high-speed "jets" have replaced propeller planes on long flights.

The *ramjet,* or "flying stovepipe," is much simpler. It has no moving parts. The ramjet works only at very high speeds. At such speeds, the air is rammed into the intake under pressure, and so no compressor-turbine is needed. Turbojet engines are used to bring the plane to a speed near that of sound, and then the ramjets are turned on. Another version of a ramjet is an *afterburner* which operates on the high-velocity gases coming from the exhaust of a turbojet. Afterburners are used primarily on military aircraft. They deliver more power at a higher efficiency.

The *turboprop,* or *propjet,* employs propellers that are turned by a gas turbine. The propjet is more powerful and smoother than the usual reciprocating engine.

Jet engines are not space engines. Despite their great power, jets are not space engines. Unlike rockets, which carry their own supplies of oxidizer, jets need oxygen from the atmosphere. Thus jets cannot operate in space where oxygen does not exist. However, they may serve as boosters for space vehicles during the early part of their flight through the atmosphere. It is this part of a space flight which takes the greatest amount of fuel, so jet engines may be of considerable value.

What is the mass-ratio of a rocket? Tremendous take-off thrust is needed to climb out of a planet's "gravity pit." At present, only powerful rocket engines burning chemical fuels can produce this large thrust. Even so, a payload can be lifted off the earth only with efficient fuels and engines, and with rockets that have a good *mass-ratio. The mass-ratio of a rocket is obtained by dividing take-off weight by final weight after all the fuel is spent.* For example, if a rocket weighs 50 tons at take-off and only 10 tons at burn-out, its mass-ratio is 5.

With the chemical fuels now in use, a *one-step* rocket cannot escape from the earth's gravity. Hence, long-range rockets are built in steps or stages, each mounted "piggyback" above the other, as shown in Fig. 15-11. As each stage reaches fuel burn-out, it drops off and the next stage fires. The use of stages increases the mass-ratio very sharply. For example, a three-stage rocket, with each stage having an individual mass-ratio of 5, combine to give the entire rocket a mass-ratio of 125.

Specific impulse and thrust. *Specific impulse* is defined as the number of seconds it takes to burn a pound of fuel at a rate which produces a one-pound thrust. Typical chemical rocket fuels have specific impulses of 250 to 300 seconds. The higher the specific impulse, the greater is the efficiency of the fuel and engine. What is generally surprising, however, is that a high specific impulse is usually associated with *very low thrust.* For example, a typical ion engine with a specific impulse of *2000 seconds* is not likely to develop more than a pound of thrust. Of course, such a rocket could never develop enough thrust to lift itself off a launching pad.

It is only the relatively inefficient chemical rockets that develop the "brute force" to lift a vehicle into space. They burn for only a few minutes, however, and their fuel is all spent. An ion engine, on the other hand, could deliver its tiny thrust for many days, weeks, and months at a time. A high-efficiency rocket with low thrust, therefore, is valuable for flights starting from orbits in space since brute force is not needed there to move a vehicle.

Ion or plasma propulsion. We have seen that a highly ionized gas is often called plasma. As indicated above, ion-plasma-propulsion is a highly efficient method of utilizing energy and may be very useful in space travel. *Electrically charged atoms, or ions, can be accelerated by high voltages.* They then shoot from the exhaust nozzles at much higher speeds than do the hot gases from burning fuels. An ion engine would be suitable for long range interplanetary travel. For example, ten tons of the element cesium would provide enough fuel for a manned space flight to Mars and back, assuming that the starting and ending points would be an orbiting station above the earth.

The electric energy needed for ion or plasma propulsion can be generated by nuclear reactors. The reactors, how-

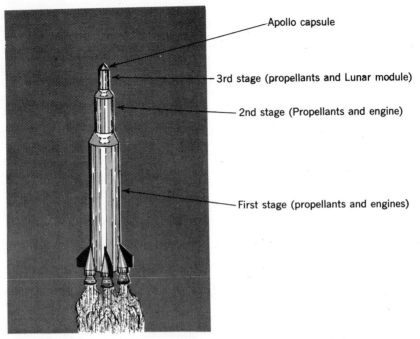

Apollo capsule

3rd stage (propellants and Lunar module)

2nd stage (Propellants and engine)

First stage (propellants and engines)

15-11. The Saturn V is a good example of a step rocket.

ever, have the disadvantage of being heavy. Hence, *solar batteries*, drawing on the energy of the sun, may provide power for ion engines of the future.

As already stated, hydrogen is another good fuel for rocket engines. Instead of burning the hydrogen atoms or accelerating them with electricity, we could use heat from nuclear reactors or from the sun to heat up the hydrogen and exhaust it from the nozzles at high speeds.

Uses of rockets. Rocket engines are used to power rocket planes, guided missiles, satellites, and space vehicles. Rocket planes with small thin wings can fly very rapidly through the thin upper air. The X-15 rocket plane was designed to reach a height of 100 miles and speeds of over 4000 mph. It is the forerunner of a manned rocket plane capable of orbiting the earth. (See Fig. 15-12.)

Rockets may be used for military or scientific, purposes, or for space travel. Powerful rockets such as the *Minuteman* and *Titan*, can deliver warheads on targets thousands of miles away with accuracy. (See Fig. 15-13.) Such rockets are called *ballistic missiles* and are aimed at definite targets before being fired. Rocket engines are also used to power *guided missiles*. Some guided missiles are directed to their targets by radio signals from the ground or from an airplane. Others may contain "homing" devices that can pick up heat waves from the target, or use radar to locate it. Two such guided missiles are the *Sidewinder* and the *Nike-Zeus*.

The largest of all rockets are used to launch space vehicles. *Saturn I*, for example, is about 1,200,000 pounds in weight, has engines that generate 1,500,000 pounds of take-off thrust, and can place up to 35,000 pounds into an orbit three-hundred-miles high. (See Fig. 15-14.)

A still more advanced vehicle called *Saturn V* weighs 6,000,000 pounds, has engines that generate 7,500,000 pounds of thrust, and is capable of placing 250,000 pounds into a 300-mile-high orbit around the earth. It can also send 90,000 pounds to the moon and is designed to carry a manned mission to the moon and back.

Quick Quiz

1. What causes a plane to stall?
2. Name four forces acting on a plane in flight.
3. What is an airfoil? Name two of them.
4. Name and explain two ways in which lift is produced on a wing.
5. Name the four main types of movement of an airplane.
6. What is meant by Mach 2.5?
7. Why is it safe to stall a plane only at a high altitude?
8. Explain the action of a propeller.
9. How can you increase the lift of an airplane?
10. Why are supersonic aircraft designed in "coke-bottle" shapes?
11. In what major way is a rocket engine like a jet engine? How is it different?
12. What is the advantage of low-efficiency chemical rockets over some of the high-efficiency rockets?
13. Describe how a three-stage rocket works.

15-12. The X-15 was designed to attain speeds in excess of 4000 miles per hour. (North American Aviation, Inc.)

15-13. The Titan II missile stands alert on its launching pad ready to respond to enemy attack. (US Dept. of Defense)

B ASTRONAUTICS

Where does outer space begin? We do not usually think of outer space as beginning only six miles above the earth. Yet at this altitude man would die from the lack of oxygen. He could also suffer from the expansion of gases in his body caused by the lack of air pressure at this altitude. This condition is called *"the bends"* and is usually associated with deep sea divers who come to the surface too fast. In this condition, bubbles form in the blood stream and bodily fluids much as they form in a bottle of soda when the cap is removed.

At an altitude of about 12 miles, the atmospheric pressure is so slight that body fluids would boil at 98.6° F (normal body temperature). This would cause death to an unprotected person in a matter of seconds. Thus, man enters an environment called *partial space equivalence* at a relatively low altitude above the earth.

At a level of 70 to 90 miles above the earth aerodynamic forces usually begin to build up on a re-entering space capsule. Above this level, satellites can maintain orbits around the earth without being rapidly slowed by atmospheric drag. Thus, we may consider as *space equivalence* an altitude of about 90 miles or more above the earth, or in other words, the least distance above the earth at which satellites can orbit.

This region is still not completely free of the earth's atmosphere, however, because traces of air extend up to about 1000 miles during periods of intense solar activity. Therefore, a *true* space environment may not exist until we go beyond 1000 miles above the earth.

Though the *gravitational field* of the earth extends indefinitely, it is significant to space flight to a distance of about a million miles. This sets the limit to *terrestrial space.* Beyond this point, the earth's gravity could not hold a satellite in orbit.

Interstellar space is the space occupied by the stars of our galaxy, the Milky Way.

Preparing for space travel. Scientists are steadily learning how to overcome many problems related to space travel. Among these are pressurization of spaceships and space suits, oxygen supply, temperature control, "weightlessness," excessive acceleration, protection from deadly radiations, and from meteoroids, and the techniques of effective navigation. Also the physical and mental limitations of man are being carefully researched.

All the problems mentioned above are included in a branch of science called *astronautics.* The prefix *"astro"* refers to the stars, but it has come to apply also to outer space in general. Thus, *astrobiology* is the science that deals with life in outer space.

Radiation is a hazard to space travel. Outer space is filled with dangerous radiations—*ultraviolet, X rays,* and *cosmic rays.* On earth, we are almost entirely protected from them by the atmosphere, which absorbs all the X rays and most of the ultraviolet and cosmic rays. The amount of radiation in space varies at different times and different places.

Special dangers exist in the *Van Allen belt,* the extensive doughnut-shaped band which is filled with *high-energy particles.* This band starts a few hundred miles above the earth and extends for tens of thousands of miles. See Fig. 15-15. It was named for the American scientist who was in charge of the project that discovered it. When electrons in the Van Allen belt strike the metal of a spaceship, they produce X rays. Astronauts would need extra shielding for an extended stay in this

15-14. The first of eight engines is installed on a Saturn booster (left). The booster has a center tank containing liquid oxygen and eight smaller tanks clustered around it. Four contain liquid oxygen and four hold a high-grade kerosene fuel. The completely assembled rocket is shown on the right. (NASA)

area. However, it is not likely that a quick passage through the belt would be hazardous.

Space travelers also need some way of controlling the amount of heat and light absorbed from the sun. Our experience with satellites shows that it is possible to maintain a livable temperature by using the proper type of surface on the spacecraft. Where the surface is polished and *highly reflecting, little heat is absorbed.* By presenting a *rough, dark surface* to the sun, much of the sun's rays can be *absorbed* to warm up the ship.

Meteoroids and space travel. Most of the meteoric material in space is in the form of dust. This is unlikely to do more than mar the surface of space vehicles. Particles as large as grains of sand are very rare, but are potentially dangerous if hits occur, because they have the *kinetic energy* of high-speed bullets. However, experiments with sandwich type layers of thin *me-*

tallic sheets and *glass wool* show that a lightweight meteor "bumper" will give satisfactory protection. Collision with a large-sized meteoroid certainly would be disastrous, but is not likely to happen.

Space travel and acceleration. *Acceleration* is a major problem during *take-off* and *landing.* A rocket uses its fuel most efficiently when it is moving at high speeds. Hence, it is desirable to accelerate as rapidly as possible, with the engines turned on "full blast." However, the human body can tolerate only a few "g's" of acceleration, and then only for a short time. (Remember that an *acceleration of one g means a gain in speed of 32 ft/sec every second.*) During a "high-g" take-off or re-entry, an astronaut reclines in a foam-rubber support so that the g forces are distributed evenly over his entire body.

How does gravity affect space flight? It is not hard to realize that

15-15. The Van Allen radiation belt is trapped by the magnetic fields of the earth. It is made up of several regions of high and medium intensity electrons and protons.

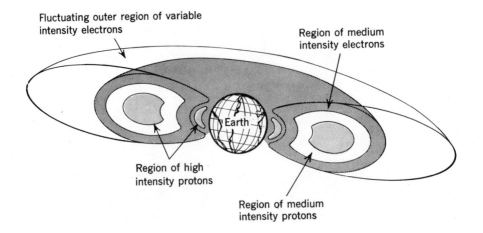

Fluctuating outer region of variable intensity electrons

Region of medium intensity electrons

Earth

Region of high intensity protons

Region of medium intensity protons

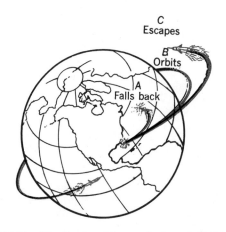

C
Escapes

B
Orbits

A
Falls back

15-16. Missile A, with a velocity of 10,000 mph, falls back to the earth. Missile B, with a velocity of almost 18,000 mph, orbits the earth. And Missile C, with a velocity of 25,000 mph, escapes completely from the earth.

gravity resists flight into air or space. Gravity must be overcome to launch a missile from a pad, to place a vehicle into orbit, or to travel to the moon or planets.

When a *sub-orbital* missile is launched down a missile range, its inertia is not great enough to be in equilibrium with the force of gravity. After the missile is hurled into the air, it follows a curved path or *trajectory* (tra-*jek*-tor-ee) back to earth. When rocket power is great enough, however, a space vehicle can be given enough speed so that it will never fall back to the earth. Such an escape is possible if an object is thrown off the earth with a velocity of at least 25,000 miles per hour. Hence, this is called *escape velocity.* (See Fig. 15-16.)

Theoretically, a rocket can leave the earth without attaining this speed. It can just keep on burning fuel to maintain thrust and speed, and eventually escape from the earth. However, it is more efficient to accelerate as rapidly as possible until escape velocity is reached. The engines are then shut off, and the rocket coasts away from the earth.

If an object reaches escape velocity, it can leave *terrestrial space* and enter *interplanetary space.* It is then controlled by the sun's gravitational field instead of the earth's.

Satellite orbits. If an object outside the atmosphere is given a high enough *horizontal velocity,* it will circle the earth as an *artificial satellite. For every height there is just one particular speed that will permit it to circle about the earth.* The force of gravity will be just great enough to bend the straight-line path of the satellite into a circular orbit about the earth. For satellites within a few hundred miles of the earth, this orbiting speed is about 18,000 miles an hour.

A satellite seldom travels in a circular path, but instead, follows an *elliptical* or oval orbit. Its lowest point above the earth is called its **perigee** (*purr*-ih-jee) and its highest point the **apogee** (*ap*-oh-jee). The speed of the satellite at its low point in orbit is great enough to balance the force of the earth's gravity and thus remain in orbit. At the apogee the satellite is traveling at its slowest speed. (See Fig. 15-17.)

A satellite will continue in its orbit forever if there is nothing reducing its speed. However, since traces of air reach out to about 1000 miles above the earth, satellites below this altitude are subjected to a very slight but constant drag. This causes each orbit to be somewhat closer to the earth. Thus, these satellites slowly but surely spiral their way into the earth's atmosphere.

Gravitational fields in the solar system. Travel to other planets in the solar system may be compared to travel between cities that lie very far apart on a gently sloping plain. Each city lies at the bottom of a deep "pit," as shown in Fig. 15-19. The hardest part of the trip is climbing out of this pit. In space travel, this corresponds to overcoming the gravitational pull of a planet as you blast off from its surface. The depth of the pit depends upon the gravitational field of the planet. Note how much easier it would be to take off from the moon, whose gravitational field is only about one-sixth as strong as that of the earth.

Fuel is used up most rapidly during this initial climb. But once out of the pit, you can coast great distances without much expenditure of fuel. By checking the table of minimum launch velocities on page 597, you will note that after leaving the earth at 25,000

15-18. Satellite tracking cameras are positioned all over the world. (NASA)

miles per hour, there is comparatively little additional speed needed to travel to most of the planets in the solar system.

Observe in Fig. 15-19, that in going away from the sun there is a slight uphill slope. For example, to go from Earth to Mars, rocket power is needed to gain speed to get ahead of the earth in its path about the sun. The spaceship then spirals out from the earth's orbit and, if properly navigated, intersects the orbit of Mars at just the right time to make contact with that planet.

A "downhill" trip from Earth to Venus requires the launching of a spaceship in the direction opposite to the earth's path around the sun. Thus, the spaceship would lag behind the earth and then spiral inward from the earth's orbit toward that of Venus. Again, precise navigation is needed to reach the orbit of Venus just as this planet is passing by.

15-17. An orbiting satellite will be in apogee when it is farthest from the earth.

MINIMUM LAUNCH VELOCITIES WITH TIME REQUIREMENTS TO REACH THE PLANETS

Planet	Length of Trip	Minimum Velocity (miles per hour)
Mercury	110 days	30,000
Venus	150 days	26,000
Mars	260 days	26,000
Jupiter	2.7 years	31,400
Saturn	6 years	33,500
Uranus	16 years	34,800
Neptune	31 years	35,500
Pluto	46 years	36,000

The launch velocities are the minimum needed for trips to the various planets. By increasing the launch velocity, the length of the trip time can be reduced.

Sliding safely down into the pit of the destination planet also poses some problems. As a spaceship nears a planet, it is pulled toward it by gravity. If nothing offsets this, the ship will fall faster and faster, and smash into the planet like a meteorite. If the planet has an atmosphere, air friction can be used to help reduce speed. However, this process generates heat and, if it is not carefully controlled, will result in burning up the ship and its contents. If there is no atmosphere, the ship must be slowed down by burning precious fuel in *retro-rockets*.

Trips to the moon. There are several ways of traveling to and from the moon. Perhaps the simplest way is by making a *direct flight* by a single rocket, as is done by the Ranger and Surveyor moon probes. However, using this method to land a manned vehicle on the moon and return it to earth would require the use of an extremely large rocket weighing as much as 20,000,000 pounds.

Other means of carrying out the manned landing on the moon require the joining together of two or more vehicles in orbit. Such procedures per-

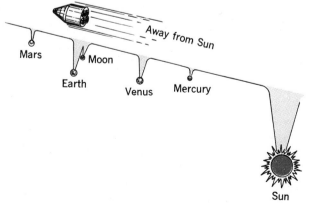

15-19. Great thrust is needed to climb out of the "gravity pit" of the planets. After this is accomplished, it is comparatively easy to travel great distances through space with very little thrust. To escape from the gravity of the sun would require another large increase in thrust.

mit the use of smaller rockets than are needed in a direct flight, but require difficult *docking* or *rendezvous* maneuvers.

Still another method of landing astronauts on the moon is scheduled to be used by the National Aeronautics and Space Administration in *Project Apollo.* A large Saturn V rocket weighing 6,000,000 pounds is scheduled to launch a spaceship into an orbit around the moon. From this lunar orbiting platform a small *lunar excursion module* will be detached to make a descent to the moon's surface. It will use retrorockets to land. After completing their explorations on the moon, the astronauts will blast off in the tiny module and return to the orbiting spaceship. (See Fig. 15-20.)

Parts or sections of the spacecraft and launch vehicle are discarded after they are no longer needed. By the time the astronauts are ready to re-enter the earth's atmosphere, only the *Apollo capsule* remains of the original 6,000,000 pound Saturn V vehicle. The parts are abandoned so that precious fuel is not used to haul the unneeded hardware.

Eventually moon trips will be made using *specialized vehicles* as well as *permanent orbiting platforms* around the earth and moon. A *high-thrust* vehicle with an ability to maneuver in the air will serve as the shuttle rocket from the ground to the earth-orbiting platform. Here the space passengers will transfer to a *low-thrust high efficiency* vehicle for the trip to the moon-orbiting platform. At the lunar platform they will again transfer to a *high thrust* vehicle for the descent to the moon's surface. This vehicle need not be streamlined because there is no

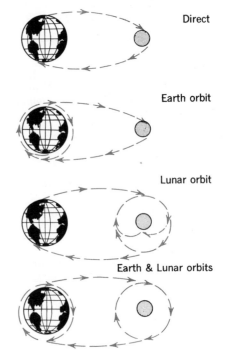

15-20. Flight to the moon may include: direct flight, earth orbit rendezvous, lunar orbit rendezvous, and orbiting platforms at both the earth and moon.

significant atmosphere on the moon.

Space travel and navigation. To appreciate the difficulties of space navigation, or **astrogation,** consider a trip to Mars. You are leaving a moving platform, the earth, which is spinning at the rate of 1000 mph at the equator and also traveling at the speed of 66,000 miles per hour around the sun. You are heading for a destination that is also traveling at high speed, but at a different speed and in a different direction. You might think that all you would have to do would be to locate your "target" in a telescope and then chase after it. But this would not do at all. You must calculate where Mars will be after some 260 days of flight time, and plan to get there at the same time that it does.

It is important to realize that although the trip to Mars may take 260 days, only about 10 minutes of that time is powered flight. The rest of the time the spaceship merely coasts. Any mistakes during the ten minutes of flight can be very serious. Some small errors can be corrected by *mid-course maneuvers,* but a big mistake would be fatal. The spaceship could become another satellite of the earth, or another asteroid forever circling the sun.

Gyroscopes help to control flights. A basic principle of inertia is used to help control the flight of rockets. A spinning object tends to keep its axis of spin unchanged. A rifle bullet or football is given a spin so that it will not tumble end-over-end. You can easily balance on a moving bicycle because the spinning wheels tend to keep their axles horizontal. A device that is designed to make use of this form of inertia is called a *gyroscope.* A spinning top, balancing on its point, is a simple gyroscope. (See Fig. 15-23.)

This principle is used in a *gyro-compass,* which tends to keep its axis lined up with the axis of the earth. Because it is not affected by magnetic influences, it has some advantages over the ordinary magnetic compass, which is subject to various types of errors.

The flight of a rocket may be radio-controlled, but this system has several disadvantages. For example, there could be atmospheric or other interferences with the transmission of signals controlling the flight. A better system depends upon *inertial guidance.* This uses a combination of accelerometers and gyroscopes. (Accelerometers

15-21. Gemini two-man space capsule. (McDonnell Aircraft Corp.)

15-22. Apollo three-man space capsule. (NASA)

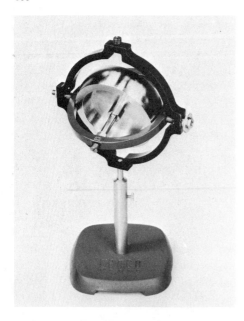

15-23. The basic gyroscope (top). Three miniature gyroscopes, contained in the package being adjusted by the engineer, will serve as a guidance system for the satellite. (Top: Central Scientific Co.; Bottom: Minneapolis-Honeywell)

measure the amount of acceleration.) In this system, all the instructions for controlling the flight are aboard the vehicle.

How can a speeding capsule be returned to earth? Putting a manned capsule into space is an important accomplishment, but the job is not completed until the capsule and its human cargo are returned safely to earth. To slow down a speeding capsule, retro-rockets may be used. However, this uses precious fuel and reduces the payload of any space flight. Thus, scientists usually rely on atmospheric braking to slow down a re-entering capsule. However, in the process, enough heat is generated to vaporize the capsule if the heat is permitted to enter it.

This heat is caused by friction, or rubbing of air against the surface of the speeding capsule. This is similar to the heat that can be generated by rubbing your hands together briskly. Heat is also caused by *compression.* This results from air building up on the front part of the nose cone or capsule.

A blunt-nosed capsule resists heating. When a blunt-nosed vehicle such as Gemini or Apollo re-enters the atmosphere, a powerful shock wave is built up. This shock wave carries off a large part of the heat energy created during re-entry. A relatively *dormant layer* of *ionized air* or *plasma* is formed immediately in front of the capsule and insulates it from the extreme temperatures of the shock wave. A sharp-nosed vehicle does not create a very large shock wave, and hence, does not carry away as much of the re-entry heat. Instead, the air rubs against the missile and heats it by *friction.* (See Fig. 15-24.)

The blunt-nosed capsule, therefore, is superior in its ability to survive re-entry heat. Such a capsule, however, lacks maneuverability in the atmosphere. It also hits the atmosphere with considerable impact and subjects the astronauts to *high deceleration loads*. Finally, the astronauts are subjected to the discomforts of a parachute landing.

A sharp-nosed vehicle has advantages in that it can easily be made maneuverable so that it can be controlled and landed without parachutes. In addition, the deceleration forces are less severe as compared to those of the blunt-nosed vehicle. Before the sharp-nosed vehicle is used, however, its heating problems must be overcome. This may be done by the development of heat resistant materials such as ceramics, or new metal alloys.

Entry corridors. Re-entry from the moon or planets must be made with extreme caution and accuracy. If a spaceship re-enters the atmosphere at too slight an angle, it will skip off the top of the atmosphere like a high-speed stone off water. Thus, it will be bounced out to space and may be lost forever. If, on the other hand, it comes into the atmosphere at too steep an angle, it can be destroyed by heat and impact. A safe path between these two extremes is a *corridor* just eight miles wide for a ballistic vehicle coming from the moon. (See Fig. 15-25.) The re-entry corridor is even less for a vehicle coming from the planets. This corridor can be widened considerably, however, if the re-entry vehicle has even a small amount of lift and is capable of being maneuvered. It could then be guided into the corridor if its initial approach were somewhat in error.

15-24. The blunt-nosed capsule builds up a shock wave which carries away most of the heat generated during re-entry. The pointed capsule has much of the heat transferred into it.

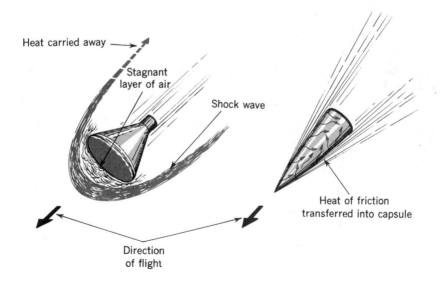

Heat carried away

Stagnant layer of air

Shock wave

Heat of friction transferred into capsule

Direction of flight

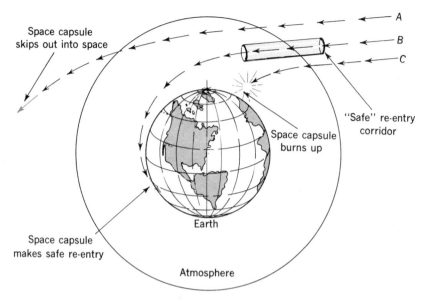

15-25. A ballistic vehicle returning from the moon is limited to a narrow path or corridor for a safe entry into the atmosphere of the earth. In this diagram, the depth of the earth's atmosphere is exaggerated in proportion to the size of the planet in order to show the possible re-entry paths more clearly.

Many useful satellites orbit the earth. Long-term scientific studies are made by instruments in satellites placed in orbit by rocket power. The *Tiros* and *Nimbus* series of weather satellites are equipped with TV cameras to take pictures of storms and cloud formations all over the globe. They are of great aid to the meteorologist in forecasting the weather.

The *Midas* satellites are also television-equipped and are used for military reconnaissance. They can detect the launching of enemy rockets by picking up their infra-red or heat rays.

The *Transit* series of satellites acts as navigational aids. By accurately timing signals from these satellites, the navigator can determine his precise location on the earth's surface. These satellites can also be used for surveys to measure the exact size and shape of the earth.

We have already read about a series of orbiting laboratories in Chapter 14 called the *Orbiting Solar Observatory* (OSO), the *Orbiting Geophysical Observatory* (OGO), and the *Orbiting Astronomical Observatory* (OAO). These are designed to help us learn more about our earth, sun, solar system, and stars.

How do communication satellites work? Communication satellites are useful for long-distance radio, radio-telephone, and television communication. There are several types of communication satellites. The *Echo* satellites, for example, are huge aluminized plastic balloons. They contain no electronic equipment but merely have large surfaces off which signals can be bounced. They are known as *passive satellites.*

Other types are crammed with electronic equipment capable of receiving radio and television signals, then amplifying, and transmitting them back to earth. These are known as *active satellites.*

Satellite systems can be placed in low, medium, or high orbits. Naturally, it requires more power to send signals to and from high satellites than it does to send them to and from low-orbiting satellites. However, the high satellites have greater earth coverage, and so fewer are needed to operate a world-wide communication system.

Satellites can also be placed into *random* and *synchronous orbits.* A random orbit is a typical path of most satellites around the earth. To an observer on the ground, a satellite in a random orbit is seen to rise from one horizon, travel across the heavens, and disappear below the horizon in another part of the sky. In a synchronous orbit, however, the satellite travels in the same direction and the same speed as the earth turns, so to an observer on the ground, *it appears to be stationary in the sky.* A synchronous satellite travels at about 22,300 miles above the equator and is sometimes called *Syncom* for *syn*chronous *com*munication. Only three synchronous satellites are needed for communications coverage over all of the inhabited earth. (See Fig. 15-26.)

15-26. Syncom (synchronous communication) satellites can cover all of the inhabited earth with a network of three satellites.

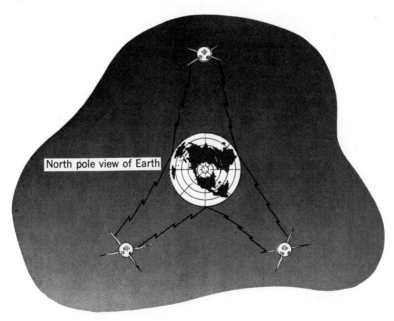

North pole view of Earth

Quick Quiz

1. Where does space begin?
2. Name some of the subdivisions of outer space.
3. Which part of a space trip uses up most fuel? Why?
4. What is meant by an artificial satellite?
5. How can a space vehicle reduce speed for a safe landing on a planet?
6. Which satellite travels faster, one in a high orbit or one in a low orbit?
7. What is escape velocity from the earth?
8. What keeps a satellite from flying off into space?
9. Explain why space environment may be hostile to man. What precautions must be observed?
10. What are some of the advantages and the disadvantages of a blunt-nosed reentry capsule?
11. What is an advantage of a high-orbiting communication satellite system over a low-orbiting system?

SUMMARY

Four forces act on an airplane in flight. They are thrust, drag, lift, and weight. The wing gets its lift from the kite effect and also from Bernoulli's principle. Wings, propellers, and various control surfaces are airfoils that are shaped to produce useful aerodynamic forces. Streamlining reduces drag and is important at high speeds. The propeller is an airfoil that produces thrust to overcome drag and to accelerate the plane. The pilot controls the plane by means of the throttle, elevators, ailerons, rudder, and flaps.

Helicopters and VTOL planes can take off and land vertically, hover over one spot, or travel horizontally. STOL planes can land and take off on very short runways. A "coke bottle" shape increases the speed and reduces the drag of a supersonic plane. Mach number is the ratio between the plane's speed and the speed of sound. The sonic boom is caused by the shock wave of air built up by an aircraft flying faster than the speed of sound.

Planes must be provided with many instruments to help the pilot stay on course, avoid accidents, and check on the operation of the plane and engines.

Outer space, which begins beyond most of our atmosphere, is classed as terrestrial, interplanetary, or interstellar. Travel through outer space presents many hazards such as meteoroids, radiation, extremes of temperature, and excessive acceleration.

A booster rocket with great thrust is needed to break free from the earth's gravity. Thereafter, a spaceship can coast through space with little expenditure of fuel. If an object in terrestrial space is given sufficient speed parallel to the earth's surface, it will orbit the earth as an artificial satellite. It usually has an elliptical orbit, the highest point of which is its apogee and the lowest its perigee.

High temperatures are built up on a spaceship when it re-enters the earth's atmosphere. A blunt-nosed capsule resists heating better than a sharp-nosed capsule. Vehicles returning from the moon or planets must enter the atmosphere in a carefully selected entry corridor.

Jet engines produce more thrust than reciprocal engines, but rockets are the most powerful of all. Chemical rockets build up great amounts of thrust and are used for launching vehicles from the ground. New types of power such as ion propulsion, which have low thrust but high efficiency, may be used for flight once the vehicle is in space.

CHAPTER REVIEW

Vocabulary

Match the words in Column A with the *best* response in Column B. Do not write in your book.

Column A	Column B
1. lift	a. an upward force on an airfoil
2. thrust	b. any surface of a plane that produces lift or other useful forces
3. drag	
4. angle of attack	c. a highly-ionized gas
5. kite effect	d. control surfaces on the rear edges of an airplane wing used to bank the plane
6. airfoil	
7. supersonic	e. efficiency rating of a rocket propellant
8. sonic boom	f. faster than the speed of sound
9. Mach number	g. force which retards the forward motion of an airplane
10. oxidizer	
11. ailerons	h. forward force of a propeller, or jet exhaust gases, on a plane or rocket
12. altimeter	
13. VTOL	i. instrument used to determine altitude
14. mass-ratio	j. lift given to an aircraft because of wind striking the underside of a wing
15. specific impulse	
16. plasma	k. minimum speed that a projectile must have to coast free of earth's gravity
17. astronautics	
18. escape velocity	l. plane capable of vertical take-off and landing
19. apogee	m. stationary communications satellite
20. Syncom	n. point in a satellite's orbit farthest from the earth
	o. ratio of the speed of a vehicle to the speed of sound
	p. ratio of the weights of a rocket before and after launching and burnout
	q. shock wave caused by supersonic airplane
	r. space science
	s. substance needed to burn rocket fuels
	t. tilt of wing in relation to relative wind striking an airplane

Questions: Group A

1. Explain two uses of wind tunnels.
2. Name and explain three main movable control surfaces of the plane.
3. State two uses of flaps.

4. What type of engine do most jet planes use?
5. What famous Italian was a pioneer of aircraft design?
6. List three uses of a plane's radio receiver.
7. How does a spaceship get from the earth's orbit into a planetary orbit farther from the sun?
8. How is the mass-ratio of a rocket calculated?
9. Describe some important problems of space travel.
10. Name three kinds of dangerous radiations in outer space.
11. Describe how Syncom can have a "stationary" orbit.
12. Why is a satellite traveling faster at perigee than at apogee?

Questions: Group B

1. Explain how the kite effect and Bernoulli's principle produce lift.
2. What is the difference between a ramjet and a turbojet?
3. Tell how the radio-altimeter and the ordinary altimeter work.
4. Explain the advantage of a "variable-pitch" propeller.
5. Explain how ion propulsion works. What advantage has it over chemical fuels?
6. How has meteorology been aided by space exploration?
7. What shape is best to resist heating in a re-entering space capsule? Why?
8. How does the area rule or "coke bottle" shape affect an aircraft's speed?
9. Why are chemical rockets with relatively low efficiency used to launch space vehicles instead of high-efficiency ion rockets?
10. What advantage is there in accelerating as rapidly as possible when launching a satellite into orbit?
11. What is the main difference between an active and passive communication satellite?

Problems

1. A guided missile is traveling at Mach 3 at sea level. About how fast is it going in miles per hour?
2. A plane has a wing area of 1000 ft². The average lift on the wings is ¼ lb/in.² Find the total lift.
3. A satellite is orbiting the earth at a speed of 18,000 mph. About how long will it take to make one revolution? (*Assume orbit diameter of 9000 miles.*)
4. Escape velocity from planet Earth is 25,200 mph. This is equal to a speed of how many miles *per second?* (Show calculations.)
5. What is the mass-ratio of a 125,000 lb three-stage rocket which places a 1000-lb final stage into orbit?

GROUPS

Light metals

Metals

Nonmetals

Noble gases

	atomic number
0	1
	H — symbol
	1.0080 — atomic weight

PERIODS	IA	IIA	IIIB	IVB	VB	VIB	VIIB	VIIIB			IB	IIB	IIIA	IVA	VA	VIA	VIIA	VIIIA
1	1 H 1.008																	2 He 4.003
2	3 Li 6.939	4 Be 9.012											5 B 10.811	6 C 12.011	7 N 14.007	8 O 15.999	9 F 18.998	10 Ne 20.183
3	11 Na 22.990	12 Mg 24.312											13 Al 26.982	14 Si 28.086	15 P 30.974	16 S 32.064	17 Cl 35.453	18 Ar 39.948
4	19 K 39.102	20 Ca 40.08	21 Sc 44.956	22 Ti 47.90	23 V 50.942	24 Cr 51.996	25 Mn 54.938	26 Fe 55.847	27 Co 58.933	28 Ni 58.71	29 Cu 63.54	30 Zn 65.37	31 Ga 69.72	32 Ge 72.59	33 As 74.922	34 Se 78.96	35 Br 79.909	36 Kr 83.80
5	37 Rb 85.47	38 Sr 87.62	39 Y 88.905	40 Zr 91.22	41 Nb 92.906	42 Mo 95.94	43 Tc (98)	44 Ru 101.07	45 Rh 102.905	46 Pd 106.4	47 Ag 107.870	48 Cd 112.40	49 In 114.82	50 Sn 118.69	51 Sb 121.75	52 Te 127.60	53 I 126.904	54 Xe 131.30
6	55 Cs 132.905	56 Ba 137.34	57-71 *	72 Hf 178.49	73 Ta 180.948	74 W 183.85	75 Re 186.2	76 Os 190.2	77 Ir 192.2	78 Pt 195.09	79 Au 196.967	80 Hg 200.59	81 Tl 204.37	82 Pb 207.19	83 Bi 208.980	84 Po (210)	85 At (210)	86 Rn (222)
7	87 Fr (223)	88 Ra (226)	89-103 **	(104)	(105)	(106)	(107)	(108)										

* Elements 57-71 closely resemble each other and are called the rare earths.

** Elements 89-103 comprise a related series which includes man-made elements.

GLOSSARY

absolute zero. Lowest temperature theoretically possible, $-273.16°$ C or $-459.69°$ F.

acceleration. Velocity change in unit time.

accelerators. Catalysts that speed up chemical reactions in the vulcanization process.

accelerometer. A device that indicates a change in velocity of a moving object.

acid. Substance that yields hydrogen (hydronium, H_3O+) ions in solution.

acoustics. The science of sound.

actual mechanical advantage (AMA). The ratio of the resistance force of a machine (R) to the effort (E) force.

adhesion. The force of attraction between *unlike* molecules.

air mass. A large body of air that has about the same temperature and moisture content throughout.

airfoil. Any surface af a plane that produces lift or other useful forces.

alkali. Strong soluble base. Usually refers to any base.

alkane. A straight or branched-chain hydrocarbon in which the carbon atoms are linked together by *single* bonds.

alkene. A straight or branched-chain hydrocarbon in which two carbon atoms are connected by a *double* bond.

alkyne. A straight or branched-chain hydrocarbon in which two carbon atoms are connected by a *triple* bond.

alloy. Material composed of two or more metals in solid solution, mixture, or metallic compound.

alpha particles. Positively charged helium nuclei given off by radioactive elements.

alternating current. Current that flows first in one direction and then in other.

altimeter. Instrument used to determine altitude.

ammeter. Instrument to measure rate of flow of electric current.

amorphous. A non-crystalline substance; having a random distribution of particles.

ampere. The unit of electric current, 6.25×10^{18} electrons per second.

amplifier. Radio tube or circuit used to strengthen feeble electric currents.

amplitude. Maximum distance the particles in a wave are displaced from the normal position of rest.

anemometer. Instrument for measuring wind speed.

anesthetic. Substance used in medicine to make one insensitive to pain.

anneal. Process of cooling glass slowly to keep it from becoming too brittle.

anode. Positive (+) terminal of an electrolytic cell.

antibiotic. Substance obtained from certain molds and bacteria, used for destroying or inhibiting the growth of many infection-producing organisms.

anticyclone (high). A whirlpool of air at high atmospheric pressure.

anti-matter. Matter made of anti-particles.

anti-oxidants. Substances used to keep rubber from becoming stiff and brittle.

anti-particle. A particle having the same mass as its counterpart in ordinary matter, but which has an opposite charge.

apogee. Point in a satellite's orbit that is farthest from the earth.

area rule. The principle of design in supersonic aircraft that reduces drag and produces the "cokebottle" shape.

armature. Part of an electric motor or generator that cuts magnetic lines of force.

asteroids. Small masses which encircle the sun in their own orbits, like the planets; planetoids.

atmosphere. The gaseous envelope surrounding the earth. The "ocean" of air.

atom. The smallest particle of an element that can exist either alone or in combination with other elements.

atomic mass. The mass of an atom based on the standard mass of 12 mass units for a C-12 atom. The number expressing the sum of the neutrons and protons in an atomic nucleus.

atomic number. The number of protons in the nucleus of an atom. Also equal to the number of electrons in a neutral atom.

atomic pile. Device in which controlled fission of radioactive material produces new radioactive substances and energy.

audio-frequency (a-f). Frequency of sound to which the ear responds.

barometer. Instrument used to measure the pressure of the atmosphere.

base. Substance that yields hydroxide (OH−) ions in solution.

battery. Two or more electric cells connected in series or in parallel.

beats. Pulsations of two sound waves caused by interference.

Bernoulli's principle. Whenever a liquid or gas speeds up, its pressure becomes less.

beta rays. High-speed electrons given off by the nuclei of radioactive atoms.

binary stars. Pairs of stars rotating around a common center.

bleaching. The operation by which color is partially or wholly removed from a colored material.

block mountains. Mountains that result from faulting.

boiling point. The temperature at which the molecules of a liquid have enough energy to overcome the attractive forces between molecules and escape into the air.

bond. One pair of shared electrons connecting two atoms together; represented by the symbol (−).

British thermal unit (Btu). The heat required to raise the temperature of one pound of water one Fahrenheit degree.

bubble chamber. Device in which nuclear particles leave a visible trail of bubbles as they pass through a gas.

buoyancy. The force that pushes up on objects when placed in a fluid.

butte. A steep-walled, flat-top hill.

calorie. The quantity of heat necessary to raise the temperature of one gram of water one Celsius degree.

candlepower. Unit of brightness equal to a standard candle.

capacitor. A combination of conducting plates separated by an insulator, used to store electric charge.

capillary action. The rise (or fall) of liquids in fine, hairlike tubes.

carding. Spreading a tangled mass of fibers into filmy web-like sheet.

carrier waves. High-frequency electromagnetic waves used for radio broadcasting.

catalyst. Chemical substance; used to alter the speed of a chemical reaction.

cathode. The negative (−) terminal of an electrolytic cell.

cathode rays. Streams of high-speed electrons leaving the negative electrode.

Celsius scale. The centigrade thermometer scale using the ice point as zero and the steam point as 100.

cement. A substance made from limestone and clay which, after mixing with water, sets to a hard mass.

center of curvature. The center of the sphere of which a mirror or a lens is a segment.

center of gravity. That point at which all of the weight of a body may be considered to be concentrated.

centigrade scale. See *Celsius scale.*

centrifugal force. Outward force exerted by a revolving body away from the center of revolution.

centrifuge. Device used to separate substances by spinning them at high speeds.

centripetal force. Inward force that pulls a revolving body out of a straight-line path.

chain reaction. Any nuclear reaction that is self-sustaining.

chemical change. Change in which a new substance is produced.

chemical equation. An expression that tells by formulas and symbols what is used and what is obtained in a chemical reaction.

chemical formula. Chemical symbols for a compound telling the number and kind of elements in a molecule.

chemical properties. Properties that describe the behavior of substances reacting with other substances.

chemical symbol. A single capital letter or a capital letter and a small letter used as an abbreviation for an element.

circuit breaker. Electromagnetic switch that breaks an electric circuit when it is overloaded.

cirrus cloud. Thin, wispy cloud of ice crystals at a high altitude.

climate. The general conditions of the atmosphere over an extended period of time.

closed pipe. Resonant air column closed at one end.

coefficient of linear expansion. The fractional increase in length of a solid per degree rise in temperature.

coefficient of volume expansion. The fractional increase in volume of a substance per degree rise in temperature.

coherent waves. Light waves in which the crests and troughs are all in step; property of a laser light.

cohesion. The attraction of *like* molecules of a substance for each other.

cold front. Boundary formed when a mass of cold air displaces a mass of warm air.

color. Property of light that depends on its wavelength.

combustion. Rapid oxidation accompanied by heat and light; burning.

combustion turbine. Engine that burns fuel and uses exhaust gases to turn a turbine.

comet. Brilliant heavenly body often having a long tail.

commutator. Device on electric generators that changes AC produced in the armature to DC in the external circuit.

complementary colors. Two colors which produce white light when combined.

compound. A substance composed of two or more different elements that are chemically united.

compound machine. Machine consisting of two or more simple machines.

compression. Region of a longitudinal wave in which vibrating particles are closer than their normal distance.

compression ratio. Volume a fuel mixture takes up before compression compared to its volume after compression.

concave lens. A lens which diverges parallel light rays.

conduction. Transfer of heat from molecules to adjoining molecules.

continental shelf. The submerged land between the shore line and the ocean floor.

convection. The transfer of heat energy by movement of fluids.

convex lens. A lens which converges parallel light rays.

core. Innermost layer of the lithosphere.

corona. Glow around the sun; seen only during an eclipse, caused by ionized gases from the sun.

cosmic rays. High-energy radiations from outer space.

coulomb. The change carried by a current; of one ampere in one second, 6.25×10^{18} electrons (6.25 billion billion).

crest. A region of "upward" displacement in a transverse wave.

critical mass. Smallest mass of fissionable material that will undergo explosive fission.

crust. The rock material forming the outer surface of the lithosphere.

crystal. Particles of a substance having or capable of having a definite geometrical form as part of its microstructure.

cumulus cloud. Large, woolly cloud forms at moderate heights.

cyclone (low). A large whirlpool of air at low atmospheric pressure.

cyclotron. Atom smasher that accelerates nuclear particles in a spiral path.

deceleration. The rate at which the velocity of a moving object decreases; the opposite of acceleration.

decibel. Unit of sound intensity or loudness.

dehydrating agent. Substance that removes water from other substances.

delta. A triangular-shaped deposit at the mouth of a river.

density. Weight (or mass) per unit volume of a substance.

detector. Radio tube or other device that separates the audio-frequency wave from the carrier wave, a process called *detection*.

deuterium. Heavy hydrogen; the hydrogen isotope.

dew point. Temperature at which moisture from the air begins to condense on the earth's surface.

diesel engine. Internal combustion engine in which the fuel as ignited in the cylinder by the heat of compression of air.

diffraction grating. Device used in a spectroscope to produce a spectrum.

diffusion. The mixing of two substances by molecular motion; the scattering of light rays.

diode. Electronic tube containing only two electrodes, a cathode and a plate.

direct current. Current that flows in one direction only.

dispersion. The separation of light into its component wavelengths.

distillation. Process of evaporating a liquid followed by condensing of vapors in a separate vessel.

doldrums. Zone of calm or shifting winds near the equator.

domain. A microscopic magnetic region composed of a group of atoms having a magnetic field aligned in a given direction.

Doppler effect. Change in frequency of a wave due to relative motion between the wave source and the observer.

dosimeter. A pocket electroscope which measures the quantity of radiation.

drag. Force which retards the forward motion of an airplane.

dry cell. Electric cell that has a moist paste instead of a liquid electrolyte.

earthquake. The cracking and sliding of large masses of rock of the earth's crust.

eclipse. Passage of moon between the sun and the earth, or when the moon enters the earth's shadow.

Edison effect. The flow of current from a hot cathode to a positively-charged plate.

elastic limit. Maximum distortion beyond which an object will not return to its original shape.

elasticity. The property of matter that causes it to resume its original shape when a distorting force is removed.

electric cell. Device for producing an electric current by chemical action.

electric circuit. Complete conducting path of an electric current.

electric current. Flow of electrons along a conductor.

electric field. The region in which an electric force acts on a charge when placed into the region.

electric induction. Process whereby a charged object produces an opposite charge on a nearby object.

electric motor. Device for changing electrical energy into mechanical energy.

electrode. Terminal of an electrolytic cell, plate, or "pole."

electrolysis. Chemical change in matter produced by an electric current.

electromagnet. An iron core that becomes a magnet when current is passed through a coil that is wrapped around it.

electromagnetic induction. Process of producing a current by moving a magnet near a conductor or vice-versa.

electromagnetic spectrum. Range of radiations, such as heat, light, ultraviolet, and X rays.

electromotive force (emf). Voltage of electric pressure.

electron cloud. The aggregate of electrons about the nucleus of an atom.

electron volt. Energy acquired by an electron falling through a field of one volt.

electroplating. Deposition of a metal on a surface by means of an electric current.

electroscope. Device to detect electrical charges.

element. Substances that cannot be broken up into simpler substances by ordinary chemical means.

energy. That which produces change in matter; the capacity to do work.

energy, kinetic. Energy due to the motion of a body.

energy, potential. Energy that is due to the position or condition; stored energy.

English system. System of measurement most commonly used in the United States and Great Britain.

equinox. Time of year when the sun rises due east and sets due west. It marks the beginning of spring and of fall.

erosion. The wearing away of the crust of the earth.

escape velocity. Minimum speed that must be given to a projectile for it to coast free of the earth's gravitational field.

exosphere. Outermost layer of the atmosphere.

Fahrenheit scale. Temperature scale on which the ice point is 32° and the steam point is 212°.

fall line. A line joining points on the border of the coastal plain and higher land.

farsightedness. Defect of the eyeball or lens whereby light rays are focused behind the retina.

fathometer. Instrument used to determine the depth of water by reflection of sound waves from the ocean bottom.

fault. Crack in the earth's surface that permits a large rock mass to rise or fall to a new level.

fission. Splitting of the atomic nucleus into fragments of more or less equal mass.

flotation. Process used to separate certain ores from worthless rock by preferential wetting.

fluid. Gas or liquid phase of matter.

fluoroscope. Device consisting of an X-ray tube and a fluorescent screen.

focal length. Distance from a mirror or lens to its principal focus.

focus. A point at which light rays meet or from which light rays diverge.

folded mountains. Mountains resulting from the folding of huge rock masses.

foot-candle. Unit of illumination equal to one lumen/ft². The brightness of light one foot from one-candlepower light source.

force. That which can change the state of rest or motion of a body; a push or pull.

force, resultant. A single force that has the same effect as two or more forces acting together.

forced vibrations. Vibrations produced in matter by direct contact with a vibrating object.

fossil. Evidences of early forms of life as recorded in rock.

four-stroke-cycle engine. The most common type of gasoline engine: intake, compression, power, exhaust.

fractional distillation. Process of separating a mixture of liquids having different boiling points.

frame of reference. A basis of comparison for motions in space.

freezing point. Temperature at which a liquid changes to a solid at normal pressure.

frequency. Number of vibrations, waves, or cycles per second.

frequency modulation (FM). Process of varying the frequency of a carrier wave to conform to an information signal.

friction. Force opposing motion of a body.

fuel cell. A cell in which chemical energy is changed to electrical energy by means of a continuous supply of fuel.

fusion, nuclear. Merging of two or more atomic nuclei to form a single heavier nucleus.

galaxy. Rotating group of billions of stars moving through space.

galvanometer. Instrument for detecting very small currents.

gamma rays. Electromagnetic radiations from radioactive substances, similar to high-energy X rays.

Geiger counter. Sensitive instrument for detecting radiation.

generator. Device that changes mechanical energy to electrical energy by electromagnetic induction.

g-force. The amount of force expressed in terms of 32 ft/sec per second, the acceleration of gravity of the earth.

glacier. A huge mass of ice that moves down slowly from a mountain area.

globular cluster. Swarm of stars on the outskirts of a galaxy.

gram. Unit of mass (weight) in the metric system; 454 grams = 1 lb.

gravitation. The attractive force which masses exert on each other.

greenhouse effect. Process by which the atmosphere traps short-wavelength solar radiations and reradiates these as longer wavelengths.

Greenwich time. Time as measured on the prime meridian, used to determine longitude.

ground water. Subsurface water; water that saturates the water table.

gyroscope. A spinning device that tends to keep its axis of spin unchanged.

half-life. Time required for half of the atoms of a sample of a radioactive element to disintegrate.

harmony. Combination of musical tones which is pleasing to the ears.

heat. A form of energy produced by the motion of molecules of a substance.

heat of fusion. Amount of heat absorbed by a substance in melting.

heat of vaporization. Amount of heat absorbed by a liquid in changing to a gas.

high. A region of high atmospheric pressure; an anticyclone.

horsepower. The unit for measuring power, equivalent to 550 ft-lb/sec.

humidity. The quantity of moisture in a given volume of the atmosphere.

hurricane. A violent cyclone of tropical origin.

hydraulic. Refers to any device that operates because of pressure applied to a liquid.

hydrocarbon. A compound containing hydrogen and carbon.

hydroelectric power. Electric power generated by falling water.

hydrogenation. The chemical addition of hydrogen to a substance.

hydrolysis. The reaction of a salt and water to form a solution that is acidic or basic.

hydrometer. Instrument used to determine the specific gravity of liquids.

hydronium ion. A proton attached to a water molecule, H_3O+ ion.

hydrosphere. The water-covered portion of the earth.

hygrometer. Instrument to determine relative humidity of the atmosphere.

iconoscope. Camera tube used for taking the picture in television.

ideal mechanical advantage (IMA). The ratio of the distance the effort force (E) moves in a machine to the distance the resistance force (R) moves.

igneous rock. Rock formed from molten mixture of minerals.

image orthicon. Sensitive electronic tube in a television camera.

immiscible. Not capable of being mixed.

inclination. The tilting of a planet's axis in relation to its orbit around the sun.

inclined plane. Plane, ramp, or slanting surface used as a simple machine.

index of refraction. Ratio of speed of light in a vacuum (air) to its speed in a given transparent substance.

induced current. One caused by electromagnetic induction.

inertia. Property of matter which resists change in motion.

inhibitor. A catalyst that slows down a chemical reaction.

inorganic matter. Nonliving or mineral matter.

input work. The product of the effort force (E) and the distance through which it acts.

intensity. Loudness of a sound.

interference. The effect produced by two waves as they are "in phase" (strengthen) or "out of phase" (destroy).

internal combustion engine. Engine that burns fuel inside its cylinders.

ion. Atom or group of atoms that has lost or gained electrons.

ion exchange. Process of replacing an ion of one atom with that of another of like electric charge.

ion propulsion. Thrust obtained by a jet or gaseous ions speeded up by electric or magnetic fields.

ionic bonding. The bonding between atoms produced by transfer of electrons from one atom to another.

ionosphere. Layer of the atmosphere above and adjacent to the stratosphere.

isobars. Lines on a weather map indicating equal barometric pressure.

isomers. Compounds whose molecules have the same number and kind of atoms but a different arrangement of atoms.

isotherms. Lines on a weather map indicating equal temperature.

isotopes. Atoms of the same element that differ from each other only in the number of neutrons in the nucleus.

jet engine. Engine that gets thrust from high-speed exhaust gases.

jet stream. Narrow band of very strong winds in the stratosphere.

kilogram. The standard of mass in the metric system; about 2.2 lb.

kilowatt. Unit for measuring electric power. It is equal to 1000 watts.

kilowatt-hour. Unit of electrical energy equivalent to using 1000 watts of power for one hour.

kindling temperature. The lowest temperature at which a substance begins to burn.

kinetic energy. Energy that matter has because of its motion.

kinetic theory of matter. Scientific generalization stating that all atoms and molecules are in constant, random motion.

laser. Light amplification by stimulated emission of radiation.

latitude. Distance measured in degrees north and south from the equator.

lever. Rigid bar free to turn about a fixed point called a fulcrum.

lift. Force which tends to lift an airfoil, a wing, or a plane upward.

light. A form of energy that radiates from atoms when they are violently disturbed by heat or electricity; a visible portion of the electromagnetic spectrum.

light year. Distance light travels in one year, about 6 trillion (6×10^{12}) miles.

linear accelerator. Atom smasher that speeds up "atomic bullets" through a long, straight tube.

lines of force. Imaginary lines representing the strength and direction of the magnetic, electric, or gravitational force.

liter. The metric unit of volume, equal to 1.06 quarts.

lithosphere. The solid part of the earth.

litmus. A dye used as an indicator for acids and bases.

longitude. Distance measured in degrees east and west from the prime meridian.

longitudinal wave. A wave in which the particles of the medium vibrate to-and-fro along the direction of wave travel.

loudness. The effect of the intensity of sound energy on the ears.

lumen. The unit of illumination. The amount of light striking one square foot of a surface that is one foot from a light source of one candle.

luminous. Giving off light. Stars

Mach number. Ratio of speed of vehicle to speed of sound.

machine. A device that changes the amount, speed, or direction of a force.

machines, law of. Neglecting friction, the output work from any machine equals its input work.

magnetic field. Space around a magnet that contains lines of force.

magnetic induction. Process whereby a magnetic pole produces an opposite pole in a nearby substance.

malleability. Property of a metal which enables it to be hammered or rolled into thin sheets.

mantle. The intermediate zone between the earth's crust and the core.

mass. A measure of the quantity of matter; a measure of the inertia of a body.

mass defect. The difference in mass between an atomic nucleus and the combined mass of its component particles.

mass number. The sum of the number of protons and neutrons in the nucleus of an atom. A whole number expressing that atomic weight.

mass-ratio. Ratio of mass of rocket with fuel to that without fuel.

matter. Anything that has weight and occupies space.

mechanical advantage. Number that shows how many times a machine multiplies the force applied to it.

mechanical equivalent of heat. The conversion factor that relates heat units to work units. One Btu is equivalent to 778 ft-lb.

medium. The material that carries energy of a wave.

meson. Nuclear particle between electron and proton in mass.

metallic mixture. Crystals of one metal scattered throughout the mass of another metal.

metals. Elements that have luster, conduct heat and electricity, and usually have a positive valence number.

metamorphic rock. Rock formed by the effect of heat and pressure on other rocks.

meteor. Particles from outer space moving at high speed through the atmosphere that burn up before reaching the earth's surface.

meteorite. Chunk of matter (meteor) that has fallen to the earth's surface.

meter. The metric unit of length, equivalent to 39.37 inches.

mev. Million electron volts.

millibar. The unit of pressure used by meteorologists; 30 inches of mercury is equivalent to 1016 millibars.

mixture. Material containing different substances that have not been chemically united.

moderator. Agent used to slow down neutrons in a controlled chain reaction.

modulation. Adding a low-frequency wave to higher frequency carrier waves.

Mohole. Hole being drilled through the earth's crust to the Moho.

molecule. The smallest particles of an element or compound that contains the properties of that substance.

moment. Product of force and perpendicular distance from the fulcrum; torque.

momentum. Product of velocity and mass.

monomer. A single molecule or single unit structure of a polymer.

month. Time from one new moon to the next.

mordant. A substance used to make certain dyes cling to textile fibers.

mortar. Hard mass made from calcium, sand, and water.

musical tone. Sound produced by regular vibrations in matter.

mutation. A new inherited trait resulting from changes in a gene or chromosome.

native metal. Metal that is found free in nature; that is, not combined chemically with another element.

natural gas. Fuel gas found under ground, containing about 90% methane.

neap tides. Lower than usual tides produced when sun and moon are at right angles.

nearsightedness. Defect of the eyeball or lens whereby the light rays are focused in front of the retina.

negative charge. Electric charge resulting from a gain of electrons.

neutralization. The reaction of the hydronium (hydrogen) ions of an acid and the hydroxide ions of a base to form water.

neutralizing. Combining equal amounts of positive and negative electricity.

noise. Sound waves of irregular vibration in matter.

nonelectrolytes. Solutions that do not conduct an electric current.

nonmetals. Elements that are very poor conductors of heat and electricity, and usually have a negative valence number.

nova. A star that has become much hotter and brighter than it was previously.

nuclear reactor. Device in which controlled fission or radioactive material produces new radioactive substances and energy.

nucleus. The positively charged center of an atom containing protons and neutrons.

octave. The interval between a given musical tone and one that is double or half the frequency.

ohm. Unit of electrical resistance.

opaque. Not able to transmit light.

open pipe. Resonant air column open at each end.

orbit. Oval path of one body revolving around another.

organic matter. Material from an animal or plant source.

oscillator. Radio tube or circuit that produces steady, alternating currents, usually at high frequency.

oscilloscope. Type of cathode-ray tube used to make visible the pattern of electrical vibrations, sound waves, etc.

output work. The product of the resistance force and the distance through which it acts.

overtone. Tone of higher pitch than the fundamental, made by the shorter segments of the vibrating object.

oxidation. The process whereby oxygen unites with other substances.

oxidizing agent. Substance that gives up oxygen units with other substances.

parallax. The apparent displacement of an object when viewed from two different points.

parallel circuit. An electrical circuit containing two or more branches through which the current may flow.

parallel forces. Forces that act in either the same or in opposite directions.

penstock. Large pipes that conduct water to the turbines from the basin.

perigee. Point of satellite's orbit that is nearest to the earth.

period. The time required for one complete cycle or vibration. A horizontal row of elements in the Periodic Table.

Periodic Table. An arrangement of elements according to their atomic numbers and properties. (See page 607).

phosphorescence. Capacity of a substance to glow after exposure to light.

photoelectric effect. The release of electrons from certain metals by the action of light.

photometer. Instrument for measuring light intensity.

photon. A single pocket (quantum) of light energy.

photosphere. Layer of brilliantly glowing gases beneath the chromosphere, source of most of the radiant energy from the sun.

photosynthesis. The food-making process in green plants.

phototube. Electronic tube that generates an electric current when exposed to light.

physical change. A change that does not produce a new substance.

pickling. Removing the surface impurities from a metal with an acid bath.

piezoelectric effect. Producing tiny currents by applying pressures or distorting certain crystals.

pitch. The effect of the frequency of sound waves on the ears. The distance between the threads of a screw. The angle of the blades of an airplane propeller.

plane mirror. Flat mirror, without curved surfaces.

planet. Heavenly body that revolves around the sun and reflects the light of the sun.

planetoids. Small masses which encircle the sun in their own orbits, like planets; asteroids.

plasma. A gaseous mixture of highly-ionized particles.

plastic. A substance containing giant molecules that can be formed or shaped by molding.

polarized light. Light which vibrates in only one plane.

polymer. A giant molecule formed by smaller molecules joining together.

positive charge. Electric charge resulting from a loss of electrons.

positron. The anti-particle of the electron.

potable water. Water that is fit to drink.

potential energy. Stored energy of matter because of its position or condition.

pound. The standard unit of force in the English system.

power. A measure of the amount of work that can be done in a unit of time.

precession. Wobbling motion of the earth's axis, like a spinning top.

precipitate. An insoluble solid that separates from a solution.

precipitation. Moisture falling to the earth in the form of rain, snow, hail, sleet, or drizzle.

pressure. Force acting on a unit area of surface.

prevailing westerlies. Winds originating in the horse latitudes blowing toward the poles.

primary coil. Coil of insulated wire attached to the source of electric current.

primary colors. Red, green, and blue-violet light, that mix to produce white light.

primary waves. Compression-type earthquake waves; longitudinal waves.

prime meridian. Line of zero longitude drawn through both poles and Greenwich, England.

principal focus. Point at which parallel rays of light converge after passing through a lens or hitting a concave mirror.

propellant. Source of power for rocket engine, consisting of a fuel and oxidizer.

quality. The effect of a tone on the ear based on the overtones present in the sound wave.

quantum theory. Theory that radiation is emitted and absorbed in tiny units, each containing a "packet" of energy which depends on its frequency.

radar. Device used to locate objects by means of high-frequency radio waves.

radar-astronomy. Science that studies the heavenly bodies of the universe by means of reflected electromagnetic radiations.

radiation. Transfer of energy in waves through space.

radical. A group of atoms that acts as if it were a single atom.

radioactivity. The giving off of alpha and beta particles and gamma rays as certain atoms decompose spontaneously.

radio-astronomy. Science that studies the heavenly bodies of the universe through radio waves they emit.

radio-frequency (r-f). Electromagnetic radiations produced by very rapid reverses of current in a conductor.

radioisotopes. Isotopes that are radioactive.

radiosonde. Balloon equipped with instruments that transmit weather information from the upper atmosphere to the earth.

real image. Image that can be projected on a screen; it is always inverted.

reciprocating engine. Engine which converts heat energy to mechanical energy by the back-and-forth motion of a piston in a cylinder.

rectifier. Device for changing alternating current to direct current.

relative humidity. Amount of water vapor in a certain volume of air compared to the maximum amount it can hold at that temperature.

relief map. Map showing the irregularities of the earth's surface.

resistance, electrical. Opposition of a substance to an electric current passing through it.

resonance. The ability of anything to be set in vibration by absorbing energy of its own natural frequency.

revolution. The movement of a body in its orbit.

rheostat. A variable resistance.

ring compound. Compound in which the ends of the chain of carbon atoms are linked together.

rocket. Device propelled by exhaust gases that can operate beyond the atmosphere.

rotation. The turning of a body on its axis.

salt. A compound formed when the positive ions from a base and the negative ions from an acid react.

satellite. Object that revolves around a larger body, as the moon around the earth.

saturated solution. Solution in which the concentration of solute is the maximum possible under the existing conditions.

scintillation counter. Device in which a flash of light occurs when a nuclear particle strikes a sensitive substance.

screw. Inclined plane wrapped around a cylinder; a simple machine.

secondary coil. Insulated coil of wire in which current is induced.

secondary waves. Earthquake waves that vibrate at right angles to the direction of travel; transverse waves.

seismograph. Instrument that records movements in the earth's surface.

semi-conductors. A material such as germanium or silicon whose electrical resistance is somewhere between conductors and insulators.

series circuit. Electric circuit which contains no branches through which the current may flow.

side-chain hydrocarbon. Hydrocarbon compounds in which the carbon atoms are linked together with branches attached to the main string of carbon atoms.

sidereal time. Time based on the actual rotation of the earth; star time.

slaking. The addition of water to quick-lime (CaO), to produce hydrated lime ($Ca(OH)_2$).

slow oxidation. An oxidation process such as decay or rusting producing some heat but no light.

soapless detergent. A cleaner that lowers the surface tension of water.

solar day. One sun day, or the time from the noon of one day to the next noon.

solar prominences. Streamers of rose-colored gases that swirl up many thousands of miles above the surface of the sun.

solar system. The sun and heavenly bodies that revolve around it.

solstice. Time of year when the sun rises farthest to the south or north. It marks the beginning of winter and of summer.

solubility. The amount of a solute that can be dissolved in a given amount of solvent, under specified conditions.

solute. Any material that is dissolved in a solution.

solution. Liquid formed by dissolving a solute in a solvent.

solvent. Liquid in which a solute dissolves.

sonar. A system of underwater communication using pulses of ultrasonic waves.

sound. A form of energy produced by vibrating matter.

sounding. Method used to determine depth of water.

specific gravity. Density of a substance divided by the density of water.

specific heat. The number of calories required to raise the temperature of one gram of a substance one Celsius degree. The number of Btu required to raise the temperature of one pound of substance one Fahrenheit degree.

specific impulse. Unit of propellant efficiency of a rocket engine; determined by multiplying thrust by burning time and dividing by the weight of the propellant.

spectroscope. Instrument that uses a prism or grating to separate light of different wavelengths.

spectrum. Band of colors formed when white light passes through a prism.

speed. Rate of motion of an object, regardless of direction.

spontaneous combustion. Combustion resulting from the accumulation of heat from slow oxidation.

spring equinox. Equal day and night occurring about March 21.

spring tides. Tides produced when the sun and moon are in line with the earth.

standard pressure. Pressure equivalent to 760 mm of mercury.

standard temperature. Temperature of 0° C.

static electricity. Accumulation of positive or negative charges on an object.

storage battery. An electric battery that can be repeatedly recharged.

straight-chain hydrocarbon. Hydrocarbon compound in which the carbon atoms are linked together in long, straight chains.

stratosphere. Layer of the atmosphere above and adjacent to the troposphere.

stratus clouds. Thin, flat, layer-like clouds close to the earth's surface.

stroboscope. Device that permits repetitive-moving objects to be viewed as though standing still.

sublimation. The passing of matter from a solid to a gas without passing through the liquid phase.

summer solstice. Time of year when the sun reaches its most northerly point, about June 21.

sunspots. Dark spots on the sun caused by a disturbance in the sun's atmosphere.

superconductor. A conductor in which there is no resistance to electrical current.

supersonic. Faster than the speed of sound.

surface tension. The drawing together, or skin effect, of the surface of a liquid.

synchrotron. A very powerful atom smasher that accelerates nuclear particles in a circular path.

temperature. A measure of the tendency of an object to transfer heat to, or absorb heat from, other objects.

tempered scale. A musical scale with 12 equal-frequency ratio intervals between the successive notes of an octave.

tempering. The heating of steel, followed by rapid or slow cooling to produce a degree of hardness desired.

tensile strength. The capacity of a metal to withstand a stretching force.

terminal velocity. The velocity attained by a freely falling object when the fluid friction of the atmosphere equals the force of gravitational attraction.

thermionic effect. Driving electrons from a substance by heating it.

thermonuclear reaction. See fusion, nuclear.

thermoplastic. Can be softened by heat.

thrust. Forward force of a propeller or jet exhaust gases on a plane or rocket.

thunderstorm. A storm accompanied by lightning, thunder, and usually heavy rains.

tides. Regular rise and fall of large bodies of water on the earth due to the gravitational force of the sun and moon.

tornado. Very violent whirlwind that occurs over a narrow path.

torque. Product of force and the perpendicular distance from a fulcrum; a moment.

tracers. Radioactive or "tagged" atoms, used in scientific research.

transformer. Device for changing voltage of an alternating current.

transistor. An electronic device which can be used in place of a vacuum tube to control electric current.

translucent. Able to transmit light, but not enough to see through clearly.

transparent. Able to transmit light so that objects can be seen clearly through it.

transverse wave. Wave in which the particles vibrate at right angles to the direction of wave travel.

triode. Radio tube containing grid, cathode, and plate.

troposphere. Layer of the atmosphere nearest to the earth's surface.

turbojet engine. Jet engine in which the burned gases turn turbine blades before shooting out of the exhaust gases.

valence number. A number representing the combining power of an element with other elements.

Van Allen belt. Band of intense radiation surrounding the earth.

vapor pressure. The production of a vapor or gas from a liquid.

velocity. Speed in a definite direction.

virtual image. Image that cannot be projected on a screen.

viscosity. Property of a fluid that offers resistance to flow.

volt. Unit of electrical pressure.

voltmeter. Instrument to measure voltage.

water of hydration. Water present as a structural part of certain crystals.

water table. Surface below which the ground is saturated with water.

watt. Unit of electric power.

wavelength. Distance between any two corresponding points of a wave.

weather. Condition of the atmosphere at a particular time and place.

wedge. Double inclined plane used to split or separate objects.

weight. A measure of the force of attraction of the earth for an object.

wheel and axle. Simple machine consisting of a large wheel rigidly attached to a smaller axle.

winter solstice. Time of year when the sun reaches its most southerly point, about December 22.

word equation. A brief statement which identifies the reactants and the products formed in a chemical reaction.

work. The result of a force moving an object a certain distance. It is determined by multiplying the force by the distance through which the force acts.

X rays. Invisible radiations of great penetrating power, produced in vacuum tubes.

year. Time required for the earth to complete one full revolution around the sun, or 365¼ days.